iWrite Math

Pre-Calculus Mathematics 11 Book

- Sequences and Series
- Operations on Radicals
- Trigonometry
- Factoring and Applications
- Quadratic Functions and Equations
- Rational Expressions and Equations
- Absolute Value Functions and Reciprocal Functions
- Linear and Quadratic Systems and Inequalities

Publisher: Absolute Value Publications

Authors: Alan Appleby, Greg Ranieri

Printed in Canada.

ISBN 978-1-926979-03-8

For information contact:

Absolute Value Publications Inc.
P.O. Box 71096
8060 Silver Springs Blvd. N.W.
Calgary, Alberta
T3B 5K1

Bus: (403) 313-1442
Fax: (403) 313-2042

e-mail: avp@avpbooks.com
avp@absolutevaluepublications.com

web site: www.avpbooks.com
www.absolutevaluepublications.com

Advantages for Students

- Students write in the book so that the math theory, worked examples, and assignments are all in one place for easy review.
- Students can write on the diagrams and graphs.
- Provides class examples and assignments so that students can use their time more efficiently. By focusing on solving problems and making their own notes, students improve their study skills.
- For independent learners, the book plus solution manual fosters self-paced learning.
- Encourages inquiry-based learning, group learning, and peer tutoring.
- The design of the book ensures that students are fully aware of the course expectations.
- The iWrite Math book is also available as an app at the Apple iTunes Store.
- We hope you enjoy using this book and that with the help of your teacher you realize the success that thousands of students each year are achieving using the book series.

Advantages for Teachers

- Written by teachers experienced in preparing students for success in high school and diploma examinations.
- Comprehensively covers the Western and Northern Canadian curriculum.
- Can be used as the main resource, or in conjunction with a textbook, or for extra assignments, or review.
- Reduces school photocopying costs and time.
- Allows for easy lesson planning in the case of teacher or student absence.
- The iWrite Math series is available in the following fromats:
    - Book
    - App form for tablets
    - Promethean Flipchart
    - One Note
    - Smart Notebook
    - Windows Journal

Student, teacher, and parent responses to the iWrite Math book series have been very positive. We welcome your feedback. It enables us to produce a high quality resource meeting our goal of success for both students and teachers.

iWrite Math Pre-Calculus Mathematics 11 Book

The iWrite Math Pre-Calculus Grade 11 book is a complete resource and a 100% fit for the combined Western and Northern Canadian mathematics curriculum. In addition, there is some enrichment material which can be completed individually or in groups.

There are eight curricular units. Each curricular unit is subdivided into individual lessons. The last lesson in each unit is a practice test containing 15 multiple choice questions, 5 numeric response questions, and 1 extended response question.

Most lessons can be covered in one hour (plus homework time), but some may require more time to complete. Most lessons are composed of four parts:

- ***Investigations, Explorations, or Review***
  which include inquiry based learning that can be teacher led, student led, or a combination of both.
- ***Class Examples***
  which are applications of the investigations, explorations, or review.
- ***Assignments***
  which include short response, extended response, multiple choice, and numeric response questions provided for student practice.
- ***Answer Key***
  which contains the answers to the assignment questions.

The **Teacher Solution Manual** is a complete copy of the book with detailed solutions to all the investigations/explorations/review, class examples, and assignments.

The **Student Solution Manual** provides detailed solutions to all the investigations/explorations/review, class examples, and assignment questions. It does not include the actual questions.

Acknowledgments

We would like to acknowledge the following people for their contributions in the production of this workbook:

- Victoria Lozinski, Susan Appleby, Rose Ranieri, and Tony Audia, for their help in proofreading, editing, and reviewing the material.
- Our students for their suggestions, opinions, and encouragement.
- Numerous colleagues for their advice, feedback, and continued support.

iWrite Math Pre-Calculus Mathematics 11 Book

Table of Contents

Sequences and Series

Lesson 1......... Investigating Patterns and Sequences....................1
Lesson 2......... Arithmetic Sequences....................15
Lesson 3......... Arithmetic Growth and Decay....................25
Lesson 4......... Arithmetic Series....................33
Lesson 5......... Geometric Sequences....................43
Lesson 6......... Geometric Growth and Decay....................53
Lesson 7......... Geometric Series....................63
Lesson 8......... Infinite Geometric Series....................75
Lesson 9......... Practice Test....................85

Operations on Radicals

Lesson 1......... Entire Radicals and Mixed Radicals....................91
Lesson 2......... Adding and Subtracting Radicals....................101
Lesson 3......... Multiplying Radicals....................109
Lesson 4......... Dividing Radicals - Part One....................117
Lesson 5......... Dividing Radicals - Part Two....................125
Lesson 6......... Practice Test....................131

Trigonometry

Lesson 1......... Rotation Angles and Reference Angles....................137
Lesson 2......... Trigonometric Ratios for Angles from 0° to 360°....................147
Lesson 3......... Applications of Reference Angles and the CAST Rule....................157
Lesson 4......... Special Triangles, Exact Values, and the Unit Circle....................167
Lesson 5......... The Sine Law....................181
Lesson 6......... The Cosine Law....................189
Lesson 7......... Problem Solving and The Ambiguous Case of the Sine Law....................197
Lesson 8......... Further Applications Involving the Sine Law and the Cosine Law....................205
Lesson 9......... Practice Test....................217

Factoring and Applications

Lesson 1......... Review of Factoring....................225
Lesson 2......... Factoring Trinomials of the Form $ax^2 + bx + c$....................231
Lesson 3......... Factoring Trinomials of the Form $a\left(f(x)\right)^2 + b\left(f(x)\right) + c$....................241
Lesson 4......... Factoring $a^2x^2 - b^2y^2$ and $a^2\left(f(x)\right)^2 + b^2\left(g(x)\right)^2$....................249
Lesson 5......... Solving Quadratic Equations using Factoring....................257
Lesson 6......... Solving Radical Equations using Factoring - Part One....................265
Lesson 7......... Solving Radical Equations using Factoring - Part Two....................275
Lesson 8......... Practice Test....................285

Quadratic Functions and Equations

Lesson 1......... Connecting Zeros, Roots, and x-intercepts......... 291
Lesson 2......... Analyzing Quadratic Functions - Part One......... 301
Lesson 3......... Analyzing Quadratic Functions - Part Two......... 309
Lesson 4......... Equations and Intercepts from the Vertex and the Point......... 317
Lesson 5......... Converting from General Form to Standard Form by Completing the Square. 325
Lesson 6......... Roots of Quadratic Equations - The Quadratic Formula......... 333
Lesson 7......... Roots of Quadratic Equations - The Discriminant......... 339
Lesson 8......... Applications of Quadratic Functions - A Graphical Approach......... 347
Lesson 9......... Applications of Quadratic Functions - An Algebraic Approach......... 355
Lesson 10........ Practice Test......... 363

Rational Expressions and Equations

Lesson 1......... Simplifying Rational Expressions - Part One......... 371
Lesson 2......... Simplifying Rational Expressions - Part Two......... 377
Lesson 3......... Addition and Subtraction of Rational Expressions - Part One......... 385
Lesson 4......... Addition and Subtraction of Rational Expressions - Part Two......... 393
Lesson 5......... Multiplication of Rational Expressions......... 403
Lesson 6......... Division of Rational Expressions......... 409
Lesson 7......... Rational Equations Part One......... 417
Lesson 8......... Rational Equations Part Two......... 425
Lesson 9......... Solving Problems Involving Rational Equations......... 431
Lesson 10........ Practice Test......... 439

Absolute Value Functions and Reciprocal Functions

Lesson 1......... Absolute Value Functions......... 449
Lesson 2......... Solving Absolute Value Equations - Part 1......... 457
Lesson 3......... Solving Absolute Value Equations - Part 2......... 467
Lesson 4......... Absolute Value Transformations......... 473
Lesson 5......... Reciprocal Functions......... 479
Lesson 6......... Practice Test......... 493

Linear and Quadratic Systems and Inequalities

Lesson 1......... Solving a System of Linear-Quadratic Equations......... 501
Lesson 2......... Solving a System of Quadratic-Quadratic Equations......... 509
Lesson 3......... Solving Linear Inequalities in Two Variables Without Technology......... 515
Lesson 4......... Solving Quadratic Inequalities in Two Variables Without Technology......... 523
Lesson 5......... Solving Inequalities in Two Variables Using Technology......... 529
Lesson 6......... Solving Quadratic Inequalities in One Variable by Case Analysis......... 535
Lesson 7......... Solving Quadratic Inequalities in One Variable by Sign Analysis......... 543
Lesson 8......... Practice Test......... 551

Sequences and Series Lesson #1: Investigating Patterns and Sequences

Overview

In this unit, we investigate patterns to define two types of sequences; arithmetic and geometric. We derive rules for determining the general term of each type of sequence and for the sum of n terms of the corresponding series. We also derive a rule for determining the sum of an infinite geometric series, and we solve problems involving arithmetic or geometric sequences and series.

Investigation 1

Jesse is making a tower using playing cards. The top three rows of the tower are shown.

The top row (Row 1) requires three playing cards.

The second row (Row 2) requires six additional playing cards.

Continue the pattern for two more rows, and complete Tables A and B below.

Table A

Row Number	1	2	3	4	5
Number of Additional Cards in the Row	3	6			

Table B

Row Number	1	2	3	4	5
Number of Triangles in the Row	1	3			

Investigation 2

Each row in the triangle, named after French mathematician Blaise Pascal, begins and ends with the number 1.

	Row
1	1
1 1	2
1 2 1	
1 3 3 1	

Apart from the ones, every other number in a particular row can be determined by adding the two numbers diagonally above it.

Continue the pattern for rows 5, 6, and 7, and complete Table C.

Table C

Row Number	1	2	3	4	5	6	7
Sum of the Numbers in the Row	1	2	4				

Investigation 3

An equilateral triangle (triangle 1) has sides of length 32 cm. A smaller triangle (triangle 2) is placed inside triangle 1 by joining the midpoints of triangle 1 (as illustrated in Diagram 2). The pattern is continued as illustrated in Diagram 3.

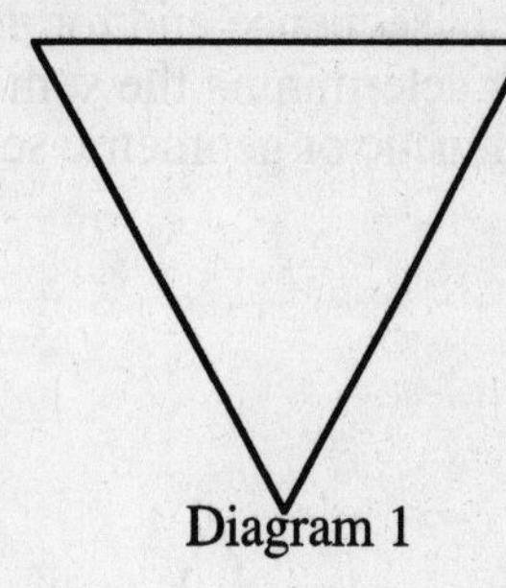
Diagram 1

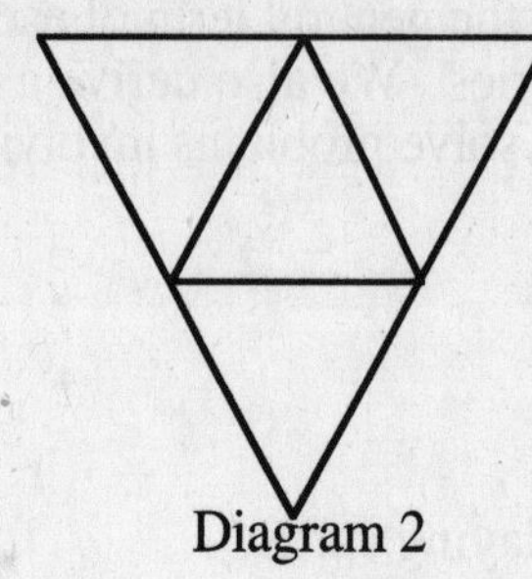
Diagram 2

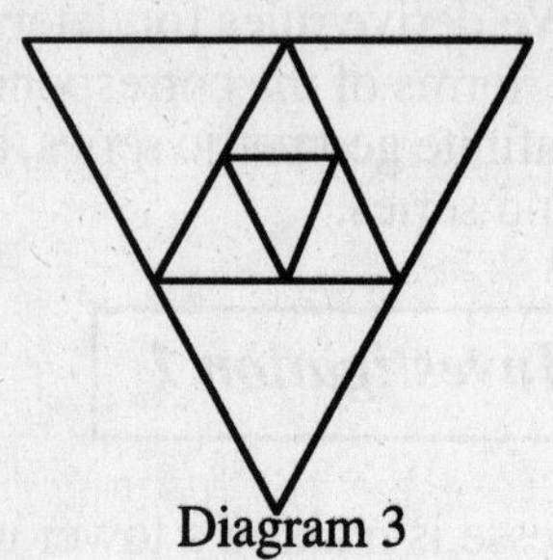
Diagram 3

a) Diagrams 4 and 5 in the sequence have not been completed. Complete each diagram.

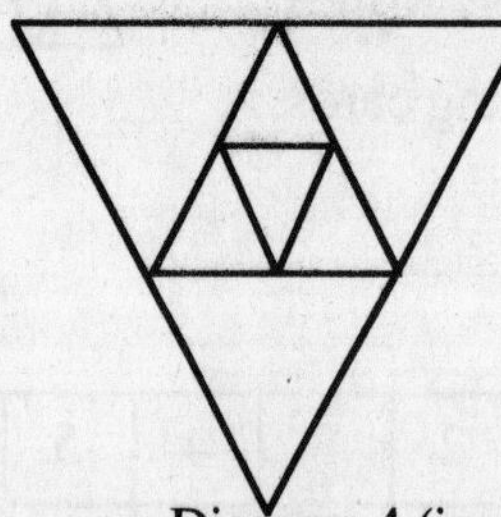
Diagram 4 (incomplete)

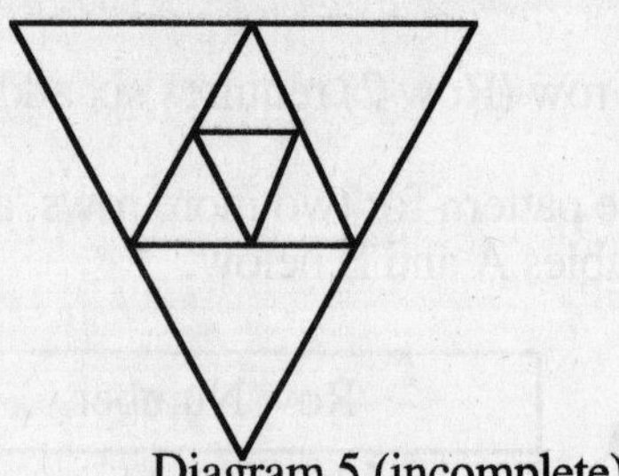
Diagram 5 (incomplete)

b) Complete Tables D and E below.

Table D

Triangle Number	1	2	3	4	5
Length of Side of Triangle (cm)	32				

Table E

Diagram Number	1	2	3	4	5
Number of Triangles of any Size in the Diagram	1	5			

Investigation 4

The mean daily temperature in Calgary on Jan 1 was 8°C. For the next ten days, the mean daily temperature decreased by 4°C each day.

Complete Table F below.

Table F

Day Number	1	2	3	4	5
Temperature (°C)	8				

In each of the tables A - F, the top row consists of the **natural numbers** 1, 2, 3, 4, etc., and the bottom row consists of a **sequence** of numbers related to the natural numbers in a specific order.

The first table you completed was **Table A**

Row Number	1	2	3	4	5
Number of Cards in the Row	3	6	9	12	15

The sequence formed is 3, 6, 9, 12, 15. The sequence consists of **terms**.

The first term, written t_1, is equal to 3. The second term, t_2, is equal to 6; $t_3 = 9$ etc.

In each of the following:

a) Complete the table using the information from Tables A - F.

b) Complete the statement, explaining how to find the next term in the sequence from the previous term using only addition or multiplication.

c) State the next two terms of the sequence.

Table A

n	1	2	3	4	5
t_n	3	6			

The next term can be calculated by ______________ the previous term.

$t_6 =$ ________ and $t_7 =$ ________ .

Table B

n	1	2	3	4	5
t_n					

The next term can be calculated by ______________ the previous term.

$t_6 =$ ________ and $t_7 =$ ________ .

Table C

n	1	2	3	4	5	6	7
t_n							

The next term can be calculated by

______________________________ .

$t_8 =$ ________ and $t_9 =$ ________ .

Table D

n	1	2	3	4	5
t_n					

The next term can be calculated by

______________________________ .

$t_6 =$ ________ and $t_7 =$ ________ .

Table E

n	1	2	3	4	5
t_n					

The next term can be calculated by ______________ the previous term.

$t_6 =$ ________ and $t_7 =$ ________ .

Table F

n	1	2	3	4	5
t_n					

The next term can be calculated by ______________ the previous term.

$t_6 =$ ________ and $t_7 =$ ________ .

Types of Sequences

There are different types of sequences.

A sequence in which the next term is formed by adding a constant (positive or negative) to the previous term is called an **arithmetic sequence**.

A sequence in which the next term is formed by multiplying the previous term by a constant (positive or negative) is called a **geometric sequence**.

Other sequences, which are not arithmetic or geometric, are possible.

For example: Sequence of Prime Numbers 2, 3, 5, 7, 11, ...

A Fibonacci Sequence, 1, 1, 2, 3, 5, 8, 13, ... , is a special type of sequence which occurs in nature in such things as seed growth, leaves on stems, petals on flowers, etc.

In the remaining lessons in this unit, we focus on arithmetic sequences and geometric sequences.

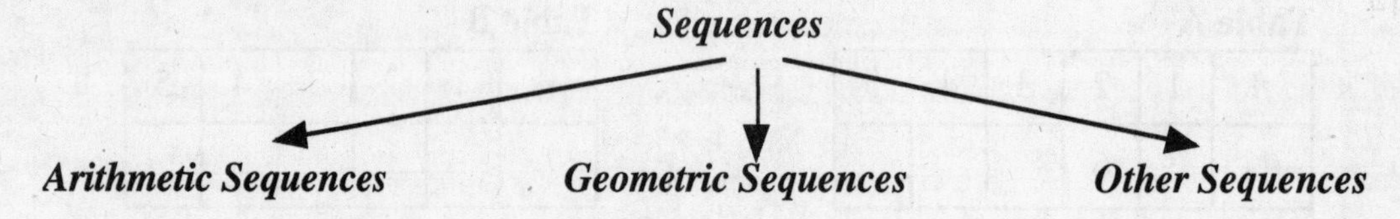

Classify the sequences in Tables A - F as arithmetic sequences or geometric sequences.

Finite and Infinite Sequences

Finite Sequence - a sequence that has a specific number of terms.

eg. 4, 10, 16, 22, 28 or 2, 4, 8, 16, ... 256.

Infinite Sequence - a sequence that has an unlimited number of terms.

eg. 4, 10, 16, 22, 28 ... or 2, 4, 8, 16, ...

A Sequence as a Function

A sequence can be regarded as a **function** relating the set of natural numbers to the terms of the sequence.

The **domain** of the function is the set of natural numbers.

The **range** of the function is the set of terms of the sequence.

Some sequences can be represented by linear functions, and some can be represented by non-linear functions.

Using the information in Tables A - F, plot the points (n, t_n) on the grids. In each case, state whether the function represented by the sequence is linear or non-linear.

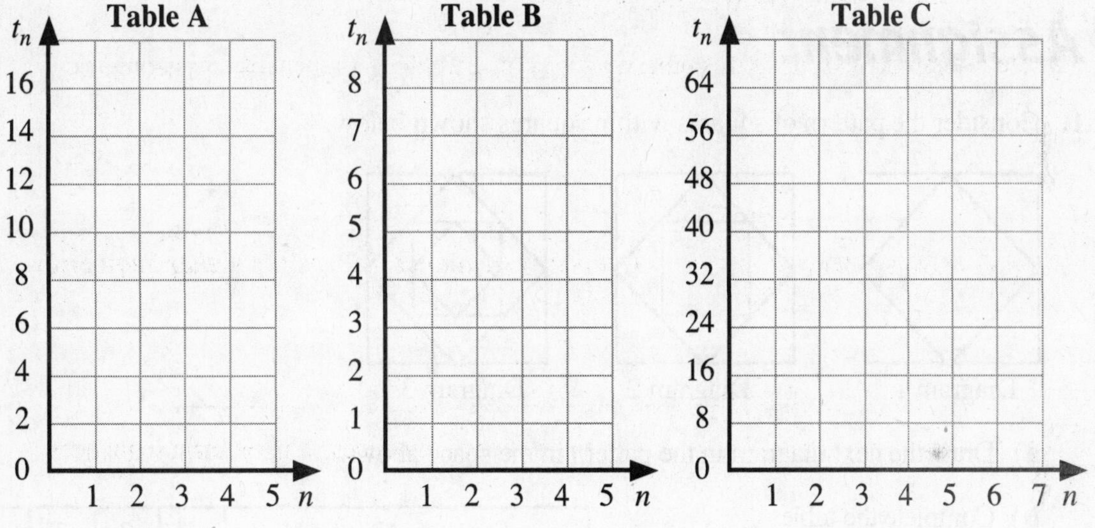

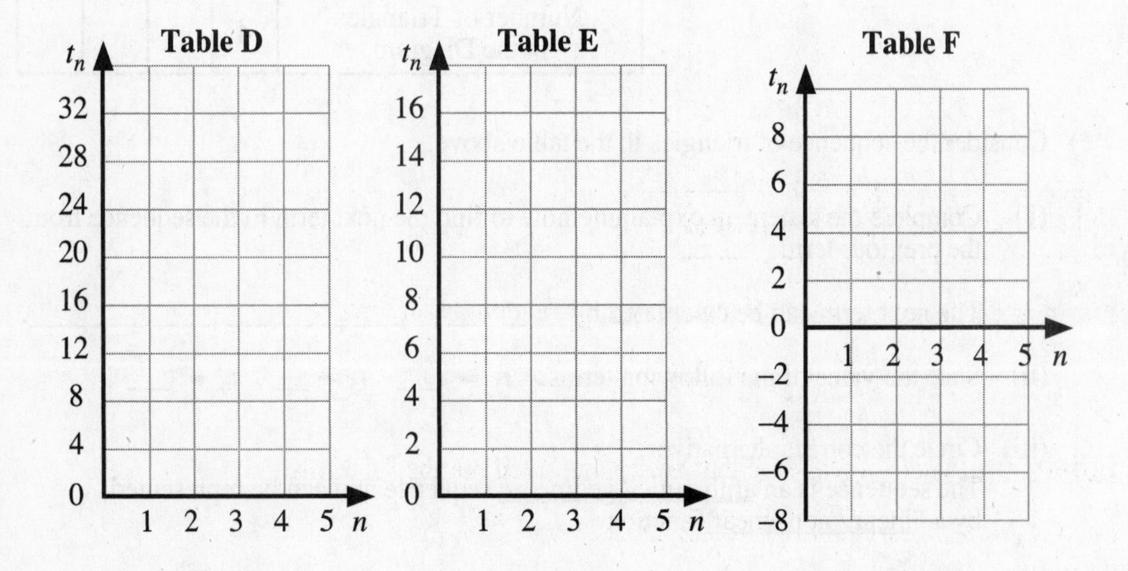

Circle the correct alternative in the following statements.

a) A sequence in which the next term is determined by adding a constant to the previous term is an arithmetic / geometric sequence.

The sequence can be represented by a linear / non-linear function.

b) A sequence in which the next term is determined by multiplying the previous term by a constant is an arithmetic / geometric sequence.

The sequence can be represented by a linear / non-linear function.

Complete Assignment Questions #1 - #15

Assignment

1. Consider the pattern of squares within squares shown below.

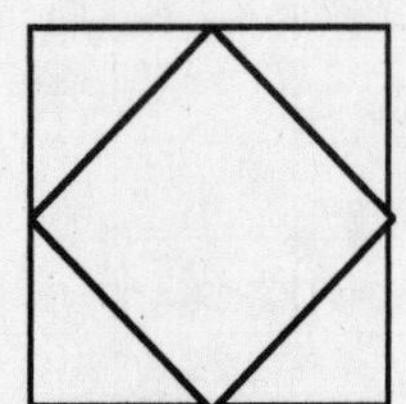
Diagram 1

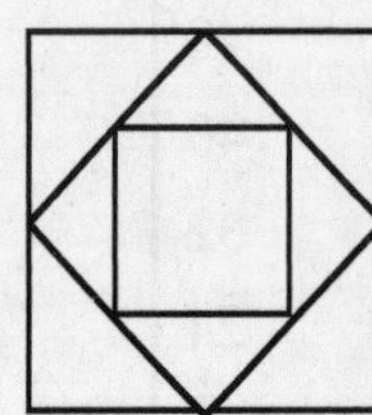
Diagram 2

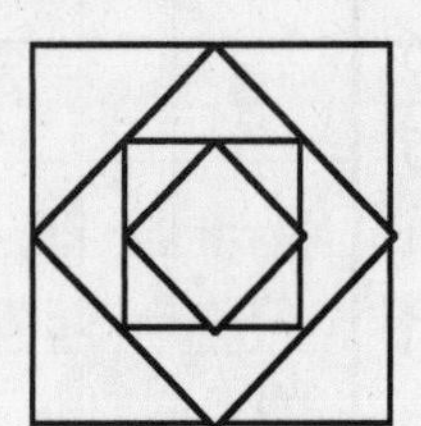
Diagram 3

a) Draw the next diagram in the pattern in the space above.

b) Complete the table.

Diagram Number	1	2	3	4
Number of Triangles in the Diagram	4			

c) Consider the sequence of triangles in the table above.

(i) Complete the statement explaining how to find the next term in the sequence from the previous term.

The next term can be calculated by ______________________.

(ii) State the value of the following terms. t_1 = ___ t_5 = ___ t_6 = ___

(iii) Circle the correct alternatives.
The sequence is an arithmetic / geometric sequence and can be represented by a linear / non-linear function.

2. Consider the following pattern of squares.

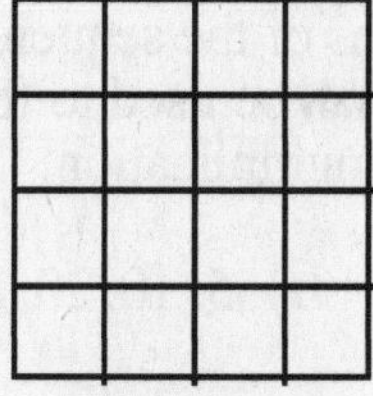
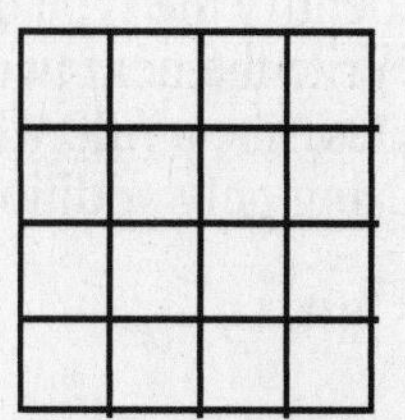

Diagram 1 Diagram 2 Diagram 3 Diagram 4 (incomplete)

a) Complete diagram 4 in the pattern.

b) Complete the table.

Diagram Number	1	2	3	4
Number of Congruent Squares in the Diagram				

c) Consider the sequence of triangles in the table above.

(i) Complete the statement explaining how to find the next term in the sequence from the previous term.

The next term can be calculated by ______________________________.

(ii) State the value of the following terms. t_4 = ___ t_5 = ___ t_6 = ___

(iii) Circle the correct alternatives.
The sequence is an arithmetic / geometric sequence and can be represented by a linear / non-linear function.

3. For each of the following sequences, determine if the sequence is arithmetic, geometric, or neither.

a) $1, 2, 3$ **b)** $-1, 1, -1, \ldots$ **c)** $12, 60, 300, \ldots$.

d) $\frac{1}{3}, \frac{1}{9}, \frac{1}{27}, \ldots, \frac{1}{2187}$ **e)** $1, 1, 2, 3, \ldots$ **f)** $250, 200, 150, \ldots$

4. Classify each sequence in question #3 as a finite sequence or an infinite sequence.

a) **b)** **c)**

d) **e)** **f)**

5. Write the next three terms of each of the infinite sequences in question #3.

6. For each of the following sequence of numbers:
- Identify the type of sequence as arithmetic or geometric.
- Write the next two terms of the sequence.
- Describe a rule which can be used to form the sequence using only addition or multiplication.

a) $5, 10, 15, ...$ **b)** $5, 10, 20, ...$ **c)** $4050, 1350, 450, ...$

d) $100, 250, 625, ...$ **e)** $25, 18, 11, ...$ **f)** $60, 80, \frac{320}{3}, ...$

7. A fractal is a fragmented geometric shape that can be subdivided into parts, each of which is a reduced-size copy of the whole. There is increased complexity of the shape at each step. An example is shown below.

Diagram 1 Diagram 2 Diagram 3

a) Diagram 4 has been started below. Complete the diagram.

Diagram 4

b) Complete the table below.

Diagram Number	1	2	3	4
Number of New Triangles in the Diagram	1			

c) Classify the sequence as arithmetic, geometric, or neither.

d) Determine the eighth term of the sequence.

8. The reproduction of bees in nature follows an interesting sequence. Whereas the female bee has two parents (a mother and a father), the male bee has only one parent (a mother).

a) Complete three more generations of the family tree for the male bee below.

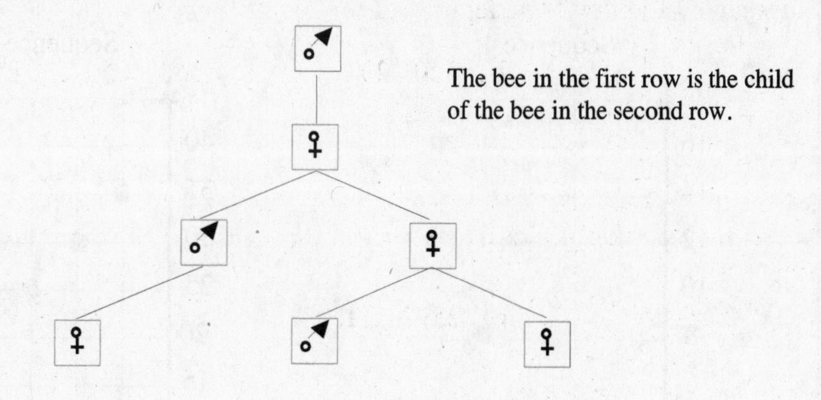
The bee in the first row is the child of the bee in the second row.

b) Complete the following table.

Row Number	1	2	3	4	5	6	7
Number of Bees in the Row	1	1					

c) Is the sequence represented in the table arithmetic, geometric or neither?

d) How many female bees are in row 7?

e) How many bees are in the eighth row?

Use the following information to answer the next four questions.

The graphical representations of two sequences are shown in the grids below.

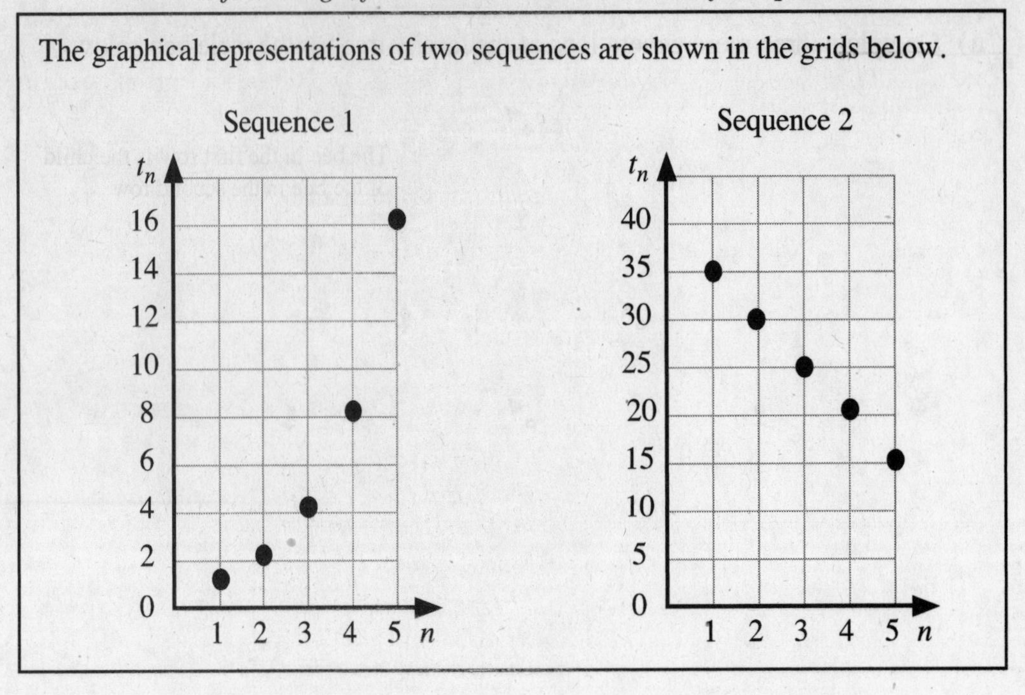

9. Explain how you can determine which one of the sequences is arithmetic.

10. Consider the sequence which is not arithmetic. How can you tell if this sequence is geometric or not?

11. For each sequence, describe a rule for determining the next term from the previous term.

12. Determine the eighth term of each sequence.

Use the following information to answer questions #13 to #15.

In the puzzle called the "Towers of Hanoi", a person is asked to move rings from one peg and stack them in order on another peg. You can make as many moves as you want, but only one ring per move. Also, no ring may be placed on top of a smaller ring. For example, the minimum number of moves required to move 1 ring is 1 move, 2 rings is 3 moves, 3 rings is 7 moves, 4 rings is 15 moves, and 5 rings is 31 moves.

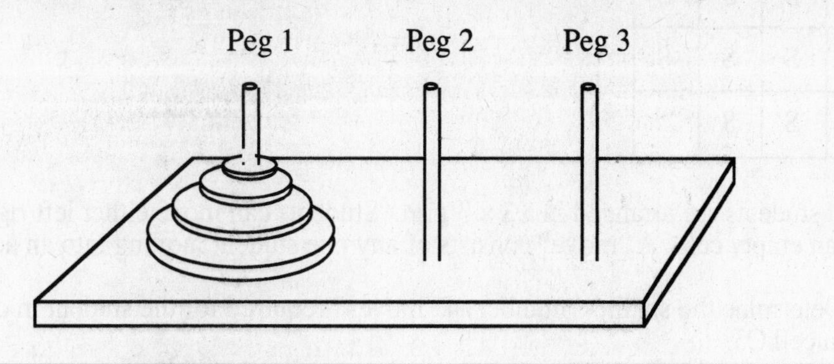

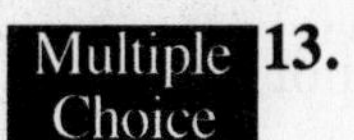

13. The sequence represented by the number of moves is

A. an arithmetic sequence

B. a geometric sequence

C. a Fibonacci sequence

D. none of the above

14. The difference between consecutive terms forms

A. an arithmetic sequence

B. a geometric sequence

C. a Fibonacci sequence

D. none of the above

15. The minimum number of moves required to move 6 rings is

A. 45

B. 55

C. 63

D. 65

The following investigation could be used as a lead-in to the next lesson. The solution can be obtained by drawing a grid and using counters or coins; however, greater understanding may be obtained by having students act out the situation.

	A	B	C
1	S	S	S
2	S	S	S
3	S	S	

Eight students are arranged in a 3×3 grid. Students can move either left/right or up/down into an empty cell. A "move" consists of any one student moving into an adjacent cell.

a) Determine the smallest number of "moves" required for the student in cell A1 to end up in cell C3.

b) Extend your thinking by developing a strategy for determining the smallest number of "moves" required to move a student from cell A1 to cell Z26 in a 26×26 grid.

Answer Key

1. a)

b) 8, 12, 16

c) **i)** adding four to the previous term

ii) $t_1 = 4, t_5 = 20, t_6 = 24$

iii) arithmetic, linear

2. a)

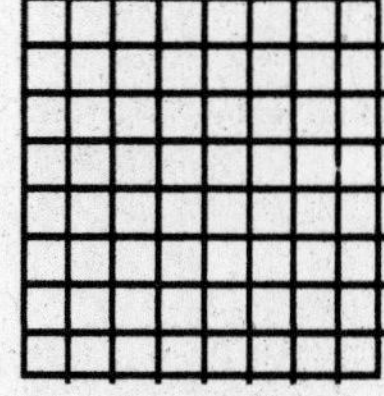

b) 1, 4, 16, 64

c) **i)** multiplying the previous term by 4

ii) $t_4 = 64, t_5 = 256, t_6 = 1024$

iii) geometric, non-linear

3. a) arithmetic **b)** geometric **c)** geometric **d)** geometric **e)** neither **f)** arithmetic

4. a) finite **b)** infinite **c)** infinite **d)** finite **e)** infinite **f)** infinite

5. b) 1, –1, 1 **c)** 1 500, 7 500, 37 500 **e)** 5, 8, 13 **f)** 100, 50, 0

6. a) Arithmetic. 20, 25. Add 5 to the previous term.

b) Geometric. 40, 80. Multiply the previous term by 2.

c) Geometric. 150, 50. Multiply the previous term by $\frac{1}{3}$.

d) Geometric. 1562.5, 3906.25. Multiply the previous term by 2.5.

e) Arithmetic. 4, –3. Add –7 to the previous term.

f) Geometric. $\frac{1280}{9}$, $\frac{5120}{27}$. Multiply the previous term by $\frac{4}{3}$.

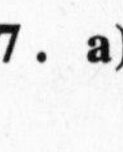

7. a)

b) 3, 9, 27 **c)** Geometric **d)** 2187

8. a)

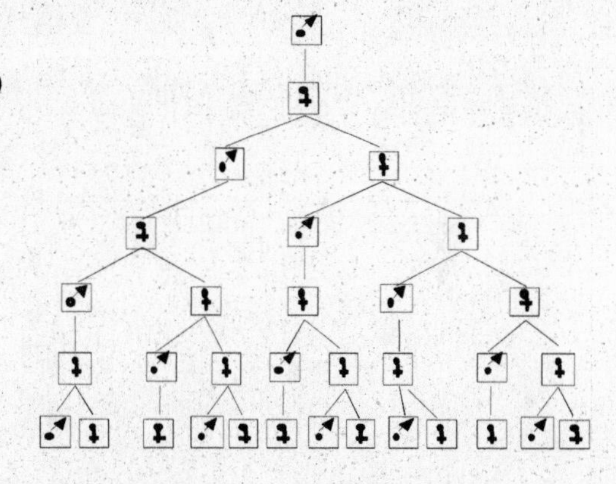

b) 2, 3, 5, 8, 13 **c)** Neither **d)** 8 **e)** 21

9. If the graph is linear, the sequence is arithmetic. Sequence 2 is arithmetic.

10. Write the terms of the sequence. If each term is formed from the previous term by multiplying by a constant, the sequence is geometric. The sequence is 1, 2, 4, 8, 16 so the sequence is geometric.

11. For sequence 1, multiply the previous term by 2. For sequence 2, add –5 to the previous term.

12. 128, 0 **13.** D **14.** B **15.** C

Group Investigation

a) 13

b) 2 x 2 grid → 5 moves. 3 x 3 grid → 13 moves. 4 x 4 grid → 21 moves.

Extend the pattern: 26 x 26 grid → 197 moves.

Sequences and Series Lesson #2:
Arithmetic Sequences

Arithmetic Sequence

An **arithmetic sequence** is a sequence in which each term is formed from the preceding term by ***adding*** a constant (positive or negative).

Complete the following for the sequence 7, 10, 13, 16, ...

- Each term is determined by adding ____ to the previous term.
- Calculate the differences: $t_2 - t_1$ = ____ $t_3 - t_2$ = ____ $t_4 - t_3$ = ____

Notice that there is a **common difference** between successive terms.

The common difference in this example is ____.

Finding a Common Difference

To find a common difference in an arithmetic sequence, we can subtract any term from the term after it.

For example $t_2 - t_1$ = common difference, or
$t_5 - t_4$ = common difference, etc.

common difference = $t_n - t_{n-1}$

Consider the sequence 16, 13, 10, 7, ...

The **common difference** in the sequence is ____ .

For each of the following
- determine which sequences are arithmetic, and
- find the common difference for those sequences which are arithmetic

a) 2, 4, 6, 8, ... **b)** $\frac{1}{2}, \frac{1}{4}, \frac{1}{8}, \frac{1}{16}, ...$ **c)** −10, −4, 2, 8, ... **d)** 4, 8, 16, 32, ...

In an arithmetic sequence we often use the following terminology.

The **first term** in an arithmetic sequence is represented by t_1, or a, and the **common difference** is represented by d.

State the values of a and d in the following sequences:

i) $-8, 2, 12, 22, \ldots$ **ii)** $15, 10, 5, 0 \ldots .$

Investigation

Investigating the Formula for the General Term of an Arithmetic Sequence

Consider the sequence $2, 12, 22, 32, 42 \ldots .$

a) State the following

$t_1 =$ $t_2 =$ $t_3 =$ $t_4 =$ $t_5 =$ $a =$ $d =$

b) Complete the following pattern which describes each term in the sequence in terms of the first term, a, and the common difference, d.

$t_1 = 2$	$t_1 = a$
$t_2 = 2 + 1(10) = 12$	$t_2 = a + (1)d$
$t_3 = 2 + 2(10) = 22$	$t_3 = a + 2d$
$t_4 =$	$t_4 =$
$t_5 =$	$t_5 =$
$t_{30} =$	$t_{30} =$
$t_n =$	$t_n =$

The Formula for the General Term of an Arithmetic Sequence

The formula for the general term of an arithmetic sequence is

$$\mathbf{t_n = t_1 + (n-1)d} \quad \text{or} \quad \mathbf{t_n = a + (n-1)d}$$

where, t_n is the general term of the arithmetic sequence
$a = t_1$, is the first term
d is the common difference
n is the position of the term in the sequence

The general arithmetic sequence is $a, a+d, a+2d, a+3d, \ldots a+(n-1)d$.

Consider the arithmetic sequence $-6, -1, 4, 9, \ldots$.

a) Determine the formula for the general term of the sequence.

b) Determine the value of the twelfth term of the sequence.

Find the number of terms in the arithmetic sequence $3, -1, -5, \ldots, -117$.

Complete Assignment Questions #1 - #10

Arithmetic Means

The terms placed between two non-consecutive terms of an arithmetic sequence are called **arithmetic means**. For example, in the sequence $5, 10, 15, 20,$ the numbers 10 and 15 are arithmetic means between 5 and 20. In order to determine arithmetic means between two given terms, it is helpful to think of the two given terms as the **first** and **last** terms of a sequence.

Place three arithmetic means between -4 and 8.

Solving Sequence Problems Where Both "a" and "d" are Unknown

Consider the sequence $x + 2, 3x - 1, 2x + 1$.

a) Determine the value of x such that $x + 2, 3x - 1$, and $2x + 1$ form an arithmetic sequence.

b) Determine the numerical value of the three terms.

The next two class examples show two different ways of solving the same problem. Class Example #8 uses arithmetic means, and Class Example #9 uses a system of linear equations.

The third and eighth terms of an arithmetic sequence are 12 and –18, respectively.

a) Use arithmetic means to determine the fifth term of the sequence.

b) State the first term, a, and the common difference, d, of the sequence.

c) Complete the following: $\dfrac{t_8 - t_3}{8 - 3} = \underline{\qquad\qquad} = \underline{\qquad\qquad}$

d) Write t_3 and t_8 in terms of a and d and prove that $\dfrac{t_8 - t_3}{8 - 3} = d$.

e) Suggest a formula for finding the common difference of a sequence if you are given the value of the p th term and the q th term.

The third and eighth terms of an arithmetic sequence are 12 and −18, respectively. Use a system of linear equations to determine the values of the first term and the common difference. Hence, determine the fifth term of the sequence.

Complete Assignment Questions #11 - #20

Assignment

1. For the following arithmetic sequences:
i) Determine the common difference. **ii)** Find the next three terms of the sequence.

a) $8, 14, 20, \ldots$ **b)** $-5, 7, 19, \ldots$ **c)** $70, 53, 36, 19, \ldots$

d) $7.1, 4.2, 1.3, \ldots$ **e)** $\frac{2}{3}, \frac{1}{15}, -\frac{8}{15}, \ldots$ **f)** $-2x + 3y, -5x + y, -8x - y, \ldots$

2. In each of the following sequences, the value of one term is given. Write the missing terms of the sequence if the common difference is as indicated.

a) ____, ____, 0, ____, ____: $d = 3$ **b)** ____, ____, ____, −3, ____: $d = -7$

c) ____, ____, 1, ____, ____: $d = -2$ **d)** ____, ____, ____, ____, 15: $d = 2.5$

3. Calculate the first four terms of the arithmetic sequences with given term and common difference, d.

a) $t_1 = 5, d = 6$ **b)** $t_3 = 15, d = -2$ **c)** $t_5 = 20, d = -1$

4. Consider the sequence $12, 5, -2, -9, \ldots$.

a) Determine the formula for the general term of the sequence.

b) Determine the nineteenth term of the sequence.

c) Which of the numbers -268 and -350 are terms of the sequence?

5. Determine the indicated terms in each arithmetic sequence.

a) $-1, -4, -7, -10, \ldots .\ t_5,\ t_{24},\ t_n$

b) $-21, -6, 9, 24, \ldots .\ t_{10},\ t_{90},\ t_n$

c) $-b, 2a-b, 4a-b, 6a-b, \ldots .\ t_{12},\ t_n$

6. Consider the pattern of L-shapes shown.

a) State the number of stars in each of the first four patterns.

b) How many stars are in the 34th pattern?

7. Determine the number of terms in each sequence.

a) $4, 7, 10, ..., 49$ **b)** $-52, -56, -60, ..., -148$

8. How many multiples of 5 are there from 25 to 315, inclusive?

9. Consider the sequence of multiples of 7 between 51 and 275.

a) State the first and last terms of the sequence.

b) How many multiples of 7 are there between 51 and 275?

10. How many multiples of 12 are there between 179 and 892?

11. a) Place five arithmetic means between 20 and –76.

b) Determine the 4th, 5th, 6th, and 7th terms of the arithmetic sequence in which $t_3 = -24$ and $t_8 = -94$.

12. The terms $2x + 3$, $3x + 1$, and $8x - 1$ are consecutive terms in an arithmetic sequence. Calculate the value of x, and state the three terms.

13. The terms $x + 3$, $3x - 1$, and $7x - 2$ are consecutive terms in an arithmetic sequence. Calculate the value of x, and determine the general term of the sequence.

14. In an arithmetic sequence, the seventh term is 3 and the sixteenth term is 9.

a) Use arithmetic means to determine the common difference and the first term of the sequence.

b) Use a system of equations to determine the common difference and the first term of the sequence.

c) Calculate t_{19} and determine the general term of the sequence.

15. Use linear systems to determine a, d and t_n for the sequences in which the following two terms are given.

a) $t_5 = 21, t_{10} = 41$

b) $t_4 = -9, t_{15} = -31$

Multiple Choice

16. Which of the following represents an arithmetic sequence with a common difference of -4?

A. $8, 4, 2, 1 \ldots$ **B.** $20, 24, 28, 32 \ldots$ **C.** $32, -8, 2, -0.5 \ldots$ **D.** $20, 16, 12, 8 \ldots$

17. $p - 1,\ p + 3,\ 3p - 1$, in that order, form an arithmetic sequence.
Which of the following is/are true about p?

1. p is even
2. p is odd
3. p is a perfect square

A. 1 only
B. 1 and 3 only
C. 2 only
D. 2 and 3 only

18. Two students are asked to write the first four terms of an arithmetic sequence.
Rob writes the sequence $-14, -6, 2, 10 \ldots.$
Jason writes the sequence $166, 162, 158, 154 \ldots..$

Which statement is true about the fifteenth term of these sequences?

A. t_{15} is the same in each sequence
B. t_{15} is smaller in Rob's sequence
C. t_{15} is smaller in Jason's sequence
D. there is not enough information to answer the question

19. If $x+2$, $3x-4$, and $7x-6$ are the first three terms of an arithmetic sequence, then the first term of the sequence has a numerical value of

A. −2
B. 0
C. 2
D. 4

Numerical Response **20.** Twenty-seven arithmetic means are inserted between the first and last terms of a sequence. The number of terms in the sequence is _______ .

(Record your answer in the numerical response box from left to right.)

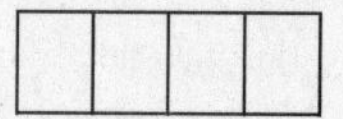

Answer Key

1. a) i) 6 ii) $t_4 = 26, t_5 = 32, t_6 = 38$ **b)** i) 12 ii) $t_4 = 31, t_5 = 43, t_6 = 55$
c) i) −17 ii) $t_5 = 2, t_6 = -15, t_7 = -32$ **d)** i) −2.9 ii) $t_4 = -1.6, t_5 = -4.5, t_6 = -7.4$
e) i) $-3/5$ ii) $t_4 = -17/15, t_5 = -26/15, t_6 = -7/3$
f) i) $-3x - 2y$, ii) $t_4 = -11x - 3y, t_5 = -14x - 5y, t_6 = -17x - 7y$

2. a) −6, −3, 0, 3, 6 **b)** 18, 11, 4, −3, −10 **c)** 5, 3, 1, −1, −3 **d)** 5, 7.5, 10, 12.5, 15

3. a) 5, 11, 17, 23 **b)** 19, 17, 15, 13 **c)** 24, 23, 22, 21

4. a) $t_n = 19 - 7n$ **b)** −114 **c)** −268 is the 41st term

5. a) −13, −70, $t_n = 2 - 3n$ **b)** 114, 1314, $t_n = 15n - 36$ **c)** $22a - b$, $t_n = 2an - 2a - b$

6. a) 4, 6, 8, 10 **b)** 70

7. a) 16 **b)** 25 **8.** 59 **9. a)** 56 and 273 **b)** 32

10. 60 **11. a)** 4, −12, −28, −44, −60 **b)** −38, −52, −66, −80

12. $x = 0$; 3, 1, −1 **13.** $x = -\frac{3}{2}$; $t_n = \frac{17}{2} - 7n$

14. a) $d = \frac{2}{3}, t_1 = -1$; **b)** $d = \frac{2}{3}, a = -1$; **c)** $t_{19} = 11$, $t_n = \frac{2}{3}n - \frac{5}{3}$

15. a) $a = 5, d = 4, t_n = 4n + 1$ **b)** $a = -3, d = -2, t_n = -2n - 1$

16. D **17.** B **18.** B **19.** B **20.**

2	9		

Sequences and Series Lesson #3:
Arithmetic Growth and Decay

Generating Number Patterns Exhibiting Arithmetic Growth

Many real-life scenarios can be represented by a pattern of numbers which exhibit arithmetic growth.

BP Birthplace Forest program in Calgary enables parents to honour their children by planting a tree when their child is born. At the same time, this shows concern for the urban environment by encouraging the growth of city forests. Some of the trees which have been planted are evergreen trees which grow an average of 12 to 18 inches per year. The program was launched in the year 2000.

a) An evergreen tree, 6 inches high, was planted in June 2000 and has a growth rate of 15 inches per year. Two students were asked to determine the height of the tree in June 2011. Joel formed an arithmetic sequence beginning 6, 21, 36, ... and Jenna formed an arithmetic sequence beginning 21, 36, 51 ... . Use the formulas in the previous lesson to determine each student's answer to the problem.

b) Determine the formula for the general term of Joel's arithmetic sequence.

c) Determine the formula for the general term of Jenna's arithmetic sequence.

d) Explain why the formulas in b) and c) are different.

e) If the tree continues to grow at the same rate, in which year will it reach a height of 28 ft?

Generating Number Patterns Exhibiting Arithmetic Decay

Many real-life scenarios can be represented by a pattern of numbers which exhibit arithmetic decay or arithmetic depreciation.

Class Ex. #2

A printing press was bought in the year 1992. It depreciates in value by the same amount each year. Five years after it was bought, the printing press had a value of $311 000. It had a scrap value of $2900 in the year 2010.

a) Use an arithmetic sequence to determine the amount of the annual depreciation.

b) Determine the purchase price of the printing press.

Relating Arithmetic Sequences to Linear Functions

We can relate arithmetic sequences to linear functions over the natural numbers. Consider the following example:

A pile of bricks is arranged in rows. There are 28 bricks in the first row, and the number of bricks in each row is two more than in the previous row.

a) Complete the table of values showing the number of bricks in each of the first 10 rows.

Row Number, r	Number of Bricks, n

b) Plot the ordered pairs on the grid. and classify the relationship as linear or non-linear.

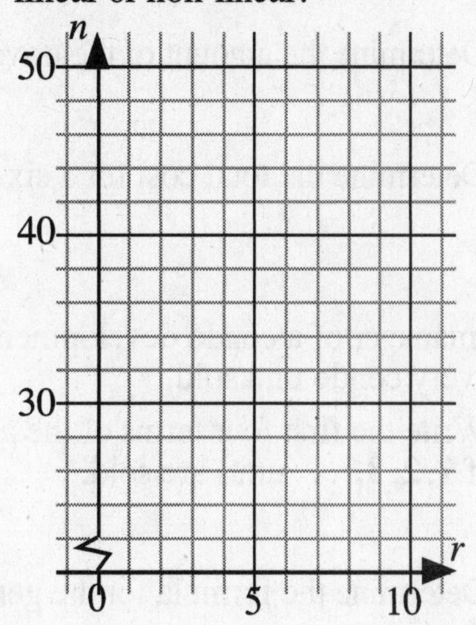

c) Determine if the range is an arithmetic sequence.

d) State the domain of the relationship.

e) Why does the graph not have an intercept on the vertical axis?

f) Write the equation for the number of bricks in a row, n, as a function of the row number, r.

Complete Assignment Questions #1 - #10

Assignment

1. A contractor charges $68 for the first hour of work. This includes a rate of one hour of work and a fixed travel fee. For a two hour job, the contractor charges $110, and for a three hour job, the contractor charges $152.

a) Using these three numbers as the first three terms of an arithmetic sequence, determine the values of a and d.

b) State the rate for each additional hour of work.

c) Determine the amount of the travel fee.

d) Determine the total cost for a six hour job.

2. The manager of a condo development receives a base salary of $15 000 per year plus $800 for every condo unit sold.

a) Write the first four terms of the arithmetic sequence for the manager's earnings if 1, 2, 3, . . . units are sold.

b) Determine the formula for the general term of the arithmetic sequence in the form $t_n = a + (n - 1)d$.

c) Use the general term formula to calculate his earnings if

i) 23 units are sold **ii)** 54 units are sold

d) Write the equation for the manager's earnings, E, as a linear function of the number, n, of units sold. Write the equation in the form $E = mn + b$.

e) Use the linear function in d) to calculate his earnings if

i) 23 units are sold **ii)** 54 units are sold

3. For a forthcoming horticultural exhibition, bulbs were planted in rows. The number of bulbs in each row forms an arithmetic sequence. There are 58 bulbs in the eighth row and 107 bulbs in the fifteenth row.

How many bulbs in total are in the first three rows?

4. Consider the linear function with equation $y = 3x + 5$.

a) Sketch the graph of the linear function on the grid.

b) Restrict the domain to the set of natural numbers. Mark with dots points on the graph which represent the function on the restricted domain.

c) Write the first five elements of the range in numerical order.

d) Show that the elements of the range form an arithmetic sequence and state the common difference.

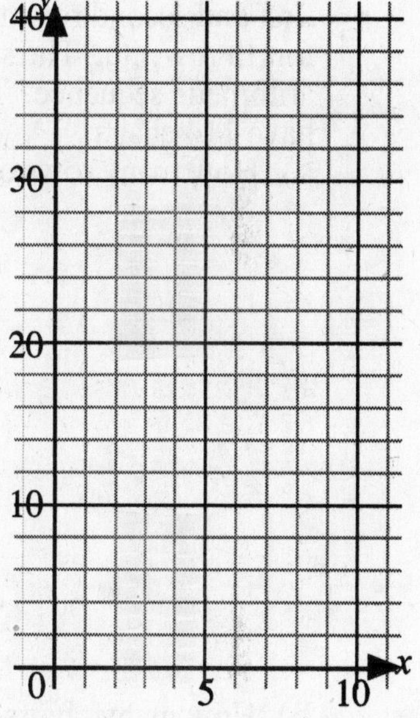

5. Charity starts a new job as a geologist in the oil industry. Her rate of pay for the first year is \$36 000, with an increase of \$2750 per year thereafter.

a) Calculate her rate of pay in the seventh year.

b) In which year will she first earn more than \$60 000?

6. A sports utility vehicle sells for \$35 000. The vehicle depreciates \$5000 the first year and \$2400 each year thereafter. Calculate the value at the vehicle at the end of the eleventh year.

7. Chairs in an auditorium are arranged in rows in such a way that the first two rows each have the same number of chairs. The third and fourth rows each have three more chairs than the first and second row; the fifth and sixth rows each have three more chairs than the third and fourth row, etc. The sequence of number of chairs for every second row forms an arithmetic sequence. The first two rows each have 27 chairs, and the last two rows each have 114 chairs.

a) How many rows of chairs are there?

b) How many chairs are in the **i)** thirteenth **ii)** thirtieth row?

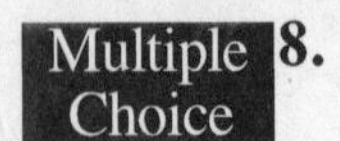

8. As part of a fitness program, Melissa walks for 35 minutes on day 1 and increases the walking time by 8 minutes each day. She completes the fitness program on the day she first spends more than 3 hours walking. The program is completed on day _____ .

A. 17
B. 18
C. 19
D. 20

Use the following graph to answer questions #9 and #10.

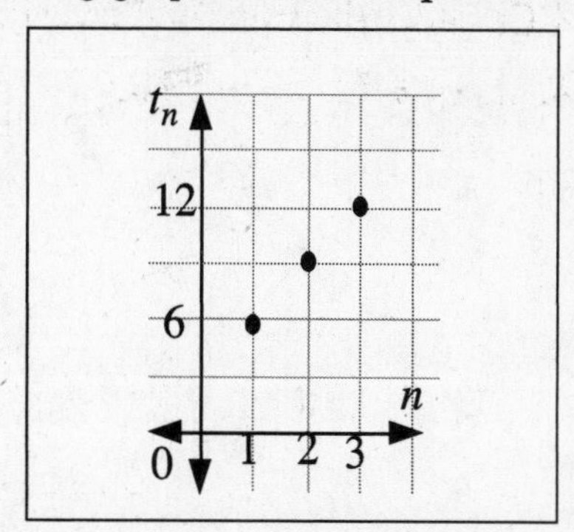

9. The graph above represents arithmetic growth. If the graph continues indefinitely, then the fifteenth term of the sequence is

A. 48
B. 51
C. 90
D. 153

Numerical Response **10.** The formula for this sequence is $t_n = mn + b$.
The value of b is ______ .
(Record your answer in the numerical response box from left to right.)

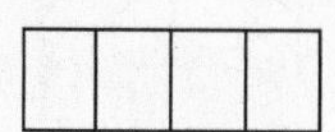

Answer Key

1. a) $a = 68$, $d = 42$ **b)** \$42 **c)** \$26 **d)** \$278

2. a) 15800, 16600,17400,18200 **b)** $t_n = 15800 + (n - 1)(800)$
c) i) \$33400 ii) \$58200 **d)** $E = 800n + 15000$ **e)** i) \$33400 ii) \$58200

3. 48 **4. c)** 8, 11, 14, 17, 20 **d)** common difference = 3

5. a) \$52500 **b)** year 10 **6.** \$6000 **7. a)** 60 **b) i)** 45 **ii)** 69

8. D **9.** A **10.** 3

Sequences and Series Lesson #4: Arithmetic Series

Arithmetic Series

When the terms of an arithmetic sequence are added, the result is known as an **arithmetic series**.

For example $\quad 3, 5, 7, 9, 11 \quad \rightarrow \quad$ arithmetic sequence

$\quad 3 + 5 + 7 + 9 + 11 \quad \rightarrow \quad$ arithmetic series.

The symbol, S_n is used to represent the sum of n terms of an arithmetic series.

In the example above $S_5 =$ _____ .

Investigation

Investigating the Sum of an Arithmetic Series

To illustrate the method for determining a formula for the sum of n terms of an arithmetic series, the story of the great mathematician Karl Gauss (1777-1855) is frequently told.

> When Karl was about 10 years old, he was placed in Master Buttner's arithmetic class. Master Buttner often gave his class long arithmetic problems to keep them quiet for a time. On one particular day, Master Buttner asked his class to add the whole numbers from 1 to 100. While all the students began to work madly on this assignment, Karl laid his slate on the desk and informed Master Buttner he was finished. Master Buttner asked Karl what his answer was. To Master Buttner's astonishment, Karl gave the correct answer of 5050.

Here we apply a method similar to his to determine the answer.

$$S_{100} = 1 + 2 + 3 + 4 + 5 + \ldots + 96 + 97 + 98 + 99 + 100$$

$$S_{100} = 100 + 99 + 98 + 97 + 96 + \ldots + 5 + 4 + 3 + 2 + 1$$

Add the rows and complete the work to show that $S_{100} = 5050$.

$$2\,S_{100} = 101 + 101 +$$

Formulas for the Sum of an Arithmetic Series

In an arithmetic series of n terms,

the first term is a, the second term is $a + d$, and the last term, $t_n = a + (n - 1)d$.

The sum of n terms of the series can be written as

$$S_n = a + (a + d) + (a + 2d) + \ . \ . \ . \ + (a + (n - 3)d) + (a + (n - 2)d) + (a + (n - 1)d$$

OR

$$S_n = (a + (n - 1)d) + (a + (n - 2)d) + (a + (n - 3)d.+ ... + (a + 2d) + (a + d) + a$$

Adding these two lines together gives

$$2S_n = (2a + (n - 1)d) + (2a + (n - 1)d) + (2a + (n - 1)d) + ... + (2a + (n - 1)d)$$
$$+ (2a + (n - 1)d) + (2a + (n - 1)d)$$
$$2S_n = n(2a + (n - 1)d)$$

Dividing by 2 gives the **formula for the sum of n terms of an arithmetic series.**

$$S_n = \frac{n[2a + (n - 1)d]}{2}$$

This formula connects a, d, n, and S_n.
If any three of these values are known, the fourth can be determined.

However, when the common difference of the series is not known, another **formula for the sum of n terms of an arithmetic series** can be formed by replacing $a + (n - 1)d$ by t_n to give

$$S_n = \frac{n(a + t_n)}{2}$$

The above formula can be thought of as the average of the first and last terms multiplied by the number of terms.

Determine the sum of the first fourteen terms of the arithmetic series 9 + 15 + 21 + ...

Determine the sum of 22 terms of an arithmetic sequence with $t_1 = -18$ and $t_{22} = 45$.

Find the sum of the terms in the sequence 17, 12, 7, ... −38.

Peter starts work at a salary of $16 000 per annum. He receives annual increases of $850. He works for the firm for twelve years.

a) Calculate his salary in the twelfth year.

b) How much has he earned in total over the twelve years?

Complete Assignment Questions #1 - #6

Investigation #2 *Investigating an Arithmetic Series Defined in Terms of S_n.*

Corrie was given two questions on a sequences and series assignment. The first question is listed below.

"Find the first four terms of the series defined by $S_n = 2n^2 - n$."

a) Complete her work below to find the first four terms.

$S_n = 2n^2 - n$

$S_1 = 2(1)^2 - 1 = 1$ $\Rightarrow t_1 = S_1$ $\therefore t_1 = 1$

$S_2 = 2(2)^2 - 2 = 6$ $\Rightarrow S_2 = S_1 + t_2$ $\Rightarrow t_2 = S_2 - S_1$ $\Rightarrow t_2 = 6 - 1$ $\therefore t_2 =$

$S_3 = 2(3)^2 - 3 = 15$ $\Rightarrow S_3 = \_ +$ $\Rightarrow t_3 = \_ - \_$ $\Rightarrow t_3 = \quad -$ $\therefore t_3 =$

$S_4 = \qquad =$ $\Rightarrow S_4 = \_ + \_$ $\Rightarrow t_4 =$ $\Rightarrow t_4 =$ $\therefore t_4 =$

b) Express t_{10} in terms of S.

c) Express t_n in terms of S.

d) The second question Corrie received was "Find t_n if $S_n = 2n^2 - n$."

i) Find t_n using the formula $t_n = a + (n - 1)d$

ii) Find t_n using the formula in c)

Remember the formula $t_n = S_n - S_{n-1},\ n \geq 2, n \in N$

For a certain arithmetic series, $S_n = \frac{1}{2}n(11 - n)$.
Determine the first four terms of the corresponding arithmetic sequence.

Complete Assignment Questions #7 - #16

Assignment

1. Find the sum of each series.

a) $2 + 3 + 4 + \ldots$ (first 30 terms)

b) $(-8) + (-4) + 0 + \ldots$ (first 27 terms)

c) $2.5 + 2.7 + 2.9 + \ldots$ to 16 terms

d) $\frac{5}{2} + \frac{11}{6} + \frac{7}{6} + \frac{1}{2} + \ldots$ to 12 terms

2. Find the sum of each arithmetic series given the first and last terms.

a) $a = 8, t_{15} = 120$ **b)** $t_1 = -11, t_{23} = -253$

3. Find the sum of each series.

a) $11 + 23 + 35 + 47 + ... + 179$ **b)** $29 + 21 + 13 + 5 + ... -27$

4. As payment for his daughter's yard work, a father agrees to give his daughter an allowance of $3.50 in the first week of the year with an increase of 50 cents each week until the last week of the year.

a) How much money did she receive for an allowance in the last week of the year?

b) What was the total amount of money her father gave her in allowances for the year?

5. Joe, from Perfection Millworks, has fourteen counter tops to deliver to fourteen floors in an office building. Because of the size of the counter tops, he can only get one counter top into the elevator at a time. He starts at the main floor and takes the first counter top to the first floor, returns to the main floor, picks up the second counter top and takes it to the second floor, and so on. He continues in this way until all fourteen countertops have been delivered. If the distance between floors is exactly 7 m, how far has the elevator travelled when Joe has delivered all the counter tops and returns to the main floor?

6. Bob "Bubbles" Burble was asked on a math assignment to find the sum of eight arithmetic means placed between –15 and 12. Bubbles proceeded to find the eight arithmetic means and determine the sum. Along comes Sally "Sequential" Sequence and asks Bubbles why he is first finding all the means. Sally told Bubbles he does not have to find the means at all! Is Sally correct in stating that Bubbles does not have to find all the means? If so, show clearly Sally's method, and determine the sum.

7. Consider the series defined by $S_n = 3n - 1$.

a) Find the first four terms of the series.

b) Is the sequence arithmetic? Explain.

8. Consider the series defined by $S_n = 3n^2 - n$.

a) Find the first four terms of the series.

b) Determine the eighth term of the corresponding sequence.

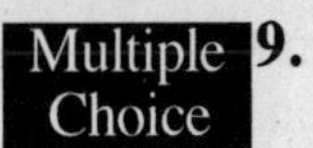

9. Which of the following is an arithmetic series?

A. $1 + 4 + 9 + 16 + 25$
B. $1, 3, 5, 7, \ldots$
C. $6 + 2 + (-2) + (-6)$
D. $8, -8, 8, -8$

10. The sum of the first 100 terms of the arithmetic series $3 + 1 + (-1) + (-3) + \ldots$ is

A. -1020
B. -1005
C. -9705
D. -9600

Use the following information to answer questions #11 and #12.

Mary Ann was a statistician. She was paid according to a salary grid with annual increases from year one to year ten. The sequence of salaries from years one to ten formed an arithmetic sequence. After year ten she reached her maximum salary. She earned $65 328 in the fifth year and $81 276 in the ninth year. She worked as a statistician for twelve years.

11. Mary Ann's pay in her first year of work was

A. $49 380
B. $53 367
C. $57 354
D. none of the above

12. The total amount that Mary Ann earned as a statistician was

A. $85 263
B. $673 215
C. $843 741
D. $1 346 430

Use the following information to answer questions #13 - #14.

A child arranges animal blocks in rows on a floor. There are 64 animal blocks in the fifth row and 92 animal blocks in the ninth and last row. Assume that the number of animal blocks from row to row form an arithmetic sequence.

Numerical Response

13. The number of animal blocks in the first row is _____ .

(Record your answer in the numerical response box from left to right.)

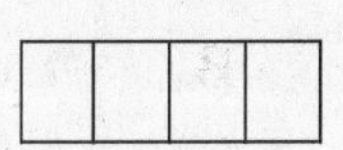

14. The total number of blocks used in the arrangement is _____ .

(Record your answer in the numerical response box from left to right.)

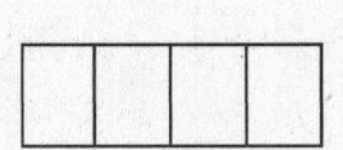

15. The graph shown plots the sum of n terms of an arithmetic sequence as a function of $n \in N$. Each point on the graph is of the form (n, S_n), where S_n is the sum of n terms of the sequence.

The sum of the second and third terms of the sequence is _____.

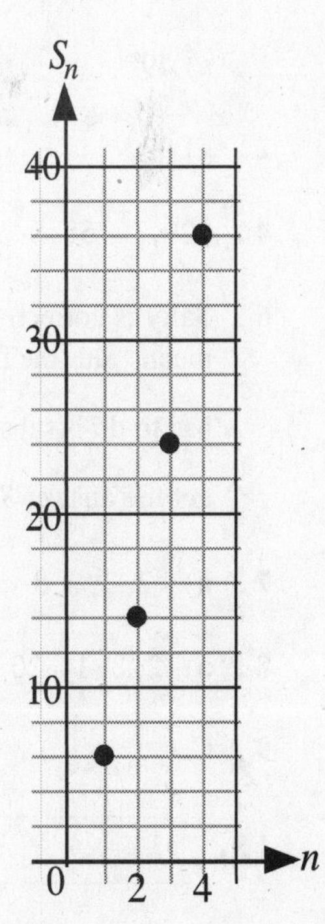

(Record your answer in the numerical response box from left to right.)

16. If the nth term of an arithmetic series is $3n - 7$, then the sum of the first 18 terms is ______ .

(Record your answer in the numerical response box from left to right.)

Answer Key

1. **a)** 495 **b)** 1188 **c)** 64 **d)** –14

2. **a)** 960 **b)** –3036 **3.** **a)** 1425 **b)** 8

4. \$29, \$845 **5.** 1470 m

6. Sally is correct. We are given: i) the first and last terms, ii) the number of terms, 10 (eight arithmetic means plus the first and last term) and iii) the series is arithmetic. ∴ given this information, all Bubbles has to do is substitute the appropriate numbers in the general arithmetic series formula $S_n = \dfrac{n(a + t_n)}{2}$ to get the answer S_{10}. Subtract the first and last terms to get the answer of –12.

7. **a)** 2, 3, 3, 3 **b)** no, because there is no common difference between successive terms.

8. **a)** 2, 8, 14, 20 **b)** 44

9. C **10.** D **11.** A **12.** C

13.

3	6		

14.

5	7	6	

15.

1	8		

16.

3	8	7	

Sequences and Series Lesson #5: Geometric Sequences

Warm-Up

Consider the following two sequences: **i)** 2, 4, 6, 8, ... **ii)** 2, 4, 8, 16, ...
Explain how to calculate t_5 and t_6 for each sequence. State the value of each term.

Geometric Sequence

A sequence where each term is obtained by **multiplying** the preceding term by a constant is called a **geometric sequence**.

For example, 3, 6, 12, 24, ... is a geometric sequence.

The value of the constant can be found by dividing the second term by the first term or by dividing any term by the previous term.

eg. $\frac{t_2}{t_1}$, or $\frac{t_4}{t_3}$, etc. In the example the constant is ____.

The constant in a geometric sequence is called the **common ratio** and can be found by the following formula:

$$\textbf{common ratio} = \textbf{r} = \frac{t_n}{t_{n-1}} \quad \text{where } n \geq 2, n \in N$$

Explain why each of the geometric sequences is geometric.

a) 6, 12, 24, 48 ... **b)** −1, 5, −25, 125 ... **c)** $-10, -5, -\frac{5}{2}, -\frac{5}{4}$ ...

For the following sequences:
- Identify the type of sequence (arithmetic or geometric).
- State the common difference or common ratio depending on the sequence.
- State the fifth and sixth term for each.

a) 8, 24, 72, 216, ... **b)** 108, 72, 36, 0, ... **c)** $-3, 2, -\frac{4}{3}, \frac{8}{9}$, ...

Complete Assignment Questions #1 - #4

Investigation ***Investigating the Formula for the General Term of a Geometric Sequence***

Consider the following scenario:
A university marine biology student studies the growth of a strand of moss by observing the change in its weight every day. The table shows the mass of the moss, in grams, at 12 noon on each of the first four days.

Days	1	2	3	4
Mass (g)	8	12	18	27

a) The masses form a geometric sequence. State the common ratio.

b) Let $a =$ the first term, and $r =$ the common ratio. Complete the following table:

t_1	First term = 8	$t_1 = a$
t_2	$8 \times 1.5 = 12$	$t_2 = ar$
t_3	$8 \times 1.5 \times 1.5 = 18$	$t_3 = ar^2$
t_4	$8 \times 1.5 \times 1.5 \times$ ___ =	$t_4 =$
t_5		$t_5 =$
t_n		$t_n =$

c) The formula for the general term of a geometric sequence is $t_n =$

The Formula for the General Term of a Geometric Sequence

The formula for the general term of an geometric sequence is:

$$t_n = ar^{n-1} \quad \text{or} \quad t_n = t_1r^{n-1}$$

where
t_n is the general term of the geometric sequence,
$a = t_1$, is the first term,
r is the common ratio,
and n is the position of the term being considered.

Apply the following pattern for the terms of a geometric sequence:

$$\underset{t_1,}{\_\_\_,}\ \underset{t_2,}{\_\_\_,}\ \underset{t_3,}{\_\_\_,}\ \underset{t_4,}{\_\_\_,}\ \ldots\ \underset{t_n}{\_\_\_}$$

$$a,\quad ar,\quad ar^2,\quad ar^3,\quad \ldots\quad ar^{n-1}$$

Determine the formula for the general term and hence calculate the indicated term for each of the following:

a) 5, 15, 45 ... Calculate t_9.

b) $\frac{1}{3}, -\frac{1}{6}, \frac{1}{12}, \ldots$ Calculate t_7.

Determining the Number of Terms in a Geometric Sequence

Janice and Gary were trying to determine the number of terms in the sequence 32, 64, 128 ... , 16 384.

a) Use the general term formula to write and simplify an equation which could be solved to determine the number of terms.

b) Janice used "guess and check" to write each side of the equation in a) with a common base. Determine the solution by this method.

c) Gary used the intersect feature of a graphing calculator to solve the equation in a). Determine the solution to the problem by this method.

Complete Assignment Questions #5 - #10

Geometric Means

The terms placed between two non-consecutive terms of a geometric sequence are called **geometric means**. For example, in the sequence 5, 10, 20, 40, the numbers 10 and 20 are geometric means between 5 and 40. In order to determine geometric means between two given terms, it is helpful to think of the two given terms as the **first** and **last** terms of a sequence.

Insert four geometric means between 81 and $\frac{1}{729}$.

Solving Sequence Problems Where Both "a" and "r" Are Unknown

Three consecutive terms of a geometric sequence are $x + 3, x$, and $x - 5$. Use the concept of common ratio to determine the value of x and the three terms.

The fourth term and the seventh term of a geometric sequence are –54 and 1458 respectively. Use a system of equations to determine the values of the first term and the common ratio. Hence, determine the formula for the general term of the sequence.

Complete Assignment Questions #11 - #22

Assignment

1. Consider the sequence $3, 6, ...$
Is there enough information to determine whether the sequence is arithmetic or geometric? Explain.

2. For the following sequences:
- Identify the type of sequence (arithmetic or geometric or neither).
- State the common difference or common ratio (where relevant).
- Determine the next two terms.

a) $4, 12, 36, 108, ...$ **b)** $512, 64, 8, 1, ...$ **c)** $2, 4, 7, 11, 16, ...$

d) $20, 10, 0, -10, ...$ **e)** $\frac{9}{14}, \frac{3}{7}, \frac{2}{7}, \frac{4}{21}, ...$ **f)** $-6.25, 5, -4, 3.2, ...$

g) $b, bc, bc^2, bc^3 ...$ **h)** $2, 3, 5, 8, 13, ...$

3. The number of bacteria is tripling every hour.

a) Starting with 1 bacterium at 1 pm, write a sequence for the number of bacteria at 1 pm, 2 pm, 3 pm, up to 7 pm.

b) Is the sequence in a) arithmetic or geometric?
State the common difference or common ratio.

c) Plot the ordered pairs (time, # bacteria) on the grid.
Does the graph represent a linear relationship?

4. State the common ratio and find the next two terms of each sequence.

a) $6, -18, 54, -162, ...$ **b)** $2, -\frac{4}{3}, \frac{8}{9}, -\frac{16}{27}, ...$ **c)** $5, 5\sqrt{3}, 15, ...$

5. Determine the general term in each of the following sequences.

a) $4, 12, 36, 108, ...$ **b)** $3, 1.5, 0.75, 0.375, ...$

c) $5, -10, 20, -40, ...$ **d)** $-3, \frac{3}{2}, -\frac{3}{4}, \frac{3}{8}, ...$

6. Consider the sequence $8, 16, 32, 64, ...$
Janeen determined the general term to be $t_n = 8(2)^{n-1}$.
Damien determined the general term to be $t_n = 2^{n+2}$.

a) Explain why both students are correct.

b) Whose general term would be considered "simplest form"?

c) Write the general term for the sequence $9, 27, 81, 243, ...$ in simplest form.

7. Use the general term formula to determine the exact value of the indicated term.

a) $2, 10, 50, 250, ...$ term 9

b) $24, 12, 6, 3, ...$ term 10

c) $\frac{1}{3}, -\frac{1}{6}, \frac{1}{12}, ...$ term 8

d) $\frac{1}{48}, \frac{1}{24}, \frac{1}{12}, ...$ term 11

8. Find the number of terms in each sequence.

a) $-6, -12, -24, ..., -192$

b) $512, -256, 128, ... -1$

9. Find the position of the last term in each of the following sequences

a) $-2, 4, -8, ... 1024$

b) $\frac{1}{384}, -\frac{1}{192}, \frac{1}{96}, ..., -\frac{16}{3}$

10. The first term of a geometric sequence is 2 and the second term is 14. If the middle term is 4802, determine the number of terms in the sequence.

11. How many terms are there in a geometric sequence in which there are 7 geometric means?

12. Place three geometric means between 24 and $\frac{3}{2}$.

13. Solve class example #7 using geometric means.

14. The first three terms of a geometric sequence can be written in the form $x + 75, x - 25$, and $x - 45$.

a) Use the concept of common ratio to determine the value of x.

b) State the common ratio and the value of each of the first five terms.

15. The first three terms in a geometric sequence are $p, p + 5, p + 9$. Determine the exact value of each term.

16. In the examples below, two terms of a geometric sequence are given. Determine the first term, the common ratio, and the general term for each sequence.

a) $t_2 = 28, t_5 = 1792$

b) $t_4 = -256, t_9 = -\frac{1}{4}$

17. In a geometric sequence, $t_2 = 3$, and $t_7 = 729$. Determine t_{10}.

18. In a geometric sequence, the third term is 18, and the seventh term is $\frac{9}{8}$. Explain why there are two different sequences with the given terms, and calculate the first term and the twelfth term in each sequence.

Multiple Choice

19. Determine the nth term for the sequence 2, –6, 18, ...

A. $t_n = -3(2)^{n-1}$ **B.** $t_n = 2(-3)^{n-1}$

C. $t_n = (-6)^{n-1}$ **D.** $t_n = 2(3)^{1-n}$

Numerical Response

20. For the geometric sequence x, $2x + 1$, $4x + 10$, the value of x to the nearest hundredth is _____ .

(Record your answer in the numerical response box from left to right.)

21. The general term for the sequence 32, 16, 8, 4, ... can be expressed in the form $t_n = 2^{k-n}$. The value of k is _____ .

(Record your answer in the numerical response box from left to right.)

22. The seventh and tenth terms of a geometric sequence can be represented by the expressions $4y + 8$ and $y - 4$ respectively. If the sequence has a common ratio of 0.5, then the value of the thirteenth term of the sequence, to the nearest hundredth, is _____.

(Record your answer in the numerical response box from left to right.)

Answer Key

1. No. More than two terms are required to determine a common difference or a common ratio.

2. a) geometric, $r = 3$, terms are 324, 972 **b)** geometric, $r = \frac{1}{8}$, terms are $\frac{1}{8}, \frac{1}{64}$

c) neither, terms are 22, 29 **d)** arithmetic $d = -10$, terms are $-20, -30$

e) geometric, $r = \frac{2}{3}$, terms are $\frac{8}{63}, \frac{16}{189}$ **f)** geometric, $r = -0.8$, terms are $-2.56, 2.048$

g) geometric, $r = c$, terms are bc^4, bc^5 **h)** neither, terms are 21, 34

3. a) 1, 3, 9, 27, 81, 243, 729 **b)** geometric, common ratio = 3 **c)** no

4. a) $r = -3$; 486, -1458 **b)** $r = -\frac{2}{3}$; $\frac{32}{81}, -\frac{64}{243}$ **c)** $r = \sqrt{3}$; $15\sqrt{3}$, 45

5. a) $t_n = 4(3)^{n-1}$ **b)** $t_n = 3(0.5)^{n-1}$ **c)** $t_n = 5(-2)^{n-1}$ **d)** $t_n = -3\left(-\frac{1}{2}\right)^{n-1}$

6. a) $a = 8, r = 2$ so $t_n = 8(2)^{n-1}$ Janeen is correct. **b)** Damien
Since $8 = 2^3$, $t_n = (2)^3(2)^{n-1} = (2)^{n+2}$ Damien is correct. **c)** $t_n = 3^{n+1}$

7. a) 781 250 **b)** $\frac{3}{64}$ **c)** $-\frac{1}{384}$ **d)** $\frac{64}{3}$

8. a) 6 **b)** 10 **9. a)** 10 **b)** 12 **10.** 9

11. 9 **12.** 12, 6, 3 or $-12, 6, -3$ **13.** $t_1 = 2$, $r = -3$, $t_n = 2(-3)^{n-1}$

14.a) 50 **b)** $r = \frac{1}{5}$; 125, 25, 5, 1, $\frac{1}{5}$ **15.** $-25, -20, -16$

16.a) $t_1 = 7$, $r = 4$, $t_n = 7(4)^{n-1}$ **b)** $t_1 = -16384$, $r = \frac{1}{4}$, $t_n = -16384\left(\frac{1}{4}\right)^{n-1}$

17. 19 683

18. Since $r^4 = \frac{1}{2} \Rightarrow r = \pm\frac{1}{2}$ has two solutions, there are two sequences and two values for the twelfth term.

$t_1 = 72$, $r = \frac{1}{2}$, $t_{12} = \frac{9}{256}$ OR $t_1 = 72$, $r = -\frac{1}{2}$, $t_{12} = -\frac{9}{256}$

19. B

20.

0	.	1	7

21.

6			

22.

0	.	7	5

Sequences and Series Lesson #6:
Geometric Growth and Decay

Generating Number Patterns Exhibiting Geometric Growth

Many real-life scenarios can be represented by a pattern of numbers which exhibit **geometric growth**.

The Globe and Mail published an article in 2010 stating that the University of Victoria is struggling with an out-of control rabbit population. At the time of writing in January, 2010, there were an estimated 1500 rabbits on the UVic grounds.

a) If the rabbit population increases at the rate of 20% per year, complete the table below giving an estimate of the rabbit population in January, 2011, 2012, 2013.

Year	2010	2011	2012	2013
Number of Rabbits				

b) Show that the sequence representing the rabbit population is geometric, and state the common ratio.

c) If term 1 in the geometric sequence is the number of rabbits in 2010, which term of the sequence represents the number of rabbits in 2025?

d) If the population continues to grow at this rate, estimate the rabbit population at UVic in January, 2025.

The **geometric growth factor** is the value of the common ratio in a pattern exhibiting geometric growth. Each term in the sequence can be determined from the previous term by multiplying by the growth factor.

In the example above, the geometric growth factor is _____.

Generating Number Patterns Exhibiting Geometric Decay

Many real-life scenarios can be represented by a pattern of numbers which exhibit **geometric decay**.

Vinny borrows $10 000 from his parents to buy a car. His parents lent him the money interest free as long as he makes a payment at the end of each year. They agree on a repayment scheme which results in Vinny owing 10% less at the end of a particular year than at the beginning of that year. This repayment scheme lasts for 8 years. At the end of the 8 years, he makes one final payment to pay off the loan.

a) Complete the table by determining the amount he owes at the end of each of the first four years.

End of Year	1	2	3	4
Amount Owing ($)				

b) The values form a geometric sequence. Calculate the value of the common ratio.

c) State the geometric growth factor.

d) Determine how much he owes at the end of the seventh year.

Geometric growth where the factor is between 0 and 1 is often called **geometric decay**.

State the growth factor in each of the following situations.

a) The rate of inflation is increasing by 3.5% each year.

b) The number of fish in a lake is decreasing by 2% each year.

c) The number of rabbits in a population is doubling each year

d) The value of a computer decreases by one-fifth each year.

e) The ball rebounds to $\frac{3}{4}$ of its previous height after each bounce.

Class Ex. #4

Consider the following problem.

" A rubber ball is dropped from the top of a building 20 m high. Each time the ball bounces, it bounces back up to 80% of its previous height. Calculate, to the nearest cm, the height of the ball after the fifteenth bounce."

a) Lucasito decides to solve the problem using a geometric sequence with $t_1 = 20$.

i) Explain why the value of t_{15} does not give the answer to the problem.

ii) Solve the problem using Lucasito's method.

b) Nicolette argues that the value of t_{15} should be the solution to the problem.

i) Explain why the first term in Nicolette's sequence does not equal 20.

ii) Solve the problem using Nicolette's method.

c) For each student, write an equation which represents the height of the ball after x bounces.

d) Write an equation which could be solved to determine the minimum number of bounces required for the rebound height to be less than 2 cm.

e) Use the intersection feature of a graphing calculator to determine, to the nearest tenth, the minimum number of bounces required for the rebound height to be less than 2 cm.

Compound Interest

Mike invests $5000 in a guaranteed investment certificate (GIC). Each year 3% interest is added to the value of the investment at the beginning of that year. Consider the geometric sequence which represents the value of the investment at the end of each year.

a) State the growth factor.

b) Write a product which represents the value of the investment after one year. This product represents the first term of the geometric sequence. Do not evaluate the product at this time.

c) Write a product which represents the value of the investment after two years. Do not evaluate the product at this time.

d) Use the formula $t_n = ar^{n-1}$ to write an expression which could be used to calculate the value of the investment after ten years. Simplify, but do not evaluate, this expression.

e) State the value of the investment, to the nearest cent, after
i) one year   ii) two years   iii) ten years.

f) Use the formula $t_n = ar^{n-1}$ to write an expression which could be used to calculate the value of the investment after n years. Show that this expression can be written as a power with an exponent of n.

g) Suppose that an investment of P dollars earns interest of $i\%$ per annum. Develop a formula for the amount A of the investment after n years. This formula is know as the **compound interest formula**.

The compound interest formula is an application of the general term of a geometric sequence. This topic will be developed further in the next math course.

Complete Assignment Questions #1 - #20

Assignment

1. State the growth factor in each of the following situations.

a) Canada's population is increasing by 1% per year.

b) My car is depreciating in value by 12% per year.

c) Henri receives a salary increase of 2.4% per year.

d) Newspaper readership is declining by $7\frac{1}{2}$% per year.

e) A bouncing ball rebounds to $\frac{1}{3}$ of its previous height.

2. A pendulum swings through an arc of 120 cm (Swing #1). With each further swing, the arc length is reduced by 15%.

a) State the growth factor.

b) Calculate the length of the arc in Swing #4.

3. A small square picture measures $3\frac{1}{2}$ inches by $3\frac{1}{2}$ inches. A photocopier is set to produce copies that are an enlargement of the original such that both the length and the width are increased by 10%.

a) State the growth factor for the length and width.

b) Calculate the exact length and width of the picture after the first enlargement.

c) Determine, to the nearest 0.01 in^2, the area of the picture after four successive enlargements.

d) Determine the growth factor for the area.

4. A truck depreciates in value by 15% per year. If the truck is valued at \$40 000 on August 1, 2010 what will its value be, to the nearest dollar, on August 1, 2016?

5. The current population of Newtown is 8400. The population is projected to increase by 2.5% per year for the next six years.

a) Calculate the projected population next year.

b) Calculate the projected population at the end of the six year period.

6. The market value of a house is predicted to increase at an annual rate of 4% for the next five years. If the current market price is \$410 000, determine, to the nearest dollar, the predicted market price five years from now.

7. A government bond is bought for \$5000 on June 1, 2010. The value of the bond increases each year by 3.9% of the previous year's value, and the bond matures on June 1, 2030. Determine the value of the bond at maturity.

8. A tree grows 2.80 m during the first year since it was planted. During each subsequent year, the tree's growth is 85% of its growth the previous year.

a) Calculate, to the nearest 0.01 m, the growth of the tree in the fourth year.

b) Determine the first year in which the growth of the tree is less than half a metre.

9. A sports store is having a closing down sale. All stock has to be sold. Each day an article remains unsold, the price is discounted by 4% of the previous day's price. This discounting continues until the article is sold. The table shows the price of a mountain bike during the first five days of the sale.

1	2	3	4	5
750	720	691.20	663.55	637.01

a) State the growth factor.

b) Calculate the cost of the mountain bike on the tenth day of the sale.

c) Write an expression for the cost of the mountain bike on the *n*th day of the sale.

d) The mountain bike was eventually sold for \$359.70. On which day of the sale was it sold?

10. Each year, as a result of overfishing, the number of fish in a lake is decreasing by $\frac{1}{20}$th of the previous year's population. In January, 2010, there were 2 500 fish in the lake.

a) Determine the number of fish present in the lake after 1 year.

b) Write an equation to represent the number of fish, N, after t years.

c) How many fish can be expected to be present in January, 2015?

d) Write an equation which could be solved to determine how many years it would take for the fish population to reduce to 1100.

e) Use the intersection feature of a graphing calculator to determine the number of years it would take for the fish population to reduce to 1100.

11. A quantity of water contains 700 g of pollutants. Each time the water passes through a filter, 18% of the pollutants are removed.

a) To the nearest tenth of a gram, calculate the mass of pollutants remaining in the water after it passes through seven filters.

b) How many filters are needed to reduce the mass of pollutants to less than 80 g?

12. It is predicted that the value of a painting will increase according to the formula $V = V_0(1.13)^{t-1}$ where V_0 is the current value of the painting and $t = 1$ represents the current year.

a) State the percentage increase in the value of the painting each year.

b) Determine, to the nearest whole number, the percentage increase in the value of the painting 8 years from now.

13. Alan invests $2500 in a 5 year Government Bond paying interest at 3.7% per annum compounded annually. Calculate the value of the bond at maturity (after 5 years).

14. At the beginning of each year, a student invests $3000 in a GIC paying 3.3% per annum interest. If interest is compounded annually, determine the total value of his GIC investments just before he makes his fourth deposit.

15. After 6 years an investment of $5400 has an accumulated value of $9056. If interest is compounded annually, determine, to the nearest tenth, the annual rate of interest.

16. Andrew invests \$2000 at 4.73% interest per annum compounded annually. To the nearest year, how many years would it take for his investment to double in value?

Multiple Choice

17. In 2004, a painting was valued at \$24 000, and its value for the next six years increased by 12% of the previous year's value. If V is the value of the painting, and t is the number of years after 2004, then the equation for the value of the painting for $t \leq 6$ is

A. $V = \$24\,000(0.12)^t$
B. $V = \$24\,000(0.12)^{t-1}$
C. $V = \$24\,000(1.12)^t$
D. $V = \$24\,000(1.12)^{t-1}$

18. Katie invested P dollars at 3% compounded annually for 10 years. The ratio of the amount of money that Katie will have at the end of any particular year compared to the amount at the beginning of that year is

A. 0.03
B. 1.03
C. $0.03P$
D. $1.03P$

Use the following information to answer the next two questions.

A new motor home can be purchased for \$120 000. It depreciates by 15% in the first year and by 9% each year thereafter.

19. The value of the motor home 6 years after it is purchased is

A. \$57 923
B. \$63 651
C. \$68 144
D. \$69 946

Numerical Response **20.** The minimum number of years it takes for the value of the motor home to be less than \$30 000 is ______ .

(Record your answer in the numerical response box from left to right.)

Group Investigation Christine invests \$7000 in an investment paying 5.4% annual interest, compounded monthly. Joe invests \$6000 in an investment at an interest rate of 6.8% per year, compounded annually. After how many years will the two investments be approximately equal in value?

Answer Key

1. a) 1.01 **b)** 0.88 **c)** 1.024 **d)** 0.925 **e)** $\frac{1}{3}$ **2. a)** 0.85 **b)** 73.695 cm

3. a) 1.1 **b)** 3.85 in **c)** 26.26 in^2 **d)** 1.21 **4.** \$15 086 **5. a)** 8610 **b)** 9741

6. \$498 828 **7.** \$10 746.84 **8. a)** 1.72 m **b)** year 12

9. a) 0.96 **b)** \$519.40 **c)** \$ $750(0.96)^{n-1}$ **d)** 19th day

10.a) 2375 **b)** $N = 2375\left(\frac{19}{20}\right)^{t-1}$ or $N = 2500\left(\frac{19}{20}\right)^{t}$ **c)** 1934

d) $1100 = 2375\left(\frac{19}{20}\right)^{t-1}$ or $1100 = 2500\left(\frac{19}{20}\right)^{t}$ **e)** 16 years

11.a) 174.5 g **b)** 11 **12.a)** 13% **b)** 166% **13.** \$2998.01 **14.** \$9 607.18

15. 9.0% **16.** 15 years **17.** C **18.** B **19.** B **20.**

1	4		

Group Investigation: 13 years

Sequences and Series Lesson #7:
Geometric Series

Geometric Series

When the terms of a geometric sequence are added, the result is known as a geometric series.
For example, 2, 4, 8, 16, ... is a geometric sequence;
2 + 4 + 8 + 16 + ... is a geometric series.

Formulas for the Sum of a Geometric Series

In a geometric series of n terms,

$$S_n = a + ar + ar^2 + ar^3 + \dots + ar^{n-2} + ar^{n-1}$$

$$rS_n = ar + ar^2 + ar^3 + ar^4 + \dots + ar^{n-1} + ar^n$$

Subtract line 1 from line 2 $\Rightarrow$ $rS_n - S_n = ar^n - a$

$$S_n(r-1) = a(r^n - 1)$$

$$S_n = \frac{a(r^n - 1)}{r - 1},\ r \neq 1 \quad \text{or} \quad S_n = \frac{t_1(r^n - 1)}{r - 1},\ r \neq 1$$

This formula connects a, r, n, and S_n.
If any three of these values are known, the fourth can be determined.

However, when the number of terms in the series (n) is not known but t_n is known , another **formula for the sum of n terms of a geometric series** can be formed by replacing ar^{n-1} by t_n. The formula can now be written as

$$S_n = \frac{rt_n - a}{r - 1},\ r \neq 1 \quad \text{or} \quad S_n = \frac{rt_n - t_1}{r - 1},\ r \neq 1$$

When $r = 1$, the series is $a + a + a + \dots = na$.

Show how the formula $S_n = \dfrac{rt_n - a}{r - 1}$ can be developed from the formula $S_n = \dfrac{a(r^n - 1)}{r - 1}$.

Determine the sum of the first fifteen terms of the sequence $-5, 10, -20, \ldots$.

Determine the sum $4 - 12 + 36 - \ldots - 8748$.

The sum of a certain number of terms in the series $(-2) + 8 + (-32) + \ldots$ is $-104\,858$.
What is the last term that would make this series add up to $-104\,858$?

In a geometric sequence, the fifth term is 1024 and the common ratio is 4.
Find the sum of the first seven terms of the sequence.

Complete Assignment Questions #1 - #9

Determining the Number of Terms in a Geometric Series

The sum of n terms of the series $5 + 15 + 45 + \ldots$ is $16\,400$. Determine the number of terms in the series by

a) solving an equation with a common base

b) using the intersect feature of a graphing calculator

A golf ball is dropped from the top of a building 100 m above a paved road. In each bounce the ball reaches a vertical height that is $\frac{3}{4}$ the previous vertical height. Determine

a) the vertical height (to the nearest tenth of a metre) of the ball after the seventh bounce

b) the total vertical distance (to the nearest tenth) travelled by the ball when it contacts the floor for the seventh time

c) How many times does the ball need to bounce to travel approximately 675 m in vertical distance?

Consider the geometric series defined by $S_n = 5(3^n - 1)$.

a) Find the first four terms of the geometric series defined by $S_n = 5(3^n - 1)$.

b) Find t_9 without using the formula $t_n = ar^{n-1}$.

To find t_n in a series defined in terms of S_n, use the formula

$$t_n = S_n - S_{n-1}$$

For example $t_8 = S_8 - S_7$, or $t_4 = S_4 - S_3$.

Determining the Common Ratio in a Geometric Series

Scientists plate E.coli bacteria on a petri dish. At the end of the first hour 30, bacterial cells are present. The number of new bacterial cells produced each hour forms a geometric sequence. If a total of 40 950 bacterial cells are present at the end of six hours, use technology to determine how many new bacterial cells are produced in the sixth hour.

Complete Assignment Questions #10 - #20

Assignment

1. Find the sum of the indicated number of terms in each geometric series. Answer as an exact value unless otherwise indicated.

a) $4 + 16 + 64 + \ ...\ (S_8)$ **b)** $24 + 12 + 6 + ...\ (S_7)$ **c)** $64 - 32 + 16 - ...\ (S_9)$

d) $\frac{1}{8} + \frac{1}{4} + \frac{1}{2} + ...$ to 10 terms **e)** $-\frac{1}{3} + \frac{4}{9} - \frac{16}{27} + ...$to 11 terms (to the nearest tenth)

2. Find the sum of the terms in each series.
Answer as an exact value unless otherwise indicated.

a) $1 + 3 + 9 + ... + 729$

b) $512 + (-256) + 128 + ... + (-1)$

c) $-8 - 2 - \frac{1}{2} - ... - \frac{1}{128}$

d) $\frac{1}{384} - \frac{1}{192} + \frac{1}{96} - ... - \frac{16}{3}$ (to the nearest tenth)

3. Consider the geometric series with general term $t_n = -3(-2)^{1-n}$.

a) Determine the first three terms of the corresponding sequence.

b) Find the *exact* sum of the first eight terms of the geometric series.

4. For the geometric series $125 + (-25) + 5 + ...$, find

a) the sixth term

b) the sum of six terms

5. In a geometric sequence the third term is 1024 and the common ratio is 0.5.
Determine the sum of the first nine terms of the sequence.

6. A line is divided into 5 parts whose lengths form a geometric sequence. If the shortest length is 2 cm , and the longest 162 cm, find the length of the whole line.

7. A mother, during a hectic day, was convinced by her son that he should have a weekly allowance that is doubled every two weeks. In weeks one and two he would receive 1 cent per week, in weeks three and four he would receive 2 cents per week. If his allowance continues to double every two weeks, determine

a) the amount of his allowance in week 30.

b) the total amount he would receive in allowance during the thirty weeks.

8. Legend has it that long ago a king was so pleased with the game of chess that he decided to reward the inventor of the game, Sessa, with whatever he wanted. Sessa, taking the request seriously, asked for a resource instead of money. Specifically, he asked for one grain of wheat for the first square of a chessboard, two grains of wheat for the second square, four grains for the third square, and so on until the entire chess board was full. (There are 64 squares on a chess board.) Find an expression for:

a) the amount of grain on the last square of the board.

b) the total amount of grain needed to fulfill Sessa's request.
(Don't be surprised at how big this is. This amount is said to represent many times the world's annual crop of wheat!)

9. Consider the series $5 + 3 + \frac{1}{2} + \frac{1}{4} + \frac{1}{8} + \frac{1}{16} + \dots + \frac{1}{512}$.

a) Explain why you cannot use the formula $S_n = \frac{rt_n - a}{r - 1}$ with $a = 5$ to determine the sum of the series.

b) Determine the sum of the series.

10. The sum of n terms of the series $2 + 8 + 32 + \dots$ is 174 762. Determine the number of terms in the series by

a) solving an equation with a common base

b) using the intersect feature of a graphing calculator

11. How many terms are required in the series $(-6) + (-12) + (-24) \dots$ to add to a sum of -378?

12. a) In a geometric sequence, the first term is 8 and the sum of the first three terms is 78. Use technology to determine the common ratio of the sequence.

b) In a geometric sequence, the first term is 8 and the sum of the first six terms is 74 648. Use technology to determine the third term of the sequence.

13. Consider the geometric series where $S_n = \frac{75}{4}(5^n - 1)$.

a) Determine the first four terms of the geometric series.

b) Show how to calculate the value of t_{12} using two different methods.

14. In the winter, if the weather gets too severe, a works manager will close the factory. He has to devise a plan so that every employee is contacted before setting out to go to work. He sets up a telephone fan-out system. He will phone r employees (level 1). Each of these employees will phone r other employees (level 2). Each of the people contacted in level 2 will phone r other employees and this continues until every employee has been contacted.

If 3279 employees have to be contacted and this is done in 7 levels of the fan-out system, use technology to determine the number of employees that each person has to phone.

15. A rubber ball is dropped on to a concrete driveway from a garage roof 10 feet above the ground. With each rebound the ball loses 10% of its previous vertical height.

a) Calculate, to the nearest hundredth of a foot, the vertical height to which the ball rebounds after the sixth bounce.

b) Calculate, to the nearest hundredth of a foot, the total vertical distance (down and up) travelled by the ball when it contacts the ground for the fourth time.

c) How many times does the ball need to bounce to travel approximately 112.5 feet in vertical distance?

Multiple Choice

16. The first term of a geometric series is 3. The sum of the first two terms of the series is 15 and the sum of the first 3 terms of the series is 63. The common ratio is

A. 3

B. 4

C. 5

D. $\frac{63}{15}$

Numerical Response

17. The general term of a geometric sequence is $t_n = 3(2)^{n-1}, n \geq 1$. The sum of the first seven terms of the corresponding series, to the nearest whole number, is _____.

(Record your answer in the numerical response box from left to right.)

18. A hard rubber ball is dropped from a building with a height of 5 m. After each bounce, the ball rises to $\frac{4}{5}$ of its previous height. The total vertical distance the ball has travelled at the moment it hits the ground for the eighth time, to the nearest tenth of a metre, is _____ .

(Record your answer in the numerical response box from left to right.)

19. If $S_n = 2(3^n - 1)$ represents the sum of n terms of a geometric sequence, then the value of the seventh term, t_7, to the nearest whole number, is _____ .

(Record your answer in the numerical response box from left to right.)

20. Students were asked to calculate the sum of four terms of a sequence in which the first term is 0.5, the third term is 18, and all the terms are positive. Jordan assumed the sequence was arithmetic and calculated a value X for the sum. Andrea assumed the sequence was geometric and calculated a value Y for the sum. The difference Y – X is _____ .

(Record your answer in the numerical response box from left to right.)

Answer Key

1. a) 87 380 **b)** $\frac{381}{8}$ **c)** $\frac{171}{4}$ **d)** $\frac{1023}{8}$ **e)** –3.5

2. a) 1093 **b)** 341 **c)** $\frac{1365}{128}$ **d)** –3.6 **3. a)** $-3, \frac{3}{2}, -\frac{3}{4}$ **b)** $-\frac{255}{128}$

4. a) $-\frac{1}{25}$ **b)** $\frac{2604}{25}$ **5.** 8176 **6.** 242 cm **7. a)** \$163.84 **b)** \$655.34

8. a) $2^{63} = 9.22 \times 10^{18}$ grains **b)** $2^{64} - 1 = 1.84 \times 10^{19}$ grains

9. a) The series is not geometric unless you disregard the first two terms **b)** $8 + \frac{511}{512} = 8\frac{511}{512}$ or $\frac{4607}{512}$

10.a) $4^n = 262144$, 9 terms **b)** 9 terms **11.** 6 **12. a)** 2.5 **b)** 288

13.a) 75, 375, 1875, 9375 **b)** $t_{12} = ar^{11} = 75(5^{11}) =$ 3 662 109 375 or $t_{12} = S_{12} - S_{11}$

14. 3 **15.a)** 5.31 feet **b)** 58.78 feet **c)** 8 **16.** B

17.

3	8	1	

18.

3	6	.	6

19.

2	9	1	6

20.

7	5		

Sequences and Series Lesson #8:
Infinite Geometric Series

Investigation #1 ***Investigating an Infinite Geometric Series with $r = \frac{1}{2}$***

David buys a pizza. He eats half of the pizza, then half of the remaining piece, then half of the remaining piece, etc., etc. Continuing in this way, it looks like he will never finish the pizza, because there will always be half of a piece left.

a) Explain why in practice this could not happen.

b) Represent this situation with a geometric series whose first term is $\frac{1}{2}$.

c) For this series, determine the values of a and r, and find a formula for S_n.

d) Use the table feature of a graphing calculator to complete the table to three decimal places.

n	1	2	3	4	5	6	7	8	9	10
S_n										

e) Plot the values in d) on the grid. Note that n is defined only on the set of natural numbers, so do not join the points.

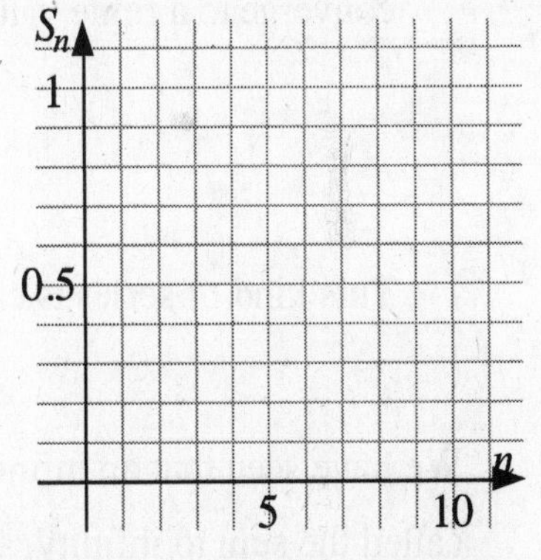

f) It would appear from the grid that as n gets larger, the sequence of sums $S_1, S_2, S_3, \ldots S_n, \ldots$ gets closer and closer to the value _____ .

This kind of series is called **convergent** as the sequence of sums converges closer and closer to a particular value. It would appear that if we added the terms of the series indefinitely, we will get closer and closer to the value 1.

We say that the sum of the infinite geometric series $\frac{1}{2} + \frac{1}{4} + \frac{1}{8} + \ldots$ is 1, or that the sum to infinity of the series is 1.

We use the symbol S or S_∞ to represent the sum of the infinite series.

Note that the sum of a finite number of terms of this series will never actually reach 1.

g) Explain with reference to the pizza why the sum of this infinite series should be 1.

Investigation #2 — *Investigating an Infinite Geometric Series with r = 2*

Consider the infinite geometric series 2 + 4 + 8 + 16 + . . .

a) For this series, determine the values of a and r, and find a formula for S_n.

b) Use the table feature of a graphing calculator to complete the table.

n	1	2	3	4	5	6	7	8	9	10
S_n										

c) Plot the values in b) on the grid.

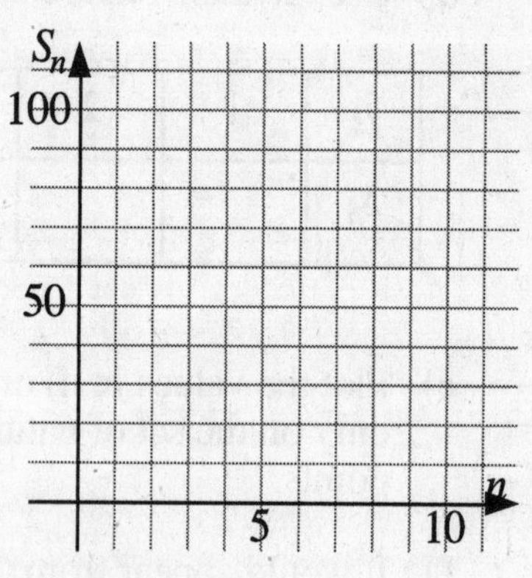

In this case, as n gets larger, the sequence of sums $S_1, S_2, S_3, \ldots S_n, \ldots$ gets larger and larger and does not converge to a finite value.

This kind of series is called **divergent** and does not have a sum to infinity.

We have seen that an infinite geometric series with $r = \frac{1}{2}$ converges to a particular value called the sum to infinity, and that an infinite geometric series with $r = 2$ diverges and does not have a sum to infinity.

Investigation #3 *Investigating Values of r^n as n Approaches Infinity*

In this investigation, we can choose:
- any value of r less than -1
- any value of r between -1 and 0
- any value of r between 0 and 1
- any value of r greater than 1.

We have suggested the values -2, $-\frac{1}{4}$, $\frac{2}{3}$, and 3, but any values in the range will do.

a) Complete the table.

	$r < -1$	$-1 < r < 0$	$0 < r < 1$	$r > 1$
eg	$r = -2$	$r = -\frac{1}{4}$	$r = \frac{2}{3}$	$r = 3$
n	r^n	r^n	r^n	r^n
1				
2				
3				
4				
10				
20				
100				

b) Complete the following statements based on your observations in a).

As n gets larger and larger:

- the sequence is convergent and approaches the value 0 if $r =$ _____ , or $r =$ _____.
- the sequence is divergent if $r =$ _____ , or $r =$ _____.

As n gets larger and larger:

- r^n gets closer and closer to 0, provided $-1 < r < 1$, i.e. $|r| < 1$.
- r^n gets larger and larger if $r < -1$ or $r > 1$, i.e. $|r| > 1$.

We can use this rule to determine a formula for the sum of an infinite geometric series.

The Formula for the Sum of an Infinite Geometric Series

Consider the infinite series $S = a + ar + ar^2 + ar^3 + \ldots$

The sum of n terms of this series is given by the formula $S_n = \dfrac{a(r^n - 1)}{r - 1}$, $r \neq 1$.

This can also be written as $S_n = \dfrac{a(1 - r^n)}{1 - r}$, $r \neq 1$.

Provided $-1 < r < 1$, r^n will get closer and closer to zero as n gets closer and closer to infinity.
This means that in determining the formula for the sum of an infinite series, S, we can replace r^n by zero in the formula for S_n.

This gives $S = \dfrac{a}{1 - r}$, provided $|r| < 1$.

If $|r| \geq 1$, the sum of an infinite geometric series is not defined.

$$S = \frac{a}{1 - r}, \quad |r| < 1$$

Overview

The following flowchart summarizes geometric series learned to this point.

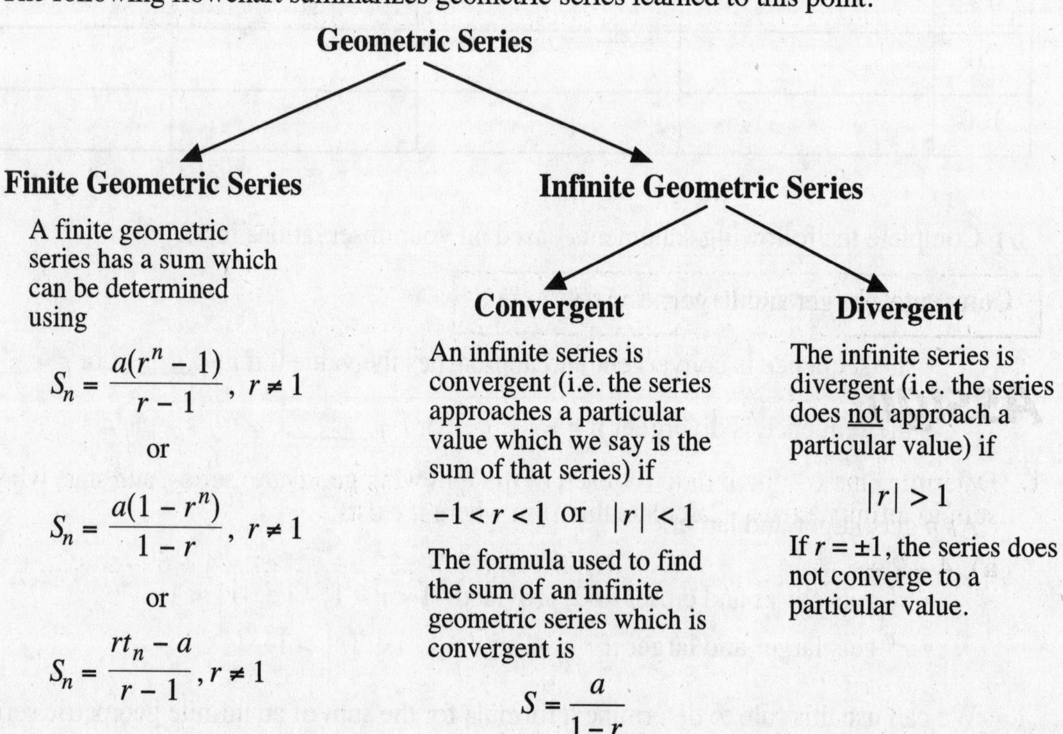

Geometric Series
Finite Geometric Series
A finite geometric series has a sum which can be determined using
$S_n = \dfrac{a(r^n - 1)}{r - 1}$, $r \neq 1$
or
$S_n = \dfrac{a(1 - r^n)}{1 - r}$, $r \neq 1$
or
$S_n = \dfrac{rt_n - a}{r - 1}$, $r \neq 1$
Infinite Geometric Series
Convergent
An infinite series is convergent (i.e. the series approaches a particular value which we say is the sum of that series) if
$-1 < r < 1$ or $|r| < 1$
The formula used to find the sum of an infinite geometric series which is convergent is
$S = \dfrac{a}{1 - r}$
Divergent
The infinite series is divergent (i.e. the series does not approach a particular value) if
$|r| > 1$
If $r = \pm 1$, the series does not converge to a particular value.

Determine the common ratio for each of the following geometric series and state whether a sum to infinity exists. Calculate this sum where it exists.

a) $1 + \frac{1}{3} + \frac{1}{9} + \ldots$ **b)** $1 - 5 + 25 - \ldots$ **c)** $2 - 1 + \frac{1}{2} - \ldots$

The first term of a geometric series is 2 and the sum to infinity is 4.
Determine the common ratio.

a) Write the repeating decimal $0.0\overline{7}$ as an infinite geometric series.

b) Find the sum to infinity of the series in a) and hence write $0.0\overline{7}$ as a fraction.

Complete Assignment Questions #1 - #11

Assignment

1. Determine the common ratio for each of the following geometric series. and state whether a sum to infinity exists. Calculate this sum where it exists.

a) $4 + 2 + 1 + \ldots$ **b)** $5 - 1 + \frac{1}{5} - \ldots$ **c)** $-4 + 6 - 9 + \ldots$

d) $1 + 1 + 1 + \ldots$ **e)** $10 - 9 + 8.1 - \ldots$ **f)** $1 - 1 + 1 - \ldots$

g) $15 - 9 + \frac{27}{5} - \ldots$ **h)** $\frac{3}{4} - \frac{3}{8} + \frac{3}{16} - \ldots$ **i)** $0.0001 + 0.001 + 0.01 + \ldots$

j) $2^6 + 2^5 + 2^4 + \ldots$ **k)** $2^4 + 2^5 + 2^6 + \ldots$

l) $\frac{3}{100} + \frac{3}{10\,000} + \frac{3}{1\,000\,000} + \ldots$ **m)** $3 + \sqrt{3} + 1 + \frac{1}{\sqrt{3}} + \ldots$

2. Consider the geometric sequence $12 + 6 + 3 + \dots$.

a) Calculate, to four decimal places, the sums for 10 and 12 terms of the sequence.

b) Explain why these sums are almost equal.

c) Predict the sum for the infinite series.

d) Calculate the sum for the infinite series.

3. The first term of a geometric series is 81 and the third term is 1. Determine the sum to infinity of each of the two possible series.

4. a) Show that $4x^{\frac{4}{3}}$, $8x^{-\frac{1}{3}}$, and $16x^{-2}$ could be the first three terms of a geometric series.

b) If $x = 8$, explain why a sum to infinity exists, and determine this sum.

5. The infinite geometric series is given by $1 - 3x + 9x^2 - 27x^3 + \dots$.
If the infinite sum is $\frac{4}{9}$, determine the numerical value of the common ratio.

6. Use an infinite series to express the following repeating decimals as fractions.

a) $0.\overline{5}$ **b)** $0.\overline{35}$ **c)** $0.3\overline{5}$

7. During the first week of operation, an oil well produced 8000 barrels of oil.
The production dropped by 2% each week.
a) Calculate to the nearest barrel;

i) the number of barrels produced in week 6

ii) the total number of barrels produced in the first ten weeks of production

iii) the total number of barrels which could be produced before the well runs dry

b) Why might the actual number of barrels produced differ from the answer to a) iii)?

Multiple Choice

8. The sum of the infinite geometric series $t + t^2 + t^3 + t^4 + ...$ is $4t$, $t \neq 0$. The value of t is

A. $\frac{4}{3}$

B. $\frac{3}{4}$

C. $\frac{1}{2}$

D. $\frac{1}{4}$

9. An expression for the sum of the infinite series $x^2 + 1 + \frac{1}{x^2} + \frac{1}{x^4} + ...$ is

A. $\frac{x^4}{x^2 - 1}$

B. $\frac{x^4}{x^2 + 1}$

C. $\frac{1}{x^2 - 1}$

D. x^4

Numerical Response

10. The common ratio of a geometric series is $-\frac{2}{3}$ and the sum to infinity is -12.
The second term, to the nearest tenth, is _____ .

(Record your answer in the numerical response box from left to right.)

11. The third term of a geometric series is $\frac{4}{3}$, and the sixth term is $\frac{32}{81}$. The difference between the sum of the first five terms and the sum to infinity of the series, correct to the nearest tenth, is _____ .

(Record your answer in the numerical response box from left to right.)

Answer Key

1. a) $r = \frac{1}{2}, s = 8$ **b)** $r = -\frac{1}{5}, s = \frac{25}{6}$ **c)** $r = -\frac{3}{2}$, s does not exist

d) $r = 1$, s does not exist **e)** $r = -\frac{9}{10}, s = \frac{100}{19}$ **f)** $r = -1$, s does not exist

g) $r = -\frac{3}{5}, s = \frac{75}{8}$ **h)** $r = -\frac{1}{2}, s = \frac{1}{2}$ **i)** $r = 10$, s does not exist

j) $r = \frac{1}{2}, s = 128$ **k)** $r = 2$, s does not exist **l)** $r = \frac{1}{100}, s = \frac{1}{33}$

m) $r = \frac{1}{\sqrt{3}}, s = \frac{3\sqrt{3}}{\sqrt{3}-1}$ or $\frac{9+3\sqrt{3}}{2}$

2. a) $S_{10} = 23.9766$, $S_{12} = 23.9941$ **b)** terms 11 and 12 are very small **c)** 24 **d)** 24

3. $S = \frac{729}{8}$ or $\frac{729}{10}$ **4.a)** $\frac{t_3}{t_2} = \frac{t_2}{t_1} = 2x^{-\frac{5}{3}}$. Common ratio so terms can form a geometric series.

b) S exists since $r = \frac{1}{16}$. $S = \frac{1024}{15}$

5. $r = -\frac{5}{4}$ **6. a)** $\frac{5}{9}$ **b)** $\frac{35}{99}$ **c)** $\frac{16}{45}$

7. a) i) 7231 **ii)** 73171 **iii)** 400 000 **b)** Once the number of barrels produced per week drops below a certain level, it becomes uneconomical to keep the well open.

8. B **9.** A

10.

1	3	.	3

11.

1	.	2	

Sequences and Series Lesson #9:
Practice Test

1. An example of a finite sequence is

A. $3, 8, 13, 18, \ldots 5n - 2, \ldots \quad n \in N.$ **B.** $3, 8, 13, 18, \ldots 5n - 2, \ldots 498, \quad n \in N.$

C. $3 + 8 + 13 + 18 + \ldots$ **D.** $3 + 8 + 13 + 18$

2. Which of the following statements regarding the sequence $2, 4, 7, 11, 16, \ldots$ is correct?

A. The sequence is arithmetic.

B. The sequence is geometric.

C. The sequence is both arithmetic and geometric.

D. The sequence is neither arithmetic nor geometric.

Numerical Response **1.** If $32, 24, 18, \ldots$ are the first three terms of a geometric sequence, then the value of the fifteenth term of the sequence, to the nearest hundredth, is _____ .

(Record your answer in the numerical response box from left to right.)

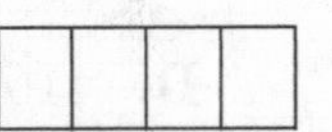

2. On a particular street, the house numbers on one side of the street form an arithmetic sequence. If the first two houses are numbered 8991 and 8995, and the last house is numbered 10039 then the number of houses on this side of the street is _____ .

(Record your answer in the numerical response box from left to right.)

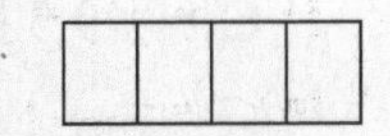

3. The common difference of the arithmetic sequence defined by $t_n = \frac{1}{3}(7 - 2n), \; n \in N,$ is

A. $\frac{7}{3}$ **B.** $-\frac{7}{3}$

C. $\frac{2}{3}$ **D.** $-\frac{2}{3}$

4. As part of a new training routine, Jesse does some burpees and push-ups. On the first day he does eight burpees and ten push-ups. Each day he increases the number of burpees by three and the number of push-ups by four. How many burpees and push-ups does he do on the nineteenth day?

A. 57 and 76

B. 62 and 82

C. 65 and 86

D. 68 and 90

5. If the 15th and 16th terms of an arithmetic sequence are 99 and 92 respectively, the 5th term is

A. 29

B. 36

C. 162

D. 169

6. A quantity of a liquid chemical contains 50 g of impurities. Each time this quantity of chemical passes through a filter, 10% of the impurities present are removed. After passing through the filter 5 times, the number of grams of impurities remaining in the liquid chemical is

A. 0 g

B. 25 g

C. 29.5 g

D. 32.8 g

7. Consider the following geometric series.

***Series* 1** : $3 + 6 + 12 + 24 + \ldots$ ***Series* 2** : $24 + 12 + 6 + 3 + \ldots$

***Series* 3** : $3 - 3 + 3 - 3 \ldots$

Which of the these series is/are convergent?

A. **1** only **B.** **2** only **C.** **1** and **2** only **D.** **2** and **3** only

8. The sum of the terms of a sequence is represented by $S_n = 6n + n^2,\ n \geq 1,\ n \in N$. The general term of the sequence is

A. $t_n = 2n + 5$

B. $t_n = 9n - 2$

C. $t_n = 7\left(\dfrac{9}{7}\right)^{n-1}$

D. $t_n = 7\left(\dfrac{16}{7}\right)^{n-1}$

9. The graph shown plots the sum of n terms of a geometric sequence as a function of $n \in N$. Each point on the graph is of the form (n, S_n), where S_n is the sum of n terms of the sequence.

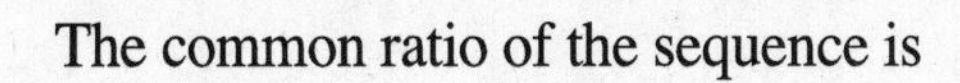

The common ratio of the sequence is

A. $\dfrac{1}{2}$

B. $\dfrac{2}{3}$

C. $\dfrac{3}{2}$

D. 8

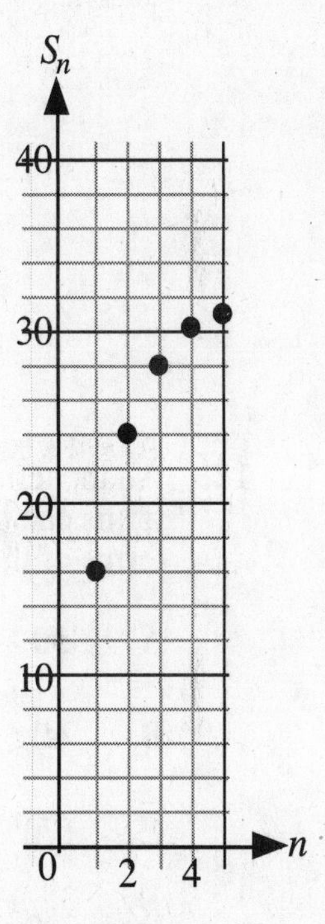

10. A bush is 2 feet high when planted. It grows 2.5 feet during the first year. Each subsequent year the bush grows $\dfrac{3}{4}$ of the previous year's growth. The maximum height of the bush is

A. 10 feet

B. 12 feet

C. 18 feet

D. unable to be determined from the given information

11. A bouncing ball returns to 64% of its previous height after each bounce. If the ball is originally dropped from a height of 10 m, its maximum height, h, after n bounces can be represented by

A. $h = 10(0.36)^{n-1}$ **B.** $h = 10(0.36)^{n}$

C. $h = 10(0.64)^{n-1}$ **D.** $h = 10(0.64)^{n}$

Numerical Response **3.** A pile driver pounds a steel column into the ground. On the first drive , the column is pounded 1.65 metres into the ground, and on each successive drive it moves 80% as far as it did on the previous drive. The least number of drives required to drive the column a total of 8.2 metres into the ground is_____ .

(Record your answer in the numerical response box from left to right.)

12. All the terms in a particular arithmetic sequence are whole numbers. If the first three terms can be represented by $2x + 10, 4x + 30$, and $8x + 60$, then the sum of the first four terms of the corresponding series is

A. 30

B. 60

C. 170

D. 340

4. In a geometric sequence, the second term is 6 000 and the fifth term is 10 368. The common ratio, as a decimal to the nearest tenth, is _____.

(Record your answer in the numerical response box from left to right.)

Numerical Response **5.** The side lengths of a triangle form an arithmetic sequence. The shortest side has a length of 10.5 cm and the perimeter of the triangle is 45 cm. The length, in cm, of the longest side is _____ .

(Record your answer in the numerical response box from left to right.)

13. If the sum of an infinite series is 72 and the common ratio is $\frac{7}{8}$, then the first term is

A. 576 **B.** 63

C. 9 **D.** $\frac{1}{576}$

14. Each of the triangles in the diagram is equilateral. The largest triangle has sides of 30 mm. The midpoints of the sides of the largest triangle are joined together to form the second largest triangle. The midpoints of the sides of the second largest triangle are joined together to form the third largest triangle.

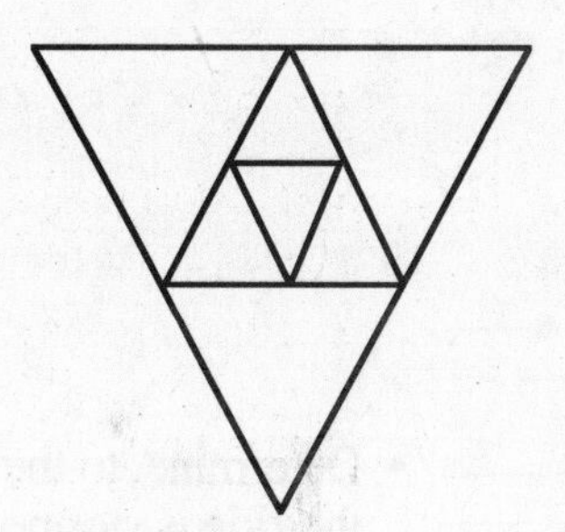

If the process is continued indefinitely, the sum of the perimeters of all of the triangles in mm is

A. 180

B. 179.8

C. 157.5

D. 60

15. A golf ball is dropped on to a concrete sidewalk from a height of 2 metres. Each time it bounces, it rebounds to $\frac{2}{3}$ of its previous height. On the sixth rebound, it will rise

A. $2\left(\frac{2}{3}\right)^6$ m **B.** $2\left(\frac{2}{3}\right)^5$ m

C. $2\left(\frac{1}{3}\right)^6$ m **D.** $2\left(\frac{1}{3}\right)^5$ m

Written Response - 5 marks

1. A new ride for young children is modelled after a pendulum involving a space capsule moving back and forth. The children board the ride at the left edge of the swing as shown in the diagram.

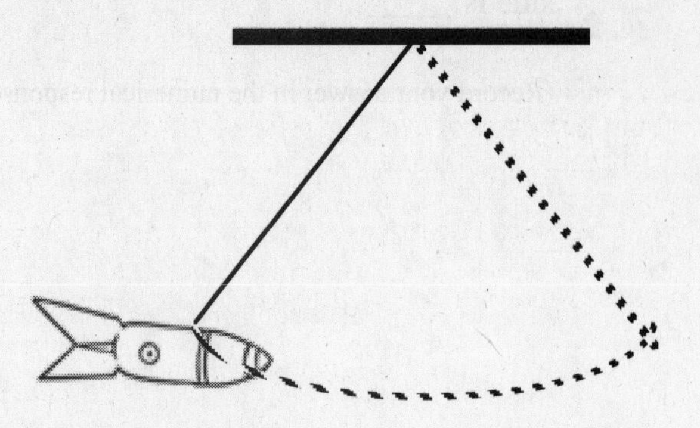

A swing is completed when the motion of the space capsule changes direction. The first swing (from left to right) is 48 metres in length. The second swing (from right to left) has a length of 95% of the first swing. The third swing (from left to right again) has a length equal to 95% of the second swing.

- Determine, to the nearest hundredth of a metre, the lengths of the second and third swings.

- The ride is stopped at the end of the first swing that is less than 18.5 metres in length. How many swings take place before the ride is stopped?

- Determine, to the nearest tenth of a metre, the total distance travelled before the ride is stopped.

- If the ride were not stopped but allowed to continue indefinitely, determine the total distance travelled by the space capsule.

Answer Key

1. B	2. D	3. D	4. B	5. D	6. C	7. B	8. A
9. A	10. B	11. D	12. B	13. C	14. A	15. A	

Numerical Response

1. | 0 | . | 5 | 7 | 2. | 2 | 6 | 3 | | 3. | 2 | 3 | | |

4. | 1 | . | 2 | | 5. | 1 | 9 | . | 5 |

Written Response

1. • 45.60 m, 43.32 m   • 20   • 615.9 m   • 960 m

Operations on Radicals Lesson #1:
Entire Radicals and Mixed Radicals

Recall the following from previous math courses.

Square Roots, Cube Roots And Other Roots

Square Roots : All positive numbers have two square roots: one a positive number and the other a negative number. The positive square root is called the **principal square root** and is denoted by the symbol $\sqrt{\ }$.

The square roots of a perfect square are rational numbers.

e.g. the square roots of 16 are 4 and –4. **NOTE:** $\sqrt{16} = 4$ <u>only</u>.

The square roots of a non-perfect square are irrational numbers.

e.g. the square roots of 17 are $\sqrt{17}$ and $-\sqrt{17}$.

Cube Roots: All numbers (positive and negative) have one cube root, denoted by the symbol $\sqrt[3]{\ }$.

The cube root of a perfect cube is a rational number.

e.g. the cube root of 1 000 is 10, i.e. $\sqrt[3]{1\,000} = 10$

the cube root of –27 is –3, i.e. $\sqrt[3]{-27} = -3$

The cube root of a non-perfect cube is an irrational number.

e.g. the cube root of 49 is $\sqrt[3]{49}$, which is irrational.

Other Roots: Complete the following statements:

The fourth roots of 16 are _____ and ______. $\sqrt[4]{16}$ = _____.

The fifth root of –32 is _____. $\sqrt[5]{-32}$ = ______.

Without using a calculator, evaluate where possible.

a) $\sqrt{64}$ **b)** $\sqrt{-64}$ **c)** $\sqrt[3]{-64}$

d) $\sqrt[5]{\dfrac{1}{32}}$ **e)** $\sqrt[4]{-16}$ **f)** $10\sqrt[3]{125}$

Using the $\sqrt[x]{\ }$ Feature of a Calculator

Use the following procedure to determine $\sqrt[4]{10\,000}$ on a calculator.

1. Press [4]. **2.** Press [MATH]. **3.** Choose **5:$\sqrt[x]{\ }$** .

4. Press 10 000 . **5.** Press [ENTER] . The answer will be 10 .

Use a calculator to determine the exact value.

a) $\sqrt[5]{243}$ **b)** $\sqrt[7]{-16\,384}$ **c)** $\sqrt[3]{\dfrac{125}{216}}$

Evaluate, to the nearest hundredth.

a) $\sqrt[5]{500}$ **b)** $\sqrt[6]{0.6}$ **c)** $\frac{2}{5}\sqrt[4]{100}$

Radicals

Numbers like $\sqrt{30}$, $\sqrt[3]{125}$, $\sqrt[4]{15}$, $\sqrt[6]{1\,000\,000}$ etc. are examples of **radicals**.

In fact, any expression of the form $\sqrt[n]{x}$, where $n \in N$, is called a radical.
n is called the **index**. In a number like $\sqrt{30}$ the index is 2.
x is called the **radicand** and $\sqrt{\ }$ is called the **radical sign**.
If the index in a radical is even, then the radicand must be positive.

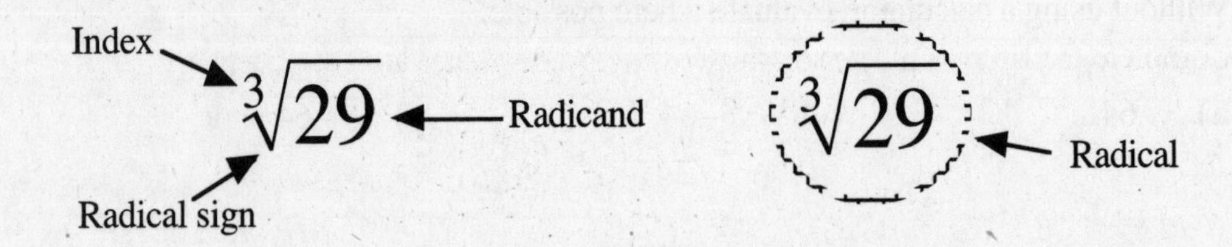

- When the index is not written in the radical, as in square root, it is assumed to be 2.
- The index is the number of times the radical must be multiplied by itself to equal the radicand.

Combining Radicals

Verify the following calculations.

$\sqrt{9} \times \sqrt{4}$ is equal to $\sqrt{9 \times 4}$ $\qquad$ $\sqrt{9} + \sqrt{4}$ is **not** equal to $\sqrt{9+4}$

$\sqrt{9} \div \sqrt{4}$ is equal to $\sqrt{9 \div 4}$ $\qquad$ $\sqrt{9} - \sqrt{4}$ is **not** equal to $\sqrt{9-4}$

The calculations above are examples of some general rules involving radicals.

i) **The product(quotient) of the roots of two numbers is equal to the root of the product(quotient) of the two numbers.**

ii) **The sum (difference) of the roots of two numbers is NOT equal to the root of the sum (difference) of the two numbers.**

In general $\sqrt{a} \times \sqrt{b} = \sqrt{ab}$ where $a, b \geq 0$ and $\dfrac{\sqrt{a}}{\sqrt{b}} = \sqrt{\dfrac{a}{b}}$ where $a \geq 0,\ b > 0$.

State whether each statement is true or false.

a) $\sqrt{3} \times \sqrt{5} = \sqrt{15}$ $\qquad$ **b)** $\dfrac{\sqrt{30}}{\sqrt{10}} = \sqrt{3}$ $\qquad$ **c)** $\sqrt{16+9} = \sqrt{16} + \sqrt{9}$

Complete Assignment Questions #1 - #5

Entire Radicals and Mixed Radicals

Use a calculator to approximate the value of each radical to 5 decimal places.

i) $\sqrt{96}$ = ____________ **ii)** $2\sqrt{24}$ = ____________ **iii)** $4\sqrt{6}$ = ____________

What do you notice about the answers? ____________________

Complete the following to explain why the three radicals are equivalent.

$\sqrt{96} = \sqrt{4 \times 24} = \sqrt{\quad} \times \sqrt{\quad} = $ _____

$\sqrt{96} = \sqrt{16 \times 6} = \sqrt{\quad} \times \sqrt{\quad} = $ _____

$\sqrt{96}$ is an example of an **entire radical**; the number is entirely under the root symbol.

$2\sqrt{24}$ and $4\sqrt{6}$ are examples of **mixed radicals**.

Entire/Pure Radicals

- Radicals expressed in the form $\sqrt[n]{b}$ are called entire (or pure) radicals.
- For example, $\sqrt{25}$, $\sqrt{80}$, $\sqrt[3]{17}$

Mixed Radicals

- Radicals expressed in the form $a\sqrt[n]{b}$ are called mixed radicals.
- For example $\frac{2}{3}\sqrt{5}$, $8\sqrt{7}$, $-9\sqrt[3]{17}$

Converting Entire Radicals to Mixed Radicals

An entire radical of index 2 may be expressed as a mixed radical when the highest perfect square has been factored out of the entire radical.
Complete the following to convert $\sqrt{72}$ to a mixed radical.

Entire Radical ⇒ *Mixed Radical*

$$\sqrt{72} = \sqrt{\quad \times 2}$$

$$= \sqrt{\quad} \times \sqrt{2}$$

$$= \_\_\_ \times \sqrt{2}$$

$\sqrt{72}$ = ______

An entire radical of index 3 may be expressed as a mixed radical when the highest perfect cube has been factored out of the entire radical.
Complete the following to convert $\sqrt[3]{108}$ to a mixed radical.

Entire Radical ⇒ *Mixed Radical*

$$\sqrt[3]{108} = \sqrt[3]{\quad \times 4}$$

$$= \sqrt[3]{\quad} \times \sqrt[3]{4}$$

$$= \_\_\_ \times \sqrt[3]{4}$$

$\sqrt[3]{108}$ = ______

A similar process is involved for indices greater than 3.

Convert the following radicals to mixed radicals in simplest form.

a) $\sqrt{320}$ **b)** $\sqrt[3]{6\,000}$ **c)** $\sqrt[5]{486}$ **d)** $2\sqrt[3]{-40}$

Application - Pythagorean Theorem or Distance Formula

Consider line segment AB shown on the grid.

Determine the exact length of the line segment, in simplest mixed radical form, using

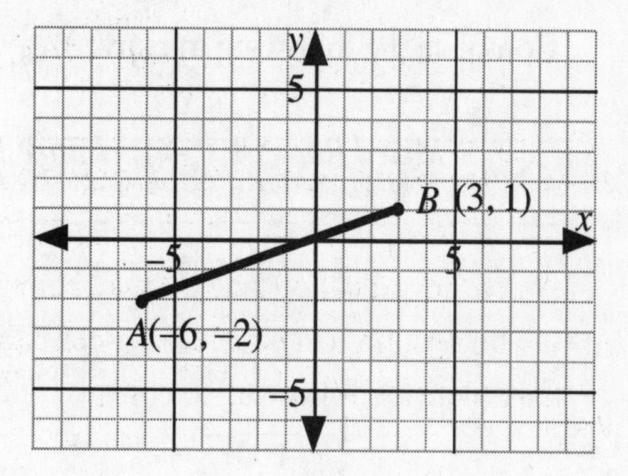

a) the Pythagorean Theorem $c^2 = a^2 + b^2$

b) the Distance Formula $d = \sqrt{(x_2 - x_1)^2 + (y_2 - y_1)^2}$

Complete Assignment Questions #6 - #9

Converting Mixed Radicals to Entire Radicals

Every mixed radical can be expressed as an entire radical.
A mixed radical of index 2 may be expressed as an entire radical by converting the number outside the radical symbol into a radical and then multiplying it by the radicand.
The number outside the radical symbol can be converted into a radical by raising it to the power of 2.

Complete the following to convert $3\sqrt{7}$ to an entire radical.

Mixed Radical ⇒ *Entire Radical*

$3\sqrt{7} \quad = \quad \sqrt{\quad} \times \sqrt{7}$

$\quad\quad = \quad \sqrt{\quad \times 7}$

$3\sqrt{7} \quad =$

A mixed radical of index 3 may be expressed as an entire radical by converting the number outside the radical symbol into a radical and then multiplying it by the radicand. The number outside the radical symbol can be converted into a radical by raising it to the power of 3.

Complete the following to convert $\frac{1}{2}\sqrt[3]{160}$ to an entire radical.

Mixed Radical $\Rightarrow$ *Entire Radical*

$$\frac{1}{2}\sqrt[3]{160} = \sqrt[3]{\quad} \times \sqrt[3]{160}$$

$$= \sqrt[3]{\quad \times 160}$$

$$\frac{1}{2}\sqrt[3]{160} =$$

Class Ex. #7

Convert the following mixed radicals to entire radicals.

a) $2\sqrt{3}$ **b)** $-5\sqrt{6}$ **c)** $-4\sqrt[3]{6}$ **d)** $5\sqrt[4]{2}$ **e)** $\frac{4}{5}\sqrt[3]{100}$

Class Ex. #8

Without using a calculator, arrange the following mixed radicals in order from greatest to least.

i) $3\sqrt{6}$ ii) $6\sqrt{3}$ iii) $\sqrt{18}$ iv) $2\sqrt{7}$ v) $7\sqrt{2}$

Complete Assignment Questions #10 - #15

Assignment

1. State whether each statement is true or false.

a) $\sqrt{20} - \sqrt{5} = \sqrt{15}$

b) $\sqrt{6} \times \sqrt{7} = \sqrt{42}$

c) $\dfrac{\sqrt{12}}{\sqrt{2}} = \sqrt{6}$

d) $\sqrt{36 + 9} = \sqrt{36} + \sqrt{9}$

2. State whether the following are true or false.

a) The square roots of 36 are ±6.

b) The cube roots of 27 are ±3.

c) $\sqrt{36} = \pm 6$

d) $\sqrt[3]{27} = \pm 3$

e) If $x^2 = 36, x \in R,$ then $x = \pm 6.$

f) If $x^3 = 27, x \in R,$ then $x = \pm 3.$

3. Without using a calculator, determine, where possible, the exact value of the following.

a) $\sqrt{81}$

b) $\sqrt{-100}$

c) $\sqrt[3]{-64}$

d) $\sqrt[5]{100\,000}$

e) $\sqrt[4]{\dfrac{81}{16}}$

f) $\sqrt[4]{-16}$

4. Without using a calculator, arrange the following radicals in order from least to greatest.

$4\sqrt[5]{1}, \quad -2\sqrt[3]{-27}, \quad \frac{3}{2}\sqrt[4]{16}, \quad 4\sqrt{\sqrt[3]{64}}$

5. Use a calculator to arrange the following radicals in order from least to greatest.

$\sqrt{10}, \quad \sqrt[3]{-729}, \quad \sqrt[5]{-243}, \quad \sqrt[4]{4\,096}, \quad \sqrt[5]{25}, \quad \sqrt[6]{242}$

6. Convert the following radicals to mixed radicals in simplest form.

a) $\sqrt{50}$ **b)** $\sqrt{60}$ **c)** $\sqrt[3]{54}$ **d)** $\frac{1}{2}\sqrt{320}$

e) $\sqrt[3]{3\,000}$ **f)** $\sqrt[3]{-81}$ **g)** $-5\sqrt[4]{162}$ **h)** $\sqrt[5]{-160}$

7. Use the Pythagorean Theorem to determine the exact length of *AB*.
Express the answer as **a)** an exact value in simplest mixed radical form
b) a decimal to the nearest hundredth

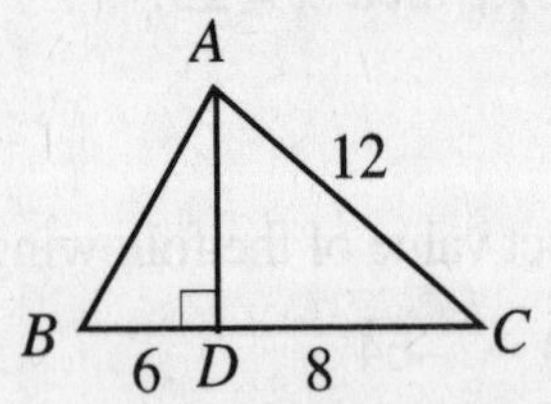

Do not use a calculator to answer question #8.

8. Given that $\sqrt{5}$ is approximately equal to 2.24, and $\sqrt{50}$ is approximately equal to 7.07, then find the approximate value of

a) $\sqrt{500}$ **b)** $\sqrt{5\,000}$ **c)** $\sqrt{20}$ **d)** $\sqrt{0.05}$ **e)** $\sqrt{0.5}$

9. Determine the exact distance between the following pairs of points.
Answer as a mixed radical in simplest form.

a) $(-3, 8)$ and $(-1, 4)$ **b)** $(3, 2)$ and $(-3, -4)$ **c)** $(15, 8)$ and $(9, 20)$

10. Convert the following mixed radicals to entire radicals.

a) $7\sqrt{5}$ **b)** $2\sqrt[3]{4}$ **c)** $-2\sqrt[4]{3}$

d) $-10\sqrt[3]{7}$ **e)** $8\sqrt{10}$ **f)** $\frac{1}{3}\sqrt[3]{9}$

11. Without using a calculator, arrange the following radicals in order from greatest to least.

$3\sqrt{5}$, $5\sqrt{3}$, $\sqrt{60}$, $2\sqrt{11}$, $\frac{1}{3}\sqrt{450}$

12. Consider the radicals $3\sqrt[3]{10}$, $4\sqrt[3]{3}$, $5\sqrt[3]{2}$, $2\sqrt[3]{31}$.

a) Explain how to arrange the radicals in order from least to greatest without using a calculator.

b) Arrange the radicals in order from least to greatest without using a calculator.

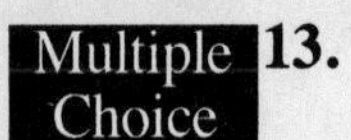

13. Without using a calculator, determine which of the following radicals is not equal to the others.

A. $8\sqrt{3}$ **B.** $\sqrt{192}$
C. $3\sqrt{24}$ **D.** $4\sqrt{12}$

Numerical Response

14. The smaller square has side length 12 cm. The side length of the larger square can be written in simplest mixed radical form as $a\sqrt{b}$, where $a, b \in N$.
The value of b^a is _____.

(Record your answer in the numerical response box from left to right.)

15. The volume of an ice cube is 32 000 mm^3. The exact length of each edge of the ice cube can be written in simplest mixed radical form as $p\sqrt[3]{q}$ where p and q are whole numbers.

The value of $p - q$ is ______.

(Record your answer in the numerical response box from left to right.)

Answer Key

1. a) false b) true c) true d) false
2. a) true b) false c) false d) false e) true f) false
3. a) 9 b) not possible c) –4 d) 10 e) $\frac{3}{2}$ f) not possible
4. $\frac{3}{2}\sqrt[4]{16}$, $4\sqrt[5]{1}$, $-2\sqrt[3]{-27}$, $4\sqrt{\sqrt[3]{64}}$ **5.** $\sqrt[3]{-729}$, $\sqrt[5]{-243}$, $\sqrt[5]{25}$, $\sqrt[6]{242}$, $\sqrt{10}$, $\sqrt[4]{4096}$
6. a) $5\sqrt{2}$ b) $2\sqrt{15}$ c) $3\sqrt[3]{2}$ d) $4\sqrt{5}$ e) $10\sqrt[3]{3}$ f) $-3\sqrt[3]{3}$ g) $-15\sqrt[4]{2}$ h) $-2\sqrt[5]{5}$
7. a) $2\sqrt{29}$ b) 10.77 **8.** a) 22.4 b) 70.7 c) 4.48 d) 0.224 e) 0.707
9. a) $2\sqrt{5}$ b) $6\sqrt{2}$ c) $6\sqrt{5}$
10. a) $\sqrt{245}$ b) $\sqrt[3]{32}$ c) $-\sqrt[4]{48}$ d) $-\sqrt[3]{7000}$ or $\sqrt[3]{-7000}$ e) $\sqrt{640}$ f) $\sqrt[3]{\frac{1}{3}}$
11. $5\sqrt{3}$, $\sqrt{60}$, $\frac{1}{3}\sqrt{450}$, $3\sqrt{5}$, $2\sqrt{11}$
12. a) Write each mixed radical as an entire radical and compare the radicands. The new radicands are determined by cubing the original coefficients and multiplying by the original radicands.
b) $4\sqrt[3]{3}$, $2\sqrt[3]{31}$, $5\sqrt[3]{2}$, $3\sqrt[3]{10}$
13. C **14.** | 4 | 0 | 9 | 6 | **15.** | 1 | 6 | | |

Operations on Radicals Lesson #2:
Adding and Subtracting Radicals

Investigation 1

In the last lesson we verified that addition of radicals cannot be done by adding the radicands.

In order to develop a rule for adding and subtracting radicals, complete the work below.

a) Use a calculator to investigate which of the following radical statements are true. Circle the statements which are true and place a single line through the expressions which are false.

i) $\sqrt{2} + 5\sqrt{2} = 6\sqrt{2}$

ii) $4\sqrt[3]{5} - 7\sqrt[3]{5} = -3\sqrt[3]{5}$

iii) $5\sqrt{8} - 2\sqrt{8} + 7\sqrt{8} = 10\sqrt{8}$

iv) $7\sqrt{5} + 7\sqrt[3]{5} = 14\sqrt[5]{5}$

v) $\sqrt[3]{3} + \sqrt[3]{2} = \sqrt[3]{5}$

b) Use the results in a) to suggest a rule for adding and subtracting radicals.

c) Simplify the following. Express the answer as a mixed radical.

i) $8\sqrt{7} - 3\sqrt{7} + 15\sqrt{7}$ **ii)** $18\sqrt[5]{10} + 12\sqrt[5]{10} - 7\sqrt[5]{10}$ **iii)** $5\sqrt{x} - 4\sqrt{x}$

Investigation 2

a) Use a calculator to verify that the following statements are true.

i) $\sqrt{2}+\sqrt{8} = 3\sqrt{2}$ **ii)** $5\sqrt{12} + 6\sqrt{48} = 34\sqrt{3}$

b) Does this appear to contradict the rule you wrote in Investigation #1 b)?

c) Complete the following by writing each radical in simplest mixed form to show that the rule can be modified.

i) $\sqrt{2}+\sqrt{8}$

$= \sqrt{2} +$

ii) $5\sqrt{12} + 6\sqrt{48}$

$=$

Adding and Subtracting Radicals

In order to add and subtract radicals, they must be able to be expressed as **like radicals**, ie. radicals with the SAME radicand **and** the SAME index.

Write each expression in terms of a single radical.

a) $\sqrt{80} - \sqrt{20}$ **b)** $\sqrt[3]{80} + \sqrt[3]{270}$ **c)** $7\sqrt{27} - 3\sqrt{75} + 2\sqrt{147}$

Simplify by combining like radicals.

a) $-5\sqrt{108} + \frac{3}{4}\sqrt{8} - \frac{5}{4}\sqrt{48} + \frac{1}{2}\sqrt{50}$

b) $\frac{\sqrt[3]{64}}{8} + 2\sqrt[3]{375} - \frac{2\sqrt[3]{54}}{3} - \frac{5\sqrt[3]{24}}{2}$

Complete Assignment Questions #1 - #5

Find the length of x

a) as an exact value
b) as a decimal to the nearest tenth.

x

$8\sqrt{2} + 2\sqrt{12}$

$5\sqrt{27} - 4\sqrt{18}$

Complete Assignment Questions #6 - #13

Assignment

1. Simplify.

a) $5\sqrt{7} - 2\sqrt{7}$ **b)** $9\sqrt[3]{13} + 2\sqrt[3]{13}$ **c)** $4\sqrt{11} - 9\sqrt{11} + \sqrt{11}$

d) $4\sqrt{5} - 2\sqrt{2} + 8\sqrt{2}$ **e)** $13\sqrt[4]{a} + 7\sqrt[4]{a}$ **f)** $-3\sqrt{2} + 6\sqrt{3} - 9\sqrt{3} + 4\sqrt{2}$

2. Write each expression in terms of a single radical.

a) $\sqrt{125} - \sqrt{5}$ **b)** $\sqrt{27} + \sqrt{12}$ **c)** $\sqrt{24} - \sqrt{54} + 2\sqrt{6}$

d) $\sqrt{150} + \sqrt{216}$ **e)** $\sqrt[3]{16} + \sqrt[3]{128}$ **f)** $-3\sqrt{175} + 8\sqrt{28} - \sqrt{63}$

g) $\sqrt[4]{16} + \sqrt[4]{162}$ **h)** $2\sqrt{700} - 6\sqrt{63}$ **i)** $-7\sqrt[3]{54} - 2\sqrt[3]{250}$

3. Simplify by combining like radicals.

a) $\sqrt{20} + \sqrt{72} - \sqrt{45}$

b) $\sqrt{27} + \sqrt{12} - \sqrt{32} - \sqrt{8}$

c) $\sqrt{98} - \sqrt{20} + \sqrt{18}$

d) $2\sqrt{252} - \sqrt{726} - 5\sqrt{63}$

e) $2\sqrt[3]{108} + \sqrt[3]{32} + 3\sqrt[3]{256}$

f) $12\sqrt{150} - 5\sqrt{54} + 3\sqrt{24}$

4. Plot the points $A(-6, 0)$, $B(10, 0)$, and C(2, 4). and determine, in simplest radical form, the perimeter of $\triangle ABC$.

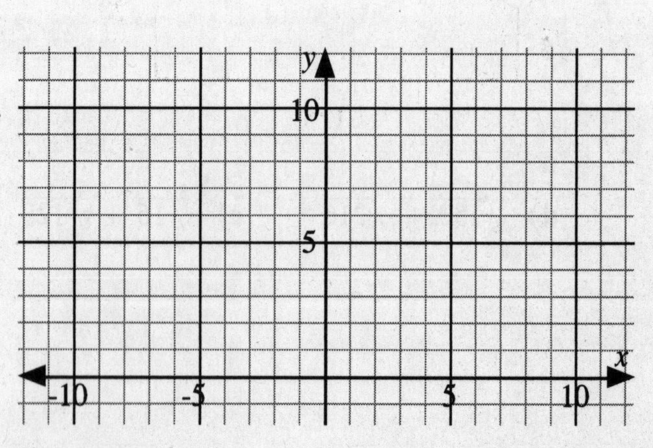

5. Write in simplest radical form.

a) $\frac{1}{3}\sqrt{63} + \frac{2}{5}\sqrt{700} - \frac{2}{3}\sqrt{112} + \frac{3}{2}\sqrt{28}$

b) $\frac{7\sqrt[3]{1024}}{2} + \frac{5\sqrt[3]{2000}}{12} - 3\sqrt[3]{686} + \frac{1}{8}\sqrt[3]{128}$

6. Determine the perimeter of the following figures in simplest radical form.

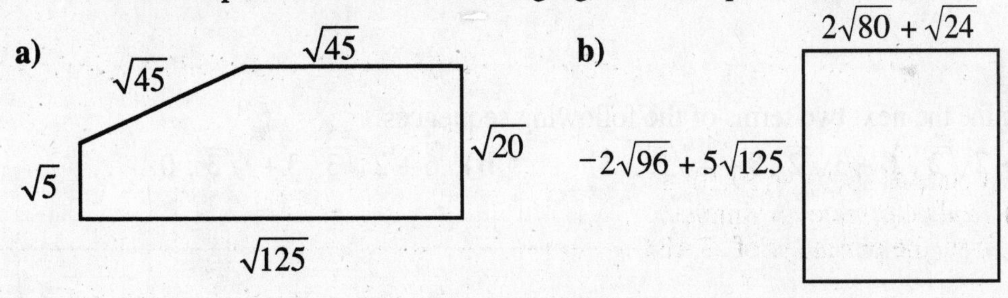

7. Determine a radical expression for the length of each of the missing sides.

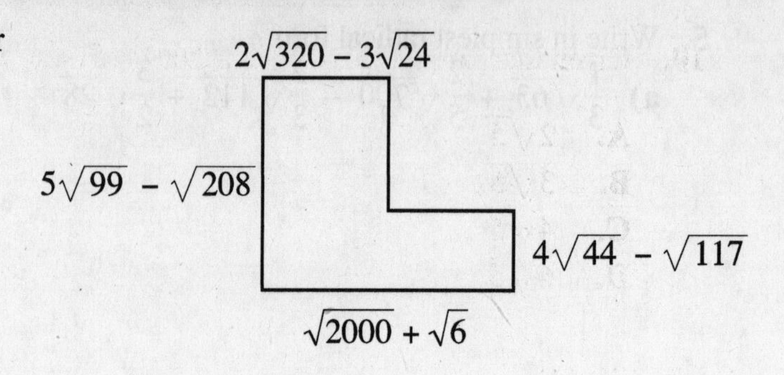

8. Determine the next two terms of the following sequences.

a) $4 + 2\sqrt{2}$, $6 + 3\sqrt{2}$, $8 + 4\sqrt{2}$, ...

b) $6 + 2\sqrt{3}$, $3 + \sqrt{3}$, 0, ...

Multiple Choice

9. $\sqrt{75} + \sqrt{3}$ equals

A. $6\sqrt{3}$
B. $26\sqrt{3}$
C. $\sqrt{78}$
D. $3\sqrt{5} + \sqrt{3}$

10. Given that $x - 2\sqrt{5} = \sqrt{45}$, then $\sqrt{5} + x$ is equal to

A. $2\sqrt{5}$
B. $3\sqrt{5}$
C. $4\sqrt{5}$
D. $6\sqrt{5}$

11. In simplest radical form the perimeter of $\Delta\, PQR$ is

A. $\sqrt{252}$
B. $6\sqrt{7}$
C. $10\sqrt{3} + 4\sqrt{6}$
D. $52\sqrt{3} + 16\sqrt{6}$

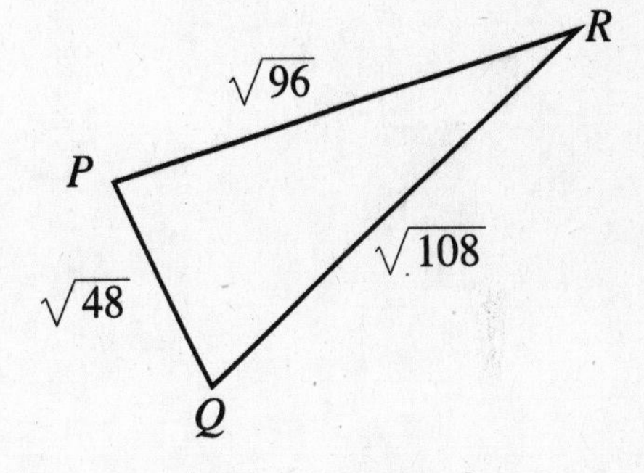

Numerical Response **12.** When simplified, the expression $\sqrt{52} + \sqrt{208} - \sqrt{13} + \sqrt{169}$ can be written in the form $p\sqrt{13} + q$. The value of pq is _____.
(Record your answer in the numerical response box from left to right.)

13. When simplified, the expression $\frac{9}{2}\sqrt[3]{48} + \frac{3}{4}\sqrt[3]{162} - \frac{3}{5}\sqrt[3]{750}$ can be written in the form $a\sqrt[3]{b}$. The value of a, to the nearest hundredth, is ______.

(Record your answer in the numerical response box from left to right.)

Answer Key

1. **a)** $3\sqrt{7}$ **b)** $11\sqrt[3]{13}$ **c)** $-4\sqrt{11}$ **d)** $4\sqrt{5} + 6\sqrt{2}$ **e)** $20\sqrt[4]{a}$ **f)** $\sqrt{2} - 3\sqrt{3}$

2. **a)** $4\sqrt{5}$ **b)** $5\sqrt{3}$ **c)** $\sqrt{6}$ **d)** $11\sqrt{6}$ **e)** $6\sqrt[3]{2}$ **f)** $-2\sqrt{7}$ **g)** $2 + 3\sqrt[4]{2}$

h) $2\sqrt{7}$ **i)** $-31\sqrt[3]{2}$

3. **a)** $6\sqrt{2} - \sqrt{5}$ **b)** $5\sqrt{3} - 6\sqrt{2}$ **c)** $10\sqrt{2} - 2\sqrt{5}$ **d)** $-3\sqrt{7} - 11\sqrt{6}$

e) $20\sqrt[3]{4}$ **f)** $51\sqrt{6}$

4. $16 + 8\sqrt{5}$

5. **a)** $\frac{16}{3}\sqrt{7}$ **b)** $\frac{35}{3}\sqrt[3]{2}$

6. **a)** $14\sqrt{5}$ **b)** $66\sqrt{5} - 12\sqrt{6}$

7. $7\sqrt{11} - \sqrt{13}$, $4\sqrt{5} + 7\sqrt{6}$

8. **a)** $10 + 5\sqrt{2}$, $12 + 6\sqrt{2}$ **b)** $-3 - \sqrt{3}$, $-6 - 2\sqrt{3}$

9. A **10.** D **11.** C

12.

6	5		

13.

8	.	2	5

Operations on Radicals Lesson #3:
Multiplying Radicals

Investigation *Investigating Multiplication Properties of Radicals*

Use a calculator to determine whether the following statements are true or false.

a) $\sqrt{2} \times \sqrt{3} = \sqrt{6}$ **b)** $\left(2\sqrt{5}\right)\left(-4\sqrt{3}\right) = -8\sqrt{15}$ **c)** $\sqrt{2} \cdot \sqrt[3]{4} = \sqrt[3]{8}$

d) $2\sqrt[3]{10} \times 3\sqrt[3]{7} = 6\sqrt[3]{70}$ **e)** $\left(4\sqrt[3]{5}\right)\left(7\sqrt{6}\right) = 28\sqrt[6]{30}$

Based on the results from a) - e), write a rule which describes the process of multiplying radicals.

Multiplying Radicals

To multiply radicals the index must be the same in each radical.

- multiply numerical coefficients by numerical coefficients
- multiply radicand by radicand
- simplify into mixed radical form if possible.

It is usually easier to convert each radical to simplest mixed form before multiplying.

Multiply and simplify where possible.

a) $\sqrt{8} \cdot \sqrt{8}$ **b)** $\left(4\sqrt{5}\right)\left(3\sqrt{6}\right)$ **c)** $\left(4\sqrt{x}\right)\left(3\sqrt{y}\right)$ **d)** $-2\sqrt{8} \times 5\sqrt{12}$

Expand and simplify.

a) $\sqrt{5}\left(2\sqrt{10} - \sqrt{5}\right)$ **b)** $2\sqrt{5}\left(3\sqrt{45} - 8\sqrt{5} + 3\sqrt{20}\right)$

c) $2\left(\sqrt{3} - \sqrt{5}\right) - \sqrt{2}\left(\sqrt{6} + \sqrt{10}\right)$ **d)** $-4\sqrt{a}\left(\sqrt{a} - 9\sqrt{b}\right)$

Write and simplify an expression for the area of each shape.

a) $4 + \sqrt{6}$

$7 - \sqrt{6}$

b)

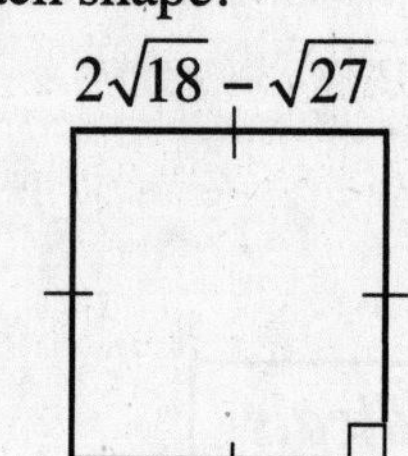

Complete Assignment Questions #1 - #10

Multiplying Conjugate Binomials

Expand the following expressions:

i) $\left(\sqrt{5} - \sqrt{2}\right)\left(\sqrt{5} + \sqrt{2}\right)$ **ii)** $\left(2\sqrt{7} + 8\right)\left(2\sqrt{7} - 8\right)$

The pairs of binomials above are called **conjugates** of each other.
What do you notice about the product of two conjugate binomials?

- Conjugate binomials are pairs of binomials in the form $a\sqrt{b}+c\sqrt{d}$ and $a\sqrt{b}-c\sqrt{d}$.
- The product of conjugate binomials is always a rational number of the form a^2b-c^2d.

Write the conjugate of each. Then multiply each pair.

a) $4\sqrt{6}+3$ **b)** $-3\sqrt{11}+\sqrt{2}$ **c)** $5\sqrt{x}-\sqrt{y}$

Complete Assignment Questions #11 - #17

Assignment

1. Multiply and simplify where possible. Do not use a calculator.

a) $(\sqrt{7})(\sqrt{3})$ **b)** $4\sqrt{3}\times 2\sqrt{5}$ **c)** $-3\sqrt{5}\times 2\sqrt{2}$ **d)** $6\sqrt{p}\times 8\sqrt{q}$

e) $(\sqrt{15})(\sqrt{3})$ **f)** $10\sqrt{5}\times 9\sqrt{5}$ **g)** $3\sqrt{6}\cdot 5\sqrt{10}$ **h)** $\sqrt{a}\times 10\sqrt{a}$

i) $7\sqrt{54}\cdot 2\sqrt{6}$ **j)** $(\sqrt{32})(\sqrt{6})$ **k)** $\sqrt{15}\times 3\sqrt{27}$

2. In each case, write each radical as the product of two mixed radicals in two different ways.

a) $15\sqrt{18}$ **b)** $35\sqrt{6}$

3. Express in simplest form. Do not use a calculator.

a) $\left(\sqrt{3}\right)^2$ **b)** $\left(4\sqrt{2}\right)^2$ **c)** $\left(-3\sqrt{5}\right)^2$ **d)** $-\left(\sqrt{12}\right)^2$ **e)** $\left(\sqrt{5}\right)^3$

4. Express in simplest form.

a) $\sqrt{5} \times 2\sqrt{3} \times 3\sqrt{2}$ **b)** $2\sqrt{6} \times 2\sqrt{3} \times 3\sqrt{2}$ **c)** $\left(-2\sqrt{6}\right)\left(2\sqrt{3}\right)\left(-3\sqrt{5}\right)$

d) $\left(\frac{2}{3}\sqrt{27}\right)\left(\sqrt{6}\right)$ **e)** $2\sqrt{\frac{8}{25}} \times 5\sqrt{2}$ **f)** $3\sqrt[3]{16} \times 2\sqrt[3]{4} \times 2\sqrt[3]{2}$

5. Consider the product $6\sqrt{5} \times 3\sqrt{8}$.

a) Use a **two decimal place approximation** for each radical to determine a two decimal place approximation for the product.

b) Determine the **exact value** of the product as a mixed radical in simplest form.

c) Determine a **two decimal place approximation** to the answer in b).

d) Which of the two decimal place approximations is more accurate? Explain.

6. Expand and simplify where possible.

a) $\sqrt{6}\left(2\sqrt{6}-\sqrt{5}\right)$ **b)** $\sqrt{2}\left(1-\sqrt{2}\right)$ **c)** $2\sqrt{3}\left(2\sqrt{7}-4\sqrt{5}\right)$

7. Expand and simplify.

a) $\sqrt{3}\left(2\sqrt{6}-\sqrt{12}\right)$ **b)** $\sqrt{8}\left(\sqrt{6}-\sqrt{2}\right)$ **c)** $\sqrt{y}\left(\sqrt{x}-9\sqrt{y}\right)$

d) $2\sqrt{11}\left(3\sqrt{2}-\sqrt{50}+3\sqrt{32}\right)$ **e)** $\sqrt{5}\left(3\sqrt{5}-\sqrt{75}+3\sqrt{3}\right)$

8. Simplify.

a) $\left(4+\sqrt{27}\right)\left(1-\sqrt{12}\right)$ **b)** $\left(2\sqrt{3}-\sqrt{10}\right)\left(\sqrt{6}-7\sqrt{20}\right)$

9. Write and simplify an expression for the area of each shape.

a)

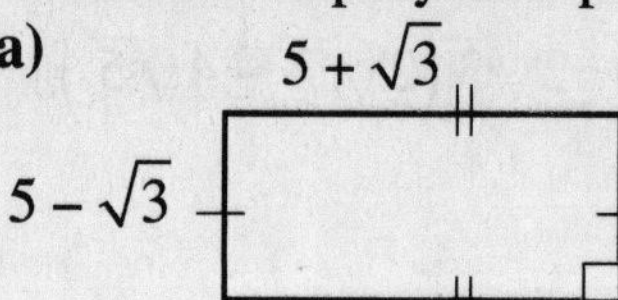

b)

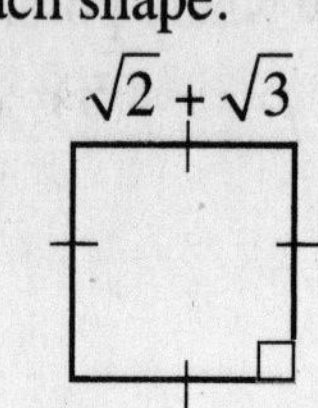

c) rectangle $2\sqrt{10}$ by $\left(\sqrt{6}+4\sqrt{5}\right)$

d) square with sides $3\sqrt{208}-8$

10. Expand and simplify.

a) $\left(5\sqrt{3}-2\right)^2$

b) $\left(4\sqrt{6}-\sqrt{2}\right)^2$

c) $2\left(\sqrt{15}-3\sqrt{5}\right)^2$

d) $\left(7\sqrt{x}-2\sqrt{y}\right)^2$

11. Expand and simplify.

a) $\left(\sqrt{5}+1\right)\left(\sqrt{5}-1\right)$ **b)** $\left(\sqrt{8}+\sqrt{7}\right)\left(\sqrt{8}-\sqrt{7}\right)$ **c)** $\left(2\sqrt{6}-\sqrt{2}\right)\left(2\sqrt{6}+\sqrt{2}\right)$

12. Write the conjugate of each.

a) $\sqrt{2}-\sqrt{5}$ **b)** $4+\sqrt{7}$ **c)** $-3\sqrt{8}-15$

13. Write the conjugate of each. Then multiply each pair.

a) $\sqrt{3}-1$ **b)** $2+\sqrt{5}$ **c)** $2\sqrt{6}-\sqrt{3}$

d) $2\sqrt{8}+\sqrt{27}$ **e)** $\sqrt{32}-\sqrt{3}$ **f)** $-3\sqrt{40}+2\sqrt{10}$

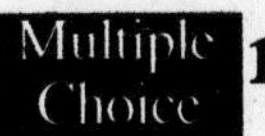

14. For all values of a and b, $\left(\sqrt{a}-\sqrt{b}\right)\left(\sqrt{a}+\sqrt{b}\right)$ is equal to

A. $\sqrt{(a-b)(a+b)}$
B. $a-b$
C. $a+b$
D. a^2-b^2

15. $\left(\sqrt{2}\right)^5$ is equal to

A. $\sqrt{10}$
B. $5\sqrt{2}$
C. $4\sqrt{2}$
D. 32

16. The expression $\sqrt{5}\left(\sqrt{10} + 12\sqrt{5}\right) - \sqrt{7}\left(\sqrt{7} - 2\sqrt{14}\right)$ can be simplified to the form $a + b\sqrt{c}$ where a, b and c are integers. The value of $a + b + c$ is _____.

(Record your answer in the numerical response box from left to right.)

17. If $p \oplus q$ means "$(p - q)$ multiplied by q" then the value of $\sqrt{6} \oplus \sqrt{3}$ can be simplified to the form $a + b\sqrt{c}$ where a, b and c are integers. The value of c is _____.

(Record your answer in the numerical response box from left to right.)

Answer Key

1. a) $\sqrt{21}$ b) $8\sqrt{15}$ c) $-6\sqrt{10}$ d) $48\sqrt{pq}$ e) $3\sqrt{5}$ f) 450 g) $30\sqrt{15}$
h) $10a$ i) 252 j) $8\sqrt{3}$ k) $27\sqrt{5}$

2. Answers may vary.
a) $(3\sqrt{3})(5\sqrt{6})$ or $(5\sqrt{3})(3\sqrt{6})$ b) $(5\sqrt{2})(7\sqrt{3})$ or $(7\sqrt{2})(5\sqrt{3})$

3. a) 3 b) 32 c) 45 d) -12 e) $5\sqrt{5}$

4. a) $6\sqrt{30}$ b) 72 c) $36\sqrt{10}$ d) $6\sqrt{2}$ e) 8 f) $48\sqrt[3]{2}$

5. a) 113.94 b) $36\sqrt{10}$ c) 113.84 d) c) because rounding is not done until the last step.

6. a) $12 - \sqrt{30}$ b) $\sqrt{2} - 2$ c) $4\sqrt{21} - 8\sqrt{15}$

7. a) $6\sqrt{2} - 6$ b) $4\sqrt{3} - 4$ c) $\sqrt{xy} - 9y$ d) $20\sqrt{22}$ e) $15 - 2\sqrt{15}$

8. a) $-14 - 5\sqrt{3}$ b) $76\sqrt{2} - 30\sqrt{15}$

9. a) 22 b) $5 + 2\sqrt{6}$ c) $4\sqrt{15} + 40\sqrt{2}$ d) $1936 - 192\sqrt{13}$

10. a) $79 - 20\sqrt{3}$ b) $98 - 16\sqrt{3}$ c) $120 - 60\sqrt{3}$ d) $49x - 28\sqrt{xy} + 4y$

11. a) 4 b) 1 c) 22

12. a) $\sqrt{2} + \sqrt{5}$ b) $4 - \sqrt{7}$ c) $-3\sqrt{8} + 15$

13. a) $\sqrt{3} + 1$, 2 b) $2 - \sqrt{5}$, -1 c) $2\sqrt{6} + \sqrt{3}$, 21
d) $2\sqrt{8} - \sqrt{27}$, 5 e) $\sqrt{32} + \sqrt{3}$, 29 f) $-3\sqrt{40} - 2\sqrt{10}$, 320

14. B **15.** C

16.

7	4		

17.

2			

Operations on Radicals Lesson #4:
Dividing Radicals - Part One

Dividing Radicals

In previous work, we discovered that $\sqrt{\dfrac{a}{b}} = \dfrac{\sqrt{a}}{\sqrt{b}}$, $a \geq 0,\ b > 0$, and $a, b \in R$.

We can use this rule to divide radicals of the form $\dfrac{m\sqrt{a}}{n\sqrt{b}}$.

To divide radicals, the index must be the same in each radical.

- divide numerical coefficients by numerical coefficients
- divide radicand by radicand
- simplify into mixed radical form if possible.

Class Ex. #1

Divide and simplify where possible.

a) $\dfrac{\sqrt{30}}{\sqrt{6}}$ b) $\dfrac{8\sqrt[3]{21}}{2\sqrt[3]{3}}$ c) $\dfrac{15\sqrt{48}}{10\sqrt{6}}$ d) $\dfrac{4\sqrt{ab}}{12\sqrt{a}}$

In some cases, converting a radical into simplest mixed radical form before dividing will make the calculation easier.

Class Ex. #2

Simplify numerator and denominator, then divide.

a) $\dfrac{4\sqrt{54}}{3\sqrt{8}}$ b) $\dfrac{8\sqrt{126}}{\sqrt{112}}$ c) $\dfrac{10\sqrt[3]{162}}{20\sqrt[3]{128}}$

Class Ex. #3

Divide each term in the numerator by the denominator, and simplify.

$$\frac{\sqrt{24} + \sqrt{48} - \sqrt{108}}{\sqrt{6}}$$

Complete Assignment Questions #1 - #4

Rationalizing the Denominator

Usually answers are written in **simplest form**, e.g. $\frac{1}{6} + \frac{1}{3} = \frac{3}{6}$ which simplifies to $\frac{1}{2}$.

In the division of radicals in this unit, regard simplest form as the form in which

i) the denominator of the fraction is a rational number, i.e. it does not contain a radical.

ii) the radicand cannot contain a fraction and is expressed in simplest mixed form.

The process of eliminating the radical from the denominator (i.e. converting the denominator from an irrational number to a rational number) is called **rationalizing the denominator**. The denominators in this lesson are all of monomial form. Denominators in binomial form will be discussed in the next lesson.

Class Ex. #4

Simplify by rationalizing the denominator.

a) $\frac{1}{\sqrt{13}}$ **b)** $\frac{\sqrt{5}}{\sqrt{2}}$ **c)** $\frac{\sqrt{2}}{-\sqrt{6}}$ **d)** $\frac{\sqrt{20}}{\sqrt{3}}$

Class Ex. #5

Simplify.

a) $\frac{7}{3\sqrt{7}}$ **b)** $\sqrt{\frac{18}{5}}$ **c)** $\frac{3\sqrt{12}}{\sqrt{72}}$

Class Ex. #6

Simplify the radical expression $\frac{3\sqrt{18} - \sqrt{12}}{\sqrt{2}}$ by:

a) rationalizing the denominator first **b)** dividing numerator and denominator by $\sqrt{2}$

Complete Assignment Questions #5 - #16

Assignment

1. Simplify.

a) $\dfrac{\sqrt{50}}{\sqrt{5}}$ **b)** $\dfrac{\sqrt{35}}{\sqrt{7}}$ **c)** $\dfrac{\sqrt[3]{39}}{\sqrt[3]{3}}$ **d)** $\dfrac{\sqrt{28}}{\sqrt{7}}$ **e)** $\dfrac{\sqrt{ab}}{\sqrt{b}}$

f) $\dfrac{8\sqrt{42}}{2\sqrt{6}}$ **g)** $\dfrac{25\sqrt{88}}{5\sqrt{8}}$ **h)** $\dfrac{12\sqrt[4]{51}}{-6\sqrt[4]{17}}$ **i)** $\dfrac{4\sqrt{50}}{8\sqrt{10}}$ **j)** $\dfrac{6\sqrt{xy^2}}{15\sqrt{xy}}$

2. Simplify.

a) $\dfrac{\sqrt{270}}{\sqrt{10}}$ **b)** $\dfrac{\sqrt{90}}{\sqrt{5}}$ **c)** $\dfrac{\sqrt{96}}{4\sqrt{3}}$ **d)** $\dfrac{3\sqrt{200}}{2\sqrt{5}}$ **e)** $\dfrac{4\sqrt[3]{144}}{\sqrt[3]{9}}$

3. Simplify.

a) $\dfrac{2\sqrt{150}}{\sqrt{8}}$ **b)** $\dfrac{4\sqrt{90}}{\sqrt{72}}$ **c)** $\dfrac{3\sqrt{240}}{\sqrt{108}}$ **d)** $\dfrac{18\sqrt{24}}{\sqrt{162}}$ **e)** $\dfrac{3\sqrt[3]{32}}{2\sqrt[3]{216}}$

4. Simplify.

a) $\dfrac{\sqrt{35} - \sqrt{21}}{\sqrt{7}}$ **b)** $\dfrac{9\sqrt{20} - 3\sqrt{10}}{3\sqrt{2}}$ **c)** $\dfrac{8\sqrt{42} + 12\sqrt{75}}{4\sqrt{3}}$

d) $\dfrac{8\sqrt{20} + 10\sqrt{125}}{2\sqrt{5}}$ **e)** $\dfrac{\sqrt{75} + \sqrt{48} - \sqrt{27}}{\sqrt{3}}$ **f)** $\dfrac{\sqrt{90} + 2\sqrt{40} - \sqrt{160}}{\sqrt{5}}$

5. Simplify by rationalizing the denominator.

a) $\dfrac{1}{\sqrt{2}}$ **b)** $\dfrac{6}{\sqrt{6}}$ **c)** $\dfrac{\sqrt{5}}{\sqrt{3}}$ **d)** $\dfrac{\sqrt{3}}{-\sqrt{2}}$

e) $\dfrac{\sqrt{10}}{\sqrt{7}}$ **f)** $\dfrac{\sqrt{12}}{\sqrt{5}}$ **g)** $\dfrac{2}{5\sqrt{6}}$ **h)** $\dfrac{\sqrt{32}}{\sqrt{18}}$

i) $\dfrac{5}{\sqrt{50}}$ **j)** $\dfrac{14}{\sqrt{98}}$ **k)** $\dfrac{-2}{\sqrt{88}}$ **l)** $\dfrac{3\sqrt{500}}{-\sqrt{27}}$

6. Simplify.

a) $\sqrt{\dfrac{27}{10}}$ **b)** $\dfrac{5\sqrt{14}}{\sqrt{70}}$ **c)** $\sqrt{\dfrac{243}{2}}$ **d)** $\dfrac{20\sqrt{12}}{12\sqrt{20}}$

7. Express the following with rational denominators.

a) $\dfrac{\sqrt{7}-\sqrt{2}}{\sqrt{2}}$ **b)** $\dfrac{\sqrt{3}+2\sqrt{2}}{2\sqrt{3}}$ **c)** $\dfrac{\sqrt{5}+\sqrt{2}}{\sqrt{6}}$

8. a) Students are asked to simplify the radical expression $\dfrac{6\sqrt{40}-8\sqrt{20}}{2\sqrt{5}}$.

Erica decides to simplify the expression by rationalizing the denominator, whereas Jaclyn divides each term in the numerator by the denominator. Determine the simplification by each method, and state which method you prefer.

b) Without doing the simplification, **explain** why Jaclyn's method would be more difficult if the radical expression was $\dfrac{6\sqrt{40}-8\sqrt{20}}{2\sqrt{7}}$.

9. Simplify and express in lowest terms.

a) $\dfrac{10\sqrt{18} - 5\sqrt{24}}{\sqrt{5}}$

b) $\dfrac{15\sqrt{18} - 3\sqrt{242}}{-3\sqrt{8}}$

10. A rectangular garden has length $3\sqrt{6}$ metres and area $\left(9\sqrt{2} - 6\sqrt{3}\right)$ square meters.

a) Write and simplify an expression for the width of the garden.

b) Determine the perimeter of the garden to the nearest tenth of a metre.

11. A triangle has an area of $\left(3\sqrt{288} - 2\sqrt{12}\right)$ square metres with a base of $3\sqrt{2}$ metres. Express the height of the triangle

a) as an exact value in simplest form **b)** as a decimal to the nearest 0.01 m.

Multiple Choice

12. Without using technology, determine which of the following expressions is **not** equivalent to the others.

A. $\dfrac{36}{\sqrt{48}}$

B. $\left(\sqrt{3}\right)^3$

C. $\sqrt{192} - \sqrt{75}$

D. $\dfrac{\sqrt{54}}{\sqrt{3}}$

13. $\dfrac{2 + \sqrt{8}}{2}$ can be simplified to

A. $1 + \sqrt{8}$ **B.** $1 + \sqrt{6}$

C. $1 + \sqrt{4}$ **D.** $1 + \sqrt{2}$

14. If $\dfrac{\sqrt{10} \times \sqrt{12}}{\sqrt{6}} = 2\sqrt{t}$, then t is equal to

A. $\sqrt{5}$

B. $\sqrt{10}$

C. 5

D. 10

15. The expression $\dfrac{1}{\sqrt{27}} - \dfrac{5\sqrt{3}}{4\sqrt{24}}$ can be written in the form $a\sqrt{3} - b\sqrt{2}$, $a, b > 0$. To the nearest hundredth, the value of b is _____.

(Record your answer in the numerical response box from left to right.)

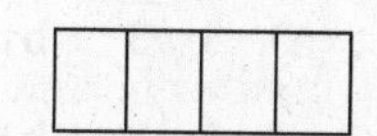

16. When the equation $\sqrt{2} + a\sqrt{5} = \sqrt{72}$ is solved for a, the solution is $a = \sqrt{t}$, where $t \in W$. The value of t is ____.

(Record your answer in the numerical response box from left to right.)

Answer Key

1. a) $\sqrt{10}$ b) $\sqrt{5}$ c) $\sqrt[3]{13}$ d) 2 e) $\sqrt{a}$
f) $4\sqrt{7}$ g) $5\sqrt{11}$ h) $-2\sqrt[4]{3}$ i) $\frac{1}{2}\sqrt{5}$ j) $\frac{2}{5}\sqrt{y}$

2. a) $3\sqrt{3}$ b) $3\sqrt{2}$ c) $\sqrt{2}$ d) $3\sqrt{10}$ e) $8\sqrt[3]{2}$

3. a) $5\sqrt{3}$ b) $2\sqrt{5}$ c) $2\sqrt{5}$ d) $4\sqrt{3}$ e) $\frac{1}{2}\sqrt[3]{4}$

4. a) $\sqrt{5} - \sqrt{3}$ b) $3\sqrt{10} - \sqrt{5}$ c) $2\sqrt{14} + 15$ d) 33 e) 6 f) $3\sqrt{2}$

5. a) $\frac{1}{2}\sqrt{2}$ b) $\sqrt{6}$ c) $\frac{1}{3}\sqrt{15}$ d) $-\frac{1}{2}\sqrt{6}$ e) $\frac{1}{7}\sqrt{70}$ f) $\frac{2}{5}\sqrt{15}$ g) $\frac{1}{15}\sqrt{6}$
h) $\frac{4}{3}$ i) $\frac{1}{2}\sqrt{2}$ j) $\sqrt{2}$ k) $-\frac{1}{22}\sqrt{22}$ l) $-\frac{10}{3}\sqrt{15}$

6. a) $\frac{3}{10}\sqrt{30}$ b) $\sqrt{5}$ c) $\frac{9}{2}\sqrt{6}$ d) $\frac{1}{3}\sqrt{15}$

7. a) $\dfrac{\sqrt{14} - 2}{2}$ b) $\dfrac{3 + 2\sqrt{6}}{6}$ c) $\dfrac{\sqrt{30} + 2\sqrt{3}}{6}$

8. a) $6\sqrt{2} - 8$ probably Jaclyn's method b) 40 and 20 do not divide exactly by 7

9. a) $6\sqrt{10} - 2\sqrt{30}$ b) -2

10. a) $\sqrt{3} - \sqrt{2}$ meters b) 15.3 metres

11. a) $\dfrac{72 - 4\sqrt{6}}{3}$ meters b) 20.73 metres **12.** D **13.** D **14.** C

15.

0	.	3	1

16.

1	0		

Operations on Radicals Lesson #5:
Dividing Radicals - Part Two

Rationalizing a Denominator in Binomial Form

When the original denominator of the fraction is of binomial form, the process of rationalizing the denominator involves multiplying both numerator and denominator of the fraction by the **conjugate** of the binomial denominator.

Simplify by rationalizing the denominator.

a) $\dfrac{2}{\sqrt{5}-\sqrt{3}}$ **b)** $\dfrac{\sqrt{6}-2}{\sqrt{6}+2}$ **c)** $\dfrac{1}{1-\sqrt{x}}$

Express $\dfrac{\sqrt{8}-\sqrt{3}}{4\sqrt{3}-\sqrt{2}}$ with a whole number in the denominator.

The area of a trapezoid is given by the formula $A = \frac{1}{2}h(a+b)$ where a and b are the lengths of the parallel sides and h is the shortest distance between the sides. If the area of a trapezoid is 20 cm^2, and the parallel sides are of lengths $\sqrt{6}$ cm and $\sqrt{5}$ cm, determine the exact value of the distance between the parallel sides. Answer with a rational denominator.

Complete Assignment Questions #1 - #12

Assignment

1. Simplify by rationalizing the denominator.

a) $\dfrac{4}{\sqrt{5}-1}$ **b)** $\dfrac{1}{\sqrt{6}+2}$ **c)** $\dfrac{3}{3-\sqrt{3}}$

d) $\dfrac{\sqrt{7}}{\sqrt{7}-2}$ **e)** $\dfrac{3}{\sqrt{2}-\sqrt{3}}$ **f)** $\dfrac{\sqrt{2}}{\sqrt{6}+\sqrt{2}}$

2. Simplify by rationalizing the denominator.

a) $\dfrac{2\sqrt{3}}{3\sqrt{2}+\sqrt{3}}$ **b)** $\dfrac{3\sqrt{11}}{3\sqrt{11}+10}$

c) $\dfrac{\sqrt{2}}{\sqrt{12}-\sqrt{8}}$ **d)** $\dfrac{\sqrt{7}}{4-\sqrt{14}}$

3. Simplify, leaving an integer in the denominator.

a) $\dfrac{\sqrt{3}-1}{\sqrt{3}+1}$

b) $\dfrac{\sqrt{5}-2}{\sqrt{5}-1}$

c) $\dfrac{\sqrt{6}+\sqrt{2}}{\sqrt{6}-\sqrt{2}}$

d) $\dfrac{5-\sqrt{10}}{3+\sqrt{10}}$

4. Simplify, leaving a whole number in the denominator.

a) $\dfrac{\sqrt{11}+5\sqrt{2}}{\sqrt{11}-2\sqrt{2}}$

b) $\dfrac{2\sqrt{6}-\sqrt{3}}{3\sqrt{3}+\sqrt{6}}$

c) $\dfrac{\sqrt{30}+3\sqrt{3}}{\sqrt{30}-3\sqrt{3}}$

d) $\dfrac{3\sqrt{5}-2\sqrt{3}}{3\sqrt{5}+2\sqrt{3}}$

5. Simplify by rationalizing the denominator.

a) $\dfrac{3}{2\sqrt{x}+3}$ **b)** $\dfrac{x+\sqrt{10}}{x-\sqrt{10}}$ **c)** $\dfrac{\sqrt{k}+\sqrt{2}}{\sqrt{k}-\sqrt{2}}$

6. The area of a rectangle is 5 m^2 and the length is $3+\sqrt{3}$ m. Calculate the width of the rectangle, expressing the answer

i) as an exact value with a whole number in the denominator
ii) as a decimal to the nearest hundredth

7. A triangle has area $\left(2\sqrt{15}-3\sqrt{6}\right)$ square units and base $(\sqrt{15}+\sqrt{6})$ units. Determine the exact value of the height of the triangle, giving the answer with a rational denominator.

Multiple Choice

8. The fraction $\frac{2}{\sqrt{5}-\sqrt{3}}$ expressed with a rational denominator is

A. $\frac{\sqrt{5}+\sqrt{3}}{4}$ **B.** $\frac{\sqrt{5}+\sqrt{3}}{8}$

C. $\sqrt{5}+\sqrt{3}$ **D.** $\frac{2\sqrt{5}+\sqrt{3}}{2}$

9. When $\frac{1}{2(2+\sqrt{3})}$ is expressed with a rational denominator, the result is

A. $\frac{2-\sqrt{3}}{2}$ **B.** $\frac{2-\sqrt{3}}{-1}$

C. $\frac{2-\sqrt{3}}{14}$ **D.** $\frac{2-\sqrt{3}}{-10}$

10. $\frac{3\sqrt{5}+\sqrt{3}}{2\sqrt{5}+\sqrt{3}}$, expressed with a rational denominator in simplest form, is

A. $\frac{33+5\sqrt{15}}{23}$

B. $\frac{33+5\sqrt{15}}{17}$

C. $\frac{27-\sqrt{15}}{23}$

D. $\frac{27-\sqrt{15}}{17}$

11. $\frac{p}{q-\sqrt{r}}$, expressed with a rational denominator, may be written as

A. $\frac{p}{q^2-r}$

B. $\frac{p\left(q+\sqrt{r}\right)}{q^2-r^2}$

C. $\frac{p\left(q+\sqrt{r}\right)}{q^2-r}$

D. $\frac{p\left(q-\sqrt{r}\right)}{q^2+r}$

Numerical Response

12. When the denominator is rationalized, $\dfrac{\sqrt{10}-\sqrt{2}}{\sqrt{10}+\sqrt{2}}$ can be expressed in the form $a-b\sqrt{5}$, where $a, b \in Q$. The value of $a+b$, to the nearest tenth, is _____.

(Record your answer in the numerical response box from left to right.)

Answer Key

1. a) $\sqrt{5}+1$ **b)** $\dfrac{\sqrt{6}-2}{2}$ **c)** $\dfrac{3+\sqrt{3}}{2}$ **d)** $\dfrac{7+2\sqrt{7}}{3}$ **e)** $-3\sqrt{2}-3\sqrt{3}$ **f)** $\dfrac{\sqrt{3}-1}{2}$

2. a) $\dfrac{2\sqrt{6}-2}{5}$ **b)** $30\sqrt{11}-99$ **c)** $\dfrac{\sqrt{6}+2}{2}$ **d)** $\dfrac{4\sqrt{7}+7\sqrt{2}}{2}$

3. a) $2-\sqrt{3}$ **b)** $\dfrac{3-\sqrt{5}}{4}$ **c)** $2+\sqrt{3}$ **d)** $8\sqrt{10}-25$

4. a) $\dfrac{31+7\sqrt{22}}{3}$ **b)** $\sqrt{2}-1$ **c)** $19+6\sqrt{10}$ **d)** $\dfrac{19-4\sqrt{15}}{11}$

5. a) $\dfrac{6\sqrt{x}-9}{4x-9}$ **b)** $\dfrac{x^2+2x\sqrt{10}+10}{x^2-10}$ **c)** $\dfrac{k+2\sqrt{2k}+2}{k-2}$

6. i) $\dfrac{15-5\sqrt{3}}{6}$ m. **ii)** 1.06 m. **7.** $\dfrac{32-10\sqrt{10}}{3}$ units.

8. C **9.** A **10.** D **11.** C **12.**

2	.	0	

Operations on Radicals Lesson #6:
Practice Test

1. $2\sqrt[3]{7}$, written as an entire radical, is

A. $\sqrt[3]{56}$ **B.** $\sqrt[3]{98}$

C. $\sqrt[3]{686}$ **D.** $\sqrt[3]{2744}$

2. Consider the following numbers. $10\sqrt{6}$, $4\sqrt{15}$, $7\sqrt{10}$, $12\sqrt{5}$

If the numbers are ranked from largest to smallest, which is the second largest value?

A. $12\sqrt{5}$

B. $4\sqrt{15}$

C. $7\sqrt{10}$

D. $10\sqrt{6}$

3. Consider the following statements

***Statement* 1** : $\sqrt{96} = 4\sqrt{6}$ ***Statement* 2** : $7\sqrt{2} = 98$

***Statement* 3** : $24 = 4\sqrt{6}$

Which of the these statements is true?

A. **1** only **B.** **1** and **2** only

C. **1, 2,** and **3** **D.** some other combination of **1, 2** and **3**

4. When $3\sqrt{80} + 4\sqrt{405}$ is written in the form $k\sqrt{5}$, the value of k is

A. 7

B. 48

C. 92

D. 372

5. The exact value of $\left(4\sqrt{11}\right)^2$ is the whole number w.
The value of w is

A. 44 **B.** 176

C. 484 **D.** 1936

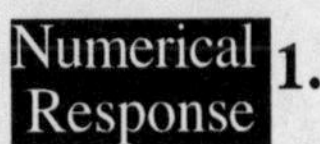

1. The expression $\sqrt{2}\left(\sqrt{5} - 12\sqrt{3}\right) - \sqrt{3}\left(\sqrt{8} - 2\sqrt{30}\right)$ can be written in simplest form $a\sqrt{b} - c\sqrt{d}$ where a, b, c, d are all positive integers.
The value of $a + b + c + d$ is _____ .
(Record your answer in the numerical response box from left to right.)

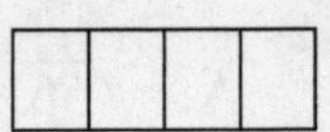

6. $\left(\sqrt{5}\right)^5$ is equivalent to

A. $5\sqrt{5}$ **B.** $10\sqrt{5}$

C. $25\sqrt{5}$ **D.** $625\sqrt{5}$

7. $\sqrt{x}\left(4 - \sqrt{x}\right)$ is equivalent to

A. $4\sqrt{x} - \sqrt{x}$ **B.** $\sqrt{4x} - x$

C. $4\sqrt{x} - x$ **D.** $4\sqrt{x} - 2\sqrt{x}$

2. $2\sqrt{3}\left(\sqrt{243} - 2\right) - \sqrt{2}\left(5 + 7\sqrt{2}\right)$ can be expanded and simplified to the form $p + q\sqrt{2} + r\sqrt{3}$. The value of $p + q + r$ is _____.
(Record your answer in the numerical response box from left to right.)

8. A square is inscribed in a circle as shown. If the area of the circle is 144π cm^2, then the exact perimeter of the square is

A. $12\sqrt{2}$ cm

B. $24\sqrt{2}$ cm

C. $36\sqrt{2}$ cm

D. $48\sqrt{2}$ cm

9. If $2\sqrt[3]{4}\left(2\sqrt[3]{54} - \sqrt[3]{x}\right)$ is equal to 16, then x is equal to

A. 2

B. 4

C. 16

D. 64

10. $5 - 3\sqrt{2}$, multiplied by its conjugate, is

A. -11 **B.** 7

C. 19 **D.** $43 + 6\sqrt{2}$

3. $\left(2\sqrt{12} + \sqrt{24}\right)^2$ can be expressed in simplest form as $a + b\sqrt{c}$.
The value of abc is _____.
(Record your answer in the numerical response box from left to right.)

11. Consider the following three equations.

$$3\sqrt[3]{64} = p, \qquad 48\sqrt{p} = q\sqrt{3}, \qquad 40\sqrt[4]{q} = r\sqrt[4]{6}.$$

Which of the statements below is correct

A. $p < q < r$

B. $p < r < q$

C. $q < r < p$

D. $r < p < q$

12. The first two terms of a geometric sequence are $6\sqrt{2}$ and 12.
The third term of the sequence is

A. $12\sqrt{2}$ **B.** $18\sqrt{2}$

C. $24\sqrt{2}$ **D.** $24 - 6\sqrt{2}$

13. If $A = 15\sqrt{48}$ and $B = 6\sqrt{150}$, then $\frac{A}{B}$ is equal to

A. $\frac{18\sqrt{2}}{5}$ **B.** $\sqrt{2}$

C. $\frac{19\sqrt{2}}{42}$ **D.** $2\sqrt{2}$

Numerical Response

4. If $m * n$ means "$(m + n)$ multiplied by m", then the value of $\sqrt{10} * \left(\sqrt{5} * \sqrt{2}\right)$ can be written as the sum of a rational number and an irrational number.
The rational number is ______.

(Record your answer in the numerical response box from left to right.)

14. $\dfrac{6}{-5\sqrt{3}+1}$, expressed with a rational denominator, is

A. $\dfrac{-15\sqrt{3}+3}{38}$

B. $\dfrac{-15\sqrt{3}+3}{37}$

C. $\dfrac{-15\sqrt{3}-3}{38}$

D. $\dfrac{-15\sqrt{3}-3}{37}$

15. $\dfrac{1}{\sqrt{q}+\sqrt{r}}$ is equivalent to

A. $\dfrac{\sqrt{q}+\sqrt{r}}{q-r}$

B. $\dfrac{\sqrt{q}+\sqrt{r}}{q+r}$

C. $\dfrac{\sqrt{q}-\sqrt{r}}{q-r}$

D. $\dfrac{\sqrt{q}-\sqrt{r}}{q^2-r^2}$

5. The expression $\dfrac{20\sqrt{5}}{\sqrt{10}} - \dfrac{16}{\sqrt{8}}$ can be expressed in the form $k\sqrt{2}$, where $k \in W$.
The value of k is _____.
(Record your answer in the numerical response box from left to right.)

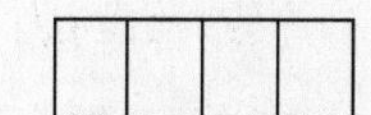

Written Response - 5 marks

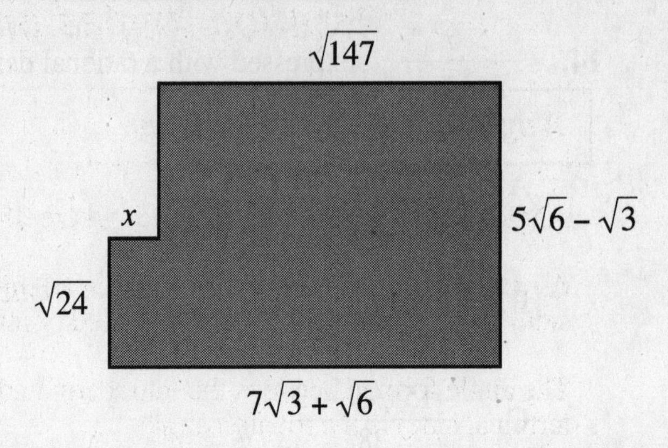

1. Consider the shaded region shown.

- Determine, in simplest radical form, an expression for x.

- Show that the area of the shaded region is equal to $105\sqrt{2} - 9$.

- Determine, in simplest radical form, an expression for the perimeter of the shaded region.

Answer Key

1. A	2. D	3. A	4. B	5. B	6. C	7. C	8. D
9. C	10. B	11. B	12. A	13. B	14. D	15. C	

Numerical Response

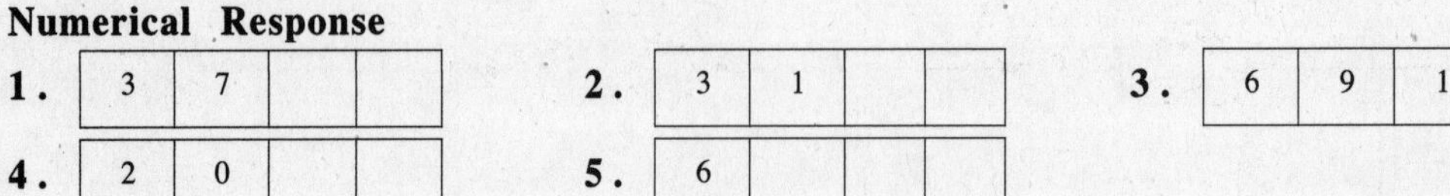

1. 3 7
2. 3 1
3. 6 9 1 2
4. 2 0
5. 6

Written Response

1. • $\sqrt{6}$ • $12\sqrt{3} + 12\sqrt{6}$

Trigonometry Lesson #1:
Rotation Angles and Reference Angles

Angles in Standard Position

Angles can be measured in degrees where 360° is one complete rotation.

A ***rotation angle*** is formed by rotating an <u>initial arm</u> (or initial side) through an angle θ ° about a fixed point (the vertex).

The angle formed between the initial arm and the terminal arm (or terminal side) is the rotation angle.

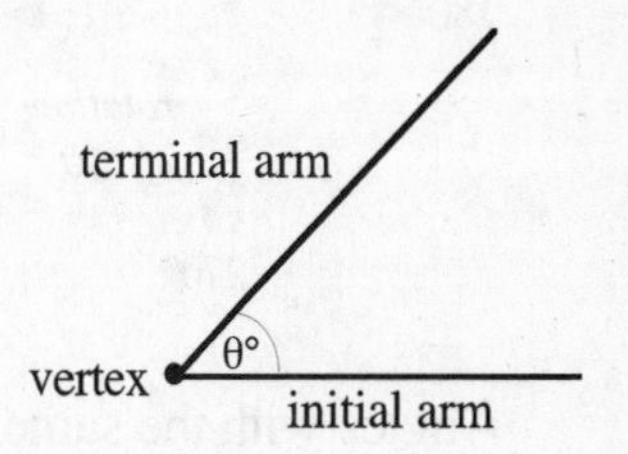

A ***positive angle*** results from a counter clockwise rotation.

A ***negative angle*** results from a clockwise rotation.

The angle shown in the diagram is said to be in ***standard position***.

On a coordinate grid, standard position means the initial arm is along the positive x-axis and the rotation is about the origin.

The diagram below shows an angle of 220° in standard position.

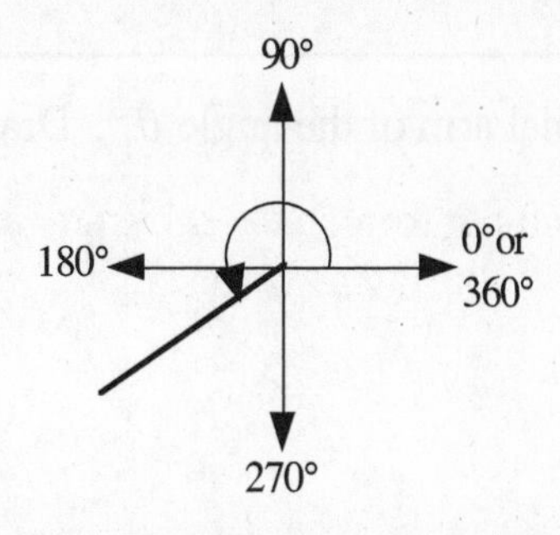

Class Ex. #1

Sketch the rotation angle in standard position and state the quadrant in which the angle terminates.

a) 120° **b)** 309° **c)** 17°

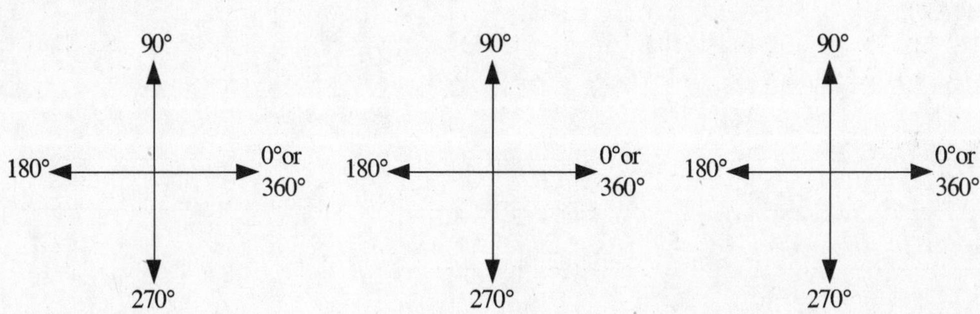

Draw the rotation angle in standard position.

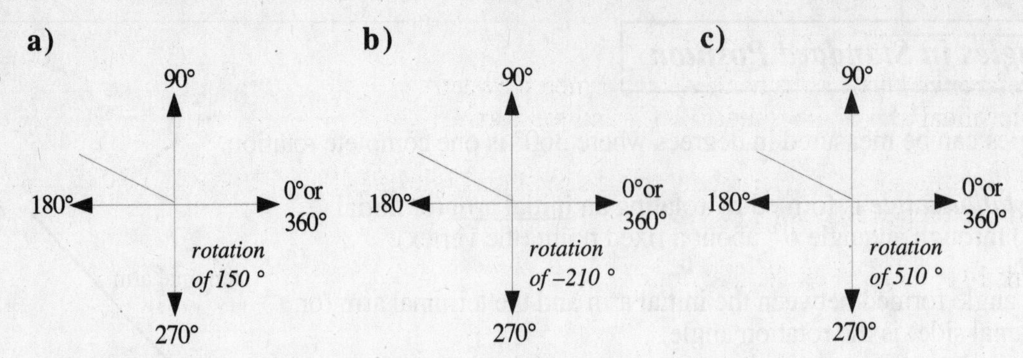

Angles with the same terminal arm are called ***coterminal angles***.

Since 150° is the measure of the smallest positive rotation angle coterminal with the angles in Class Example #2, it is called the ***principal angle***.

The principal angle will always have a measure between 0° and 360°.

There are infinitely many angles that are coterminal with a given angle.

For the purposes of this unit, we will restrict the measure of the rotation angle to be between 0° and 360°. Coterminal angles and principal angles will be studied in the next course.

The point P lies on the terminal arm of the angle $\theta°$. Draw the angle $\theta°$ in standard position.

a) $P(2, -4)$

b) $P(-5, -1)$

Complete Assignment Question #1 - #2

Reference Angles

A **reference angle** is the acute angle formed between the terminal arm of the rotation angle and the x-axis.

The diagram shows the terminal arm of a rotation angle of 141° with a reference angle of 39°.

Mark 141° and 39° on the diagram.

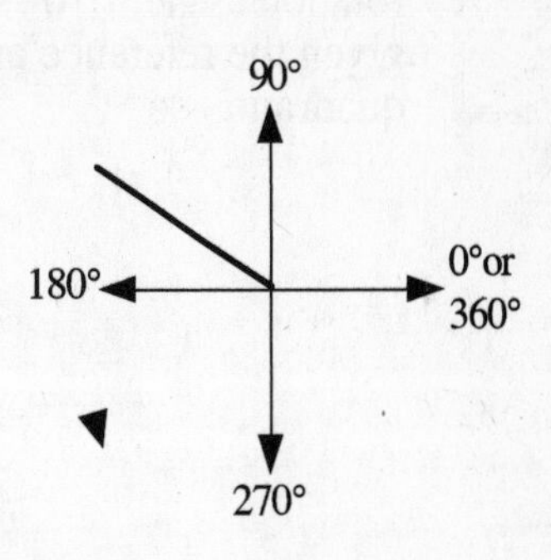

In each case, sketch the rotation angle and state the reference angle.

a) 243°

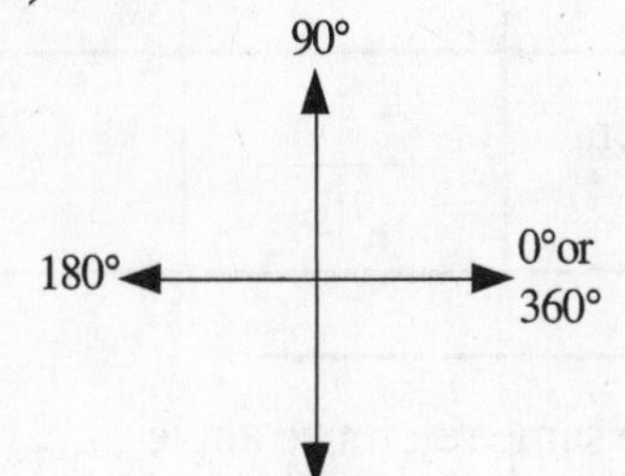

b) 337°

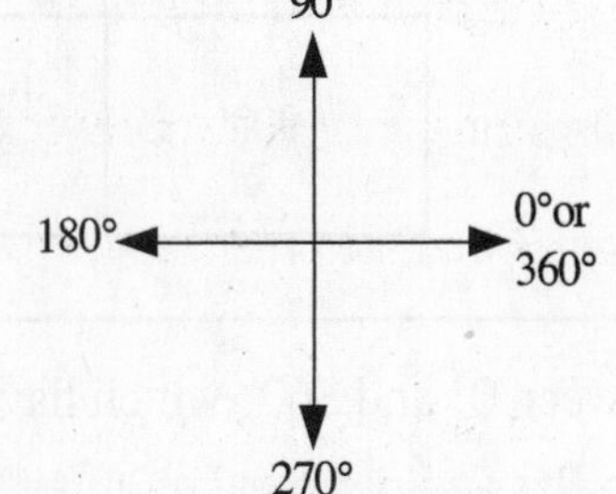

c) 70°

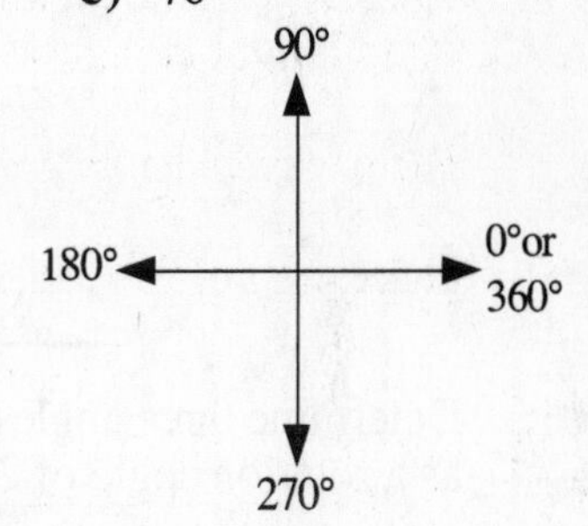

a) On the grid, draw a reference angle of 58° in each of quadrants one to four.

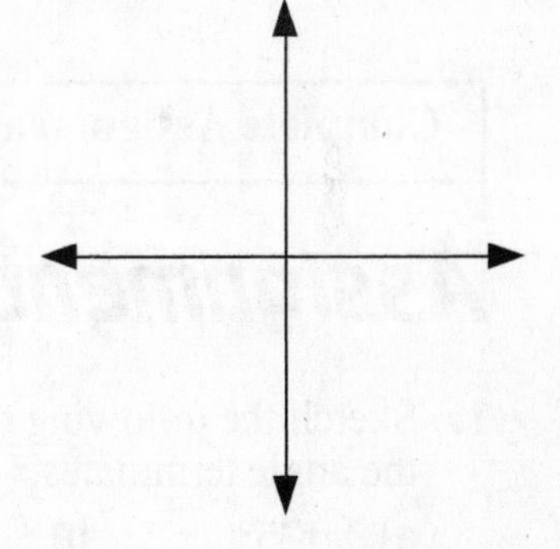

b) State the measure of the rotation angle in each quadrant.

c) Let $P(5, 8)$ be a point on the terminal arm of the rotation angle in quadrant one. State the coordinates of points Q, R, and S which are on the terminal arms of the rotation angles in quadrant two, quadrant three, and quadrant four respectively.

Determine the measure of the rotation angle, x, $0° \leq x < 360°$, given the reference angle and the quadrant.

Reference Angle	Quadrant	Sketch	Rotation Angle
25°	2		
60°	4		
8°	3		
39°	1		
90°	between 3 and 4		

Determine three angles between 0° and 360° which have the same reference angle as a rotation angle of 256°.

Complete Assignment Question #3 - #19

Assignment

1. Sketch the following rotation angles in standard position, and state the quadrant in which the angle terminates.

a) 135° **b)** 300° **c)** 190° **d)** 70° **e)** 270°

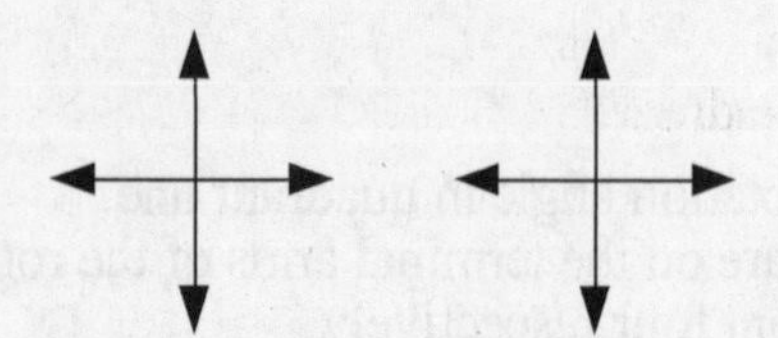
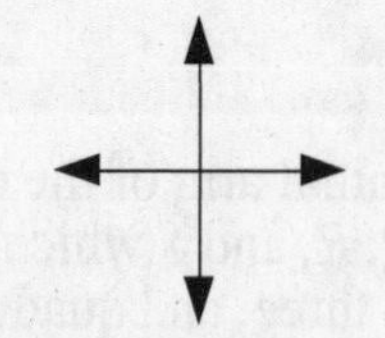
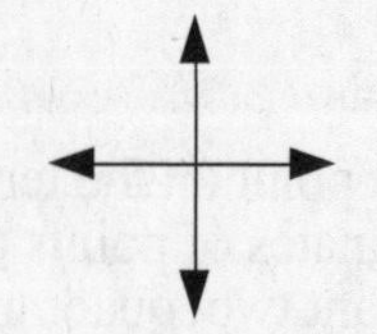
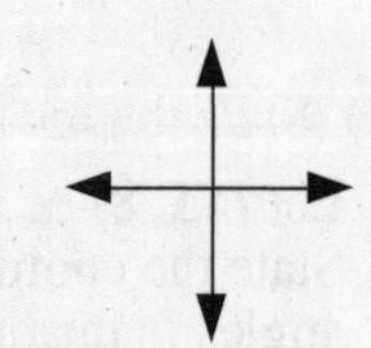

2. In each case, the given point is on the terminal arm of an angle of $\theta°$. Draw the angle $\theta°$ in standard position.

a) $P(7, -4)$ **b)** $Q(-2, 3)$ **c)** $R(-1, -4)$

3. In each case, sketch the rotation angle and state the reference angle.

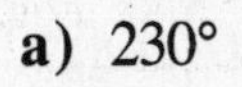

a) 230° **b)** 313° **c)** 109°

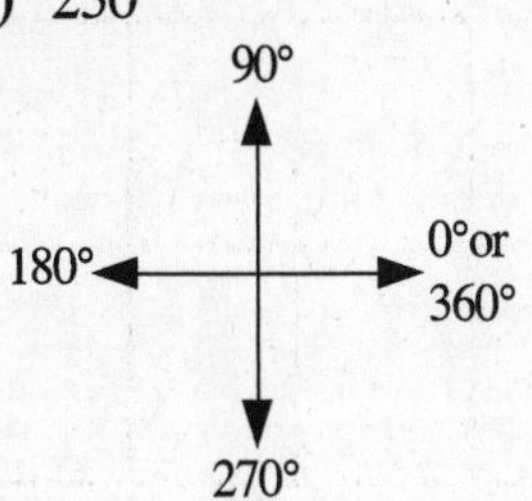

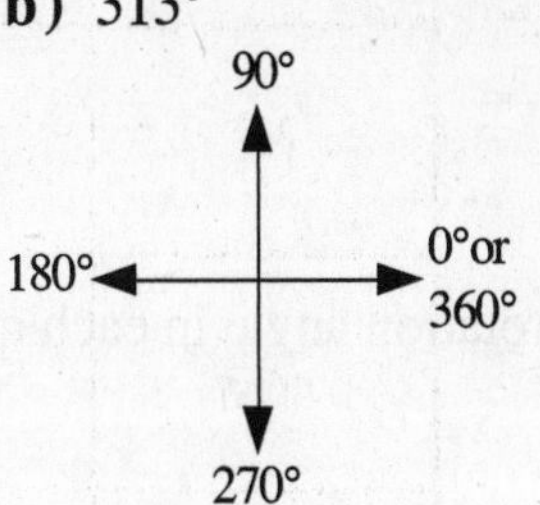

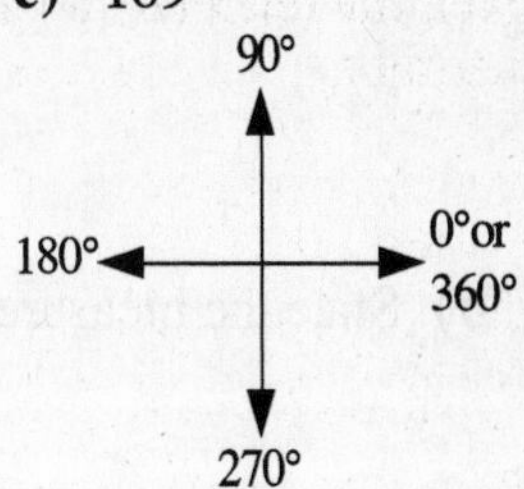

d) 20° **e)** 180° **f)** 270°

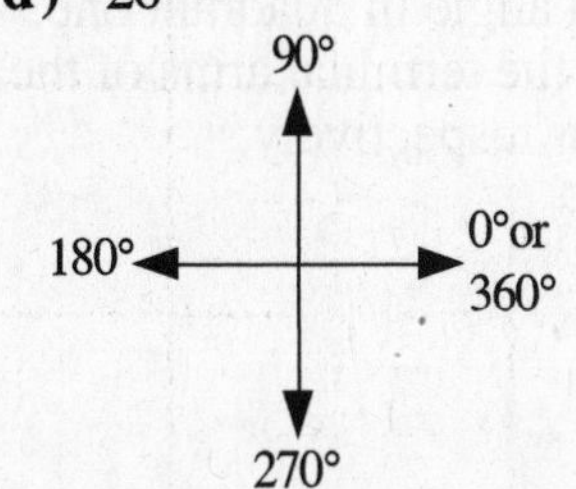

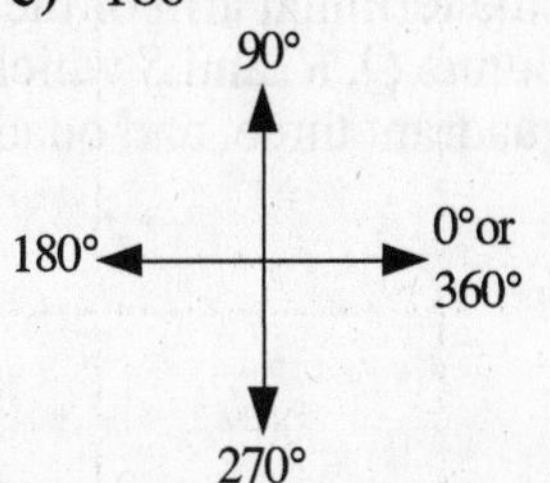

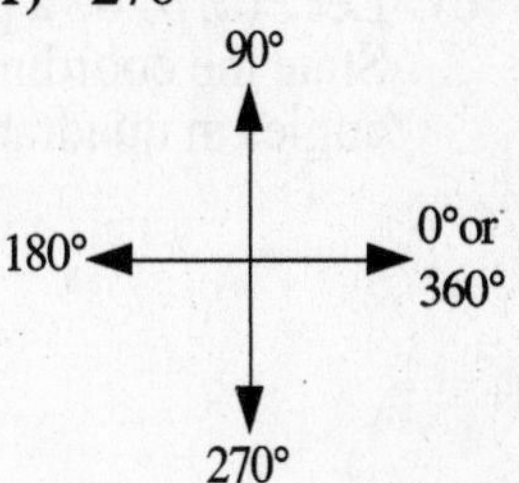

4. Find the reference angle for the following rotation angles.

a) 135° **b)** 296° **c)** 237° **d)** 90°

5. For each of the following angles, determine;
(i) the quadrant of the terminal arm of the angle **(ii)** the reference angle

a) 355° **b)** 170° **c)** 190° **d)** 51°

6. a) Sketch a diagram to show a reference angle of 30° in each of quadrants one to four.

b) State the measure of the rotation angle in each quadrant.

c) Let $P\left(\frac{\sqrt{3}}{2}, \frac{1}{2}\right)$ be a point on the terminal arm of the rotation angle in quadrant one.
State the coordinates of points Q, R and S which are on the terminal arms of the rotation angles in quadrant two, quadrant three, and quadrant four respectively.

7. a) Sketch a diagram to show a reference angle of 77° in each of quadrants one to four.

b) State the measure of the rotation angle in each quadrant.

c) Let $P(a, b)$ be a point on the terminal arm of the rotation angle in quadrant one. State the coordinates of points Q, R, and S which are on the terminal arms of the rotation angles in quadrant two, quadrant three, and quadrant four respectively.

8. Complete the following tables, given the reference angle and the quadrant.

Reference Angle	Quadrant	Sketch	Rotation Angle
30°	2		
30°	3		
60°	1		
55°	2		
15°	4		
76°	3		

Reference Angle	Quadrant	Sketch	Rotation Angle
30°	1		
30°	4		
4°	3		
89°	2		
0°	between 2 and 3		
90°	between 1 and 2		

9. Students were asked to determine the reference angle for a rotation angle of 214°.

a) Jeff gave an incorrect answer of 56°. Use a diagram to explain how he arrived at his answer.

b) Mandy gave an incorrect answer of 146°. Use a diagram to explain how she arrived at her answer.

c) State the correct answer.

10. Consider a reference angle of 50° in quadrant 1.

a) Sketch a diagram to show the reference angle reflected in the y-axis.
State the measure of the rotation angle formed.

b) Sketch a diagram to show the original reference angle reflected in the x-axis.
State the measure of the rotation angle formed.

c) Sketch a diagram to show the original reference angle reflected in both the x-axis and the y-axis.
State the measure of the rotation angle formed.

11. Given that a rotation angle of $x°$ in standard position has a terminal arm in the first quadrant, state expressions for four rotation angles between 0° and 360° which have a reference angle of $x°$.

12. Complete the following table.

Reference Angle	**Rotation Angle in:**			
	Quad 1	Quad 2	Quad 3	Quad 4
28°				
39°				
$a°$				
		114°		
			201°	
				295°

13. Determine three angles between 0° and 360° which have the same reference angle as a rotation angle of 136°.

14. Determine three angles between 0° and 360° which have the same reference angle as a rotation angle of 303°.

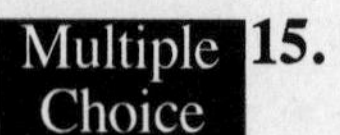

15. An angle of 134° in standard position has a reference angle of

A. 44° **B.** 46°

C. 134° **D.** 226°

Use the following information to answer the next question.

Row	Rotation Angle	Quadrant of Terminal Arm	Reference Angle
1	264°	3	96°
2	139°	2	41°
3	357°	4	3°
4	94°	1	86°

16. Which of the following rows contain an error?

A. row 1 only **B.** row 4 only

C. rows 1 and 4 only **D.** rows 1, 2, 3, and 4

Use the following information to answer the next question.

Meghan makes four statements connecting rotation angles and reference angles.

Statement I: In quadrant 1, the rotation angle is equal to the reference angle.

Statement II: In quadrant 2, the rotation angle is equal to 180° minus the reference angle.

Statement III: In quadrant 3, the rotation angle is equal to 180° plus the reference angle.

Statement IV: In quadrant 4, the rotation angle is equal to 360° minus the reference angle.

17. How many of Meghan's statements are true?

A. 1 **B.** 2 **C.** 3 **D.** 4

18. Which one of the following angles in standard position has the same reference angle as an angle of 165°?

A. 25° **B.** 205°

C. 255° **D.** 345°

Numerical Response

19. There are four angles in standard position between 0° and 360° which have a reference angle of 51°. The sum of these angles is _____ .

(Record your answer in the numerical response box from left to right.)

Answer Key

1.

a) 135° **b)** 300° **c)** 190° **d)** 70° **e)** 270°

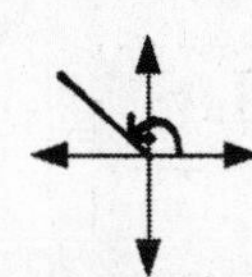
Quadrant 2

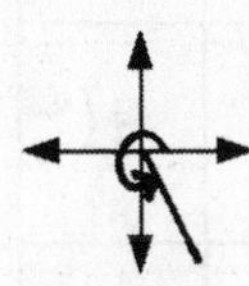
Quadrant 4

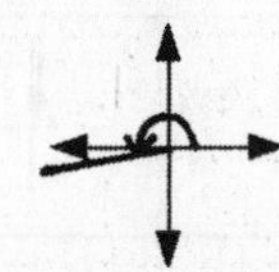
Quadrant 3

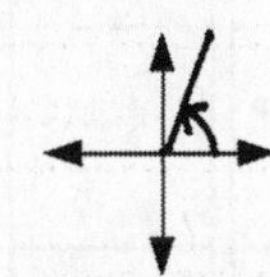
Quadrant 1

Between Quadrant 3 and Quadrant 4

2.

a) $P(7, -4)$

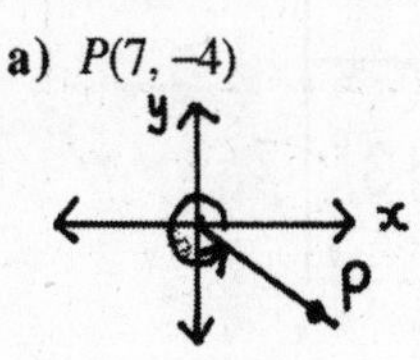

b) $Q(-2, 3)$

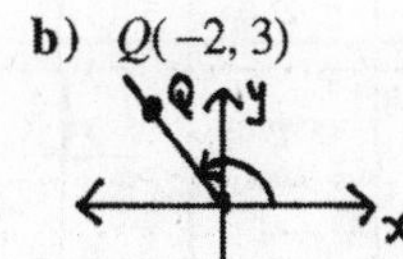

c) $R(-1, -4)$

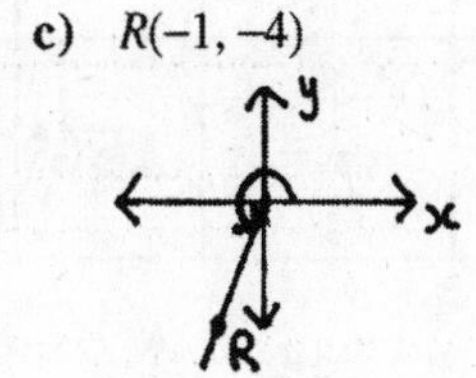

3.

a) 230°

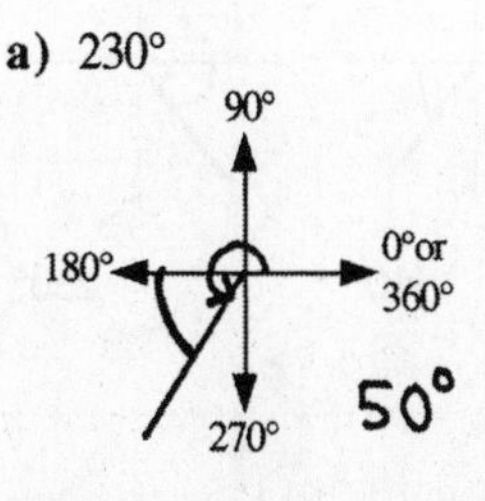

b) 313°

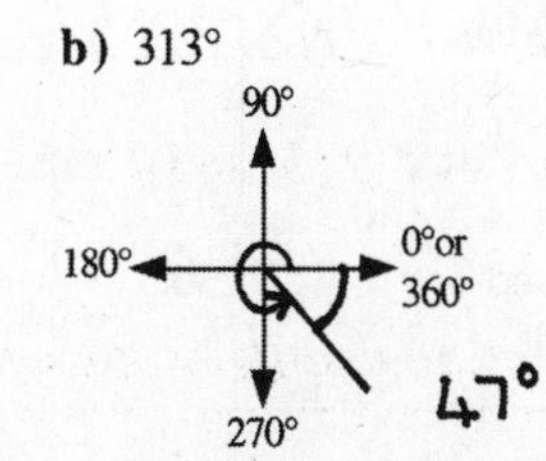

c) 109°

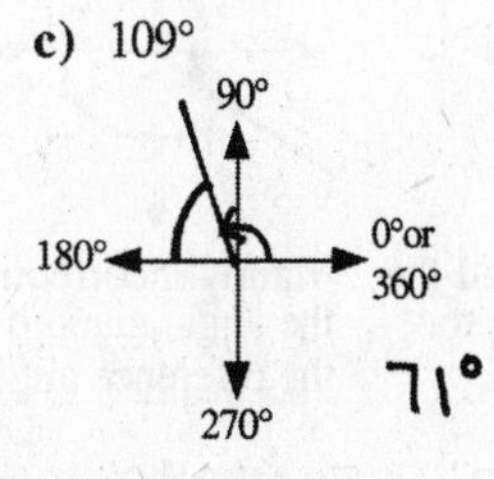

d) 20°

90° 180° 0°or 360° 270° 20°

e) 180°

90° 180° 0°or 360° 270° 0°

f) 270°

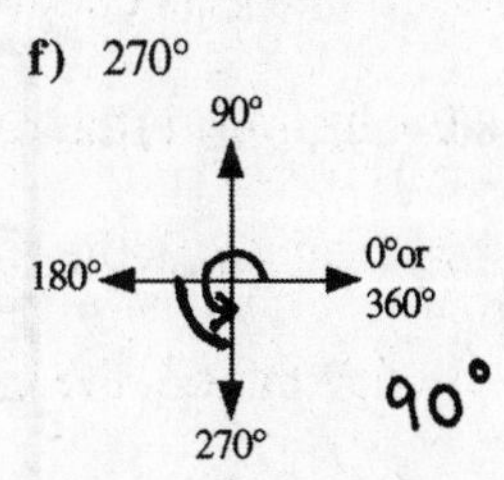

4. a) 45° **b)** 64° **c)** 57° **d)** 90°

5. a) i) 4 **ii)** 5° **b) i)** 2 **ii)** 10° **c) i)** 3 **ii)** 10° **d) i)** 1 **ii)** 51°

6. a)

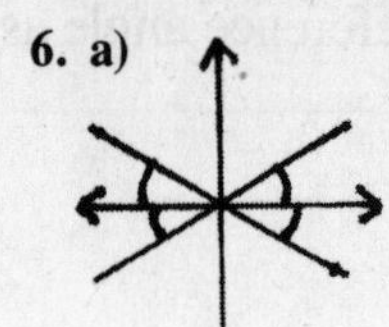

b) Quadrant 1 → 30°,
Quadrant 2 → 150°
Quadrant 3 → 210°
Quadrant 4 → 330°

c) $Q\left(-\frac{\sqrt{3}}{2}, \frac{1}{2}\right)$ $R\left(-\frac{\sqrt{3}}{2}, -\frac{1}{2}\right)$ $S\left(\frac{\sqrt{3}}{2}, -\frac{1}{2}\right)$

7. a)

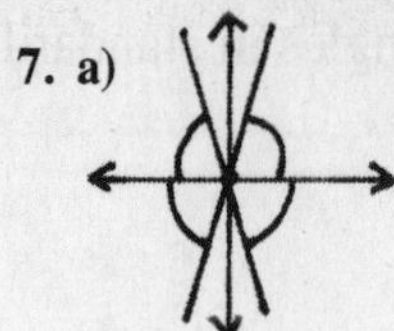

b) Quadrant 1 → 77°
Quadrant 2 → 103°
Quadrant 3 → 257°
Quadrant 4 → 283°

c) $Q(-a, b)$ $R(-a, -b)$ $S(a, -b)$

8.

Reference Angle	Quadrant	Sketch	Rotation Angle	Reference Angle	Quadrant	Sketch	Rotation Angle
30°	2		150°	30°	1		30°
30°	3		210°	30°	4		330°
60°	1		60°	4°	3		184°
55°	2		125°	89°	2		91°
15°	4		345°	0°	between 2 and 3		180°
76°	3		256°	90°	between 1 and 2		90°

9. a)

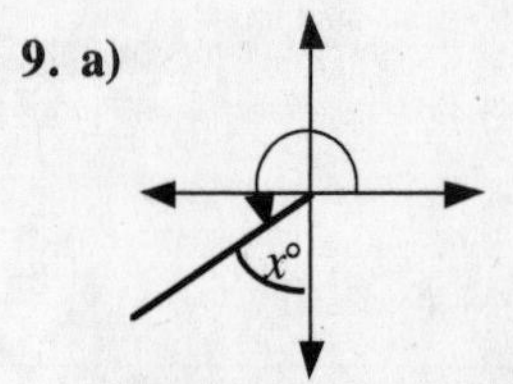

Jeff incorrectly used the angle marked $x°$ as the reference angle

b)

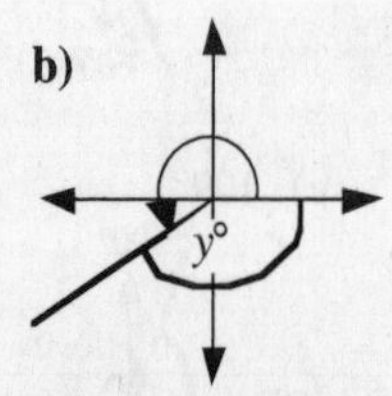

Mandy incorrectly used the angle marked $y°$ as the reference angle

c) 34°

10. a)

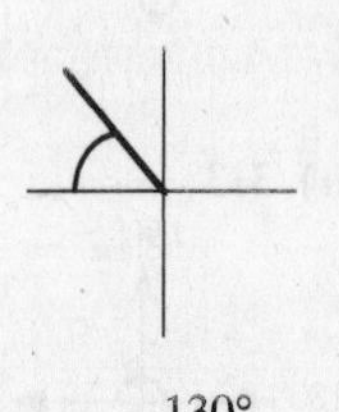

130°

b) **c)**

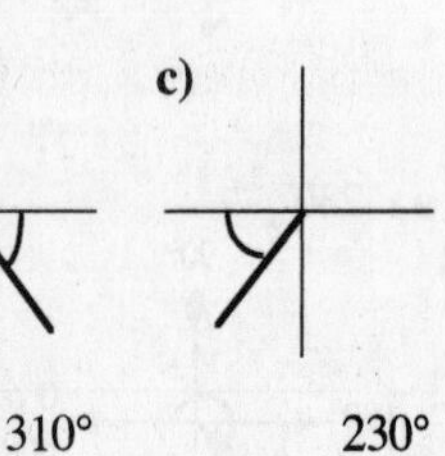

310° 230°

11. $(180 - x)°$, $(180 + x)°$, $(360 - x)°$

12.

Reference Angle	Rotation Angle in:			
	Quad 1	Quad 2	Quad 3	Quad 4
28°	28°	152°	208°	332°
39°	39°	141°	219°	321°
$a°$	$a°$	$(180 - a)°$	$(180 + a)°$	$(360 - a)°$
66°	66°	114°	246°	294°
21°	21°	159°	201°	339°
65°	65°	115°	245°	295°

13. 44°, 224°, 316°

14. 57°, 123°, 237°

15. B **16.** C **17.** D **18.** D

19.

7	2	0	

Trigonometry Lesson #2: Trigonometric Ratios for Angles from 0° to 360°

Pythagorean Theorem

The traditional formula for the Pythagorean Theorem is $c^2 = a^2 + b^2$.

In trigonometry we use x, y, and r instead of a, b, and c.

The point $P(x, y)$ lies on the terminal arm of angle θ.

The distance from the origin to point P is r, the radius of the circle formed by the rotation.

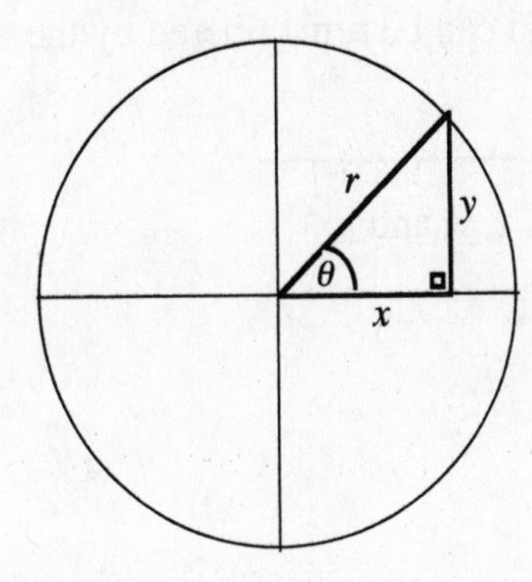

$x^2 + y^2 = r^2$, where $r > 0$

Sketch the rotation angle in standard position, and calculate the exact distance from the origin to the given point. Where appropriate, write the answer in simplest mixed radical form.

a) Point $P(-5, 12)$ on the terminal arm of angle θ.

b) Point $Q(-2, -6)$ on the terminal arm of angle A.

Trigonometric Ratios

Complete the following

sine ratio $\Rightarrow$ $\sin\theta =$

cosine ratio $\Rightarrow$ $\cos\theta =$

tangent ratio $\Rightarrow$ $\tan\theta =$

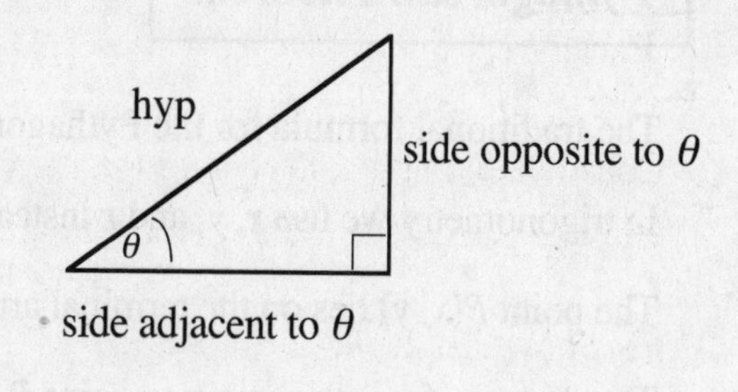

These ratios are called the ***Primary Trigonometric Ratios*** and can be remembered by the acronym **SOHCAHTOA**.

Write the primary trigonometric ratios for angle θ in terms of x, y, and r.

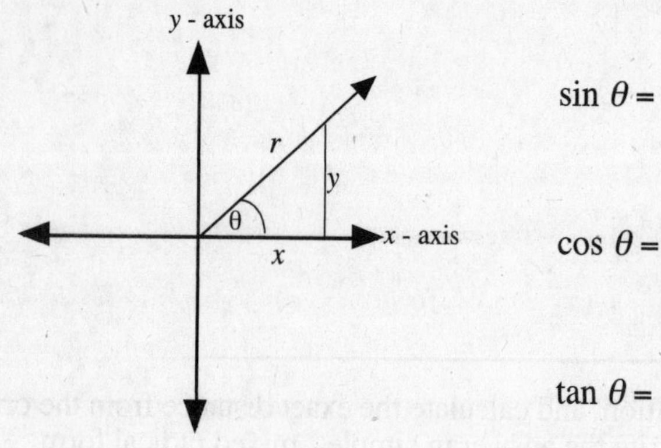

$\sin\theta =$

$\cos\theta =$

$\tan\theta =$

You should memorize these formulas.

Some students use a phrase like "**s**even **y**ellow **r**abbits" to remember $\sin\theta = \dfrac{y}{r}$.

The point (15, 8) lies on the terminal arm of an angle θ as shown. Calculate the value of r, and hence determine the exact values of the primary trigonometric ratios.

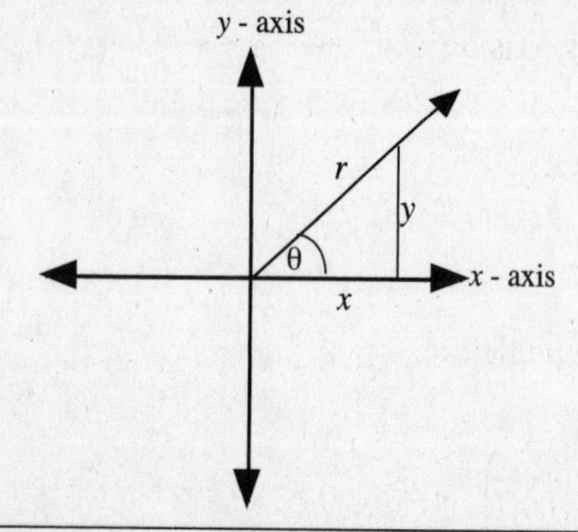

Complete Assignment Questions #1 - #6

Investigating Trigonometric Ratios for Angles Between 90° and 360°

Part 1

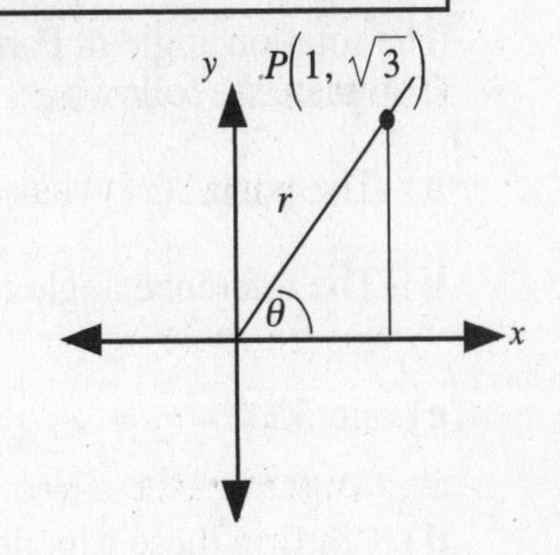

Consider an angle θ in standard position with the point $P\left(1, \sqrt{3}\right)$ on the terminal arm.

a) Show that the value of θ is 60°.

b) Calculate the value of r.

c) Complete the following, using $x =$ ______ , $y =$ ______ , and $r =$ ______ .

$\sin 60° = \dfrac{y}{r} =$ $\qquad$ $\cos 60° = \dfrac{x}{r} =$ $\qquad$ $\tan 60° = \dfrac{y}{x} =$

Part 2

The rotation angle in Part 1 is reflected in the y-axis.

Complete the following:

a) The point $Q(x, y)$ has coordinates $Q($, $)$.

b) The reference angle is _____ and the rotation angle is _____.

c) $\sin 120° = \dfrac{y}{r} =$ $\qquad$ $\cos 120° = \dfrac{x}{r} =$ $\qquad$ $\tan 120° = \dfrac{y}{x} =$

d) Confirm these trigonometric ratios on your calculator.

Part 3

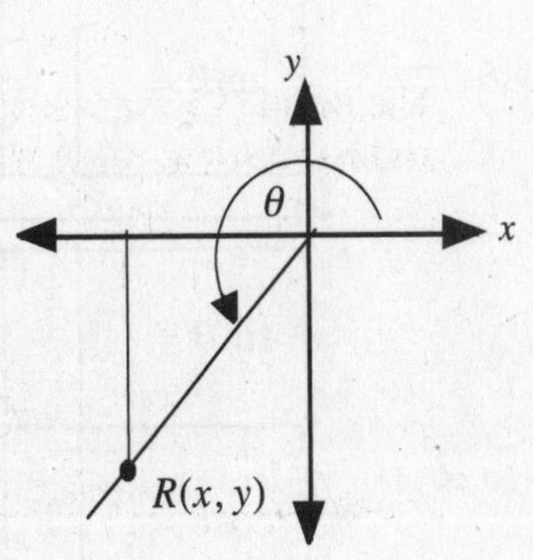

The rotation angle in Part 1 is reflected in both the x-axis and the y-axis.

Complete the following

a) The point $R(x, y)$ has coordinates $R($, $)$.

b) The reference angle is ______ and the rotation angle is ______.

c) $\sin 240° = \dfrac{y}{r} =$ $\qquad$ $\cos 240° = \dfrac{x}{r} =$ $\qquad$ $\tan 240° = \dfrac{y}{x} =$

d) Confirm these trigonometric ratios on your calculator.

Part 4

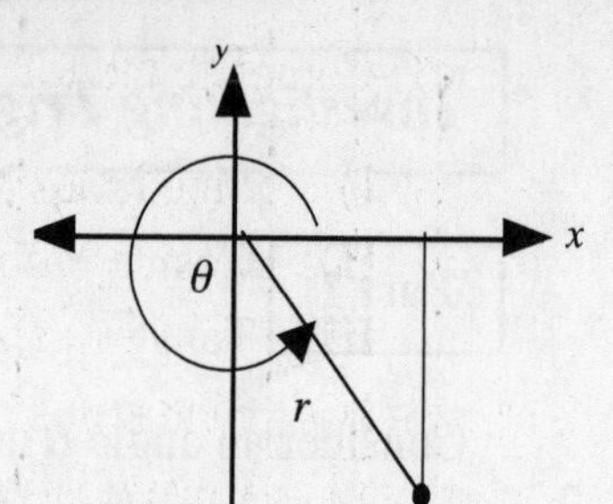

The rotation angle in Part 1 is reflected in the x-axis.
Complete the following:

a) The point $S(x, y)$ has coordinates $S($, $)$.

b) The reference angle is _____ and the rotation angle is _____.

c) $\sin 300° = \frac{y}{r} =$ $\cos 300° = \frac{x}{r} =$ $\tan 300° = \frac{y}{x} =$

d) Confirm these trigonometric ratios on your calculator.

Observations

The trigonometric ratios for angles between 90° and 360° are either the trigonometric ratios of the reference angle, or the negative of the trigonometric ratios of the reference angle.

The sign of the trigonometric ratios depends on the quadrant and whether x and y are positive or negative.

Determining the Sign of a Trigonometric Ratio

a) In quadrant 1, draw the rotation angle θ in standard position and complete the table.
b) Repeat for quadrants 2 - 4.

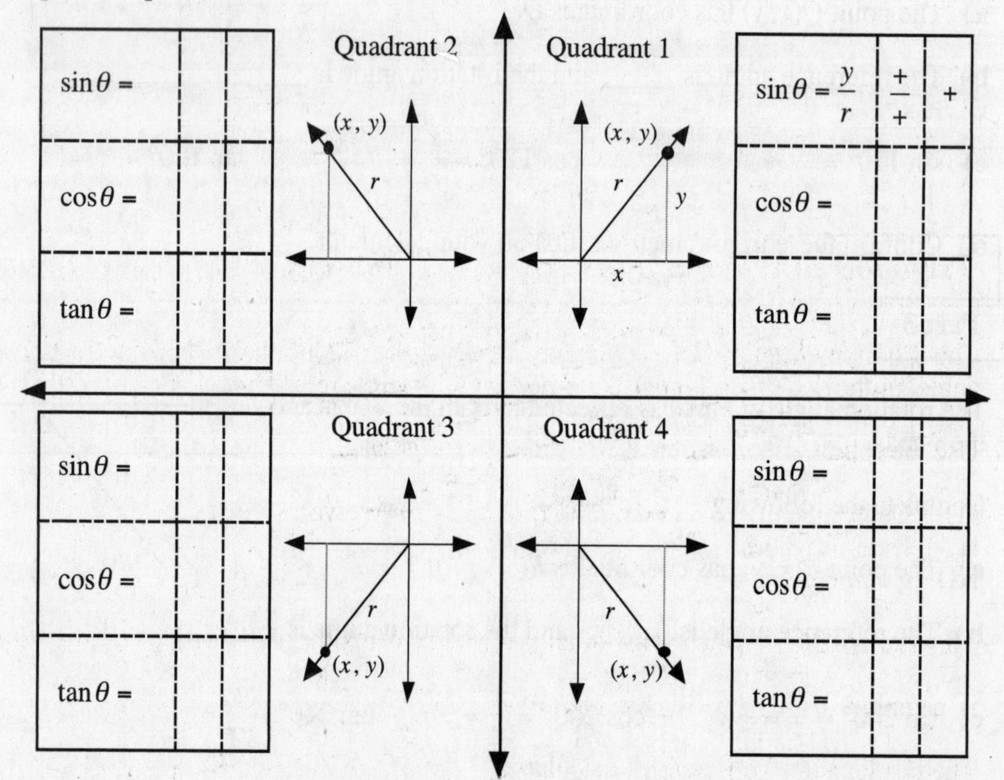

c) Complete the following statements using the results from a) and b).

i) Sine ratios have **positive** values in quadrants _____ and _____ .
ii) Cosine ratios have **positive** values in quadrants _____ and _____ .
iii) Tangent ratios have **positive** values in quadrants _____ and _____ .
iv) Sine ratios have **negative** values in quadrants _____ and _____ .
v) Cosine ratios have **negative** values in quadrants _____ and _____ .
vi) Tangent ratios have **negative** values in quadrants _____ and _____ .

CAST Rule

The results can be memorized by:

- the **CAST** rule or
- by remembering to "**A**dd **S**ugar **T**o **C**offee"

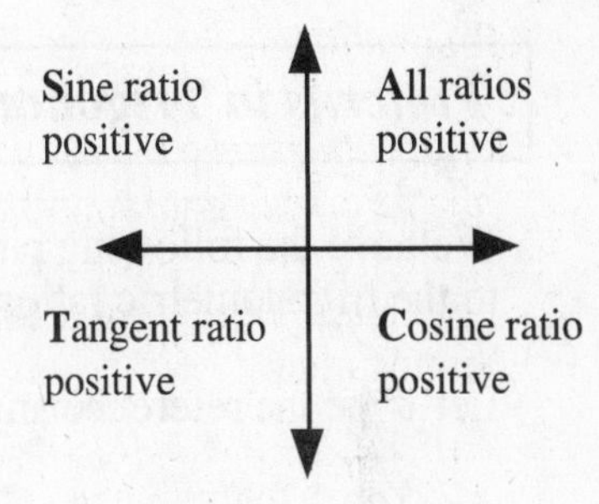

Determine, without using technology, whether the given trigonometric ratios are positive or negative.

a) sin 340° **b)** tan 227° **c)** sin 88°

d) cos 235° **e)** cos 308° **f)** tan 123°

Trigonometric Ratios of an Angle in Terms of the Reference Angle

The trigonometric ratios for any angle are either the trigonometric ratios of the reference angle, or the negative of the trigonometric ratios of the reference angle.

Use the following procedure.

i) Determine the sign of the ratio (positive or negative).
ii) Determine the measure of the reference angle.
iii) Combine i) and ii).

To write cos 260° as the cosine of an acute angle using the above procedure, we have

i) negative ii) 80° iii) cos 260° = – cos 80°.

The result can be verified on a calculator.

Rewrite as the same trigonometric function of an acute angle.

a) sin 140° **b)** tan 323° **c)** cos 165°

d) sin 287° **e)** cos 308° **f)** tan 199°

Patterns in Trigonometric Ratios

We have the following pattern of results relating the trigonometric ratios of rotation angles to the trigonometric ratios of reference angles.

Let $x°$ be the reference angle for an angle in standard position.

$\sin(180 - x)° = \sin x°$ $\cos(180 - x)° = -\cos x°$ $\tan(180 - x)° = -\tan x°$

$\sin(180 + x)° = -\sin x°$ $\cos(180 + x)° = -\cos x°$ $\tan(180 + x)° = \tan x°$

$\sin(360 - x)° = -\sin x°$ $\cos(360 - x)° = \cos x°$ $\tan(360 - x)° = -\tan x°$

Complete Assignment Questions #7 - #13

Assignment

1. Sketch the rotation angle in standard position, and calculate the exact distance from the origin to the given point.

a) Point $P(15, -8)$ on the terminal arm of angle θ.

b) Point $Q(-24, -7)$ on the terminal arm of angle B.

2. Determine the exact distance from the origin to each of the following points. Where appropriate, answer in simplest mixed radical form.

a) $(-6, -8)$ **b)** $(2, 7)$ **c)** $(-4, 4)$

3. Point $P(x, y)$ is on the terminal arm of angle θ in standard position. The distance $OP = r$, where O is the origin. Express the three primary trigonometric ratios in terms of x, y, and r.

$\sin\theta =$ $\cos\theta =$ $\tan\theta =$

4. The point (9, 12) lies on the terminal arm of an angle θ as shown. Calculate the value of r, and hence determine the exact values of the primary trigonometric ratios.

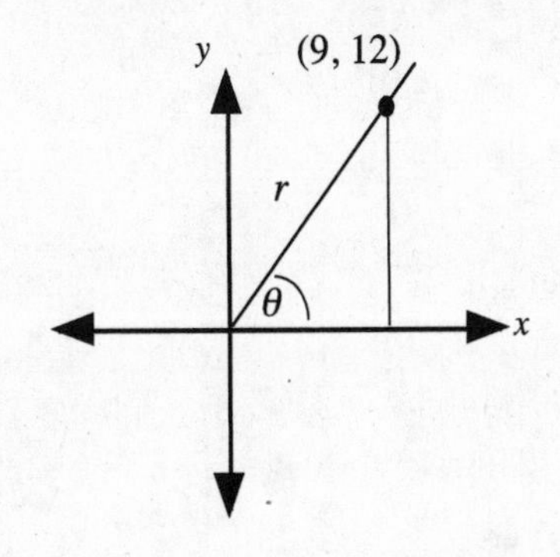

5. The point (5, 4) lies on the terminal arm of an angle θ. Determine the exact values of $\sin\theta$, $\cos\theta$, and $\tan\theta$. Answer as an exact radical with a rational denominator.

6. The point (6, 12) lies on the terminal arm of an angle θ. Determine the exact values of $\sin\theta$, $\cos\theta$, and $\tan\theta$. Answer as a mixed radical in simplest form with a rational denominator.

7. In which quadrant(s) does the terminal arm of θ lie if:

a) $\sin\theta$ is positive? **b)** $\tan\theta$ is positive? **c)** $\cos\theta$ is negative?

d) both $\sin\theta$ and $\tan\theta$ are negative? **e)** $\cos\theta$ is positive and $\sin\theta$ is negative?

8. Determine, without using technology, whether the given trigonometric ratios are positive or negative.

a) cos 310° **b)** sin 94° **c)** tan 265°

d) sin 288° **e)** tan 109° **f)** cos 207°

9. Rewrite as the same trigonometric function of a positive acute angle.

a) sin 205° = **b)** tan 193° =

c) cos 97° = **d)** sin 156° =

e) cos 321° = **f)** tan 340° =

Multiple Choice **10.** The point (4, 6) lies on the terminal arm of an angle A in standard position. The exact value of $\cos A$ is

A. $\dfrac{1}{\sqrt{13}}$ **B.** $\dfrac{2}{\sqrt{13}}$

C. $\dfrac{3}{\sqrt{13}}$ **D.** $\dfrac{3}{\sqrt{26}}$

11. Without using technology, determine which of the following has a different sign from the others.

A. tan 255° **B.** sin 272° **C.** cos 175° **D.** –tan 75°

12. Without using technology, determine which of the following has the same value as cos 297°.

A. cos 27° **B.** cos 117° **C.** –cos 243° **D.** –cos 63°

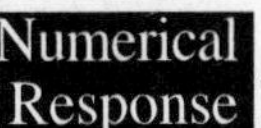

13. Consider angles A, B, and C such that $\cos A = \cos 217°$, $\tan B = \tan 298°$, and $\sin C = \sin 7°$. where $0° \leq A \leq 360°$, $0° \leq B \leq 360°$, and $0° \leq C \leq 360°$.

The value of $A + B + C$ is _____.

(Record your answer in the numerical response box from left to right.)

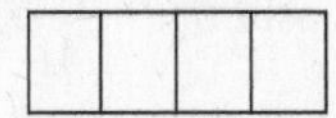

The following problems could be used as a lead in to the next lesson.

a) Sketch an angle of 30° in standard position with the point $P\left(\sqrt{3}, 1\right)$ on the terminal arm.
Without using technology, explain and carry out a strategy to determine the exact trigonometric ratios of three different angles greater than 90° and less than 360°

b) Consider an angle A in standard position with $\sin A = -\frac{3}{5}$ and $0° \leq A \leq 360°$.
Without using technology, explain and carry out a strategy to determine the exact values of cos A and tan A.

Answer Key

1. a) 17 **b)** 25

2. a) 10 **b)** $\sqrt{53}$ **c)** $4\sqrt{2}$

3. $\sin\theta = \frac{y}{r}$ $\cos\theta = \frac{x}{r}$ $\tan\theta = \frac{y}{x}$

4. $r = 15$, $\sin\theta = \frac{4}{5}$ $\cos\theta = \frac{3}{5}$ $\tan\theta = \frac{4}{3}$

5. $\sin\theta = \frac{4\sqrt{41}}{41}$ $\cos\theta = \frac{5\sqrt{41}}{41}$ $\tan\theta = \frac{4}{5}$

6. $\sin\theta = \frac{2\sqrt{5}}{5}$ $\cos\theta = \frac{\sqrt{5}}{5}$ $\tan\theta = 2$

7. a) 1 or 2 **b)** 1 or 3 **c)** 2 or 3 **d)** 4 **e)** 4

8. a) Positive **b)** Positive **c)** Positive **d)** Negative **e)** Negative **f)** Negative

9. a) –sin 25° **b)** tan 13° **c)** –cos 83° **d)** sin 24° **e)** cos 39° **f)** –tan 20°

10. B **11.** A **12.** C **13.**

4	3	4	

Group Investigation

a) $\sin 150° = \frac{1}{2}$ $\cos 150° = -\frac{\sqrt{3}}{2}$ $\tan 150° = -\frac{\sqrt{3}}{3}$

$\sin 210° = -\frac{1}{2}$ $\cos 210° = -\frac{\sqrt{3}}{2}$ $\tan 210° = \frac{\sqrt{3}}{3}$

$\sin 330° = -\frac{1}{2}$ $\cos 330° = \frac{\sqrt{3}}{2}$ $\tan 330° = -\frac{\sqrt{3}}{3}$

b) In quadrant three, $\cos A = -\frac{4}{5}$ and $\tan A = \frac{3}{4}$.

In quadrant four, $\cos A = \frac{4}{5}$ and $\tan A = -\frac{3}{4}$.

Trigonometry - Lesson #3: Applications of Reference Angles and the CAST Rule

Overview

In this lesson, we use our knowledge of rotation angles, reference angles, and the CAST rule to:

i) determine the exact trigonometric ratios for rotation angles from 0° to 360° given a point on the terminal arm.

ii) determine trigonometric ratios for a rotation angle from 0° to 360° given a different trigonometric ratio for the angle.

iii) solve equations of the form $\sin\theta = a$, $\cos\theta = a$, or $\tan\theta = a$ where $0° \leq \theta \leq 360°$.

Review

The reference angle for any rotation angle is the acute angle between the terminal arm of the rotation angle and the *x*-axis.

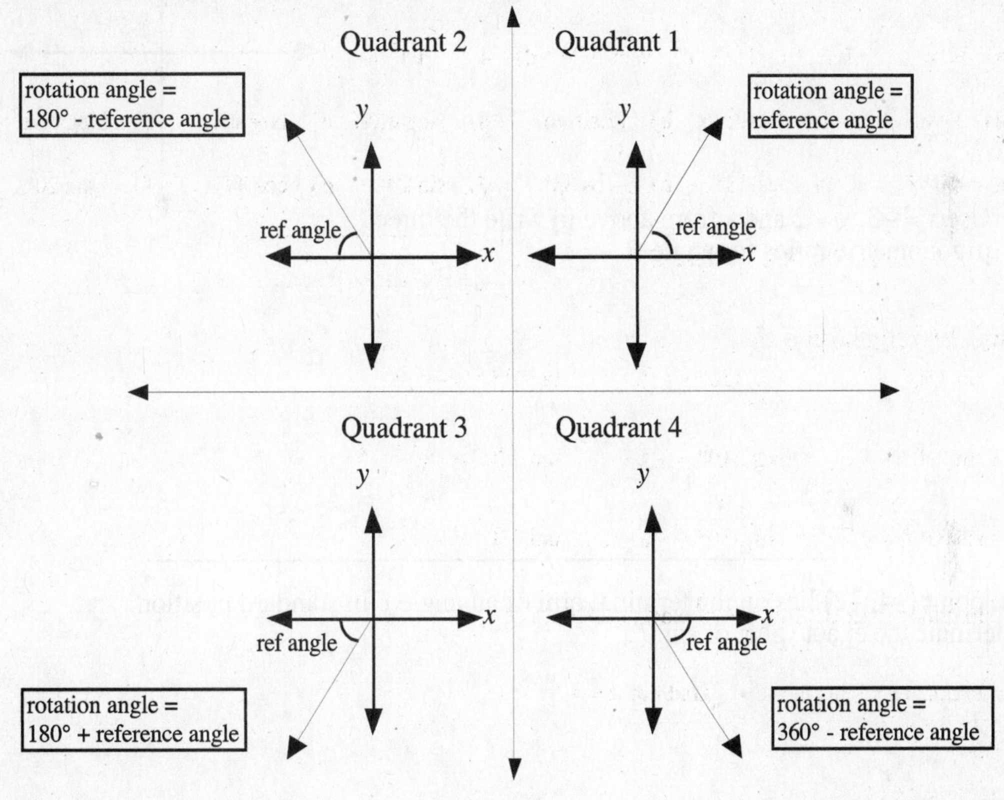

We can determine the sign of a trigonometric ratio in a particular quadrant

- by the **CAST** rule or
- by remembering to "**A**dd **S**ugar **T**o **C**offee".

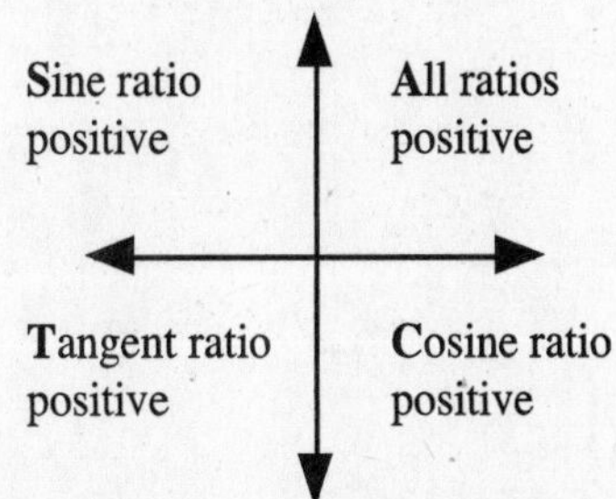

The trigonometric ratios for an angle in standard position with a point $P(x, y)$ on the terminal arm and $OP = r$ are

$$\sin\theta = \frac{y}{r} \qquad \cos\theta = \frac{x}{r} \qquad \tan\theta = \frac{y}{x}$$

Exact Values of Trigonometric Ratios Given a Point on a Terminal Arm

In the previous lesson, we were able to determine the exact values of the trigonometric ratios given a point on the terminal arm of a rotation angle in quadrant one.
In this lesson, we extend the method into quadrants two to four.

The point $P(-3, 2)$ lies on the terminal arm of an angle θ in standard position. Complete the following procedure to determine the values of the primary trigonometric ratios.

a) Sketch the rotation angle on the grid and mark the point $P(-3, 2)$ on the terminal arm.

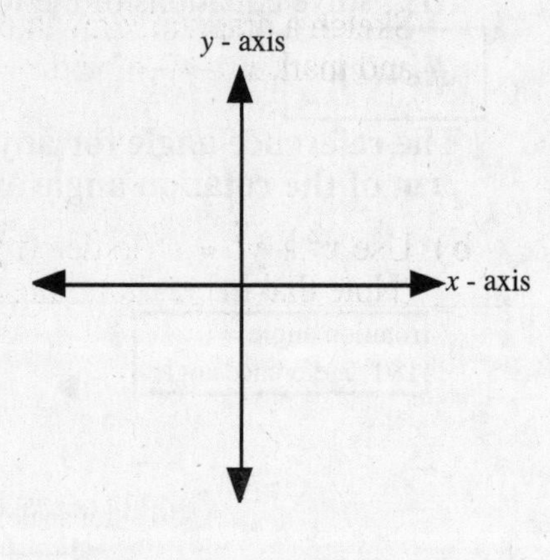

b) Calculate the exact length of $OP = r$.

c) Use $x = -3$, $y = 2$ and r from above to write the three trigonometric ratios for angle θ.

The point $(-4, -2)$ lies on the terminal arm of an angle θ in standard position. Determine the exact value of $\sin\theta$.

Value of a Trigonometric Ratio Given a Different Trigonometric Ratio

Class Ex. #3

Angle A terminates in the third quadrant with $\sin A = -\frac{4}{5}$. Complete the following procedure to determine the values of $\cos A$ and $\tan A$.

a) Since $\sin A = -\frac{4}{5} = \frac{y}{r}$ we know that the point $(x, -4)$ lies on the terminal arm in the third quadrant with $r = 5$.
Sketch a diagram, draw the reference triangle and mark x, $y = -4$, and $r = 5$ on the reference triangle.

b) Use $x^2 + y^2 = r^2$ to determine the value of x.
(Note that in quadrant three the value of x must be negative).

c) Use the values of x, y, and r to determine the exact values of $\cos A$ and $\tan A$.

Class Ex. #4

If $\tan\theta = -\frac{2}{3}$ and $\cos\theta$ is positive, then find the exact value of $\sin\theta$.

Complete Assignment Questions #1 - #9

Solving Equations Involving Sine, Cosine, or Tangent

We can use the concepts of reference angles and signs of the trigonometric ratio to solve equations of the form $\sin\theta = a$, $\cos\theta = a$, or $\tan\theta = a$, where $0° \leq \theta \leq 360°$.

Use the following procedure to solve an equation such as $\sin\theta = 0.5$, where $0° \leq \theta \leq 360°$.

Step 1: Determine the quadrant(s) the angle will be in by looking at the sign of the ratio.

Step 2: Determine the reference angle (always between 0° and 90°) and draw a rough sketch in the appropriate quadrant(s). To determine the reference angle, use
[2nd] [sin] or [2nd] [cos] or [2nd] [tan]
of the **absolute value** of the given quantity.

Step 3: Determine the rotation angle(s) using the reference angle and the quadrant(s).

- Always check the given domain to determine which quadrants are valid in the calculation. Sometimes the domain is restricted to, for example, $0° \leq \theta \leq 180°$, or $90° \leq \theta \leq 180°$.

Use the procedure above to solve $\sin\theta = 0.5$, where $0° \leq \theta \leq 360°$

Find the measure of x, to the nearest degree, where $0° \leq x \leq 360°$.

a) $\sin x = -0.8090$ **b)** $\cos x = -0.8090$ **c)** $\tan x = -2.4586$

Class Ex. #7

Solve the following equations if $0° \leq \theta \leq 360°$.

a) $\sin \theta = 1$

b) $\cos \theta = 0$

Class Ex. #8

Solve the equation $3 \tan \theta + 1 = 4$, $0° \leq \theta \leq 180°$.

Complete Assignment Questions #10 - #18

Assignment

1. The point $(8, -6)$ lies on the terminal arm of an angle θ in standard position. Determine the exact values of $\sin \theta$, $\cos \theta$, and $\tan \theta$.

2. The point $(-1, -3)$ lies on the terminal arm of an angle θ in standard position. Determine the exact values of $\sin \theta$, $\cos \theta$, and $\tan \theta$.

3. The point $(-16, 63)$ lies on the terminal arm of an angle A in standard position. Determine the exact value of $\cos A$.

4. If $\cos\theta = \frac{12}{13}$ and $270° \le \theta \le 360°$, then find the exact values of $\sin\theta$ and $\tan\theta$.

5. If $\sin\theta = -\frac{4}{7}$ and $\cos\theta$ is negative, then find the exact value of $\tan\theta$.

6. If $\tan A = -\frac{15}{8}$ and $0° \le A \le 180°$, then find the values of $\sin A$ and $\cos A$.

7. If $\tan B = 0.8$ and $\cos B$ is negative, then find the exact value of $\sin B$.

8. If $\sin X = -\frac{1}{4}$ and $\tan X$ is negative, express $\cos X$ as an exact value.

9. Solve for the required ratios in each of the following. Express each answer as an exact value with a rational denominator.

a) Angle θ terminates in the second quadrant. If $\tan\theta = -\frac{\sqrt{3}}{5}$, find $\sin\theta$ and $\cos\theta$.

b) Angle θ terminates in the fourth quadrant. If $\tan\theta = -\frac{\sqrt{3}}{5}$, find $\sin\theta$ and $\cos\theta$.

10. Solve the following equations, where $0° \leq \theta \leq 360°$.

a) $\cos\theta = \frac{1}{2}$ **b)** $\sin\theta = -\frac{\sqrt{3}}{2}$ **c)** $\tan\theta = -1$

11. Find the measure of θ, to the nearest degree, where $0° \leq \theta \leq 360°$.

a) $\sin\theta = 0.6485$ **b)** $\cos\theta = -0.8219$ **c)** $\tan\theta = 0.4668$

d) $6\sin\theta = -1$ **e)** $4\cos\theta - 3 = 0$ **f)** $\tan\theta + 5 = 0$

12. Determine the measure of A if $0° \leq A \leq 360°$.

a) $\tan A = 0$ **b)** $\cos A = 1$ **c)** $\sin A = -1$ **d)** $\sin A = 0$

13. Given that $(\tan\theta)^2$ can be written as $\tan^2\theta$, solve the following equations if $0° \leq \theta \leq 360°$.

a) $\tan^2\theta = 3$ **b)** $\cos^2\theta = \frac{3}{4}$

Multiple Choice

14. If $\cos A = -\frac{7}{25}$, and $180° \leq A \leq 270°$, then the values of $\sin A$ and $\tan A$ respectively are

A. $-\frac{24}{25}$ and $-\frac{24}{7}$

B. $-\frac{24}{25}$ and $\frac{24}{7}$

C. $-\frac{24}{25}$ and $\frac{7}{24}$

D. $\frac{24}{25}$ and $\frac{24}{7}$

15. If $\sin\theta = -\frac{1}{2}$, and $270° \leq \theta \leq 360°$, then the value of $\cos\theta$ is

A. $-\frac{1}{2}$

B. $-\frac{\sqrt{3}}{2}$

C. $\frac{1}{2}$

D. $\frac{\sqrt{3}}{2}$

16. Angle P has a terminal arm in the third quadrant. If $\tan P = \frac{1}{\sqrt{3}}$, the value of $\sin P - \cos P$ is

A. $\frac{1-\sqrt{3}}{2}$

B. $\frac{\sqrt{3}-1}{2}$

C. $\frac{1+\sqrt{3}}{2}$

D. $\frac{-1-\sqrt{3}}{2}$

17. The solution of the equation $\cos x = 0.0999$ in the interval $0° \leq x \leq 360°$ is

A. 84°, 276°
B. 96°, 264°
C. 96°, 276°
D. 264°, 276°

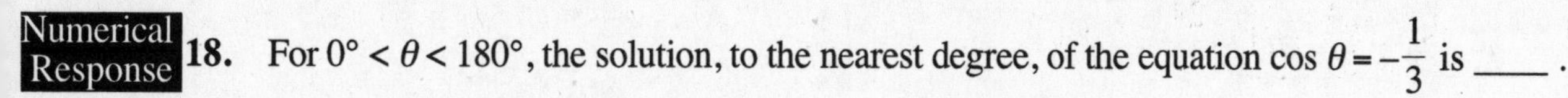

Numerical Response **18.** For $0° < \theta < 180°$, the solution, to the nearest degree, of the equation $\cos\theta = -\frac{1}{3}$ is ____ .

(Record your answer in the numerical response box from left to right.)

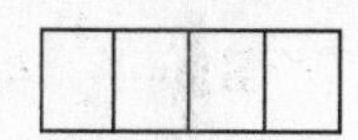

Answer Key

1. $\sin\theta = -\dfrac{3}{5}$ $\cos\theta = \dfrac{4}{5}$ $\tan\theta = -\dfrac{3}{4}$ **2.** $\sin\theta = -\dfrac{3\sqrt{10}}{10}$ $\cos\theta = -\dfrac{\sqrt{10}}{10}$ $\tan\theta = 3$

3. $\cos A = -\dfrac{16}{65}$ **4.** $\sin\theta = -\dfrac{5}{13}$ $\tan\theta = -\dfrac{5}{12}$ **5.** $\tan\theta = \dfrac{4\sqrt{33}}{33}$

6. $\sin A = \dfrac{15}{17}$ $\cos A = -\dfrac{8}{17}$ **7.** $\sin B = -\dfrac{4\sqrt{41}}{41}$ **8.** $\cos X = \dfrac{\sqrt{15}}{4}$

9. a) $\sin\theta = \dfrac{\sqrt{21}}{14}$ $\cos\theta = -\dfrac{5\sqrt{7}}{14}$ **b)** $\sin\theta = -\dfrac{\sqrt{21}}{14}$ $\cos\theta = \dfrac{5\sqrt{7}}{14}$

10.a) 60°, 300° **b)** 240°, 300° **c)** 135°, 315°

11.a) 40°, 140° **b)** 145°, 215° **c)** 25°, 205° **d)** 190°, 350° **e)** 41°, 319° **f)** 101°, 281°

12.a) 0°, 180°, 360° **b)** 0°, 360° **c)** 270° **d)** 0°, 180°, 360°

13.a) 60°, 120°, 240°, 300° **b)** 30°, 150°, 210°, 330°

14. B **15.** D **16.** B **17.** A **18.**

1	0	9	

Trigonometry - Lesson #4:
Special Triangles, Exact Values, and the Unit Circle

Overview

In this lesson, we will determine the exact value of the sine ratio, the cosine ratio, and the tangent ratio for a given angle with a reference angle of 0°, 30°, 45°, 60°, and 90°.

Investigation

a) Diagram 1 shows an angle of 45° in standard position. An isosceles triangle is drawn whose equal sides are 1 unit.

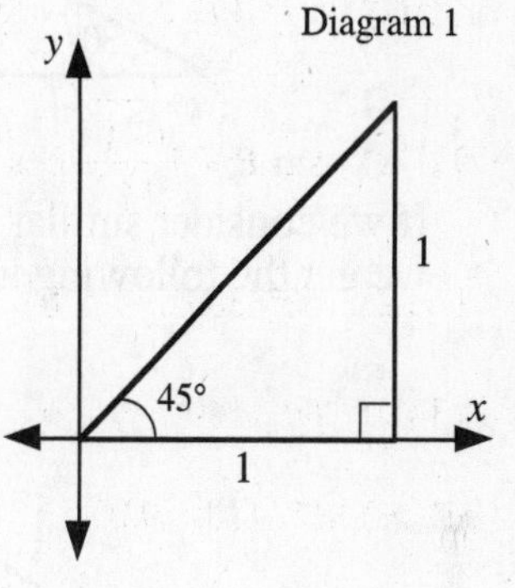

i) Determine the length of the hypotenuse.

ii) Use SOHCAHTOA or the x, y, r formulas to complete:

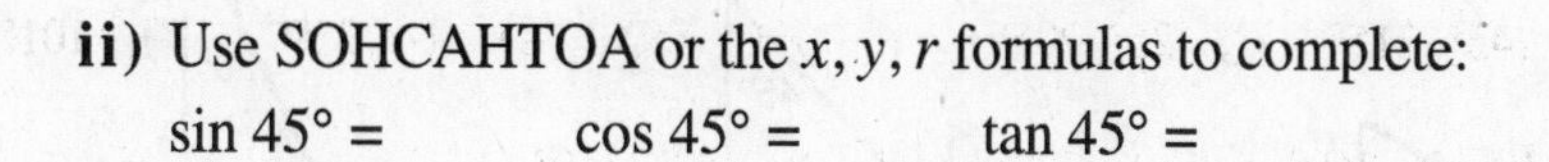

sin 45° = cos 45° = tan 45° =

b) Diagram 2 shows an angle of 60° in standard position. An equilateral triangle is drawn whose equal sides are 2 units and a vertical altitude is drawn which divides the equilateral triangle into two congruent triangles.

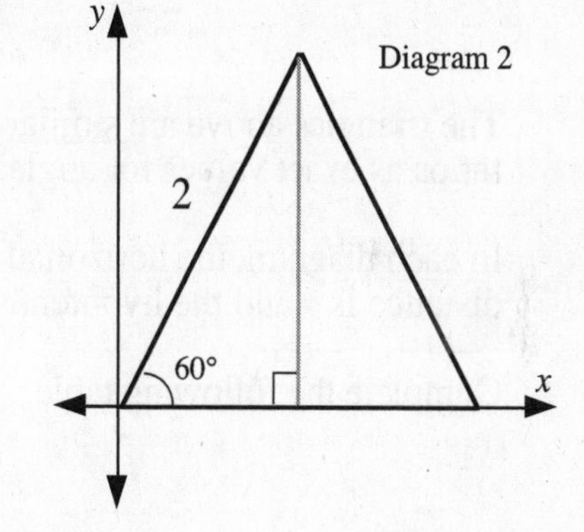

i) Determine the length of the altitude.

ii) Complete :

sin 60° = cos 60° = tan 60° =

c) Diagram 3 shows an angle of 30° in standard position. An equilateral triangle is drawn whose equal sides are 2 units and a horizontal altitude is drawn which divides the equilateral triangle into two congruent triangles.

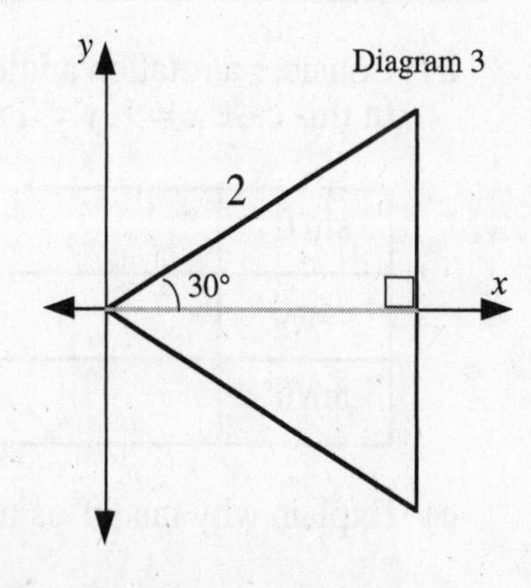

i) Complete:

sin 30° = cos 30° = tan 30° =

Special Triangles

The following triangles were developed on the previous page.

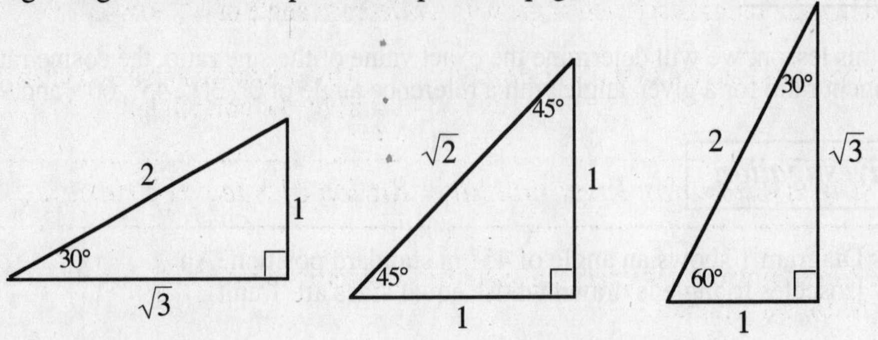

If we consider similar triangles to the above, all with hypotenuse length of one unit, we get the following triangles.

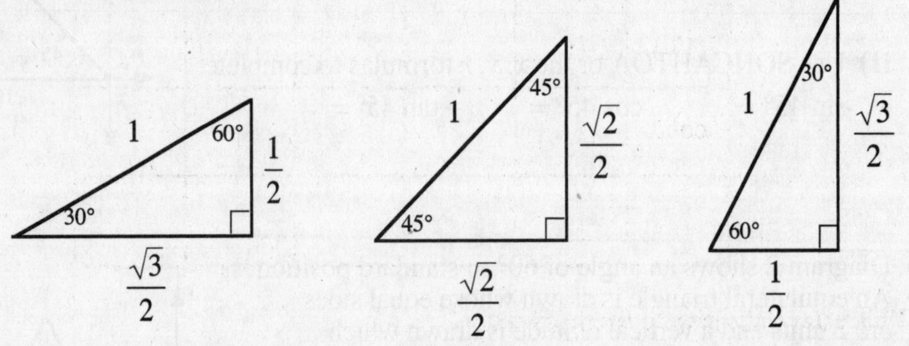

The triangles above are <u>similar</u> to the ones in the investigation and illustrate the trigonometric ratios as exact values for angles of 30°, 45° and 60°.

In each diagram, the horizontal distance is x, the vertical distance is y and the hypotenuse is $r = 1$.

Complete the following table.

$x°$	30°	45°	60°
$\sin x$			
$\cos x$			
$\tan x$			

Finding Exact Trigonometric Ratios for Angles of 0° and 90°

a) Consider a rotation angle of 0°. In this case $x = 1$, $y = 0$ and $r = 1$.

sin 0°	
cos 0°	
tan 0°	

b) Consider a rotation angle of 90°. In this case $x = 0$, $y = 1$ and $r = 1$

sin 90°	
cos 90°	
tan 90°	

c) Explain why tan 90° is undefined.

Determining Exact Values for Trigonometric Ratios of Certain Angles

There are several ways to determine, without technology, the exact value of the sine, cosine and tangent ratios of a given angle with a reference angle of $0°, 30°, 45°, 60°$, and $90°$.

We will discuss two of these methods: i) by reference angle and chart
ii) by the unit circle.

Using a Chart for Trigonometric Ratios of Special Triangles

We can summarize the exact values of trigonometric ratios of $0°, 30°, 45°, 60°$, and $90°$ in the following chart.

x	0°	30°	45°	60°	90°
$\sin x$					
$\cos x$					
$\tan x$					

This chart should be memorized.

Note the following patterns.

The sine ratios increase from 0 to 1. The cosine ratios decrease from 1 to 0.

The tangent ratios are equal to the sine ratios divided by the cosine ratios.

Determining Exact Values of Trigonometric Ratios Using the Chart

We can use the previous table, together with the concept of reference angles and the CAST rule, to determine the exact values of the trigonometric ratios of certain angles in quadrants 2, 3, and 4.

Write the following in terms of a reference angle and determine the exact value.

a) $\sin 210°$ **b)** $\cos 300°$ **c)** $\tan 225°$

Without using technology, determine the exact value(s) of θ where

a) $\cos\theta = -\frac{\sqrt{3}}{2}$, $0° \leq \theta \leq 360°$ **b)** $\tan\theta$ is undefined, $0° \leq \theta \leq 360$

The point $P\left(-3, \sqrt{3}\right)$ is on the terminal arm of an angle θ.
Without using technology, complete the following questions.

a) Draw the angle in standard position and mark the point P on the terminal arm.

b) State the values of x and y and hence the value of $\tan\theta$.

c) State the reference angle and hence the rotation angle θ.

Complete Assignment Questions #1 - #5

Creating The Unit Circle

An alternative method for determining exact values for trigonometric ratios of certain angles greater than 90° is to use the **unit circle**.

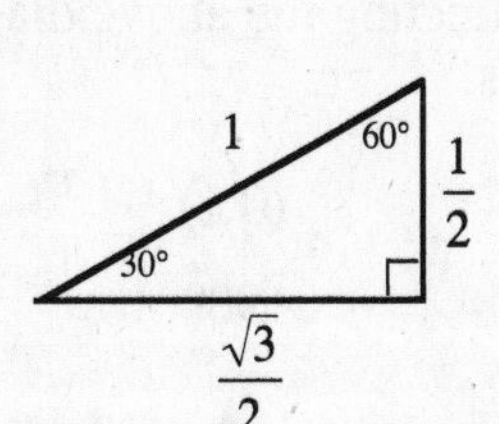

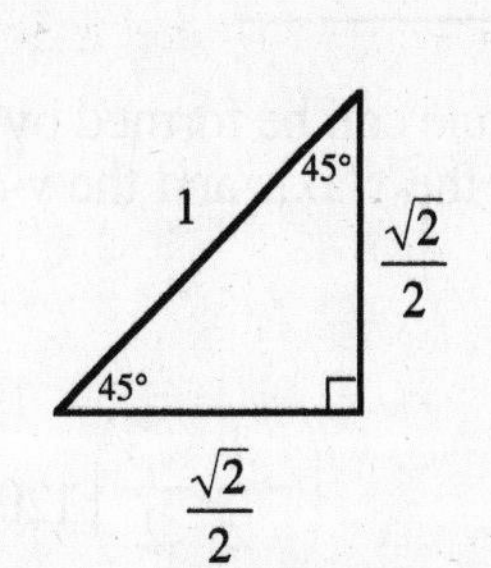

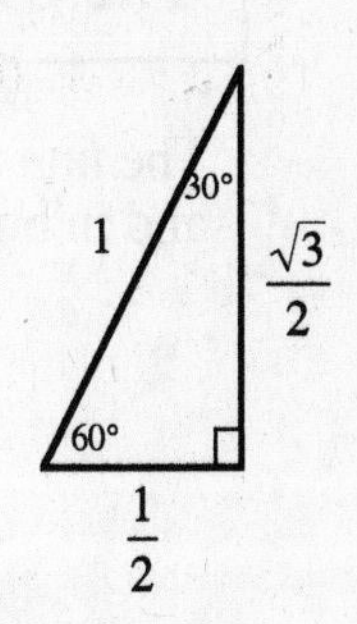

The diagram above shows the triangles developed from the investigation. In each diagram the horizontal distance is x, the vertical distance is y, and the hypotenuse is $r = 1$.

In the diagram below, these three triangles are placed in quadrant one on a Cartesian Plane.

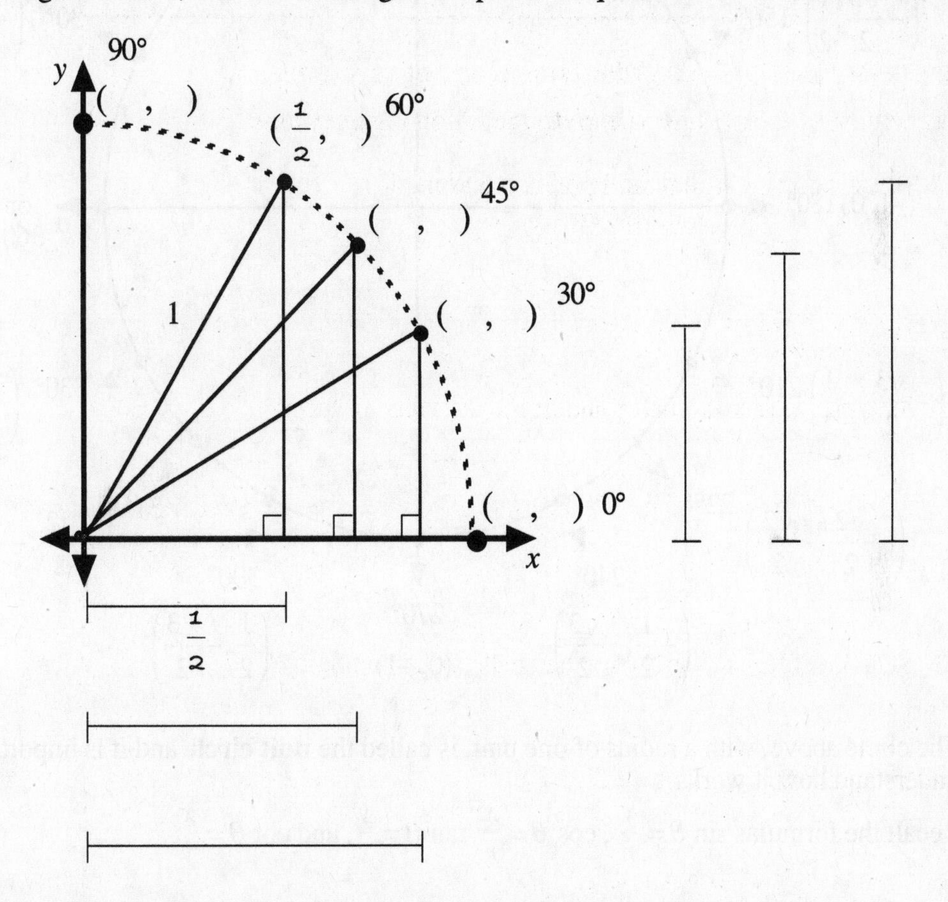

a) Write the lengths of the horizontal and vertical line segments indicated.

b) Write the coordinates of the five points marked.

c) How do the coordinates of the points relate to the measure of the rotation angles?

Complete Assignment Question #6

The Unit Circle

The unit circle can be formed by reflecting the above diagram in the x-axis, in the y-axis, and in both the x-axis and the y-axis.

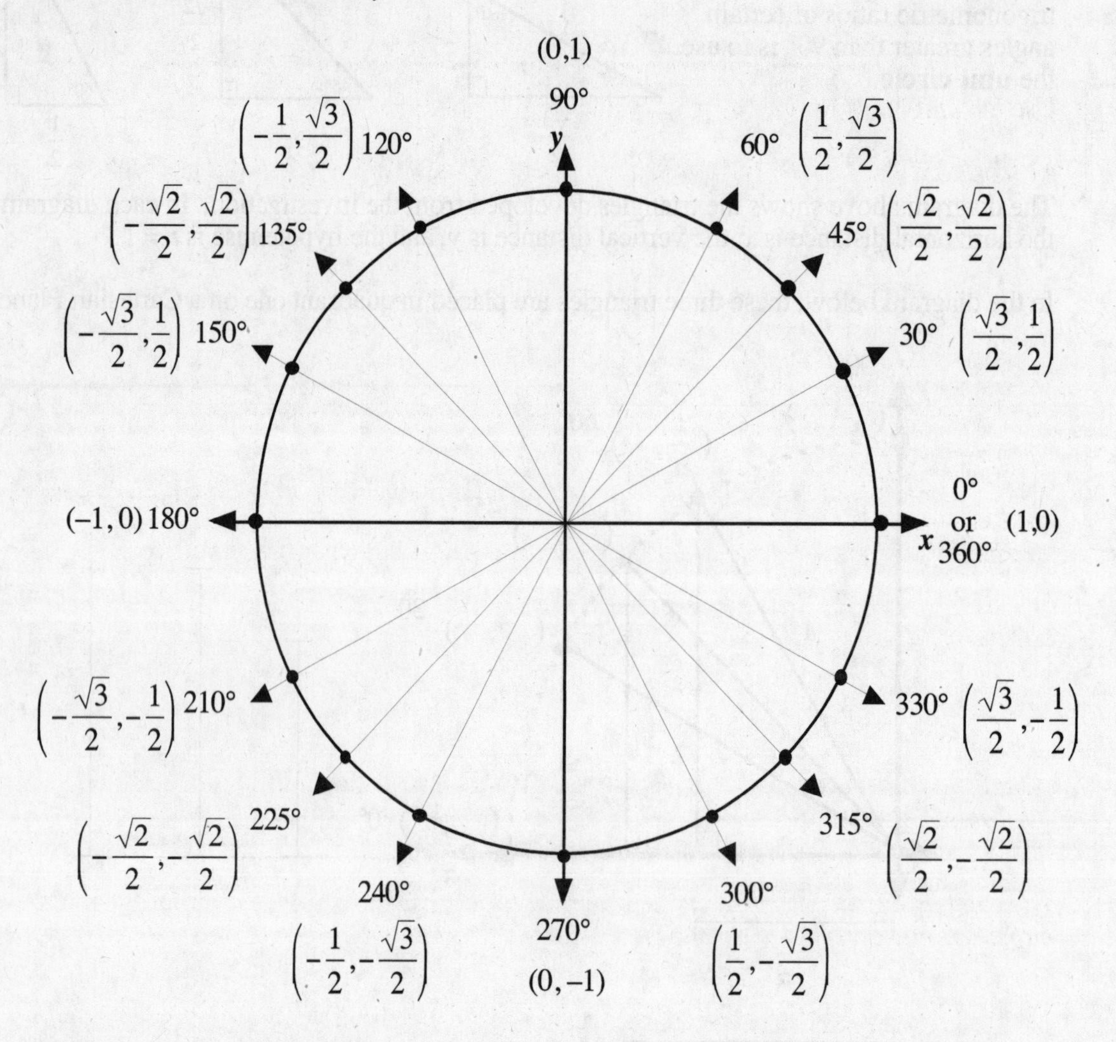

The circle above, with a radius of one unit, is called the **unit circle** and it is important to understand how it works.

Recall the formulas $\sin\theta = \frac{y}{r}$, $\cos\theta = \frac{x}{r}$, $\tan\theta = \frac{y}{x}$, and $\cot\theta = \frac{x}{y}$.

- In the unit circle, where $r = 1$, we have:

  $\sin\theta =$ ______ and $\cos\theta =$ ______

- Every point on the unit circle has coordinates (x, y) which can be written as $(\cos\theta, \sin\theta)$

- $\tan\theta = \dfrac{\sin\theta}{\cos\theta}$

Class Ex. #4

Use the unit circle to find the exact value of the trigonometric ratios for a rotation angle of 240°. Give each answer with a rational denominator.

$\sin 240° =$ $\qquad$ $\cos 240° =$ $\qquad$ $\tan 240° =$

Class Ex. #5

Use the unit circle to find the exact value of

a) $\cos 135°$ $\qquad$ **b)** $\tan 120°$ $\qquad$ **c)** $\sin 180°$ $\qquad$ **d)** $\tan 270°$

Class Ex. #6

$A\left(-\frac{\sqrt{2}}{2}, \frac{\sqrt{2}}{2}\right)$ and $B\left(-\frac{1}{2}, -\frac{\sqrt{3}}{2}\right)$ are two points on the unit circle. If an object rotates counterclockwise from point A to point B, through what angle has it rotated?

Class Ex. #7

Use a calculator to determine, to four decimal places, the coordinates of the point on the unit circle that corresponds to a rotation of 148°.

Class Ex. #8

The point $T(-0.8829, 0.4695)$ lies on the unit circle. Determine the value of θ, where θ is the angle made by the positive x-axis and the line passing though T.

We now have two methods for determining exact values of trigonometric ratios of certain angles greater than 90°. Use either method.

Use the chart or unit circle to find the exact value of :

a) $\cos 300° + \sin 330°$ **b)** $\sin^2 225° + \cos^2 225°$ **c)** $\dfrac{2\tan 150°}{1 - \tan^2 150°}$

Complete Assignment Questions #7 - #18

Assignment

1. Complete the following chart.

x	0°	30°	45°	60°	90°
$\sin x$					
$\cos x$					
$\tan x$					

2. Find the exact value of the following using the chart and reference angle method.

a) $\cos 120°$ **b)** $\tan 300°$ **c)** $\sin 135°$ **d)** $\sin 330°$ **e)** $\cos 315°$

f) $\tan 180°$ **g)** $\cos 180°$ **h)** $\sin 180°$ **i)** $\tan 150°$ **j)** $\cos 210°$

k) $\tan 270°$ **l)** $\cos 270°$ **m)** $\sin 270°$ **n)** $\tan 240°$ **o)** $\cos^2 225°$

3. Without using technology, determine the exact value(s) of θ where

a) $\sin \theta = \frac{\sqrt{2}}{2}$, $0° \leq \theta \leq 360°$ **b)** $\cos \theta = -\frac{1}{2}$, $0° \leq \theta \leq 360°$

c) $\tan \theta = -\frac{\sqrt{3}}{3}$, $0° \leq \theta \leq 360°$ **d)** $\tan \theta$ is undefined, $0° \leq \theta \leq 360$

4. The point $\left(-\sqrt{2}, -\sqrt{6}\right)$ is on the terminal arm of an angle θ.
Without using technology, complete the following questions.

a) Draw the angle in standard position and mark the point on the terminal arm.

b) State the values of x and y and hence the value of $\tan \theta$.

c) State the reference angle and hence the rotation angle θ.

5. The point (5,–5) is on the terminal arm of an angle A.
Without using technology, determine the value of angle A.

6. The diagram on page 171 has been reflected in the x-axis, the y-axis, and in both axes to produce the diagram below.

Complete the diagram by writing the coordinates and the rotation angle for each point on the circumference of the circle.

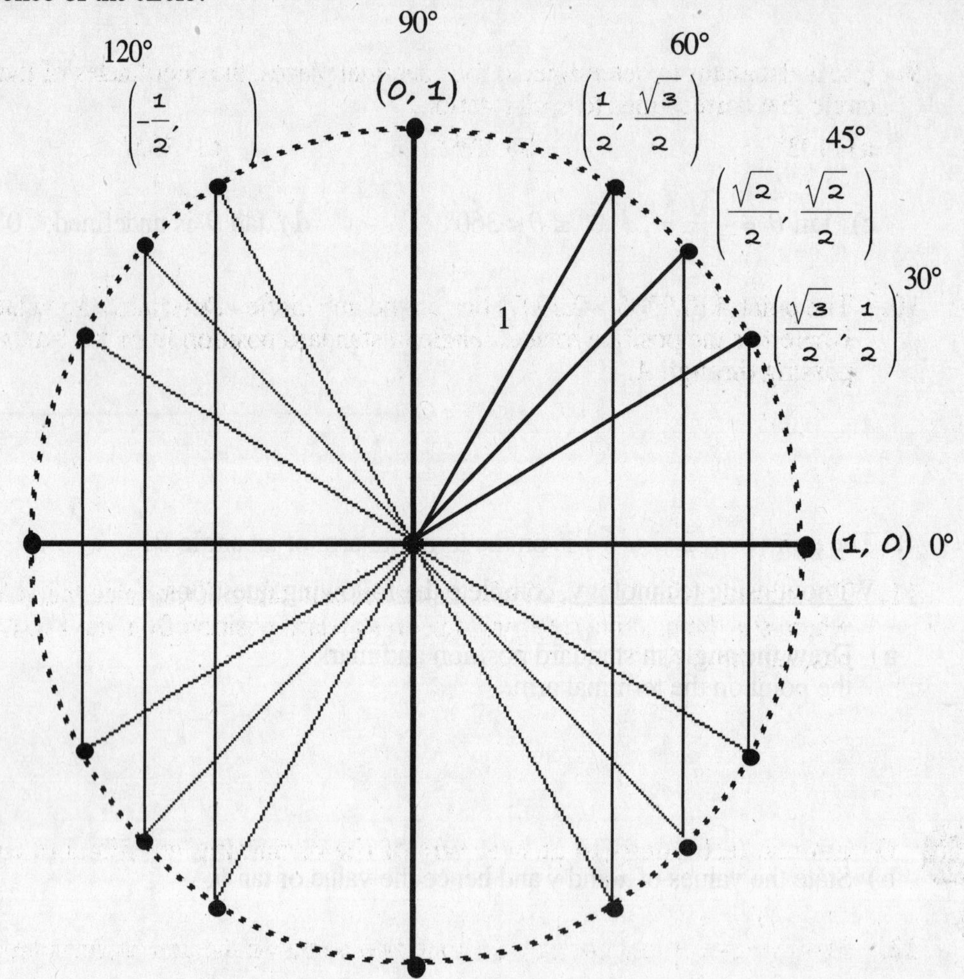

7. Find exact values for each using the unit circle.

a) cos 30° **b)** sin 90° **c)** sin 135° **d)** tan 45°

e) cos 150° **f)** tan 120° **g)** sin 300° **h)** cos 300°

i) tan 330° **j)** cos 270° **k)** tan 180° **l)** tan 270°

8. State the exact coordinates of the point on the unit circle that correspond to each rotation.

a) 270° **b)** 120° **c)** 210°

9. Use a calculator to determine, to four decimal places, the coordinates of the point on the unit circle that corresponds to each rotation.

a) 103° **b)** 298° **c)** 195°

10. The point A (0.9205, –0.3907) lies on the unit circle. Determine the value of θ, where θ is the positive rotation angle in standard position from the x-axis to the line passing through A.

11. The point B (–0.9272, –0.3746) lies on the unit circle. Determine the value of θ, where θ is the positive rotation angle in standard position from the x-axis to the line passing through B.

Do not use technology to answer any of the remaining questions in this assignment.

12. $P\left(-\frac{\sqrt{3}}{2}, -\frac{1}{2}\right)$ and $Q\left(\frac{1}{2}, \frac{\sqrt{3}}{2}\right)$ are two points on the unit circle. If an object rotates counterclockwise from point P to point Q, through what angle has it rotated?

13. If $\cos A = \frac{\sqrt{3}}{2}$, and angle A is not a first quadrant angle, determine the exact value of $\tan A$.

Use the following information to answer questions #14 and #15 (#15 is on the next page).

Katelin places a 360° protractor on grid paper. She takes a picture of it with her iPhone, downloads it to her computer, uses software to adjust the image, and then prints it.

An illustration of her printout is shown.

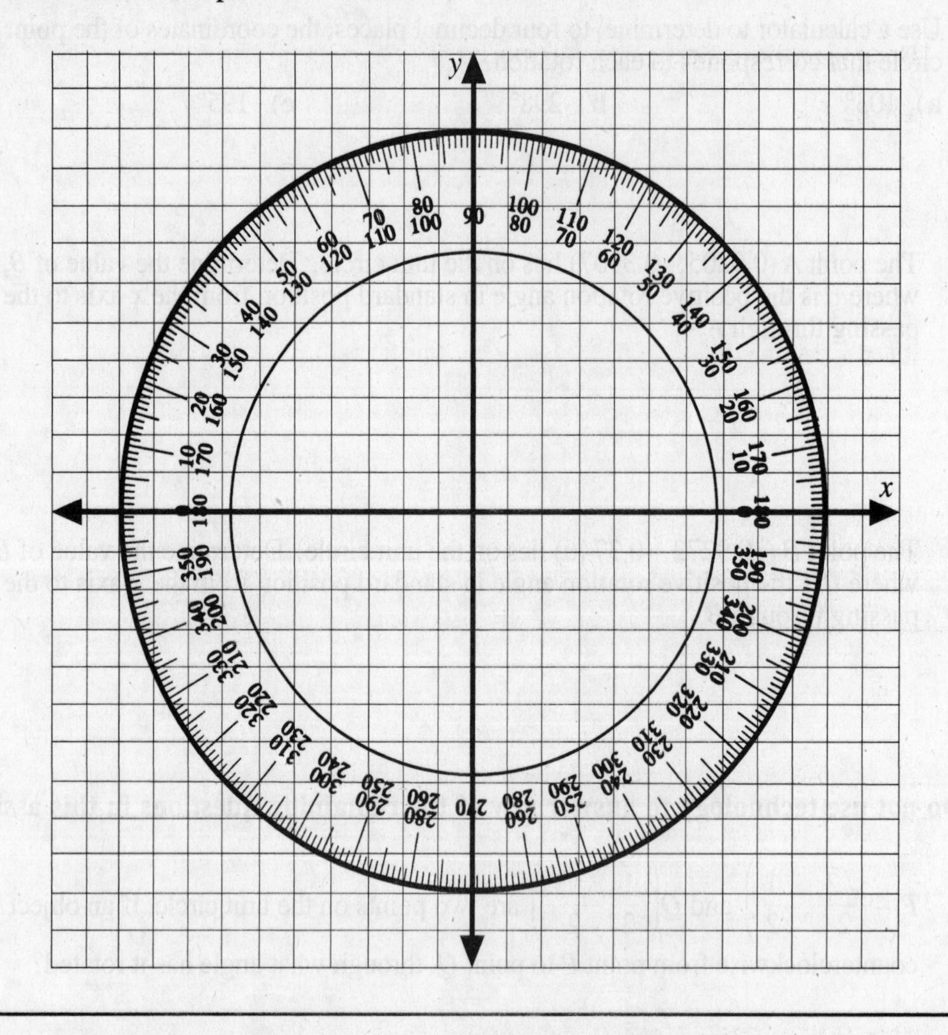

14. a) Explain how to use the illustration to estimate the sine ratio, the cosine ratio, and the tangent ratio for any angle between 0° and 360°.

b) Use the illustration to estimate the following ratios to two decimal places. Use a calculator to check the accuracy of your estimates.
i) sin 70° **ii)** cos 130° **iii)** tan 240° **iv)** sin 336°

15. Use the illustration on the previous page to estimate, to the nearest degree, the solution to the following equations on the domain $0° \le \theta \le 360°$.

a) $\sin\theta = 0.1$ **b)** $\cos\theta = -0.6$ **c)** $5\sin\theta + 1 = 0$ **d)** $\tan\theta = \frac{1}{4}$

16. Determine the exact measure of θ where $0° \le \theta \le 360°$.

a) $\sin\theta = -\frac{\sqrt{3}}{2}$ **b)** $\tan\theta = \frac{\sqrt{3}}{3}$ **c)** $\cos\theta = -\frac{1}{2}$

d) $\sin\theta = 1$ **e)** $\cos\theta = 1$ **f)** $\tan\theta = 1$

g) $\sin\theta = -1$ **h)** $\cos\theta = -1$ **i)** $\tan\theta = -1$

j) $\sin\theta = 0$ **k)** $\cos\theta = 0$ **l)** $\tan\theta = 0$

Multiple Choice

17. The smallest positive root of the equation $\tan x + \sqrt{3} = 0$ is

A. 60° **B.** 120°
C. 150° **D.** 240°

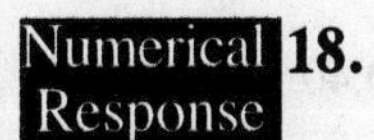

18. The solution to the equation $2\cos\theta = -\sqrt{3}$, $180° < \theta < 360°$, to the nearest degree, is ______ .

(Record your answer in the numerical response box from left to right.)

Answer Key

1. See table below

x	0°	30°	45°	60°	90°
sin x	0	$\frac{1}{2}$	$\frac{\sqrt{2}}{2}$	$\frac{\sqrt{3}}{2}$	1
cos x	1	$\frac{\sqrt{3}}{2}$	$\frac{\sqrt{2}}{2}$	$\frac{1}{2}$	0
tan x	0	$\frac{\sqrt{3}}{3}$	1	$\sqrt{3}$	undefined

2. a) $-\frac{1}{2}$ **b)** $-\sqrt{3}$ **c)** $\frac{\sqrt{2}}{2}$ **d)** $-\frac{1}{2}$ **e)** $\frac{\sqrt{2}}{2}$ **f)** 0 **g)** −1 **h)** 0
i) $-\frac{\sqrt{3}}{3}$ **j)** $-\frac{\sqrt{3}}{2}$ **k)** undefined **l)** 0 **m)** −1 **n)** $\sqrt{3}$ **o)** $\frac{1}{2}$

3. a) 45°, 135° **b)** 120°, 240° **c)** 150°, 330° **d)** 90°, 270°

4. a) see diagram below **b)** $x = -\sqrt{2}$, $y = -\sqrt{6}$, $\tan\theta = \sqrt{3}$

c) reference angle = 60°, rotation angle = 240°

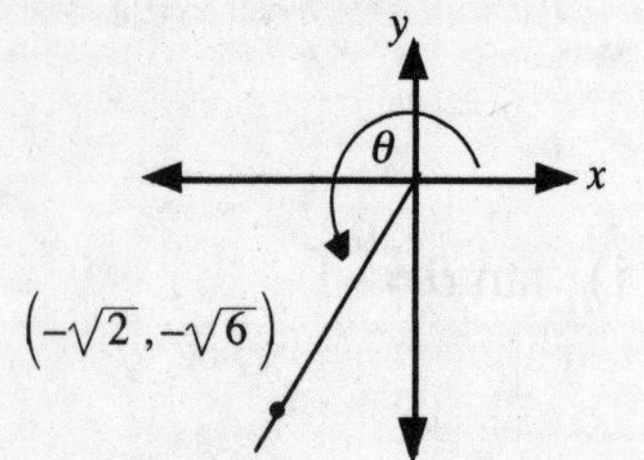

5. 315° **6.** See page 172

7. a) $\frac{\sqrt{3}}{2}$ **b)** 1 **c)** $\frac{\sqrt{2}}{2}$ **d)** 1 **e)** $-\frac{\sqrt{3}}{2}$ **f)** $-\sqrt{3}$
g) $-\frac{\sqrt{3}}{2}$ **h)** $\frac{1}{2}$ **i)** $-\frac{\sqrt{3}}{3}$ **j)** 0 **k)** 0 **l)** undefined

8. a) (0, −1) **b)** $\left(-\frac{1}{2}, \frac{\sqrt{3}}{2}\right)$ **c)** $\left(-\frac{\sqrt{3}}{2}, -\frac{1}{2}\right)$

9. a) (−0.2250, 0.9744) **b)** (0.4695, −0.8829) **c)** (−0.9659, −0.2588)

10. 337° **11.** 202° **12.** 210° **13.** $-\frac{\sqrt{3}}{3}$

14. a) Let the radius of the protractor represent 1 unit. The *y*-coordinate of any point on the circumference gives the sine ratio for a particular angle. The *x*-coordinate gives the cosine ratio and the tangent ratio is determined by dividing the *y*-coordinate by the *x*-coordinate.
b) Answers are estimates and may vary slightly. **i)** 0.94 **ii)** −0.64 **iii)** 1.72 **iv)** −0.40

15. a) 6°, 174° **b)** 127°, 233° **c)** 192°, 348° **d)** 14°, 194°

16. a) 240°, 300° **b)** 30°, 210° **c)** 120°, 240° **d)** 90° **e)** 0°, 360° **f)** 45°, 225° **g)** 270°
h) 180° **i)** 135°, 315° **j)** 0°, 180°, 360° **k)** 90°, 270° **l)** 0°, 180°, 360°

17. B **18.**

2	1	0	

Trigonometry Lesson #5:
The Sine Law

Review of Right Triangle Trigonometry

In previous courses, we studied trigonometry in right triangles using SOHCAHTOA.

In each case, determine the value of x to the nearest whole number.

a)

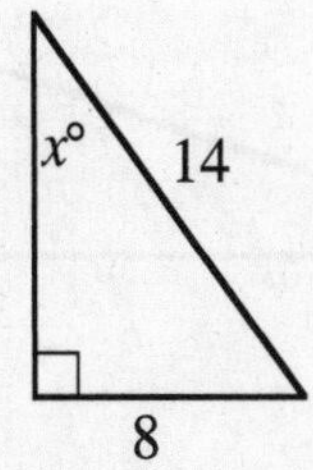

b)

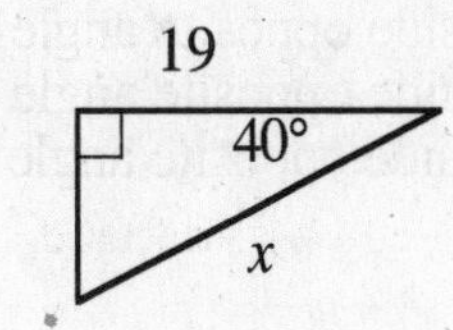

Use SOHCAHTOA to determine the length of BC. Work to three decimal places and answer to two decimal places.

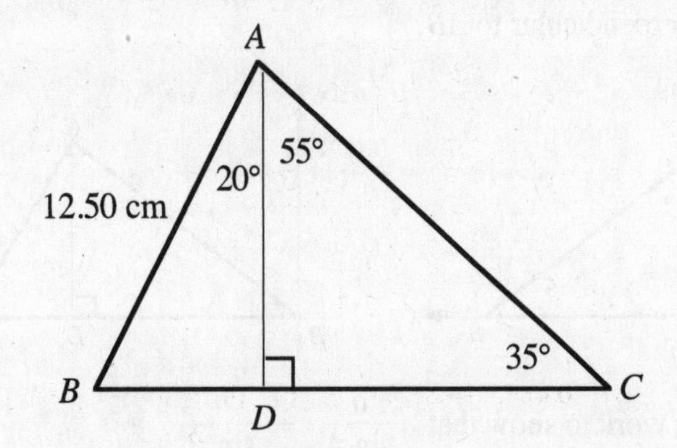

Complete Assignment Questions #1 - #2

Trigonometry in Acute Angled and Obtuse Angled Triangles

In the next three lessons, we focus on solving triangles which are not right angled and in which *SOHCAHTOA* is not valid.

Often, in trigonometry, it is convenient to use the following notation.

In triangle ABC, represent

the length of the side opposite angle A by a,
the length of the side opposite angle B by b,
and the length of the side opposite angle C by c.

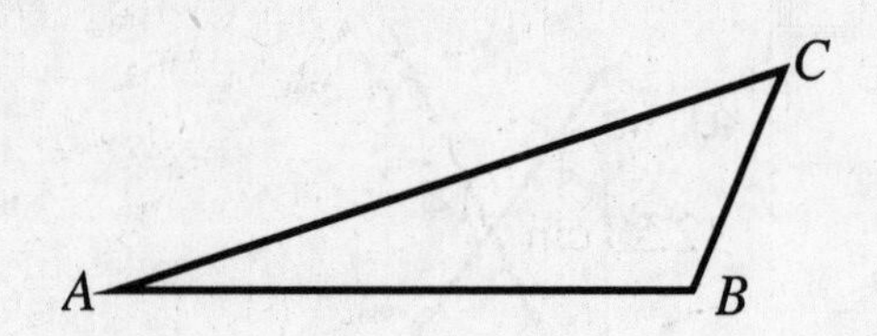

The Sine Law

In every triangle ABC, $\frac{a}{\sin A} = \frac{b}{\sin B} = \frac{c}{\sin C}$ or $\frac{\sin A}{a} = \frac{\sin B}{b} = \frac{\sin C}{c}$

Proof of the Sine Law

The diagrams show the same triangle ABC placed with base AB on the x–axis.
In diagram i) the origin is at A, and in diagram ii) the origin is at B.
The line CD is drawn perpendicular to AB.

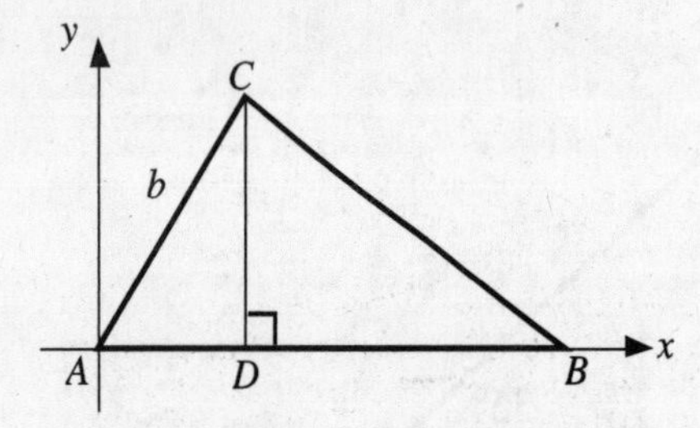

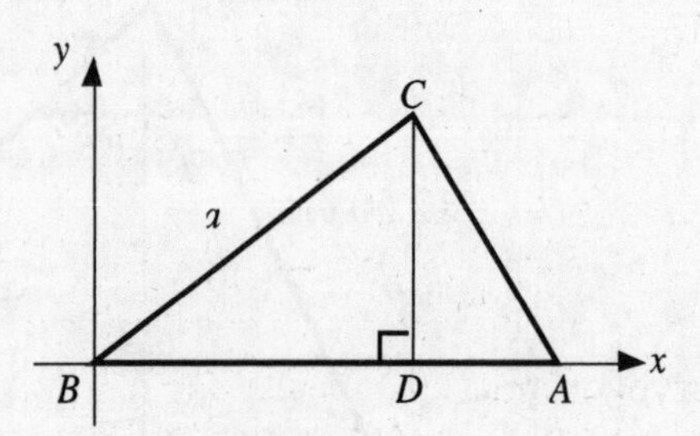

Complete the following work to show that $\frac{a}{\sin A} = \frac{b}{\sin B}$.

In i) $\sin A = \frac{CD}{AC} = \frac{CD}{b}$ In ii) $\sin B =$ $=$

$CD =$ $CD =$

It follows that $b \sin A =$

Dividing both sides by $\sin A \sin B$ gives the result

Repeating the work above with AC placed on the x–axis would give the result $\frac{a}{\sin A} = \frac{c}{\sin C}$.

Hence $\frac{a}{\sin A} = \frac{b}{\sin B} = \frac{c}{\sin C}$ or $\frac{\sin A}{a} = \frac{\sin B}{b} = \frac{\sin C}{c}$.

To use the sine law, we need to know **three** pieces of information. This information must include both numerator and denominator of one of the three fractions, i.e. we need to know an angle and the measure of its opposite side.

Triangle ABC from Class Ex. #2 is shown. Use the sine law to calculate the length of BC, and compare your answer to the SOHCAHTOA method.

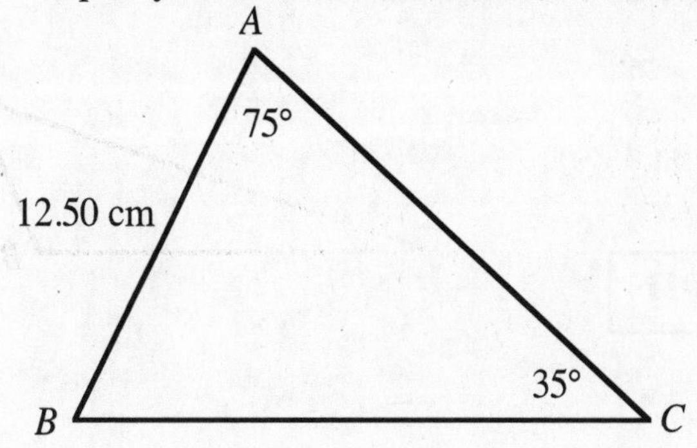

Use the sine law in the triangle shown to determine the measure of $\angle ACB$ to the nearest degree.

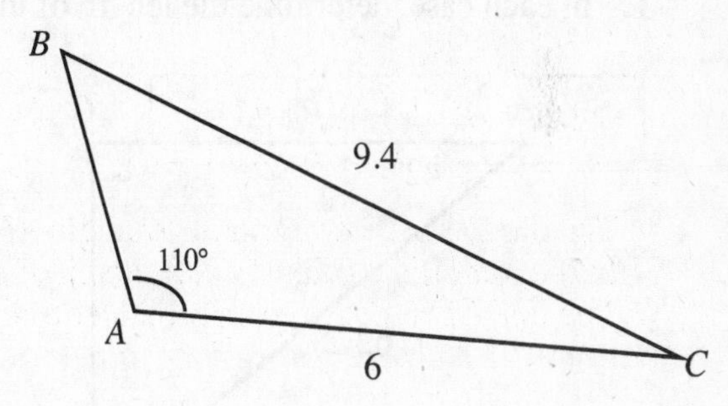

A surveyor measures a base line PQ 440 m long. He takes measurements of a landmark R from P and Q, and finds that $\angle QPR = 46°$ and $\angle PQR = 75°$.

a) Calculate the perimeter of ΔPQR to the nearest metre.

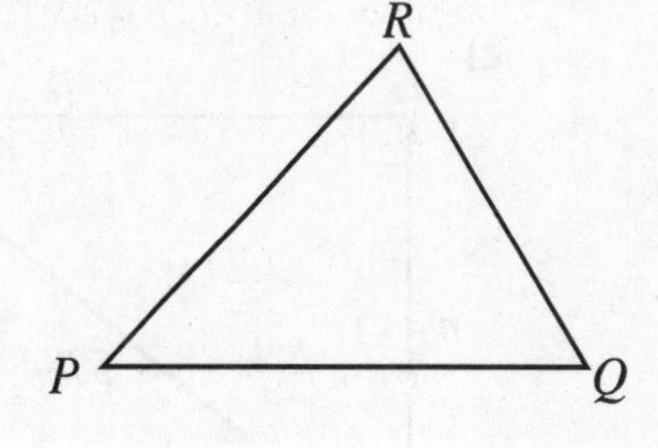

b) Calculate the area of ΔPQR to the nearest hundred square metres.

Complete Assignment Questions #3 - #11

Assignment

1. In each case, determine the length of the indicated side to the nearest tenth.

a)

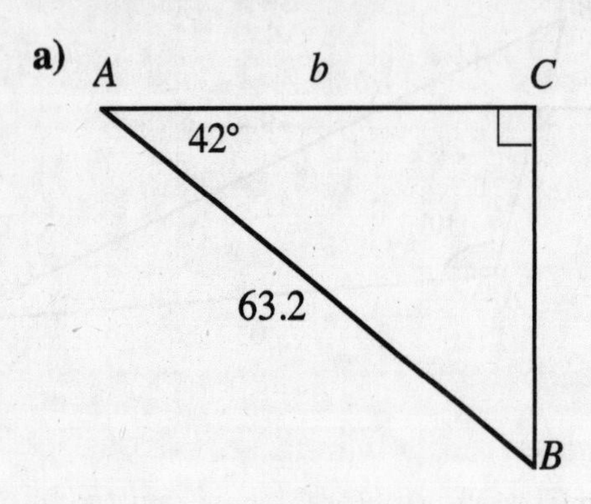

b)

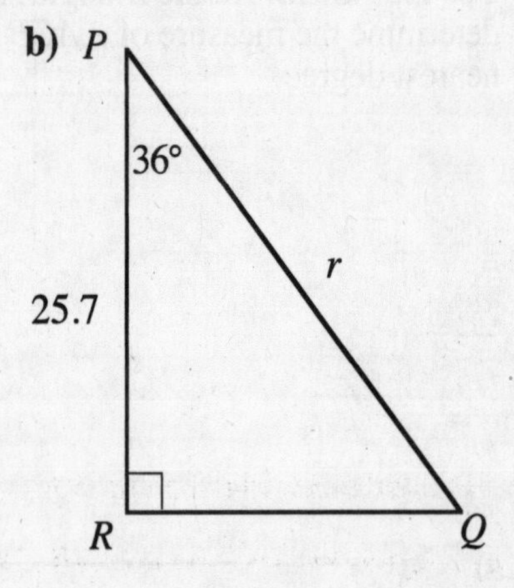

c)

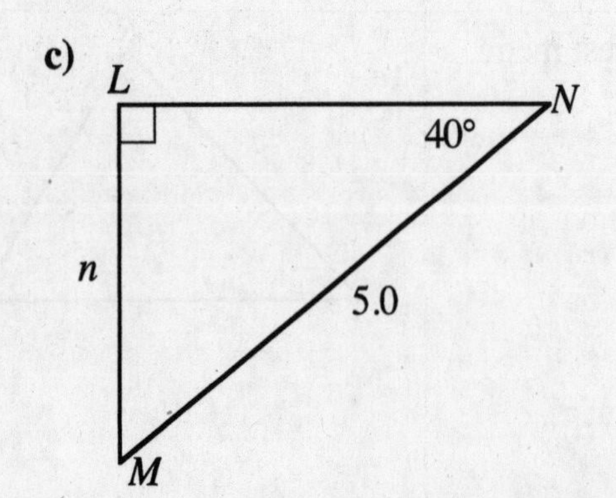

d)

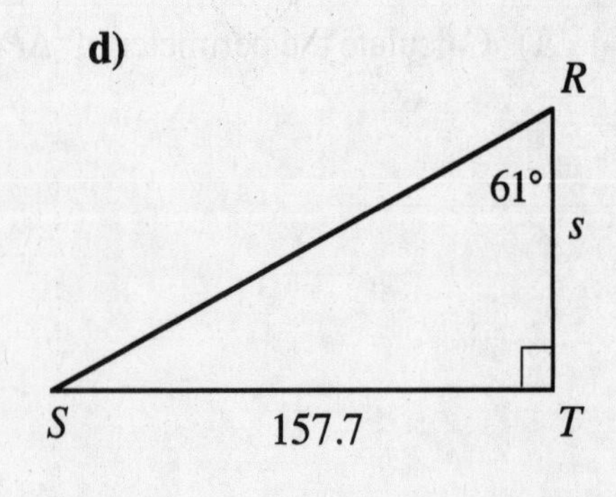

2. In each case, determine the measure of the indicated angle to the nearest degree.

a)

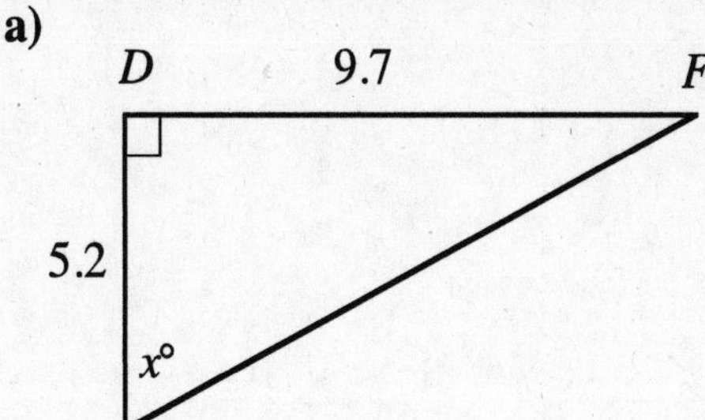

b)

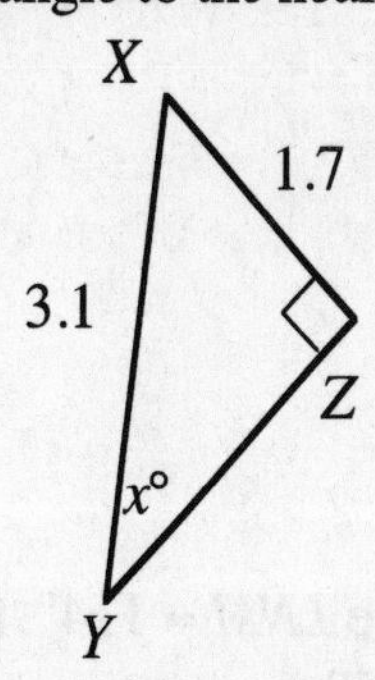

3. In each case, find the length of the indicated side to the nearest tenth.

a)

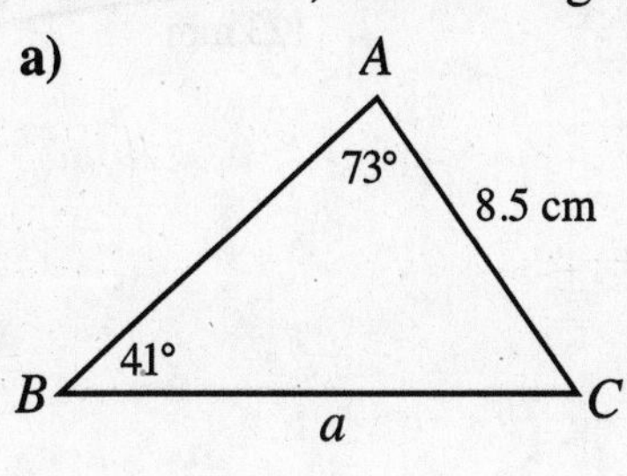

b)

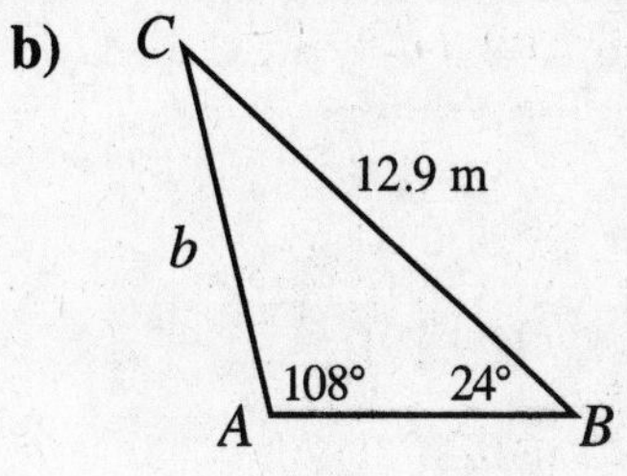

c)

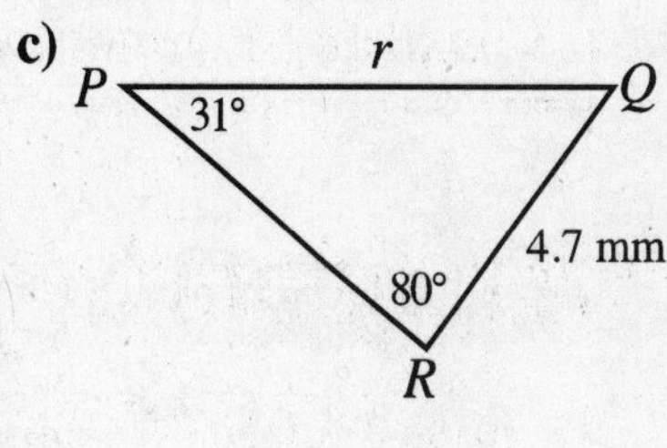

4. In each case, find the measure of the indicated angle to the nearest degree.

a)

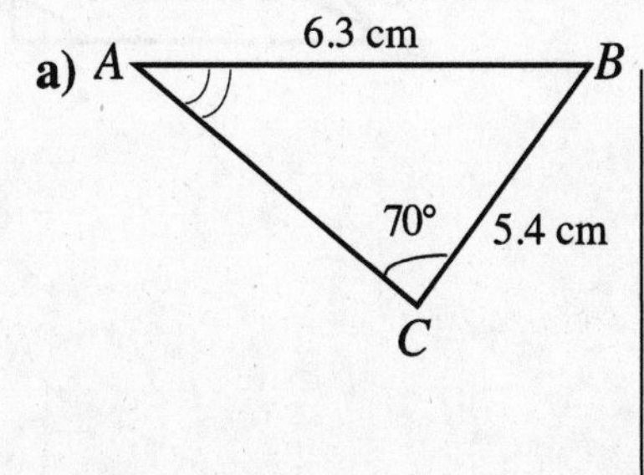

b)

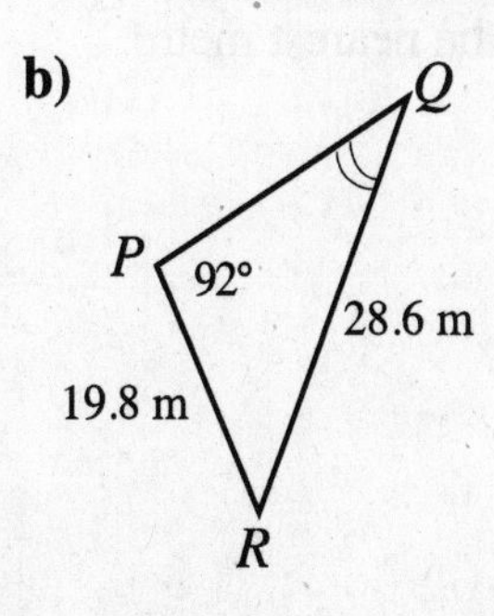

c)

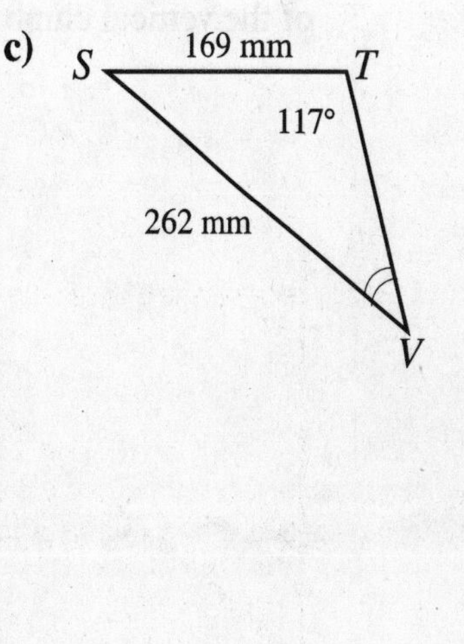

5. In ΔABC, angle $A = 49°$, angle $B = 57°$ and $a = 8$. Calculate b to the nearest tenth.

6. In ΔLMN, angle $LNM = 114°$, $LM = 123$ mm and $MN = 88$ mm.
Calculate $\angle LMN$, to the nearest degree.

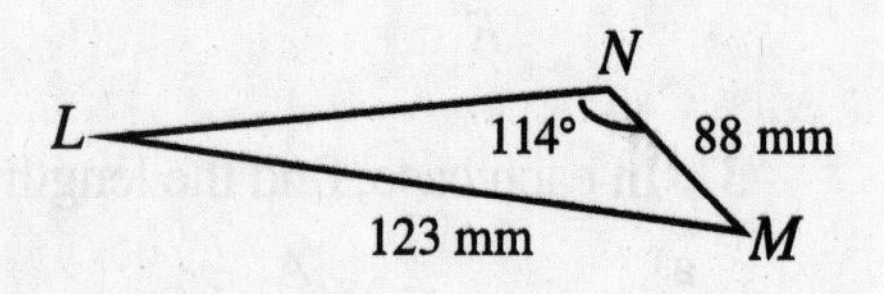

7. P and Q are two bases for a mountain climb. PQ is 600 m and QR is a vertical stretch of a rock face. The angle of elevation of Q from P is 31°, and the angle of elevation of R from P is 41°.

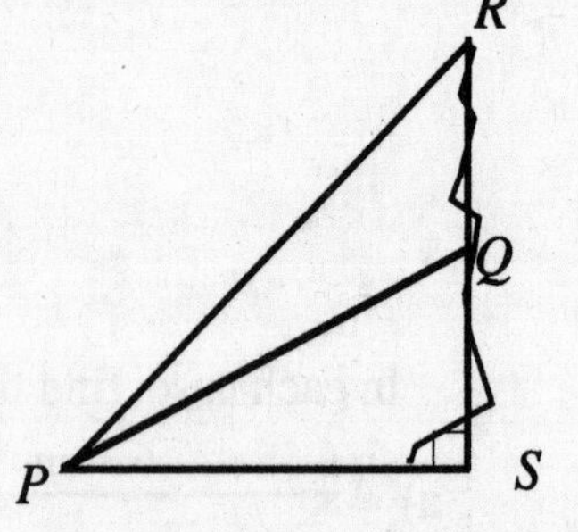

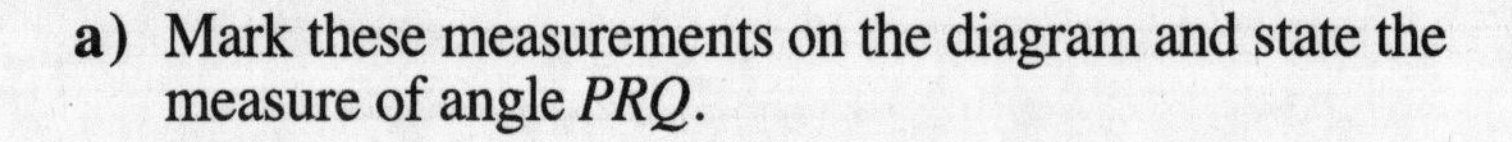

a) Mark these measurements on the diagram and state the measure of angle PRQ.

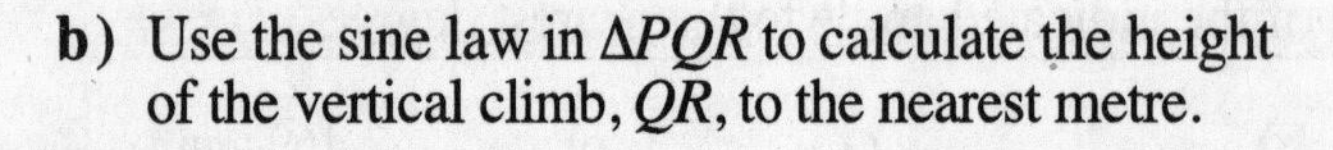

b) Use the sine law in ΔPQR to calculate the height of the vertical climb, QR, to the nearest metre.

8. Three students are trying to determine the area of the triangle in the diagram. Each student is given a different formula with which to determine the area. The area of the triangle is 53.3 m^2.

12 m

46°

65°

Show how each student arrived at this answer.

Student #1: Use the formula $A = \frac{1}{2}bh$, where b is the length of the base and h is the vertical height.

Student #2: Use Heron's formula $A = \sqrt{s(s-a)(s-b)(s-c)}$, where a, b and c are the lengths of the three sides and s is the semi-perimeter of the triangle.

Student #3: Use the formula $A = \frac{1}{2}ab \sin C$, where a and b are the lengths of two sides and angle C is the contained angle between the sides a and b.

Multiple Choice

9. In triangle PQR, angle $P = 20°$, angle $R = 150°$ and $QR = 6$ m. The length of PQ is

A. 4.1 m
B. 8.8 m
C. 15.2 m
D. 17.3 m

10. In ΔABC, $\angle A = 30°$, $BC = 10$ units and $AC = 15$ units. If $\angle B$ is acute-angled, then $\angle C$ is

A. 19.4°
B. 48.6°
C. 101.4°
D. 130.6°

Numerical Response

11. From a point A, level with the foot of a hill, the angle of elevation of the top of the hill is 16°. From a point B, 950 metres nearer the foot of the hill, the angle of elevation of the top is 35°.
The height of the hill, DC, to the nearest metre, is ____.

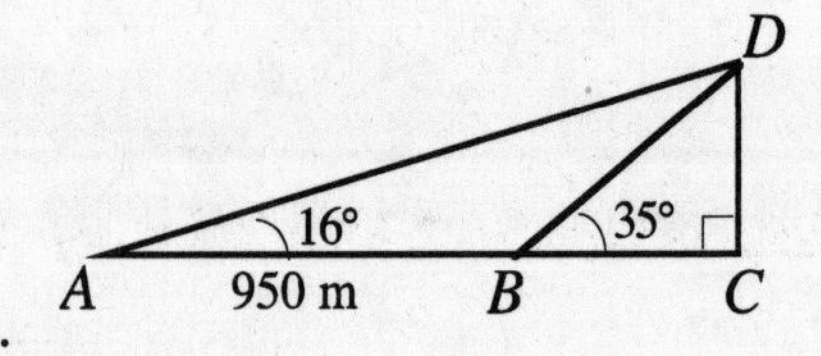

(Record your answer in the numerical response box from left to right.)

Answer Key

1. a) 47.0 **b)** 31.8 **c)** 3.2 **d)** 87.4 **2. a)** 62° **b)** 33°
3. a) 12.4 cm **b)** 5.5 m **c)** 9.0 mm **4. a)** 54° **b)** 44° **c)** 35°
5. 8.9 **6.** 25° **7. a)** 49° **b)** 138 m
9. B **10.** C **11.** | 4 | 6 | 1 | |

Trigonometry Lesson #6: The Cosine Law

Warm-Up

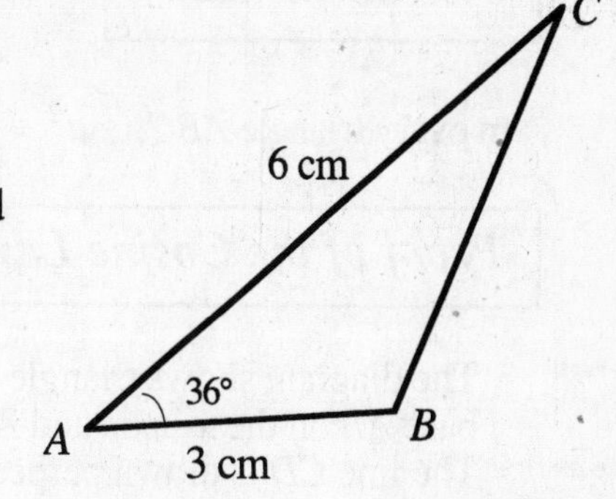

Consider triangle *ABC* in which $\angle A = 36°$, $AB = 3$ cm and $AC = 6$ cm. What happens when you try to apply the sine law to determine the length of *BC*?

In the example above, where we are given the length of two sides and the contained angle, the sine law is **not** applicable.

Use SOHCAHTOA in the diagram below to determine the length of *BC* to the nearest tenth of a cm.

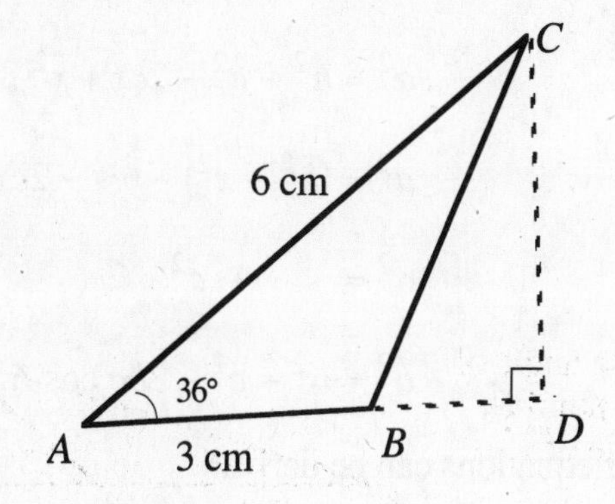

The method above is time consuming.
The length of *BC* can be determined in one step by using the **cosine law**.

The Cosine Law

In every triangle ABC, $a^2 = b^2 + c^2 - 2bc \cos A$.

Proof of the Cosine Law

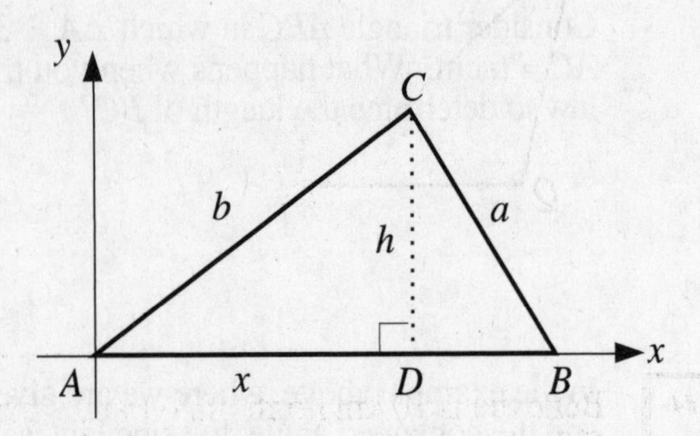

- The diagram shows triangle ABC placed with base AB on the x–axis and A at the origin.
- The line CD is drawn perpendicular to AB and is h units in length.
- $AD = x$ units so $DB = c - x$ units.

Complete the following work to show that $a^2 = b^2 + c^2 - 2bc \cos A$.

In ΔADC $\cos A = \dfrac{AD}{AC} = \dfrac{x}{b}$

so $x =$

In ΔBDC $BC^2 = CD^2 + DB^2$

$a^2 = h^2 + (c - x)^2$

$a^2 = h^2 + c^2 - 2cx + x^2$

$a^2 = (h^2 + x^2) + c^2 - 2cx$

$a^2 = \qquad + c^2 - 2c(\qquad)$

$a^2 = b^2 + c^2 - 2bc \cos A$.

By placing AC and then BC on the x–axis, similar equations can be derived.

$b^2 = c^2 + a^2 - 2ca \cos B$ $\qquad$ $c^2 = a^2 + b^2 - 2ab \cos C$

This version of the cosine law can be used in any triangle if we are given the length of two sides and the contained angle, (SAS).

Consider the ΔABC from Class Ex. #1 in which $\angle A = 36°$, $AB = 3$ cm, and $AC = 6$ cm. Determine the length of BC, to the nearest tenth of a cm, using the cosine law.

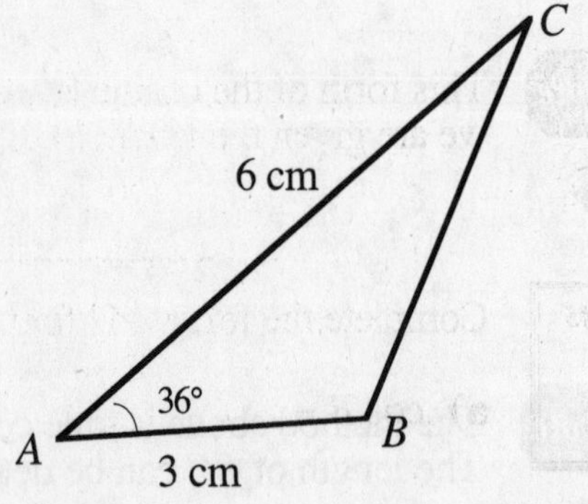

Find the length, to the nearest tenth of a cm, of the third side of ΔPQR if $QP = 1.7$ cm, $QR = 3.1$ cm and $\angle PQR = 110°$.

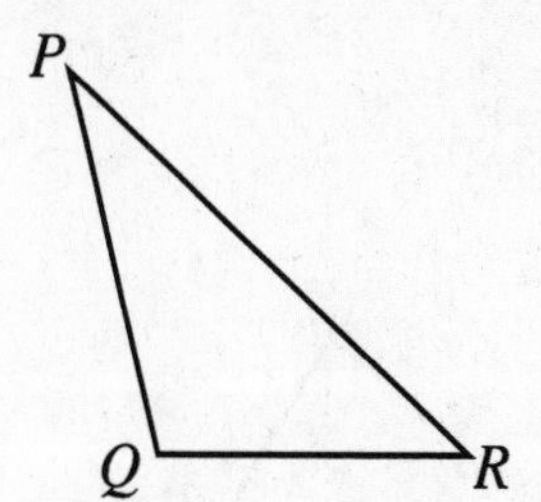

Bellevue is 30 km north of Ayr and Churchville is 18 km northwest of Ayr. Calculate the distance between Bellevue and Churchville to the nearest km.

Complete Assignment Questions #1 - #4

Alternative Form of the Cosine Law

The equation $a^2 = b^2 + c^2 - 2bc \cos A$

can be rearranged to the form $\cos A = \dfrac{b^2 + c^2 - a^2}{2bc}$.

This form of the cosine law can be used to determine any angle in a triangle when we are given the length of all three sides, (SSS)

Complete the following for triangle *ABC*.

a) $\cos B =$

b) $\cos C =$

Determine the largest angle in ΔABC if $a = 14.7$, $b = 8.9$, and $c = 12.6$.

Two ships set sail from port, P, heading in different directions. The first ship sails 7 km to R and the second ship sails 8 km to Q. If the distance between R and Q is 13 km, determine the angle between the directions of the two ships.

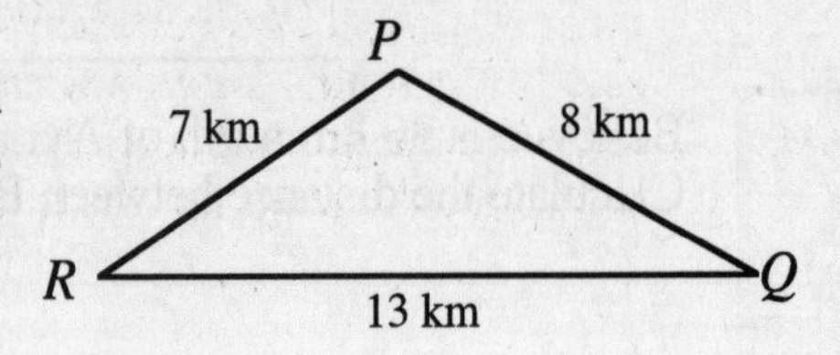

Complete Assignment Questions #5 - #12

Assignment

1. Complete the following for triangle *STV*.

   a) $s^2 =$ **b)** $v^2 =$

2. In each case, find the length of the indicated side to the nearest 0.1 cm.

a)

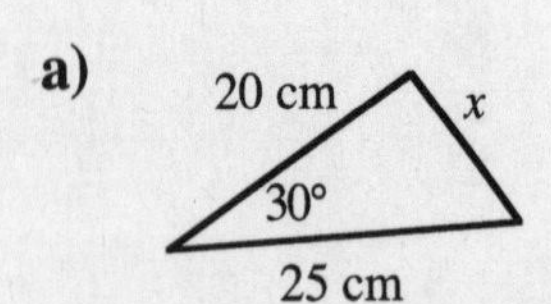

b)

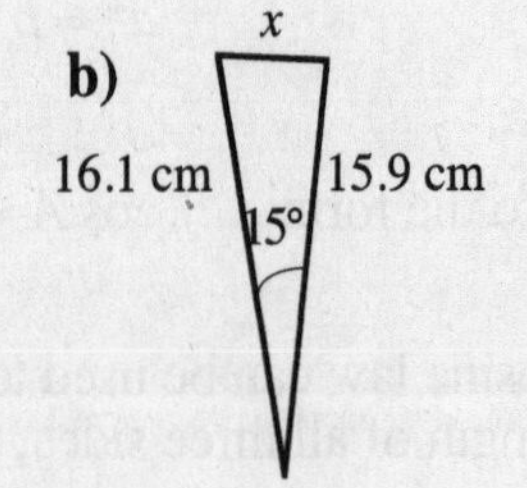

c)

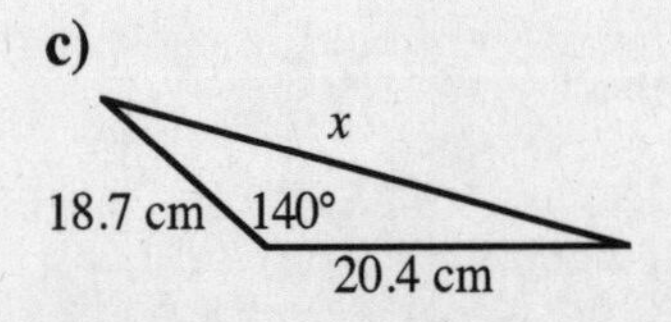

3. In ΔABC, angle $A = 49°$, $b = 24$ and $c = 37$. Calculate a to the nearest whole number.

4. In the diagram, AB represents part of a road constructed on the incline of a hill. BC represents a telephone pole 7.5 m tall at the side of the road. A guide wire attached to the top of the pole is joined to the ground at A. If $AB = 11.4$ m and $\angle ABC = 135°$, determine the length of the guide wire to the nearest 0.1 m.

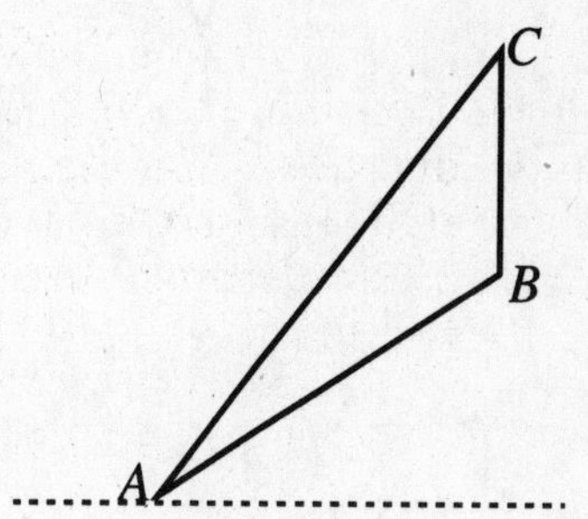

5. Solve triangle ABC in which $AB = 4.5$ cm, $BC = 7.8$ cm and angle $ABC = 79°$. Round sides to the nearest tenth of a cm and angles to the nearest tenth of a degree.

6. Complete the following for triangle DEF.

a) $\cos E =$

b) $\cos F =$

7. In each case, find the measure of the indicated angle to the nearest degree.

a)

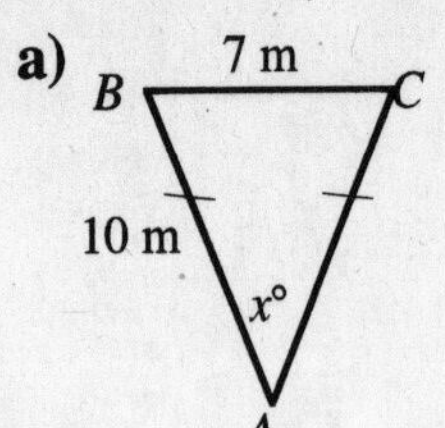

b)

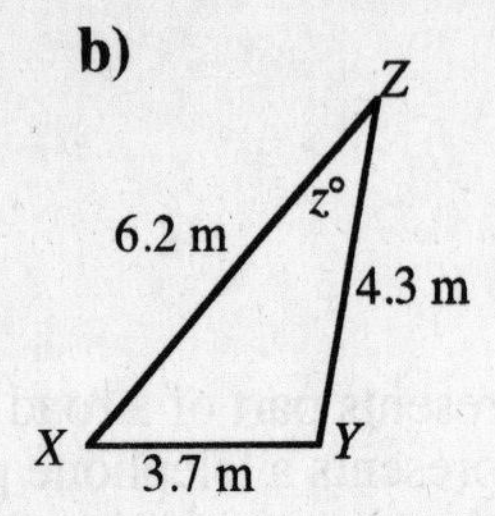

c)

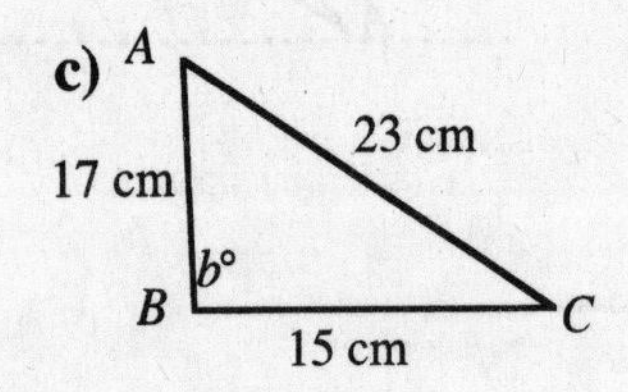

d)

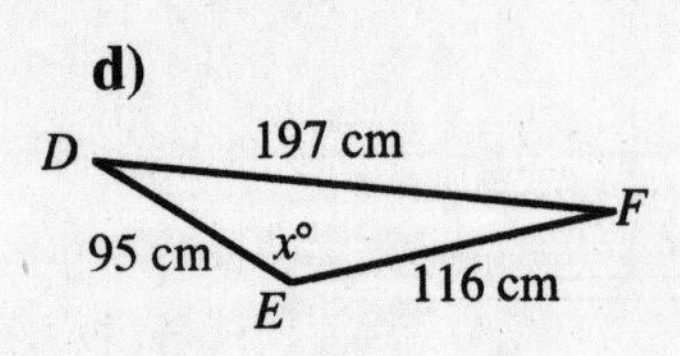

8. Anwar and Ingrid have three trees in their garden. The trees form a triangle as shown in the diagram. Determine the smallest angle between the trees.

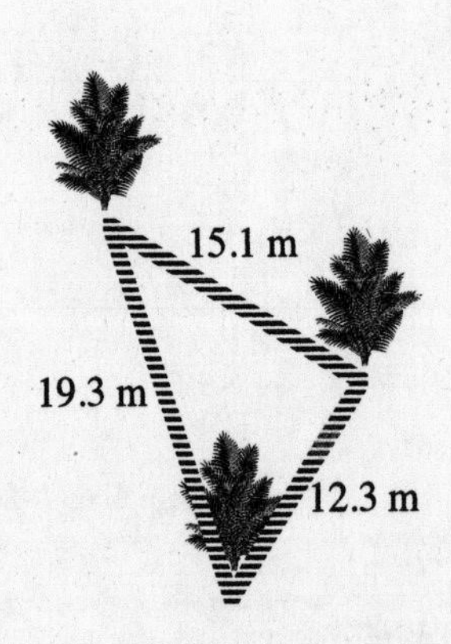

9. The solid in the diagram was formed by removing a corner from a cube of 24 cm. The length of EB is 6 cm.

a) Calculate, to the nearest tenth, the lengths of PE and PR.

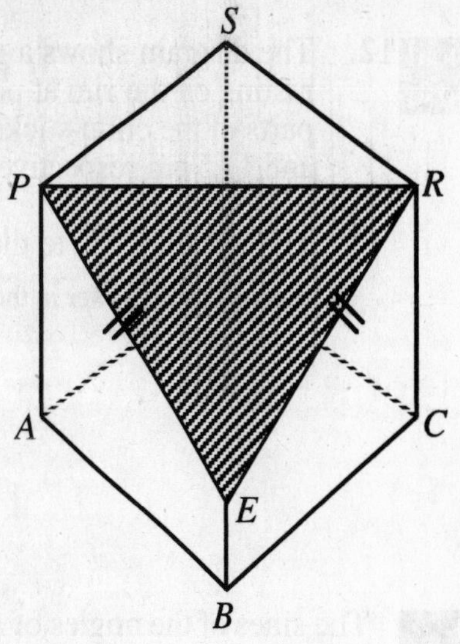

b) Calculate the measure of angle PER to the nearest degree.

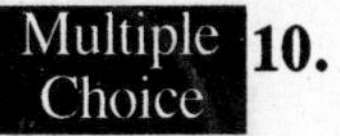

10. The value of x^2 is

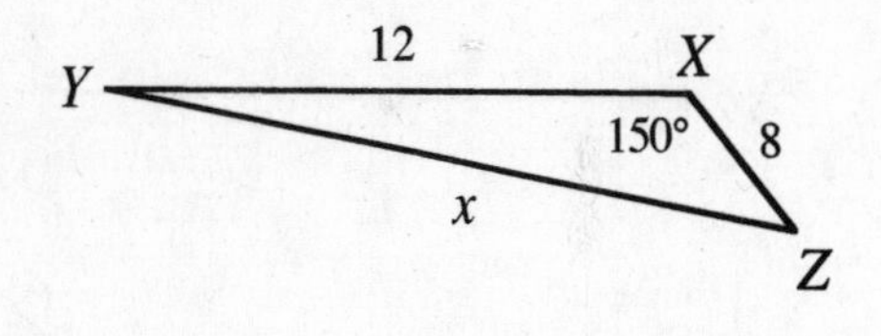

A. 112
B. 304
C. $208 - 96\sqrt{3}$
D. $208 + 96\sqrt{3}$

11. The length of BC in cm is

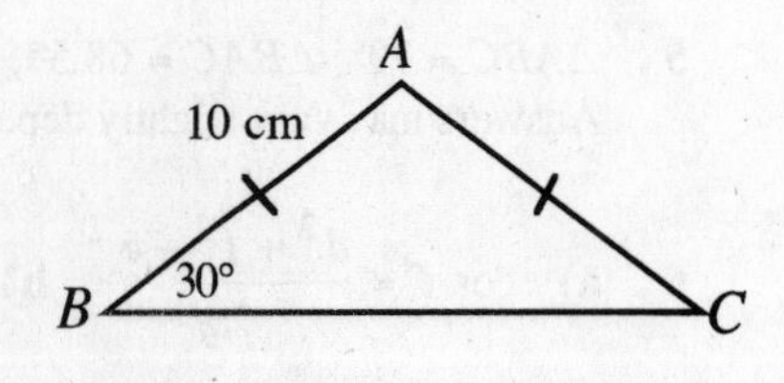

A. $5\sqrt{3}$
B. 10
C. $10\sqrt{3}$
D. 20

Numerical Response

12. The diagram shows a glass bowl with two chop-sticks resting on the rim at points S and T. The lengths of the parts of the chop-sticks inside the bowl are 9 cm and 11.5 cm respectively.

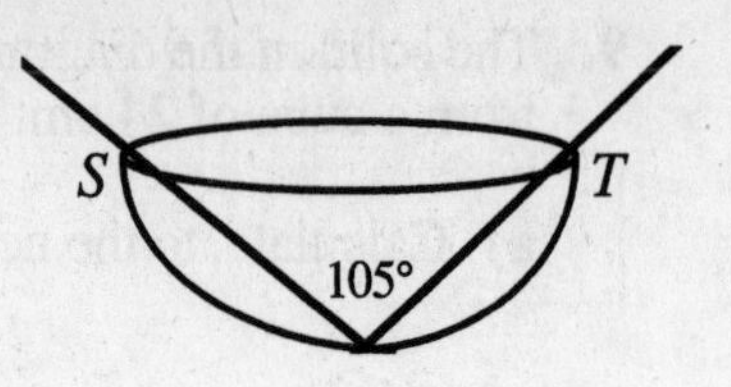

The length of ST, to the nearest tenth of a cm, is _____ .
(Record your answer in the numerical response box from left to right.)

Group Investigation

The sines of the angles of a triangle are in the ratio 2:3:4.
Determine the ratios of the cosines of the angles.

Answer Key

1. a) $s^2 = t^2 + v^2 - 2tv \cos S$ **b)** $v^2 = s^2 + t^2 - 2st \cos V$

2. a) 12.6 cm **b)** 4.2 cm **c)** 36.7 cm **3.** 28 **4.** 17.5

5. $\angle ABC = 79°$, $\angle BAC = 68.5°$, $\angle ACB = 32.5°$, $AC = 8.2$ cm, $BC = 7.8$ cm, $AB = 4.5$ cm.
Answers may vary slightly depending on method.

6. a) $\cos E = \dfrac{d^2 + f^2 - e^2}{2df}$ **b)** $\cos F = \dfrac{d^2 + e^2 - f^2}{2de}$

7. a) 41° **b)** 36° **c)** 92° **d)** 138° **8.** 40°

9. a) $PE = 30.0$ cm, $PR = 33.9$ cm **b)** 69°

10. D **11.** C **12.**

1	6	.	3

Group Investigation 14:11:–4

Trigonometry Lesson #7:
Problem Solving and The Ambiguous Case of the Sine Law

Warm-Up

Students were asked to determine the measure of angle ACB in a triangle in which $AB = 6$ cm, $AC = 4$ cm and $\angle ABC = 30°$.

Two students, Scott and Brittany, each constructed a triangle to represent the given information.

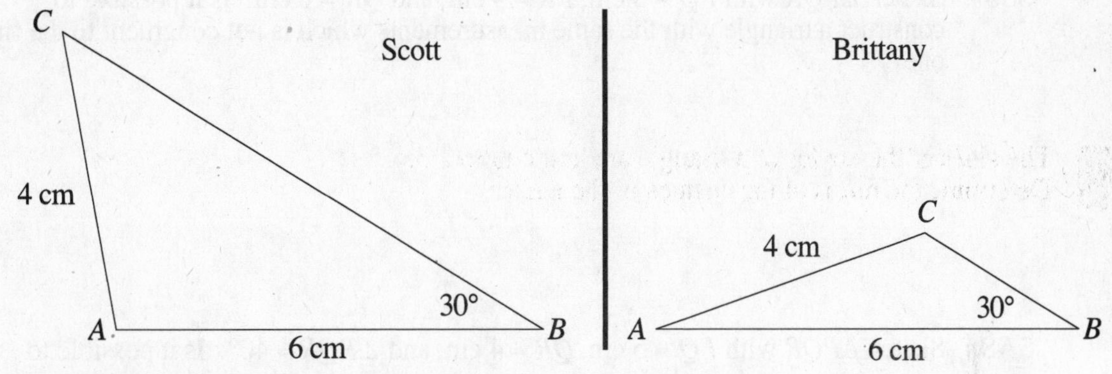

a) Use a ruler and protractor to determine if the student's triangle correctly represents the given information.

b) Without using a measuring device, estimate, to the nearest 10°, the measure of angle ACB in each case.

c) In each case, use the sine law to determine the measure of angle ACB to the nearest degree.

In this particular example, the information given allowed us to draw two different triangles which produced two different answers to the same question. This is called **the ambiguous case of the sine law**.

But how do we know if given information will produce a unique solution or two different solutions? The investigations that follow will help us determine the answer to this question.

Constructing Triangles

Triangles can be constructed given three measurements, one of which must be the length of a side. The following explorations can be completed using a compass and protractor set or software such as *Geometer's Sketchpad*.

Investigation #1 *Constructing Congruent Triangles*

SSS - Sketch ΔPQR with $PQ = 3$ cm, $PR = 4$ cm, and $QR = 6$ cm. Is it possible to construct a triangle with the same measurements which is not congruent to the first one?

SAS - Sketch ΔPQR with $PQ = 5$ cm, $QR = 4$ cm, and $\angle PQR = 40°$. Is it possible to construct a triangle with the same measurements and angle which is not congruent to the first one?

ASA - Sketch ΔPQR with $PQ = 3$ cm, $\angle PQR = 40°$ and $\angle QPR = 30°$. Is it possible to construct a triangle with the same measurements and two angles which is not congruent to the first one?

SSA - Sketch ΔPQR with $PQ = 6$ cm, $PR = 4$ cm, and $\angle PQR = 40°$. Is it possible to construct a triangle with the same measurements and angle which is not congruent to the first one?

In Investigation #1, we found that in the case of SSS, SAS, and ASA, only **one** triangle can be drawn. However, in the case of SSA (when two sides and an angle are given), we found that we can draw two different triangles. Note that the angle cannot be the contained angle.

Given SSA in a triangle, there are actually three possible situations.

Investigation #2 *Constructing Triangles using SSA*

The diagrams below will be used to construct ΔABC in which $AB = 6$ cm and $\angle ABC = 30°$. The point C will lie somewhere on line segment AD.

Case 1 *Two Possible Triangles*

- Set the compass to 3.5 cm.
- Place the pointer at A and draw an arc of a circle to intersect BD.
- How many possible positions are there for the point C?

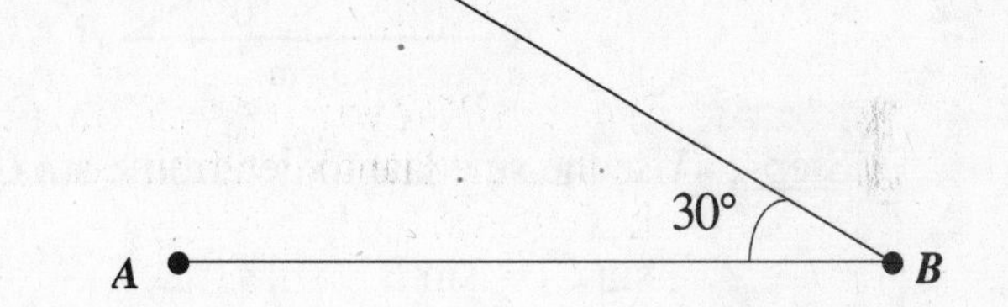

Case 2 *One Unique Triangle*

- Repeat the instructions in Case 1 with the compass set to 3 cm.
- How many possible positions are there for the point C?

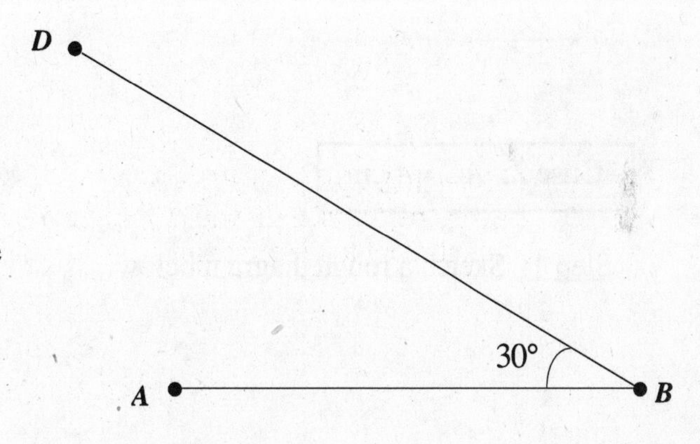

Case 3 *No Possible Triangle*

- Repeat the instructions in Case 1 with the compass set to 2 cm.
- How many possible positions are there for the point C?

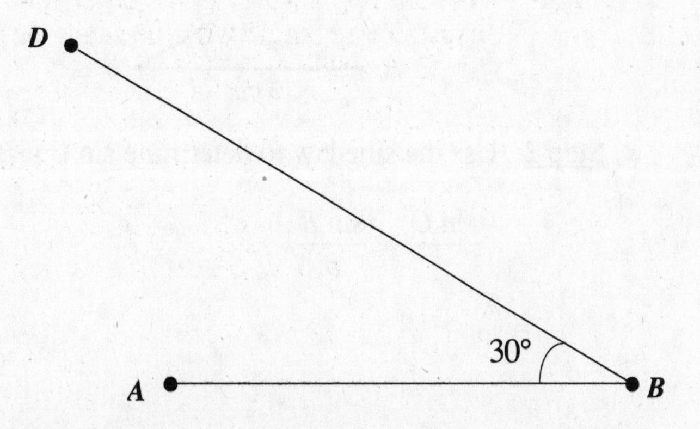

Investigating the Ambiguous Case of the Sine Law

In the previous investigations, we discovered that in the case of SSS, SAS, and ASA only one solution was possible. But in the case of SSA, zero, one, or two solutions are possible. We shall investigate the SSA scenario in this investigation.

Consider ΔABC in which $AB = 6$ cm and $\angle ABC = 30°$. We are going to consider three different measurements for AC and use the sine law to determine the measure of $\angle BAC$.

Case 1: $AC = 2.5$ cm

Step 1: Sketch a rough diagram below.

A 30° B
3 cm

Step 2: Use the sine law to determine sin C.

$$\frac{\sin C}{c} = \frac{\sin B}{b}$$

Step 3: Solve $\sin C = 0.6$.

Reference angle = 37°

$\angle C = 37°$ or $\angle C =$ ___

$\angle ACB = 37°$ or $\angle ACB =$ ____

Step 4: Determine the measure of $\angle BAC$.

Step 5: State the solution to the problem.

Case 2: $AC = 4$ cm

Step 1: Sketch a rough diagram below.

A 30° B
3 cm

Step 2: Use the sine law to determine sin C.

$$\frac{\sin C}{c} = \frac{\sin B}{b}$$

Step 3: Solve $\sin C =$

Reference angle = ____

$\angle C =$ ____

$\angle ACB =$ ____

Step 4: Determine the measure of $\angle BAC$.

Step 5: State the solution to the problem.

Case 3: $AC = 1$ cm

<u>Step 1</u>: Sketch a rough diagram below.

A ——— B, $30°$, 3 cm

<u>Step 2</u>: Use the sine law to determine sin C.

$$\frac{\sin C}{c} = \frac{\sin B}{b}$$

<u>Step 3</u>: Solve sin C =

<u>Step 4</u>: State the solution to the problem.

Conditions for the Ambigous Case of the Sine Law

The determining factor depends on how the reference angle compares to the given angle. Complete the following statements.

i) If the reference angle is greater than the given angle, there will be _____ solution(s).

ii) If the reference angle is less than the given angle, there will be _____ solution(s).

iii) If the reference angle does not exist, there will be _____ solution(s).

The case for two solutions can also be determined by looking at the two given sides.

Since $\frac{\sin C}{c} = \frac{\sin B}{b}$, then $\frac{b}{c} = \frac{\sin B}{\sin C}$.

In the case of b) above, where the reference angle C is less than the given angle B, the ratio $\frac{\sin B}{\sin C} > 1$, hence $\frac{b}{c} > 1$ and $b > c$.

This shows that:

- If the side opposite the given angle is greater than the side opposite the required angle, there is only one solution to the problem.
- If the side opposite the given angle is less than the side opposite the required angle, there are either two solutions or no solutions (depending on the height of the triangle).

Without using the sine law, determine in which of the following cases there is **exactly one** solution to the problem, i.e. there is only one triangle which can be constructed from the given information.

a) Calculate $\angle C$ in ΔABC where $\angle B = 56°$, $c = 10$ cm, and $b = 12$ cm

b) Calculate $\angle PQR$ in ΔPQR where $\angle QPR = 41°$, $RQ = 3$ cm, and $PR = 4.2$ cm

Find all possible measures of $\angle C$ in the following triangles.

a) ΔABC where $\angle A = 50°$, $a = 7.5$ cm and $c = 9.5$ cm

b) ΔABC where $\angle A = 50°$, $a = 9.5$ cm and $c = 7.5$ cm

Complete Assignment Questions #1 - #6

Assignment

1. Explain what is meant by the ambiguous case of the sine law. Describe situations in which a sine law problem may have no solution, one solution or two solutions.

2. In each case, draw a rough sketch of the triangle. **Without** using the sine law, determine in which of the following there is **exactly one** solution to the problem, i.e. there is only one triangle which can be constructed from the given information.

a) Calculate $\angle C$ in ΔABC where $\angle B = 29°$, $c = 8.2$ cm, and $b = 6.7$ cm

b) Calculate $\angle TSV$ in ΔSTV where $ST = 18$ in, $TV = 14$ in, and $\angle SVT = 36°$

c) Calculate $\angle ABC$ in ΔABC where $\angle ACB = 51°$, $AB = 3.9$ mm, and $AC = 4.9$ mm

d) Calculate $\angle PQR$ in ΔPQR where $\angle QPR = 48°$, $PQ = 4.9$ m, and $PR = 6.3$ m

3. Find all possible measures of $\angle C$ in the following triangles.

a) ΔABC where $\angle A = 31°$, $a = 4.5$ cm and $c = 4.9$ cm

b) ΔABC where $\angle A = 61°$, $a = 7.5$ cm and $c = 5.8$ cm

4. In ΔLMN, angle $LMN = 42°$, $LN = 32$ mm and $LM = 42$ mm. Calculate all possible measures of angle MLN to the nearest degree.

5. In each case, determine all possible measures of the indicated angle.

a) ΔDNA where $\angle N = 35°$, $d = 4.1$ cm and $n = 2.1$ cm
Determine $\angle D$.

b) ΔEFG where $\angle GEF = 53°$, $EF = 7.2$ cm and $GF = 6.5$ cm
Determine $\angle GFE$.

6. In triangle PQR, angle $P = 30°$, $QR = 5$ cm, and $PR = 7.5$ cm.
The measure of angle PQR is

A. 19.4°
B. 19.4° or 161.6°
C. 48.6°
D. 48.6° or 131.4°

Answer Key

2. There is exactly one solution in b, d (d is SAS and uses the cosine law to determine exactly one solution).

3. a) 34° or 146° **b)** 43° **4.** 19° or 77°

5. a) no solution **b)** 9° or 65° **6.** D

Trigonometry Lesson #8:
Further Applications
Involving the Sine Law and the Cosine Law

Problems in Trigonometry can be solved using *SOHCAHTOA*, the Sine Law, the Cosine Law or a combination of these. Use the following to determine which method is appropriate.

1. In a right triangle use *SOHCAHTOA*.

2. In a non-right triangle use:

i) the Cosine Law if you are given; • all three sides (SSS)

or

• two sides and the contained angle (SAS)

ii) the Sine Law in all other cases.

There are many practical examples in which students have to choose the appropriate method for solution. We introduce the applications of trigonometry in circles and the concept of bearings since they provide further applications of the sine and the cosine law. The assignment questions include questions on circles, bearings, and questions on other topics.

Trigonometry and Circles

Complete the following circle properties from earlier math courses. The diagrams below are provided as an aid.

a) The perpendicular from the centre of a circle to a chord ____________ the chord.

b) The measure of the central angle is equal to ___________ the measure of the inscribed angle subtended by the same arc.

c) The inscribed angles subtended by the same arc are _______________ .

d) A tangent to a circle is ____________________ to the radius at the point of tangency.

a)

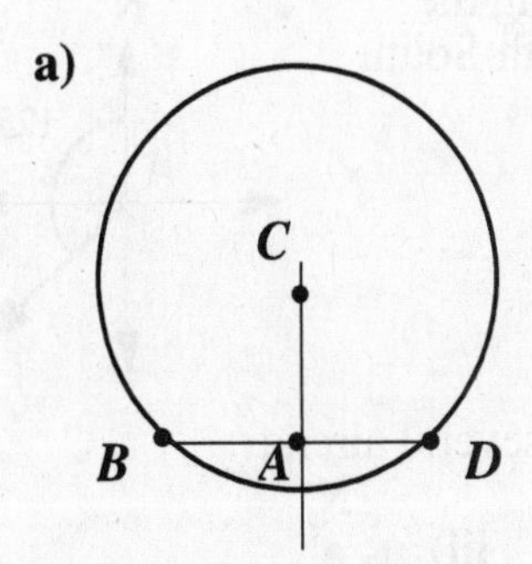

b), c)

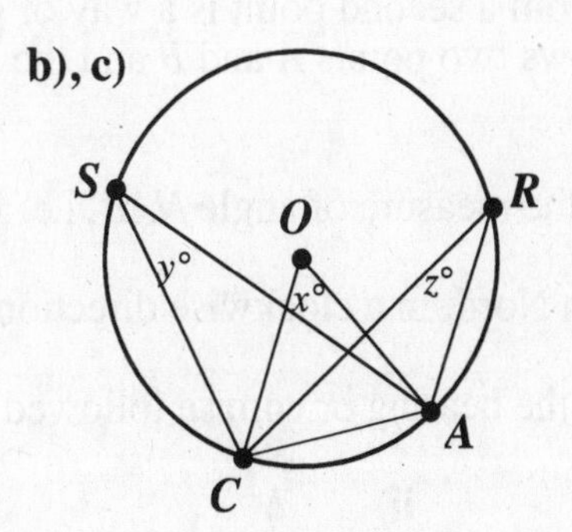

d)

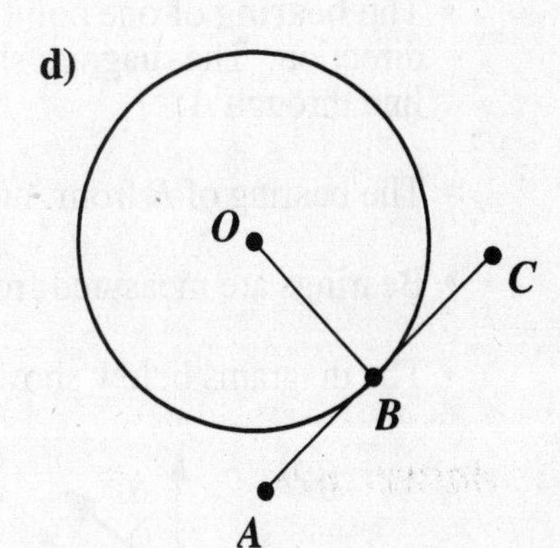

In the diagram, O is the centre of a circle of radius 3.25 cm. $QR = 2.5$ cm and $RS = 4.7$ cm. Calculate to the nearest whole number:

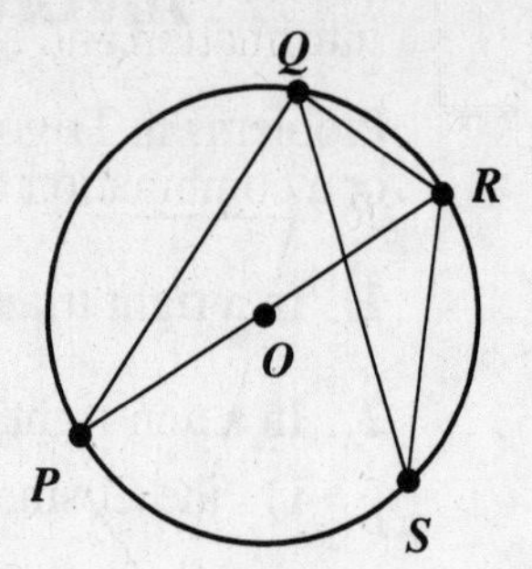

a) the length of PQ

b) the measure of $\angle QPR$

c) the measure of $\angle SQR$.

Complete Assignment Questions #1 - #5

Bearings

- The **bearing** of one point from a second point is a way of giving the direction. The diagram shows two points A and B and the North-South line through A.

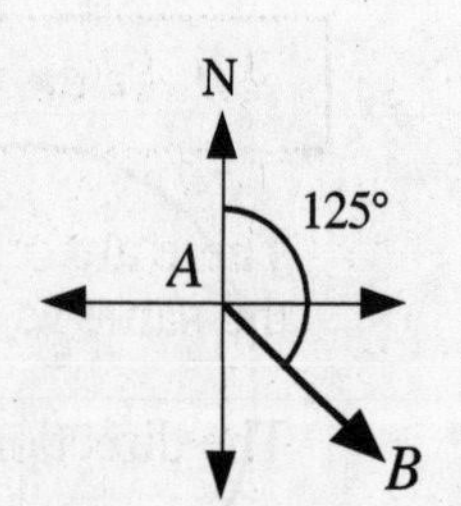

- The bearing of B from A is the measure of angle NAB, i.e. 125°.
- Bearings are measured from North in a clockwise direction.
- The diagrams below shows the bearing or **course** followed by several aircraft.

i)

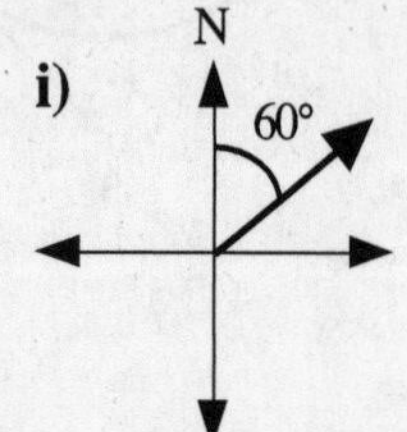

ii)

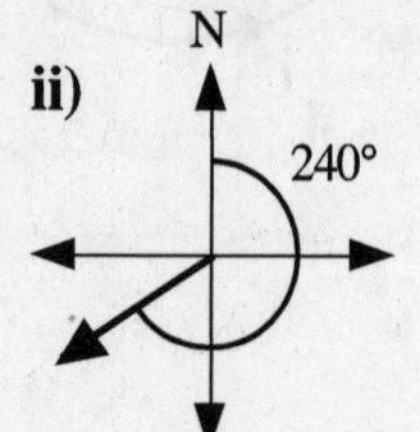

iii)

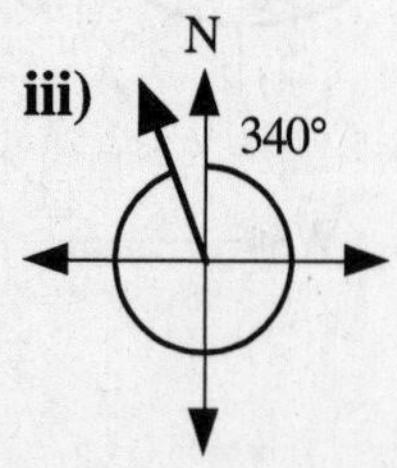

A liner leaves a port P and sails 15 km on a course of 37° to a position Q where it changes course to 270° and sails 12 km to a position R. Complete the sketch to illustrate this information and calculate the distance and course the liner must sail to return from R to P.

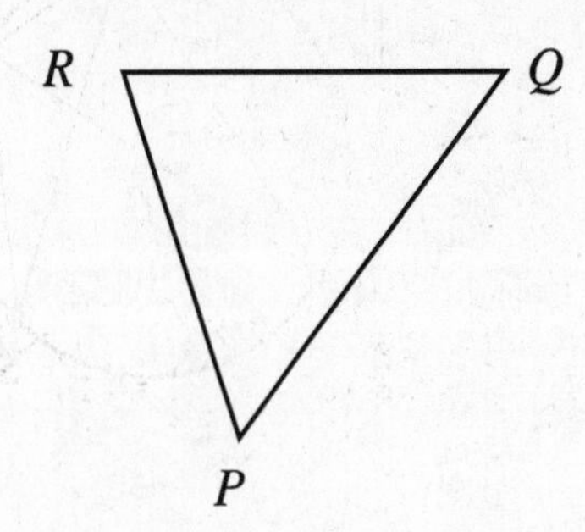

Two aircraft, A and B, leave an airport at the same time. A flies on a course of 90° at 700 km/h, and B flies on a course of 290° at 600 km/h. Calculate their distance apart after 12 minutes to the nearest kilometre.

An Alternative Way of Describing a Direction

There are other ways of describing a course. A bearing of 125° is the same as 55° E of S (read as "55° East of South").

The direction can also be given as S 55° E.

N
W E
55°
S S 55° E

The diagrams below show the course followed by the aircraft on the previous page.

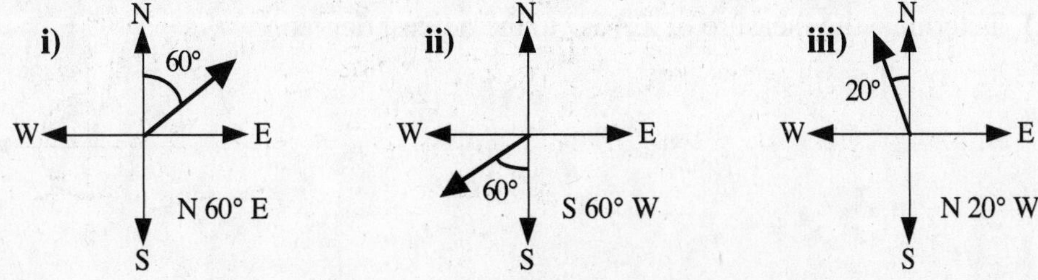

A ship observes a lighthouse in a direction 50° W of N. After sailing 36 km in a direction 35° W of S the lighthouse is observed in a direction 15° E of N.

a) Draw a sketch showing the information given.

b) Calculate the distance of the ship from the lighthouse when the second observation is made.

Complete Assignment Questions #6 - #16

Assignment

1. In the diagram, chord $PQ = 13.6$ cm, and radius $CP = 10.5$ cm. Determine the measure of angle PRQ, to the nearest degree.

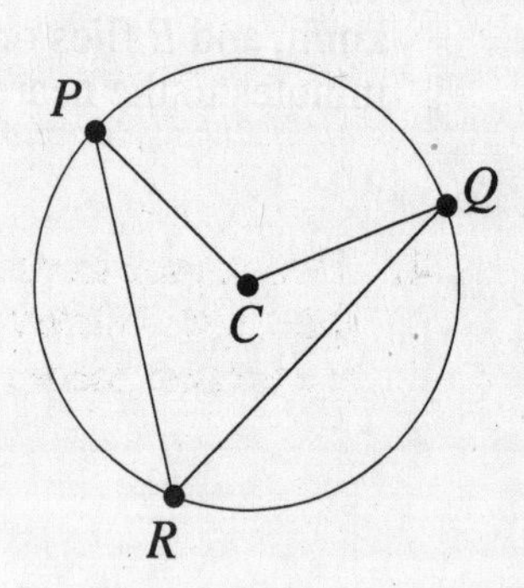

2. In the diagram, the chords AB and CD intersect at E. $EB = 12$ cm, $EA = 16$ cm, $ED = 8$ cm, and $\angle BED = 120°$.

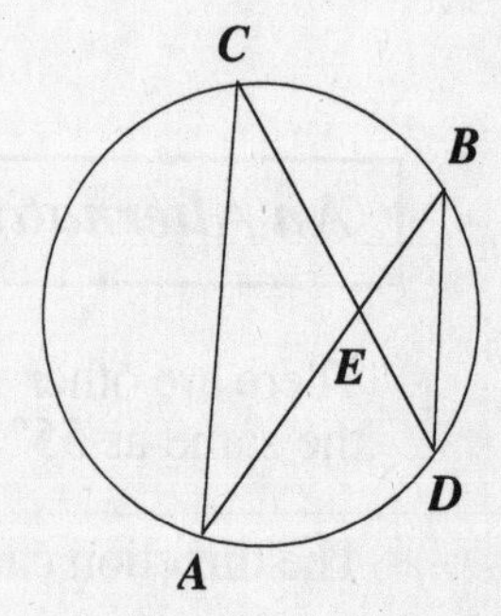

a) Calculate the length of BD to two decimal places.

b) Determine the measure of $\angle ACD$ to the nearest degree.

3. In the diagram, DA and DC are tangents to the circle with centre O. Angle $ABC = 65°$ and $AC = 4.5$ inches.

a) Explain why angle $ADC = 50°$.

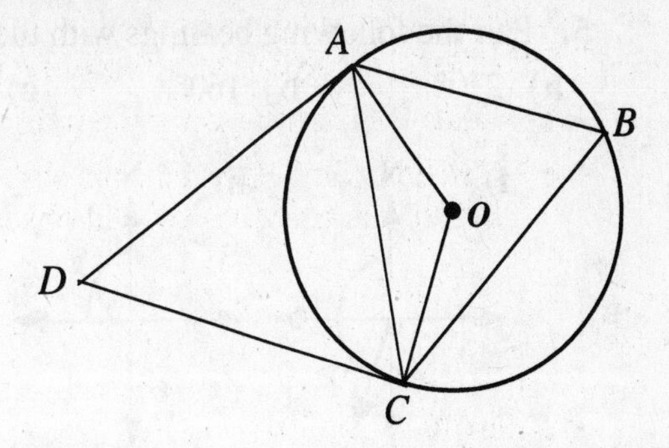

b) Determine the length of CD to the nearest tenth of an inch.

4. Two spruce trees are 100m apart. From the point on the ground halfway between the trees the angles of elevation to the tops of the trees are 21° and 39°. Determine the distance, to the nearest metre, between the tops of the two trees.

5. Pair the following bearings with the correct diagram.

a) 270° **b)** 160° **c)** 285° **d)** 90° **e)** 200°

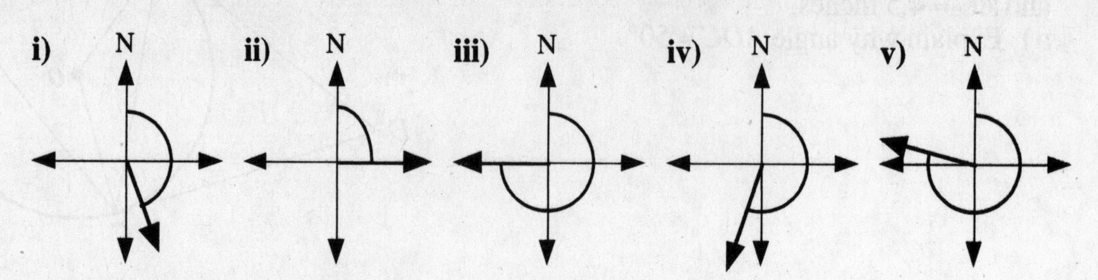

6. A ship is steaming at 16 km/h on a course of 78°, illustrated by the dotted line in the diagram. *L* represents the position of a lighthouse. At 0800 hours the ship is at *P*, which is on a bearing of 314° from *L*, and one hour later it is at *Q*, which is due north of *L*.

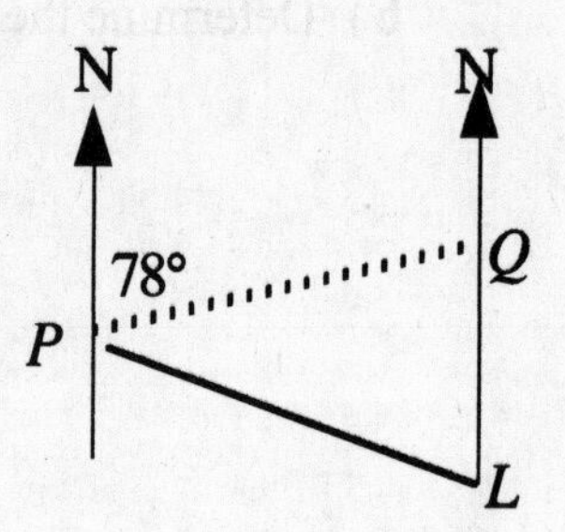

a) Determine the measures of angles *PLQ* and *LPQ*.

b) Calculate the distance *PL*, to the nearest kilometre.

c) At what time, to the nearest minute, is the ship nearest to the lighthouse?

7. At 12 noon a ship observes a lighthouse at a distance of 15 km in a direction of N50°E. It sails at 15 km/h in a direction S35°W. Find the distance and direction of the lighthouse from the ship at 3 pm. Answer to the nearest whole number.

Multiple Choice

In questions 8 -10 you are to decide which is the most appropriate method for solving the problem.

8. Yachts in a race have to sail a triangular course. First they sail in a direction of S45°E for 8 km. They change direction and sail on a course of N45°E. The last part of the course is to return to the start by sailing due West. How far was the second part of the course? The most appropriate method for solving this problem is

A. *SOHCAHTOA*

B. the Sine Law

C. the Cosine Law

D. the problem cannot be solved without further information.

9. In ΔABC, $BA = 9$ cm, $AC = 13$ cm and $\angle ABC = 113°$. Calculate the measure of $\angle BCA$. The most appropriate method for solving this problem is

A. *SOHCAHTOA*

B. the Sine Law

C. the Cosine Law

D. the problem cannot be solved without further information.

10. A pilot leaves base flying on a bearing of 340°. After 30 minutes he changes course to 108° and flies in this direction until he is due north of base. How far does he have to fly South to return to base? The most appropriate method for solving this problem is

A. *SOHCAHTOA*

B. the Sine Law

C. the Cosine Law

D. the problem cannot be solved without further information.

Numerical Response

11. Two aircraft X and Y leave an airport at the same time. X flies on a course of 70° at 720 km/h, and Y flies on a course of 350° at 600 km/h.
To the nearest kilometre, the distance between the aircraft after 5 minutes is _____.

(Record your answer in the numerical response box from left to right.)

Use the following information to answer questions #12 and #13.

In triangle ABC, angle $BAC = 60°$, $AB = 6$ cm, and $AC = 8$ cm.

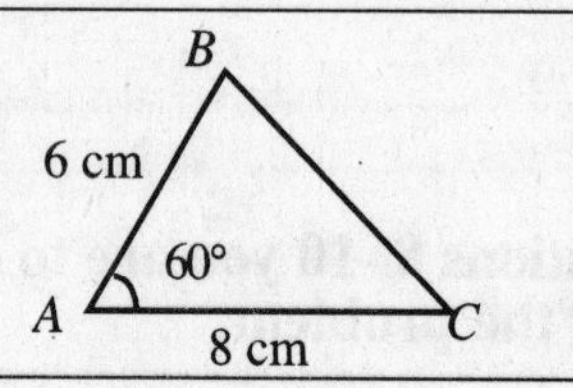

12. The length of BC, to the nearest tenth of a cm, is _____.
(Record your answer in the numerical response box from left to right.)

13. The ratio $\dfrac{\sin C}{\sin B}$, to the nearest hundredth, is _____.
(Record your answer in the numerical response box from left to right.)

Use the following information to answer questions #14 - #16.

The minute hand of a clock is 12 cm long and the hour hand is 10 cm long.

14. To the nearest degree, the angle between these hands at 5 o'clock is ____ .

(Record your answer in the numerical response box from left to right.)

15. To the nearest degree, the angle between these hands at 7:30 pm is _____ .

(Record your answer in the numerical response box from left to right.)

16. To the nearest 0.1 cm, the distance between the tips of the hands at 9:30 pm is _____ .

(Record your answer in the numerical response box from left to right.)

Billiards is a game like pool or snooker which is played by two players on a rectangular table 3.66 metres long by 1.86 metres wide. Three balls are used - white, spot white and red. The object of the game is to score points by pocketing balls (called hazards) or by hitting both other balls (called cannons).

In the diagram Bob propels his white ball on to the red ball which goes in to the corner pocket (scoring 3 points). The white ball deflects off the red ball on to the left cushion, rebounds, and strikes his opponent's spot white (scoring a further 2 points).

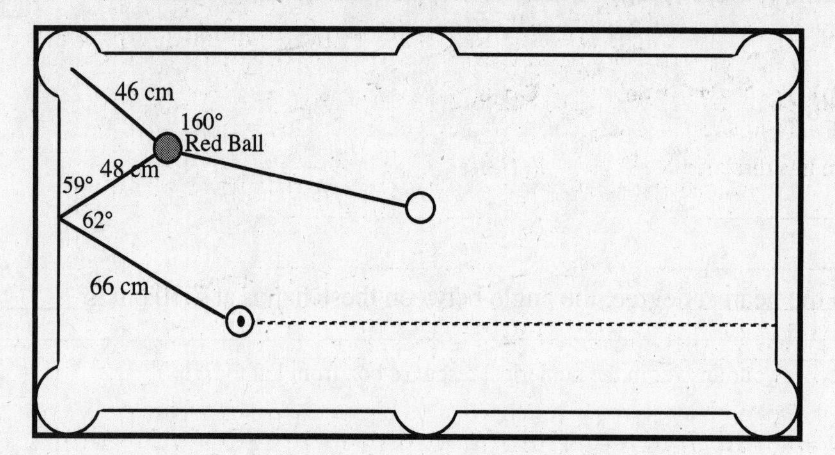

a) If the measurements are as in the diagram, calculate the distance, to the nearest cm, between the red ball and the spot white ball before Bob attempts his shot.

b) After the spot white is hit by the white ball it travels parallel to the bottom cushion until it stops just touching the right cushion. To the nearest 10 cm, calculate the distance travelled by the spot white (ignore the width of the ball in the calculation).

Answer Key

1. 40° **2. a)** 17.44 cm **b)** 23°

3. a) Angle DAO = Angle DCO = 90°, Angle $AOC = 2 \times 65 = 130°$.
Angle $ADC = 360° - 90° - 90° - 130° = 50°$
b) 5.3 inches

4. 102 m **5. a)** iii) **b)** i) **c)** v) **d)** ii) **e)** iv)

6. a) 46°, 56° **b)** 22 km **c)** 0846

7. 60 km in a direction N 39° E **8.** A **9.** B **10.** D

11.

7	1		

12.

7	.	2	

13.

0	.	7	5

14.

1	5	0	

15.

4	5		

16.

1	7	.	5

Group Work a) 61 cm **b)** 310 cm

Trigonometry Lesson #9: Practice Test

The first nine questions of this test should be done without using a calculator.

1. Which of the following pairs of angles in standard position have the same reference angle?

A. 62° and 152° **B.** 212° and 328°

C. 149° and 319° **D.** 71° and 19°

2. The point (x, y) is on the terminal arm of an angle θ° in standard positio.n Which of the following statements must be correct?

A. The point (y, x) is on the terminal arm of angle θ°.
B. The point $(x, -y)$ is on the terminal arm of angle $(180 - \theta)$°.
C. The point $(-x, -y)$ is on the terminal arm of angle $(180 + \theta)$°.
D. The point $(-x, y)$ is on the terminal arm of angle $(360 - \theta)$°.

3. In which quadrant is the sine ratio of an angle negative and the tangent ratio of the angle also negative?

A. 4 **B.** 3 **C.** 2 **D.** 1

4. The terminal arm of angle θ in standard position passes through the point $(8, -6)$. The exact value of $\sin\theta$ is

A. 0.6
B. −0.6
C. 0.8
D. −0.8

5. Which of the following statements is true?

A. $\cos 165° = \cos 15°$
B. $\sin 287° = -\sin 17°$
C. $\tan 156° = -\tan 24°$
D. $\sin 200° = \sin 20°$

6. Determine the exact value of cos 210°.

A. $-\frac{\sqrt{3}}{2}$ **B.** $\frac{\sqrt{3}}{2}$

C. $-\frac{1}{2}$ **D.** $\frac{1}{2}$

7. Angle A terminates in the fourth quadrant with $\cos A = \frac{4}{5}$. The exact value of $\tan A$ is

A. $\frac{4}{3}$

B. $\frac{3}{4}$

C. $-\frac{4}{3}$

D. $-\frac{3}{4}$

8. The largest solution to the equation $\tan \theta + 1 = 0$, $0° \leq \theta \leq 360°$, is $\theta = x°$. The value of x is

A. 45° **B.** 135°

C. 225° **D.** 315°

9. The diagram shows an initial arm of length 1 unit being rotated counterclockwise about the origin to form a circle of radius 1.

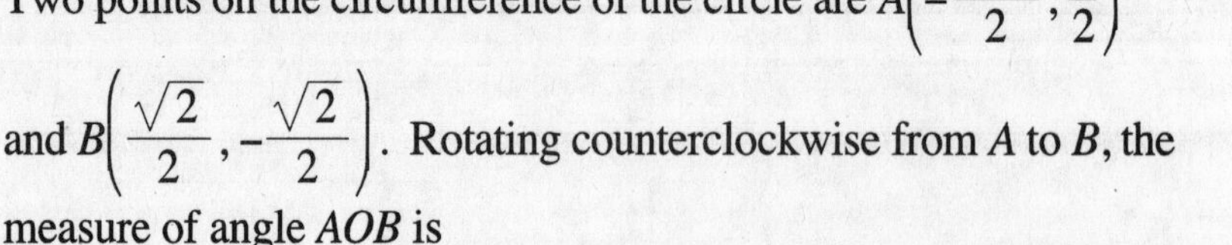

Two points on the circumference of the circle are $A\left(-\frac{\sqrt{3}}{2}, \frac{1}{2}\right)$ and $B\left(\frac{\sqrt{2}}{2}, -\frac{\sqrt{2}}{2}\right)$. Rotating counterclockwise from A to B, the measure of angle AOB is

A. 75°
B. 105°
C. 165°
D. 195°

A calculator is allowed for the remaining questions in this test.

10. Solve: $\sin A = -0.8290$, $0° \leq A \leq 360°$

A. 56°
B. 56°, 124°
C. 124°, 236°
D. 236°, 304°

1. An oil company drilling off shore has pipelines from platform Alpha and platform Beta to the same shore station Delta. Platform Alpha is 180 km on a bearing of 50° from Delta and platform Beta is 250 km on a bearing of 125° from Delta. Calculate the distance between platform Alpha and platform Beta to the nearest km.

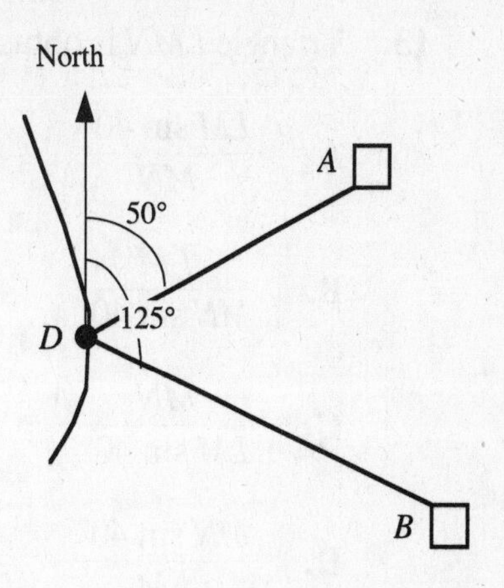

(Record your answer in the numerical response box from left to right.)

Use the following information to answer the next question .

The first hole at a golf course is 210 yards long in a direct line from the tee to the hole. Andrew Duffer hit his first shot at an angle of 15° off the direct line to the hole. The angle between his first shot and his second shot was 105°. His second shot landed in the hole.

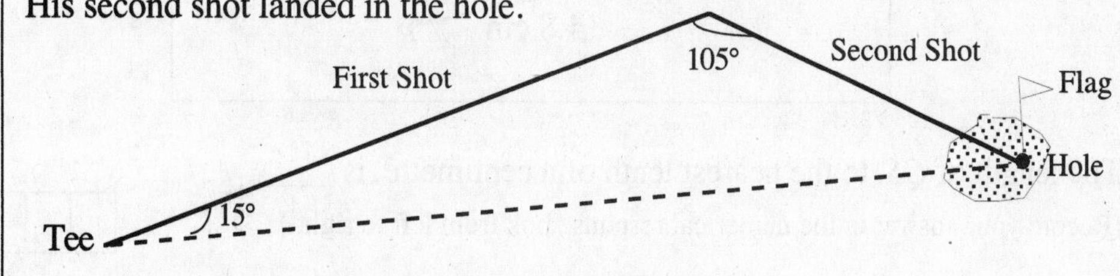

11. The length of his second shot, to the nearest yard, was

A. 30
B. 56
C. 105
D. 188

12. Triangle ABC is drawn with $AB = 3.6$ cm, $BC = 4.2$ cm, and angle $BCA = 28°$. The measure of angle ABC is

A. 33°
B. 119°
C. 33° or 147°
D. 5° or 119°

13. Triangle LMN is obtuse angled at M and $\angle MLN = 40°$. Sin LNM is equal to

A. $\dfrac{LM \sin 40°}{MN}$

B. $\dfrac{LM}{MN \sin 40°}$

C. $\dfrac{MN}{LM \sin 40°}$

D. $\dfrac{MN \sin 40°}{LM}$

Use the following diagram to answer the next two questions.

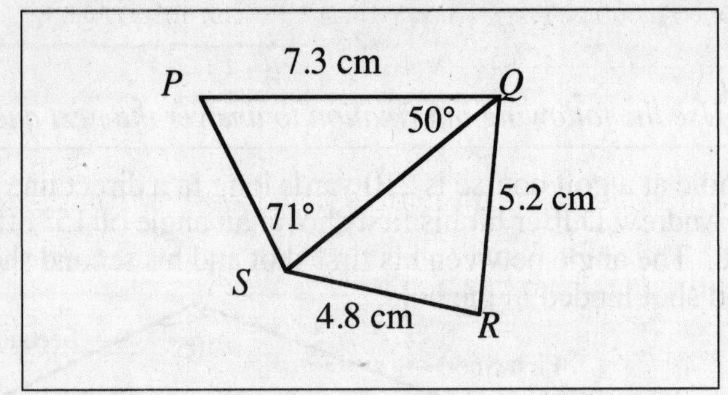

Numerical Response 2. The length of QS, to the nearest tenth of a centimetre, is _____ .
(Record your answer in the numerical response box from left to right.)

Numerical Response 3. The measure of angle QSR, to the nearest degree, is _____ .
(Record your answer in the numerical response box from left to right.)

Use the following information to answer the next question.

A student has been given the following problem to solve.

> " A pilot leaves an airport flying on a bearing of 165°. He changes direction and flies for 80 km on a bearing of 205°. He changes direction again and flies back to the airport. How far is he from the airport when he makes the second change in direction."

14. The most appropriate method for solving this problem is

A. *SOHCAHTOA*
B. the Sine Law
C. the Cosine Law
D. the problem cannot be solved without further information.

Use the following information to answer the next question.

On June 30, 1956, the world's largest free standing totem pole was erected in Beacon Hill Park in Victoria. Recently, a surveyor took measurements to verify the height, h, of the totem pole.

In the diagram, triangle ABC lies in a vertical plane and triangle BCD lies in a horizontal plane.

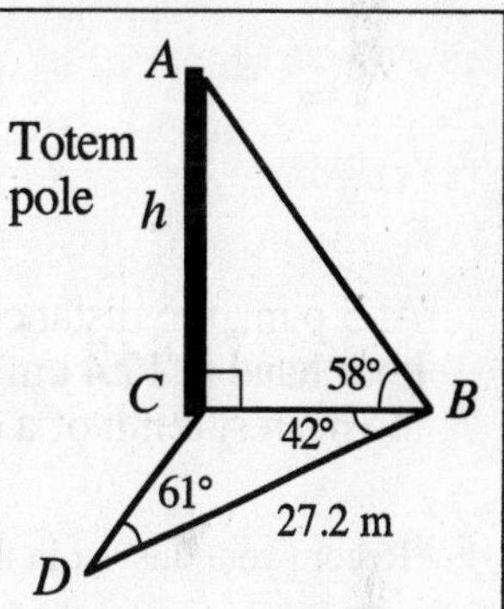

Numerical Response 4. The height of the totem pole, to the nearest metre, is _____ .

(Record your answer in the numerical response box from left to right.)

---

15. Mr. Post's two metre high fence has almost been blown down by the wind. As a temporary measure, he wants to tie a rope from the top of the fence to a peg one metre from the base of the fence.

The fence has moved so that it is leaning 25° to the vertical as shown. Determine, to the nearest tenth of a metre, the minimum length of rope required if he allows 50 cm for knots.

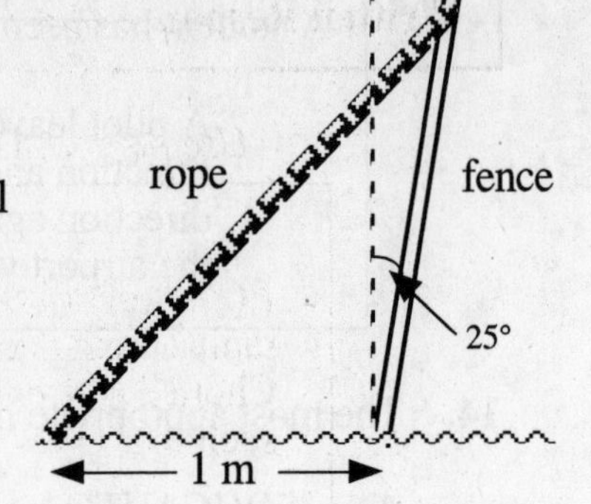

A. 1.7 m
B. 2.3 m
C. 2.6 m
D. 3.1 m

Numerical Response 5. At 5 p.m., the distance between the tip of the minute hand on a clock and the tip of the hour hand is 17.4 cm. If the minute hand is 10 cm long, the length of the hour hand, to the nearest tenth of a centimetre, is ____.

(Record your answer in the numerical response box from left to right.)

Written Response #1 - 3 marks

Use the following information to answer the next three questions.

PQ is a chord of a circle with centre *C* and radius 8 cm. Angle *CPQ* is 35°. Chord *PQ* is extended to the point *R* such that *CR* = 12 cm.

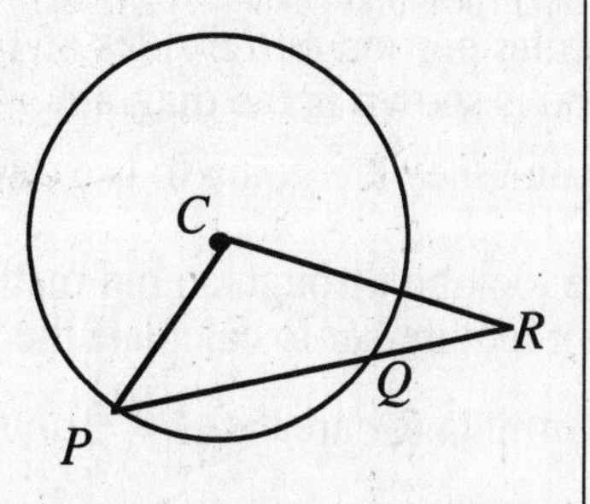

- Determine the measure of $\angle CRP$ to the nearest tenth of a degree.

- Determine, to the nearest tenth of a centimetre, the length of *PR*.

- Determine, to the nearest tenth of a centimetre, the length of the chord *PQ*.

Written Response #2 - 2 marks

Violet and Thomas have formed their own student painting company. They have been given a contract to paint a small triangular portion of the sides of 100 houses. The area to be painted is shown in the diagram.

The paint they are going to use covers 10 m^2 per litre.

6.5 m
4.3 m
8.0 m
A
B
C

While looking through an old math book, Violet found a formula for the area of a triangle that did not require her to calculate the vertical height of the triangle.

The formula for area is $A = \frac{1}{2}ab \sin C$.

Using the above formula for the area of a triangle, determine, to the nearest 10 litres, the amount of paint required to paint the sides of 100 houses.

Answer Key

1. B **2.** C **3.** A **4.** B **5.** C **6.** A **7.** D **8.** D
9. C **10.** D **11.** B **12.** D **13.** A **14.** D **15.** D

Numerical Response

1. | 2 | 6 | 8 | |

2. | 6 | . | 6 | |

3. | 5 | 1 | | |

4. | 3 | 9 | | |

5. | 8 | . | 0 | |

Written Response

1. • 22.5° • 17.6 cm • 13.1 cm
2. 140 litres

Factoring and Applications Lesson #1:
Review of Factoring

Factoring

Factoring involves writing a sum or difference of monomials as a product of polynomials. In this lesson, we will review factoring techniques learned in previous math courses, namely:

- factoring by taking out (or removing) a common factor
- factoring a difference of squares
- factoring trinomials by inspection
- factoring by grouping.

Factoring trinomials by the method of decomposition will be covered in the next lesson.

Factor each polynomial by removing the greatest common factor.

a) $15x^3 - 5x^2$ **b)** $8p^3 - 4p^2 - 4$ **c)** $3y(y+2) - 9(y+2)$

Factor, if possible, using the difference of squares method.

a) $x^2 - 81$ **b)** $25a^2 - 49$ **c)** $9x^2 + 4$ **d)** $16t^2 - 64$

Where possible, factor the following trinomials by inspection.

a) $a^2 + 11a + 30$ **b)** $b^2 - b - 30$ **c)** $x^2 - 4x + 48$ **d)** $3x^3 - 21x^2 + 36x$

Factor the following polynomials by grouping.

a) $x^2 - 5x + 2x - 10$ **b)** $6y^2 + 9y + 2y + 3$

Guidelines for Factoring a Polynomial Expression

If we are asked to factor a polynomial expression, the following guidelines should help us to determine the best method.

1. Look for a common factor. If there is one, take out the common factor and look for further factoring.

2. If there is a binomial expression, look for a difference of squares.

3. If there is a trinomial expression of the form $x^2 + bx + c$, look for factoring by inspection.

4. If there is a trinomial expression of the form $ax^2 + bx + c$, look for factoring by decomposition. (Note: This will be covered in the next lesson)

5. If there is a polynomial with four terms, look for factoring by grouping.

6. After factoring, check to see if further factoring is possible.

The guidelines can be shown in a flowchart.

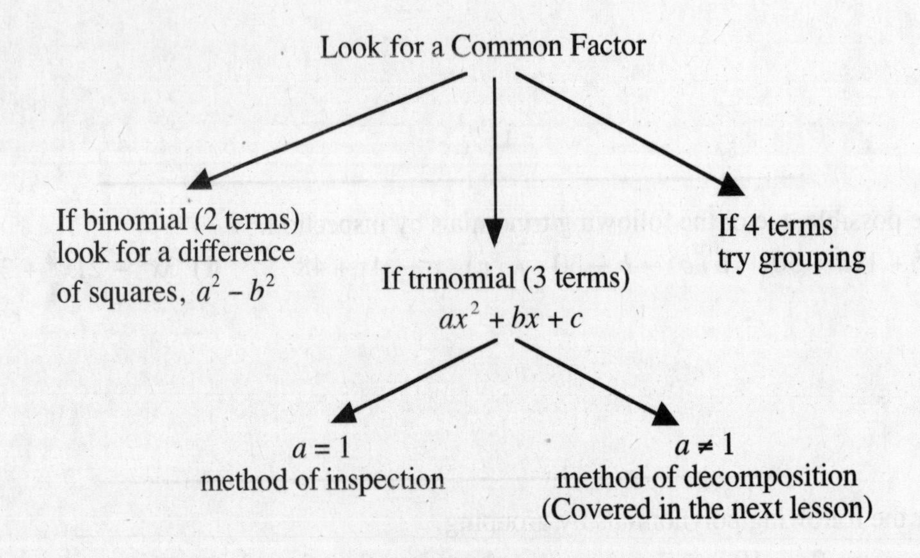
Look for a Common Factor
If binomial (2 terms) look for a difference of squares, $a^2 - b^2$
If trinomial (3 terms) $ax^2 + bx + c$
If 4 terms try grouping
$a = 1$ method of inspection
$a \neq 1$ method of decomposition (Covered in the next lesson)

Note
Always check to see if further factoring is possible.

Factor the following.

a) $36 - 9x^2$ **b)** $28 + 3x - x^2$

Complete Assignment Questions #1 - #12

Assignment

1. Factor where possible.

a) $x^2 + 5x + 6$ **b)** $x^2 + 6x + 5$ **c)** $x^2 + 9x + 10$ **d)** $x^2 + 10x + 9$

2. Factor.

a) $x^2 - 1$ **b)** $x^2 + 2x - 15$ **c)** $16x^2 + 4$

d) $16x^2 - 4$ **e)** $16x^2 - 4x$ **f)** $b^2 - 7b + 10$

g) $a^3 + a^2 + a + 1$ **h)** $p^2 - 10p - 56$ **i)** $4a^3 - a^2 - 4a + 1$

3. Factor where possible.

a) $100 - a^2$ **b)** $24 + 10x - x^2$ **c)** $c^2 + 21c + 38$

d) $9x - 4x^2$ **e)** $x^2 - 17x + 40$ **f)** $5f^2 - 45f - 50$

g) $2y^2 + 8y + 4$ **h)** $18 - 15x - 6x + 5x^2$ **i)** $48 - 4x - 4x^2$

4. Factor where possible.

a) $x^3 - 6x^2 - 4x + 24$ **b)** $6 - t - t^2$ **c)** $4 - 25t^2$

d) $x^2 + 5x + 4x - 20$ **e)** $-81 + x^2$ **f)** $x^2 + 4 - x - 4x$

5. Consider the following in which each letter represents a whole number.

$x^2 - 4x - 32 = (x - A)(x + E)$

$50x^2 - 2 = D(Lx - 1)(Lx + 1)$

$x^2 + 16x - 3x - 48 = (x - P)(x + i)$

Determine the value of each letter, and hence name the item represented by the following code.

(8) (3) (3) (5) (4) (16) (3) (8) (2)

__ __ __ __ __ __ __ __ __

Multiple Choice

6. When factored, the trinomials $x^2 - 12x + 35$ and $x^2 - 2x - 35$ have one binomial factor in common. This factor is

A. $x - 7$ **B.** $x + 7$

C. $x - 5$ **D.** $x + 5$

7. One factor of $-a^3 + a^2 + 6a$ is

A. $a - 2$ **B.** $a + 2$

C. $a + 3$ **D.** $a + 6$

8. One factor of $9 - 6x - 3x^2$ is

A. $-3x$ **B.** $x - 3$

C. $x - 2$ **D.** $x - 1$

9. The expression $x^2 - 8x + k$ **cannot** be factored if k has the value

A. 7
B. 0
C. −7
D. −9

In questions #10 and #11, <u>one or more</u> of the four responses may be correct. Answer

A. if only 1 and 2 are correct
B. if only 1, 2, and 3 are correct
C. if only 3 and 4 are correct
D. if some other response or combination of responses is correct

10. The set of factors of $6x^2 - 12x - 18$ contains
(1) $x - 1$ (2) $x + 3$ (3) $x + 1$ (4) $x - 3$

11. $x + 2$ is a factor of
(1) $x^2 + 4$ (2) $x^2 + 22x + 40$ (3) $4x^3 - 4x^2 - 24x$ (4) $x^2 - 2x + x + 2$

Numerical Response

12. Consider the polynomial $x^2 + 6x + c$, where c is a natural number. The polynomial can be factored for several values of c. The sum of all the possible values of c for which the polynomial can be factored is ______ .

(Record your answer in the numerical response box from left to right.)

Answer Key

1. a) $(x + 3)(x + 2)$ **b)** $(x + 5)(x + 1)$ **c)** not possible **d)** $(x + 9)(x + 1)$

2. a) $(x - 1)(x + 1)$ **b)** $(x + 5)(x - 3)$ **c)** $4(4x^2 + 1)$
d) $4(2x - 1)(2x + 1)$ **e)** $4x(4x - 1)$ **f)** $(b - 5)(b - 2)$
g) $(a^2 + 1)(a + 1)$ **h)** $(p - 14)(p + 4)$ **i)** $(4a - 1)(a - 1)(a + 1)$

3. a) $(10 - a)(10 + a)$ **b)** $-(x - 12)(x + 2)$ or $(12 - x)(2 + x)$ **c)** $(c + 19)(c + 2)$
d) $x(9 - 4x)$ **e)** not possible **f)** $5(f - 10)(f + 1)$
g) $2(y^2 + 4y + 2)$ **h)** $(6 - 5x)(3 - x)$ **i)** $-4(x + 4))(x - 3)$ or $4(3 - x)(4 + x)$

4. a) $(x - 6)(x - 2)(x + 2)$ **b)** $-(t + 3)(t - 2)$ or $(3 + t)(2 - t)$ **c)** $(2 - 5t)(2 + 5t)$
d) not possible **e)** $(x - 9)(x + 9)$ **f)** $(x - 4)(x - 1)$

5. APPLEiPAD **6.** A **7.** B **8.** D **9.** C **10.** C **11.** D

12.

2	2		

Factoring and Applications Lesson #2:
Factoring Trinomials of the Form $ax^2 + bx + c$

The technique for factoring $ax^2 + bx + c$ by decomposition may have been learned in an earlier course. If this is the case, the next two pages and assignment questions #1-#3 may be omitted. Class Ex. #3 to #5 may be used as practice.

Warm-Up

Complete the following:

a) $(2x + 1)(3x + 4) =$ ______________ so ______________ factors to $(2x + 1)(3x + 4)$

b) $(3x - 2)(4x + 3) =$ ______________ so ______________ factors to $(3x - 2)(4x + 3)$

Consider the following problem: What are the factors of $2x^2 + 7x + 6$?
We need to find two binomials whose product is $2x^2 + 7x + 6$. The first method we will consider is to use algebra tiles.

Factoring $ax^2 + bx + c$ using Algebra Tiles

____

a) Write a polynomial expression for the group of algebra tiles shown.

b) Arrange the algebra tiles into a rectangle and state the length and width of the rectangle.

c) Use the algebra tile diagram to express the polynomial in factored form.

Factor $5x^2 + 7x + 2$ using algebra tiles.

Complete Assignment Questions #1 - #2

Factoring using algebra tiles will work for all trinomials of the form $ax^2 + bx + c$ which have binomial factors. However, it can get rather tedious if the values of a, b, c are large.

Factoring $ax^2 + bx + c$ using the Method of Decomposition

1. In Warm-Up a) we factored
$6x^2 + 3x + 8x + 4$ or $6x^2 + 11x + 4$ to get $(2x + 1)(3x + 4)$.
In order to factor $6x^2 + 11x + 4$, we must first split $11x$ into $3x$ and $8x$ and then group.

But how do we know to split $11x$ into $3x$ and $8x$ rather than $2x$ and $9x$ or $5x$ and $6x$ etc.?
In $6x^2 + 11x + 4$, how are the numbers 8 and 3 connected to the value of a (i.e. 6), the value of b (i.e. 11) and the value of c (i.e. 4)?

2. In Warm-Up b) we factored
$12x^2 + 9x - 8x - 6$ or $12x^2 + x - 6$ to get $(3x - 2)(4x + 3)$.
In order to factor $12x^2 + x - 6$, we must first split $1x$ into $9x$ and $-8x$ and then group.

But how do we know to split $1x$ into $9x$ and $-8x$ rather than $5x$ and $-4x$ or $3x$ and $-2x$?
In $12x^2 + x - 6$, how are the numbers 9 and -8 connected to the value of a (i.e. 12), the value of b (i.e. 1) and the value of c (i.e. -6)?

The method of factoring $ax^2 + bx + c$ by splitting the value of b into two integers whose product is ac and whose sum is b is called the **method of decomposition**.

Factor, using the method of decomposition, and compare the answers with Class Examples #1 and #2.

a) $2x^2 + 7x + 6$ **b)** $5x^2 + 7x + 2$

Factor.

a) $6x^2 + 17x - 3$ **b)** $3n^2 - 2n - 8$ **c)** $12x^2 - 8x + 1$

Factor.

a) $15 - 7y - 2y^2$ **b)** $15k^2 + 5k - 10$

Factoring Trinomials of the form $ax^2 + bxy + cy^2$

The method of decomposition can be applied to trinomials of the form $ax^2 + bxy + cy^2$.

Factor.

a) $2x^2 - 5xy + 2y^2$ **b)** $2n^2 - 3nm - 35m^2$

Complete Assignment Questions #3 - #8

Perfect Square Trinomials

A **perfect square trinomial** is formed from the product of two identical binomials. Perfect square trinomials can be factored by considering the pattern displayed when squaring binomials.

Complete the following : $(p + q)^2 =$ ____________ $(p - q)^2 =$ ____________

From the above we can see that :

. The first term in the trinomial is the square of the _________ term in the binomial.

. The last term in the trinomial is the square of the _________ term in the binomial.

. The middle term in the trinomial is _________ the ___________ of the first and last terms in the binomial.

In a perfect square trinomial, e.g. $x^2 + 10x + 25$, the **first and last terms must be perfect squares** and the **middle term must be twice the product of the square roots of the first and last terms.**

Which of the following are perfect square trinomials?

a) $a^2 + 4a + 4$ **b)** $x^2 - 9x + 6$ **c)** $4x^2 - 36x + 81$ **d)** $y^2 + 8y - 16$

Fill in the blank so that each of the following is a perfect square trinomial.

a) $x^2 +$ ___ $+100$ **b)** $x^2 -$ ___ $+ 100$ **c)** $25x^2 +$ ___ $+ 36$ **d)** $9m^2 + 24m +$ ___

Factor.

a) $49x^2 - 14x + 1$ **b)** $16 + 40x + 25x^2$ **c)** $\frac{1}{9}a^2 - 2ab + 9b^2$

Complete Assignment Questions #9 - #16

Assignment

1. a) Write a polynomial expression for the group of algebra tiles shown.

b) Arrange the algebra tiles into a rectangle and state the length and width of the rectangle.

c) Use the algebra tile diagram to express the polynomial in factored form.

2. Factor the following expressions using algebra tiles.

a) $2x^2 + 5x + 3$

b) $2x^2 + 7x + 3$

c) $6x^2 + 7x + 2$

d) $4x^2 + 13x + 3$

3. Factor the following expressions.

a) $10x^2 + 17x + 3$

b) $9x^2 + 6x + 1$

c) $3x^2 + 14x + 15$

d) $3a^2 - 23a - 8$

e) $3a^2 + a - 2$

f) $2p^2 - 19p + 9$

4. Factor.

a) $3x^2 - 2x - 1$

b) $8y^2 + 2y - 3$

c) $9t^2 - 24t + 16$

d) $12m^2 - 11m - 5$

e) $12p^2 + 13p - 4$

f) $9x^2 - x - 10$

5. A rectangular garden has an area of $12a^2 - 5a - 2\ \text{m}^2$.

a) Write the area as the product of two binomials with integer coefficients.

b) The garden is to be completely enclosed by a path 1m wide.
Find and simplify an expression for the area of the path.

c) The path is concrete, poured to a depth of 10 cm.
Calculate the volume (in m^3) of concrete used if $a = 6$.

6. Factor the following expressions.

a) $12 + 8x + x^2$

b) $6 - 7x - 20x^2$

c) $3 + a - 10a^2$

d) $10a^2 + 25a - 15$

e) $12z^2 + 66z + 30$

f) $4x^3 - 7x^2 - 2x$

7. Factor.

a) $8x^2 + 22xy + 5y^2$

b) $6x^2 + 11xy - 7y^2$

c) $4a^2 - 9ab - 9b^2$

d) $2m^2 - 19mn + 9n^2$

e) $9x^2 + xy - 10y^2$

f) $8x^2 + 7xy - 15y^2$

8. Consider the following, in which each letter represents a whole number.

$4x^2 + 23x + 15 = (Dx + W)(x + R)$

$12x^2 - 52xy - 9y^2 = (Ex - Ty)(Ox + y)$

$16x^2 + 40xy - 56y^2 = I(x - Gy)(Ex + Sy)$

Determine the value of each letter, and hence name the sports celebrity represented by the following code.

(9) (8) (1) (2) (5) (3) (6) (6) (4) (7)

— — — — — — — — — —

9. Which of the following are perfect square trinomials?

a) $a^2 + 12a + 36$ **b)** $x^2 - 25x + 50$ **c)** $4x^2 - 4x + 1$ **d)** $16y^2 + 32y + 16$

e) $a^2 + 9a + 9$ **f)** $25x^2 - 90x + 81$ **g)** $1 - 16x + 64x^2$ **h)** $y^2 + 20y - 100$

10. Fill in the blank so that each of the following is a perfect square trinomial.

a) $x^2 +$ ___ $+ 49$ **b)** $x^2 -$ ___ $+ 144$ **c)** $9x^2 +$ ___ $+ 36$ **d)** $4m^2 + 24m +$ ___

e) $\frac{1}{4}a^2 +$ ___ $+1$ **f)** $225x^2 -$ ___ $+ 16$ **g)** $100x^2 +$ ___ $+ y^2$ **h)** ___ $- 30y + 9y^2$

11. Factor.

a) $16x^2 - 8x + 1$ **b)** $36 + 60x + 25x^2$ **c)** $4a^2 - 12ab + 9b^2$

d) $4x^2 - 44x + 121$ **e)** $5x^2 + 10x + 5$ **f)** $\frac{4}{9}x^2 + \frac{2}{9}x + \frac{1}{36}$

Multiple Choice

12. One factor of $20x^2 + 6x - 8$ is

A. $2x - 1$
B. $4x + 2$
C. $5x - 4$
D. $10x - 1$

13. From the expressions below, the one which does **not** represent a perfect square trinomial is

A. $x^2 - 14x + 49$ **B.** $144 + 24x + x^2$
C. $4x^2 - 12x + 36$ **D.** $9x^4 + 30x^2 + 25$

Numerical Response

14. The polynomial expression $\frac{1}{16}x^2 + \frac{1}{3}x + \frac{4}{9}$ can be written in the form $(Ax + B)^2$. The value of the product AB, to the nearest one hundredth, is _____.

(Record your answer in the numerical response box from left to right.)

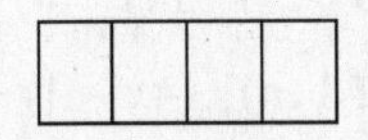

15. The factored form of $3x^2 - 14x + 8$ is $(x + a)(bx + c)$ where a, b, and c are integers. The value of b^c, to the nearest hundredth, is ________

(Record your answer in the numerical response box from left to right.)

16. The expression $24x^2 + 41x - 35$ can be written in the form $(ax - b)(cx + d)$ where a, b, c, and d are all positive integers.

Write the value of a in the first box. Write the value of b in the second box.
Write the value of c in the third box. Write the value of d in the fourth box.

(Record your answer in the numerical response box from left to right.)

Answer Key

1. **a)** $3x^2 + 7x + 2$ **b)** $3x + 1, x + 2$ **c)** $3x^2 + 7x + 2 = (3x + 1)(x + 2)$

2. **a)** $(2x + 3)(x + 1)$ **b)** $(2x + 1)(x + 3)$ **c)** $(3x + 2)(2x + 1)$ **d)** $(4x + 1)(x + 3)$

3. **a)** $(5x + 1)(2x + 3)$ **b)** $(3x + 1)^2$ **c)** $(3x + 5)(x + 3)$
d) $(3a + 1)(a - 8)$ **e)** $(3a - 2)(a + 1)$ **f)** $(2p - 1)(p - 9)$

4. **a)** $(3x + 1)(x - 1)$ **b)** $(2y - 1)(4y + 3)$ **c)** $(3t - 4)^2$
d) $(3m + 1)(4m - 5)$ **e)** $(4p - 1)(3p + 4)$ **f)** $(9x - 10)(x + 1)$

5. **a)** $(3a - 2)(4a + 1)$ **b)** $14a + 2$ m^2 **c)** 8.6 m^3

6. **a)** $(6 + x)(2 + x)$ **b)** $(3 + 4x)(2 - 5x)$ **c)** $(3 - 5a)(1 + 2a)$
d) $5(2a - 1)(a + 3)$ **e)** $6(2z + 1)(z + 5)$ **f)** $x(4x + 1)(x - 2)$

7. **a)** $(2x + 5y)(4x + y)$ **b)** $(2x - y)(3x + 7y)$ **c)** $(4a + 3b)(a - 3b)$
d) $(2m - n)(m - 9n)$ **e)** $(9x + 10y)(x - y)$ **f)** $(8x + 15y)(x - y)$

8. TIGER WOODS **9.** **a), c), d), f), g)** are all perfect square trinomials.

10. **a)** $14x$ **b)** $24x$ **c)** $36x$ **d)** 36 **e)** a **f)** $120x$ **g)** $20xy$ **h)** 25

11. **a)** $(4x - 1)^2$ **b)** $(6 + 5x)^2$ **c)** $(2a - 3b)^2$ **d)** $(2x - 11)^2$ **e)** $5(x + 1)^2$ **f)** $\left(\frac{2}{3}x + \frac{1}{6}\right)^2$

12. A **13.** C

14.

0	.	1	7

15.

0	.	1	1

16.

8	5	3	7

Factoring and Applications Lesson #3:
Factoring Trinomials of the Form $a(f(x))^2 + b(f(x)) + c$

In the previous lessons we have factored:

- trinomials of the form $x^2 + bx + c$ by inspection
- trinomials of the form $ax^2 + bx + c$, by decomposition

In this lesson, we extend this process to consider expressions in which the variable x is replaced by a function of x.

Factoring Trinomials of the form $(f(x))^2 + b(f(x)) + c$ where $f(x)$ is a Monomial

The method of inspection can be extended to factor polynomial expressions of the form $(f(x))^2 + b(f(x)) + c$, where $f(x)$ itself is a polynomial.
In this section, we will restrict f to be a monomial.

In the trinomial $x^2 + bx + c$, the degrees of the terms are 2, 1, and 0 respectively.
The method of inspection can also be used when the terms have degrees 4, 2, and 0 or 6, 3, and 0 etc.

In all cases, we make a substitution which results in a trinomial with terms of degree 2, 1, and 0.

The following example to factor $x^4 + 5x^2 + 6$ illustrates the process.

$x^4 + 5x^2 + 6$ can be written $(x^2)^2 + 5(x^2) + 6$.

Make the substitution $A = x^2$ so the expression becomes $A^2 + 5A + 6$ which factors to $(A + 2)(A + 3)$.

Replace A by x^2 to get $(x^2 + 2)(x^2 + 3)$. $\qquad x^4 + 5x^2 + 6 = (x^2 + 2)(x^2 + 3)$

With experience, this process can be done by inspection.
Note that in this example the function $f(x) = x^2$.

Factor completely.

a) $a^4 - 5a^2 - 14$ **b)** $x^4 + 4x^2 - 5$ **c)** $x^6 - 9x^3 + 14$

Factoring Trinomials of the form $a(f(x))^2 + b(f(x)) + c$ *where* $f(x)$ *is a Monomial*

The method of decomposition can be extended to factor polynomial expressions of the form $af(x)^2 + b(f(x)) + c$ where f itself is a polynomial.
In this section, we will restrict f to be a monomial.

In the trinomial $ax^2 + bx + c$, the degrees of the terms are 2, 1, and 0 respectively.
The method of decomposition can also be used when the terms have degrees 4, 2, and 0 or 6, 3, and 0 etc.

The expression $4y^4 - 11y^2 - 3$ can be factored using the method of decomposition by substituting $A = y^2$ or by splitting $-11y^2$ into two terms in y^2.

Complete the work started below.

Method 1

$4y^4 - 11y^2 - 3 = 4(y^2)^2 - 11(y^2) - 3$

Let $A = y^2$ $\quad 4A^2 - 11A - 3$

$=$

Method 2

$4y^4 - 11y^2 - 3 = 4y^4 - 12y^2 + 1y^2 - 3$

Class Ex. #2

Factor completely.

a) $4x^4 - 5x^2 - 6$

b) $2a^2b^2 - 31ab + 99$

Factor completely the expression $8x^4 + 10x^2 - 3$.

Given that $(\sin x)^2$ is written as $\sin^2 x$ and $(\cos x)^2$ is written as $\cos^2 x$, factor

a) $6 \sin^2 x - 7\sin x + 2$

b) $4 \cos^2 x + 11 \cos x - 3$

Complete Assignment Questions #1 - #4

Factoring Trinomials of the form $a(f(x))^2 + b(f(x)) + c$ ***where f(x) is a Binomial***

Factor.

a) $7(x - 3)^2 - 4(x - 3) - 3$

b) $9(a + 4)^2 + (a + 4) - 10$

Complete Assignment Questions #5 - #10

Assignment

1. Factor completely.

a) $x^4 + 9x^2 + 20$

b) $x^4 - 9x^2 + 20$

c) $a^4 - 17a^2 + 16$

d) $t^6 - 4t^3 - 21$

e) $3x^4 + 9x^2 - 30$

f) $2x^5 - 16x^3 + 32x$

2. Factor completely.

a) $6x^4 + 11x^2 + 5$

b) $2a^4 - 5a^2 + 2$

c) $5p^6 - 8p^3 - 4$

d) $16x^4 + 8x^2 - 3$

e) $4 - 9t^2 - 9t^4$

f) $4x^5 - 50x^3 + 126x$

g) $4x^2y^2 - xy - 14$

h) $4\pi^2r^2 - 9\pi r - 9$

3. Given that $(\sin x)^2$ is written as $\sin^2 x$ and $(\cos x)^2$ is written as $\cos^2 x$, factor

a) $6\sin^2 x + \sin x - 2$

b) $4\cos^2 x - 7\cos x + 3$

4. Factor the polynomial expression $16a^8 - 65a^4 + 4$.

5. Factor.

a) $4(3x + 1)^2 - 5(3x + 1) + 1$

b) $6(x - 4)^2 - (x - 4) - 2$

c) $4(a - b)^2 - 40(a - b) + 100$

d) $5(2 - 3x)^2 - 28(2 - 3x) + 15$

6. Factor $2(3a - 4)^2 - (3a - 4)(a + 2) - 6(a + 2)^2$

Multiple Choice

7. From the expressions below, the one which does **not** represent a perfect square trinomial is

A. $x^2 - 14x + 49$
B. $144 + 24x + x^2$
C. $4x^2 - 12x + 36$
D. $9x^4 + 30x^2 + 25$

8. When factored completely, the polynomial $k^4 + 16 - 17k^2$ is equal to

A. $(k^2 - 1)(k^2 - 16)$
B. $(k^2 + 1)(k^2 + 16)$
C. $k^2(k + 1)(k + 16)$
D. $(k + 1)(k - 1)(k + 4)(k - 4)$

9. One factor of $x^4 - 16x^2 + 15$ is

A. $x + 1$
B. $x^2 + 15$
C. $x + 15$
D. $x - 15$

10. The polynomial expression $\frac{1}{4}(x - 2)^2 + 3(x - 2) + 9$ can be written in the form $(Ax + B)^2$. The value of $A + B$, to the nearest tenth, is _____.
(Record your answer in the numerical response box from left to right.)

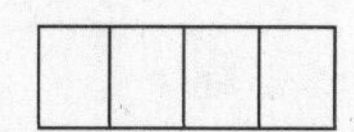

Answer Key

1. a) $(x^2 + 5)(x^2 + 4)$ b) $(x - 2)(x + 2)(x^2 - 5)$ c) $(a - 1)(a + 1)(a - 4)(a + 4)$
   d) $(t^3 - 7)(t^3 + 3)$ e) $3(x^2 + 5)(x^2 - 2)$ f) $2x(x - 2)^2(x + 2)^2$

2. a) $(6x^2 + 5)(x^2 + 1)$ b) $(2a^2 - 1)(a^2 - 2)$ c) $(5p^3 + 2)(p^3 - 2)$
   d) $(2x - 1)(2x + 1)(4x^2 + 3)$ e) $(4 + 3t^2)(1 - 3t^2)$ f) $2x(x - 3)(x + 3)(2x^2 - 7)$
   g) $(4xy + 7)(xy - 2)$ h) $(4\pi r + 3)(\pi r - 3)$

3. a) $(3 \sin x + 2)(2 \sin x - 1)$ b) $(4 \cos x - 3)(\cos x - 1)$

4. $(2a - 1)(2a + 1)(a^2 - 2)(a^2 + 2)(4a^2 + 1)$

5. a) $9x(4x + 1)$ b) $(2x - 7)(3x - 14)$
   c) $4(a - b - 5)^2$ d) $-3(7 - 15x)(1 + x)$ or $3(15x - 7)(x + 1)$

6. $(a - 8)(9a - 2)$ 7. C 8. D 9. A

10.

2	.	5	

Factoring and Applications Lesson #4:
Factoring $a^2x^2 - b^2y^2$ and $a^2(f(x))^2 - b^2(f(x))^2$

Factoring $a^2x^2 - b^2y^2$

Complete the following.

- The expanded form of $(ax - by)(ax + by)$ is ____________________ .

- The factored form of $a^2x^2 - b^2y^2$ is ____________ .

Class Ex. #1

Factor.

a) $9x^2 - 16y^2$ **b)** $3x^3y - 27xy^3$ **c)** $144p^2q^2 - 4r^2$

Class Ex. #2

A pane of glass is rectangular with an area of $49x^2 - 16y^2$ ft^2.

a) The length and width of the pane of glass can both be written in the form $(ax + by)$ where a and b are integers. Determine appropriate values for a and b, and hence write expressions in x and y for the length and width of the pane.

b) Given that the length of the pane is double the width, and the perimeter is 56 ft, develop a strategy for determining the length and width of the pane.

Complete Assignment Questions #1 - #2

Factoring $a^2(f(x))^2 - b^2(g(y))^2$ *where* $f(x)$ *and* $g(y)$ *are Monomials*

The method of difference of squares in which $a^2 - b^2 = (a - b)(a + b)$ can also be extended to include examples where a and b represent polynomials.

The following process can be used to factor $x^4 - 16y^4$.

$x^4 - 16y^4$ can be written $(x^2)^2 - (4y^2)^2$.

Make the substitution $A = x^2$ and $B = 4y^2$ so the expression becomes $A^2 - B^2$ which factors to $(A - B)(A + B)$.

Replace A by x^2 and B by $4y^2$ to get $(x^2 - 4y^2)(x^2 + 4y^2)$ which factors further to $(x - 2y)(x + 2y)(x^2 + 4y^2)$.

In this example $f(x) = x^2$ and $g(y) = y^2$.

Factor completely.

a) $k^4 - 1$ **b)** $80a^4 - 5x^4$ **c)** $2p^5q^4 - 162pt^4$

Complete Assignment Questions #3 - #4

Factoring $a^2(f(x))^2 - b^2(g(y))^2$ *where* $f(x)$ *and/or* $g(y)$ *are Binomial(s)*

Factor completely.

a) $a^2 - (b - c)^2$ **b)** $(2x - y)^2 - (x + y)^2$

Factor the expression $36(x + 5)^2 - 49(x - 8)^2$.

Complete Assignment Questions #5 - #11

Assignment

1. Factor:

a) $16x^2 - 49y^2$

b) $25a^2 - 121y^2$

c) $p^2q^2 - r^2s^2$

d) $16x^2 - 4y^2$

e) $9a^2b^2 - 36c^2$

f) $12a^2 - 75p^2q^2$

g) $4xy^3 - 169x^3y$

h) $60a^2b^2 - 15a^4b^4$

i) $4b^2g^2 - 49t^2z^2$

j) $25x^2 + 100y^2$

k) $225a^2c^2 - 16b^2d^2$

l) $xw^2y^2 - x^3z^2$

m) $1 - \cos^2 x$

n) $\sin^2 x - \cos^2 x$

o) $\frac{x^2}{64} - \frac{y^2}{49}$

2. The floor of a classroom is rectangular with an area of $81m^2 - 4n^2$ square metres.

a) The length and width of the floor can both be written in the form $(am + bn)$ where a and b are integers. Determine appropriate values for a and b, and hence write expressions in m and n for the length and width of the floor.

b) If the perimeter of the floor is 72 metres, form an equation in m and n and solve for m.

c) Determine the length and width of the floor if the length is 25% greater than the width.

3. Factor.

a) $x^4 - y^4$

b) $a^4 - 256b^4$

c) $2z^4 - 162$

d) $48x^4 - 3y^4$

e) $9a^4b^4 - 144c^4d^4$

f) $z^8 - 256$

4. Factor each expression.

a) $81a^4 - 16b^4$

b) $16p^4 - \frac{1}{81}q^4$

c) $16a^4 - 121b^2c^2$

d) $z^6 - 9$

e) $1 - a^{16}$

f) $x^4 - 0.0256y^4$

5. Factor each expression.

a) $(a - b)^2 - c^2$

b) $a^2 - (b + c)^2$

c) $(x + y)^2 - x^2$

d) $x^2 - (x - y)^2$

e) $4(p + q)^2 - 25$

f) $36(a + b)^2 - (p + q)^2$

g) $(x + 5)^2 - (x - 5)^2$

h) $9(a + b + c)^2 - 4(a - b + c)^2$

i) $256(a - 4)^2 - 100(a - 6)^2$

Use the following information to answer the next question.

The diagram shows a square of side $(2x - 3)$ metres inside a square of side $(3x + 4)$ metres. Students were asked to determine the area of the shaded region in factored form.

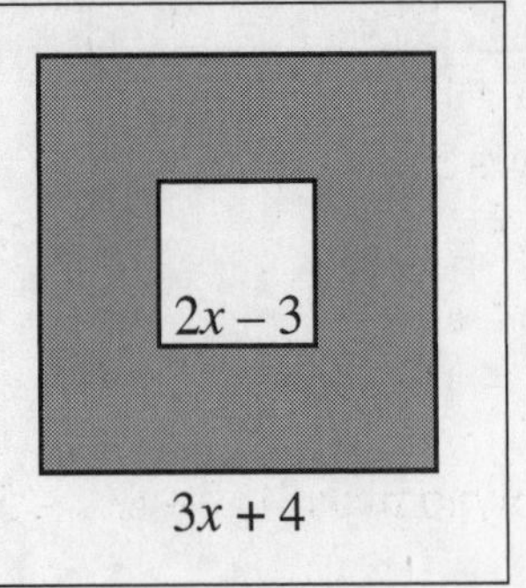

6. a) Rhonda chose to solve the problem by finding the area of each square, subtracting, and factoring the result. Use Rhonda's method to determine the area.

b) Soyee used the factoring technique of difference of squares to determine the answer. Use Soyee's method to determine the area.

c) Which method do you prefer?

7. The diagram shows a washer with outer radius $(r + 3)$ mm, and an inner radius of $(r - 1)$ mm.

a) Write, but do not simplify, an expression for the area of the surface of the washer

b) Factor this expression completely.

c) Use the factored expression to determine the area of the washer if $r = 5$.

Multiple Choice

8. One factor of $y^4 - 81$ is

A. $y + 9$
B. $y + 3$
C. $y^2 - 3$
D. $y^2 + 3$

9. The polynomials $4x^2 + 8xy - 5y^2$ and $24x^2 - 6y^2$ have in common a factor of

A. $4x + y$
B. $4x - y$
C. $2x + y$
D. $2x - y$

10. When fully factored, the expression $a^4 - (9a + 18)^2$ can be written as the product of two binomial factors and one trinomial factor. If the binomial factors are $a + p$ and $a + q$, the value of pq is _____.

(Record your answer in the numerical response box from left to right.)

11. The expression $81(x-3)^2 - 144(x-2)^2$ can be factored into the form $-a(x+b)(cx-d)$, where $a, b, c, d \in N$. The value of $a+b+c+d$ is _____.

(Record your answer in the numerical response box from left to right.)

Answer Key

1. **a)** $(4x-7y)(4x+7)$ **b)** $(5a-11y)(5a+11y)$ **c)** $(pq+rs)(pq-rs)$
d) $4(2x-y)(2x+y)$ **e)** $9(ab-2c)(ab+2c)$ **f)** $3(2a-5pq)(2a+5pq)$
g) $xy(2y-13x)(2y+13x)$ **h)** $15a^2b^2(2-ab)(2+ab)$ **i)** $(2bg-7tz)(2bg+7tz)$
j) $25(x^2+4y^2)$ **k)** $(15ac-4bd)(15ac+4bd)$ **l)** $x(wy-xz)(wy+xz)$
m) $(1-\cos x)(1+\cos x)$ **n)** $(\sin x - \cos x)(\sin x + \cos x)$ **0)** $\left(\frac{x}{8}+\frac{y}{7}\right)\left(\frac{x}{8}-\frac{y}{7}\right)$

2. **a)** $(9m+2n)$ metres, $(9m-2n)$ metres **b)** $2(9m+2n)+2(9m-2n)=72,\ m=2$
c) Length = 20 metres, Width = 16 metres.

3. **a)** $(x-y)(x+y)(x^2+y^2)$ **b)** $(a-4b)(a+4b)(a^2+16b^2)$
c) $2(z-3)(z+3)(z^2+9)$ **d)** $3(2x-y)(2x+y)(4x^2+y^2)$
e) $9(ab-2cd)(ab+2cd)(a^2b^2+4c^2d^2)$ **f)** $(z-2)(z+2)(z^2+4)(z^4+16)$

4. **a)** $(3a-2b)(3a+2b)(9a^2+4b^2)$ **b)** $\left(2p-\frac{1}{3}q\right)\left(2p+\frac{1}{3}q\right)\left(4p^2+\frac{1}{9}q^2\right)$
c) $(4a^2-11bc)(4a^2+11bc)$ **d)** $(z^3-3)(z^3+3)$
e) $(1-a)(1+a)(1+a^2)(1+a^4)(1+a^8)$ **f)** $(x-0.4y)(x+0.4y)(x^2+0.16y^2)$

5. **a)** $(a-b-c)(a-b+c)$ **b)** $(a-b-c)(a+b+c)$
c) $y(2x+y)$ **d)** $y(2x-y)$
e) $(2p+2q-5)(2p+2q+5)$ **f)** $(6a+6b-p-q)(6a+6b+p+q)$
g) $20x$ **h)** $(a+5b+c)(5a+b+5c)$
i) $4(3a-2)(13a-62)$

6. **a)** $(x+7)(5x+1)$ **b)** $(x+7)(5x+1)$

7. **a)** $\pi(r+3)^2 - \pi(r-1)^2$ **b)** $8\pi(r+1)$ **c)** 48π mm^2

8. B **9.** D

10.

1	8		

11.

3	4		

Factoring and Applications Lesson #5
Solving Quadratic Equations using Factoring

In this lesson, we introduce an application of factoring, namely the solution to polynomial equations, in particular quadratic equations. Some students may have covered this lesson as an enrichment in the Foundations of Mathematics and Pre-Calculus Grade 10 Workbook.

Investigating the Zero Product Law

Complete the following.

The statement $x - 3 = 0$ is true only if $x =$ ______.

The statement $x + 1 = 0$ is true only if $x =$ ______.

The statement $(x - 3)(x + 1) = 0$ is true if $x =$ ______ or if $x =$ ______.

The statement $x(x + 1) = 0$ is true if ____________________.

The Zero Product Law

The last two statements in the investigation above are examples of what is called The Zero Product Law which states the following:

If the **product** of multiple factors is **equal to zero,**
then at least **one of the factors must be equal zero**.

- Complete: If $a \times b = 0$, then $a =$ _____ or $b =$ _____

- Complete the following by solving for x in each equation:

a) $8x = 0$ **b)** $8(x + 2)(x - 7) = 0$ **c)** $x(x + 2)(x - 7) = 0$ **d)** $(2x + 1)(3x - 2) = 0$

e) Why is it acceptable to divide by 8 first in (a) and (b)?

f) Why is it **not** acceptable to divide by x first in (c)?

All the above equations are polynomial equations in which one side is a polynomial expression and the **other side equals zero**.

The **solution** to a polynomial equation is given by stating the value(s) of the variable which make(s) the left side and the right side equal. These values are said to **satisfy** the equation.

We can use the Zero Product Law to solve polynomial equations of various types.
In this lesson, we will focus on quadratic equations using factoring and the zero product law.

Solving Quadratic Equations

Consider the equation $x^2 - 2x - 3 = 0$. Factoring the left side leads to $(x - 3)(x + 1) = 0$. This is true if $x = 3$ or if $x = -1$. Since the equation is satisfied by both $x = 3$ and $x = -1$, the solutions to the equation are $x = 3$ **and** $x = -1$, sometimes written as $x = -1, 3$.

Class Ex. #1

Complete the solution to the equation $x^2 - 9x + 20 = 0$.

$x^2 - 9x + 20 = 0$

$(x - \quad)(x - \quad) = 0$

$x - \quad = 0$ or $x - \quad = 0$ The solutions are $x =$ ____ and $x =$ ____

$x =$ ____ or $x =$ ____ or $x =$ ____ , ____

Class Ex. #2

Solve the equation by using the Zero Product Law.

a) $x^2 - 81 = 0$ **b)** $4x^2 - 9 = 0$ **c)** $10x^2 - 90x = 0$ **d)** $10x^2 - 90 = 0$.

Class Ex. #3

Solve the equation.

a) $3x^2 - 13x - 10 = 0$ **b)** $5x^2 + 30x = -25$

Complete Assignment Questions #1 - #4

Problem Solving with Quadratic Equations

Some problems in mathematics can be solved by the following procedure.

i) Introduce a variable to represent an unknown value.

ii) Form a quadratic equation from the given information.

iii) Solve the quadratic equation using the methods in this lesson.

iv) State the solution to the problem.

In this section we will consider fairly routine problems. This topic will be extended in a higher level math course.

The area of a rectangular sheet of paper is $300\ \text{cm}^2$. The length is 5 cm more than the width. Form a polynomial equation and solve it to determine the perimeter of the rectangular sheet.

The diagram shows the cross-section of a water trough whose sloping sides AD and BC make an angle of 45° with the horizontal. The length $DC = 36$ cm.

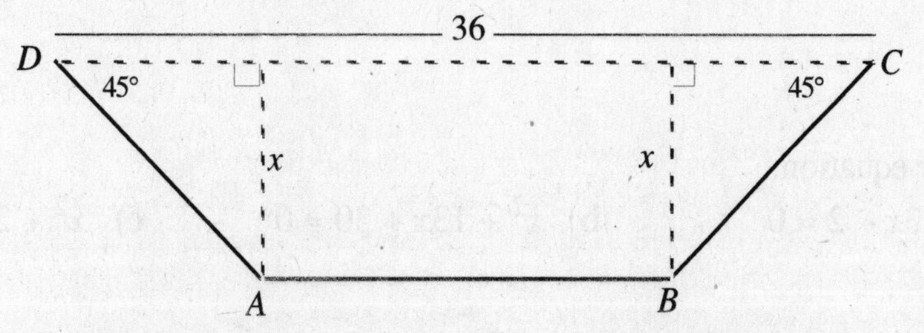

a) Show that the area of the cross-section is $x(36 - x)\ \text{cm}^2$.

b) If the area of the cross-section is 260 cm^2, determine the value of x.

Complete Assignment Questions #5 - #10

Assignment

1. Solve the equation.

a) $(x - 2)(x + 7) = 0$

b) $(3x - 2)(2x + 5) = 0$

c) $5x(10 - x) = 0$

d) $x^2 + 2x = 0$

e) $x^2 - 121 = 0$

f) $9x^2 - 100 = 0$

g) $36x^2 = 25$

h) $9x - 4x^2 = 0$

i) $4(49 - x^2) = 0$

2. Solve the equation.

a) $x^2 - 3x + 2 = 0$

b) $x^2 + 13x + 30 = 0$

c) $x^2 + 2x - 15 = 0$

d) $3x^2 - 10x + 3 = 0$ **e)** $2x^2 + 3x - 35 = 0$ **f)** $15 - 2x - x^2 = 0$

3. Solve the equation.

a) $2x^2 + 5x = 7$ **b)** $6x^2 = 7x + 3$ **c)** $x(x + 4) = 32$

d) $(x - 3)(2x + 3) = 5$ **e)** $(2x - 3)^2 = 1$ **f)** $(x + 1)(x - 1) = 5(x + 1)$

4. Solve the equation.

a) $6a^2 - 7 - 19a = 0$ **b)** $21 - 8k - 2k^2 = 2k^2$

5. The diagram shows a piece of wood of uniform width x cm.
$RS = 10$ cm and $ST = 7$ cm.

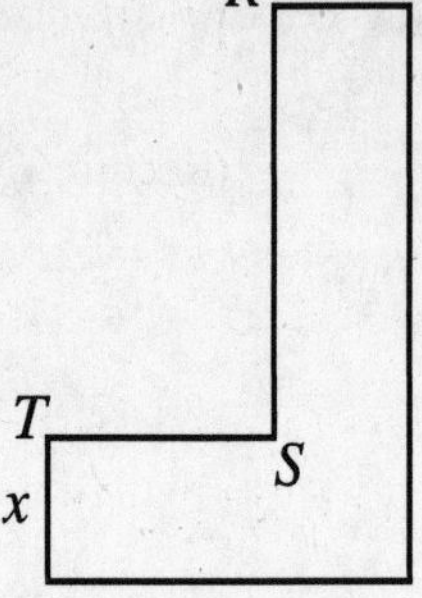

a) Find the area of the piece of wood in terms of x.

b) Find the value of x if the area is 60 cm^2.

6. Consider the arithmetic series $2 + 5 + 8 + \ldots$.
Determine the number of terms of the series required to give a sum of 222 by developing and solving a quadratic equation.

7. The height of a triangle is 8 mm more than the base. The area is 172.5 mm^2.

a) Write a polynomial equation to model this information.

b) Determine the height of the triangle.

Multiple Choice

8. The complete solution to the equation $x(x - 1) = 2$ is

A. $x = 0$ and $x = 1$
B. $x = 2$ and $x = 3$
C. $x = -1$ and $x = 2$
D. $x = -2$ and $x = 1$

Numerical Response

9. The equation $24x^2 + 2x = 15$ has solutions $x = a$ and $x = -b$, where a and b are positive rational numbers. The value of b, to the nearest hundredth, is _____.

(Record your answer in the numerical response box from left to right.)

10. The sum of the first n natural numbers is given by the formula $S = \frac{1}{2}n(n+1)$. If the first k natural numbers have a sum of 496, the value of k is _____.

(Record your answer in the numerical response box from left to right.)

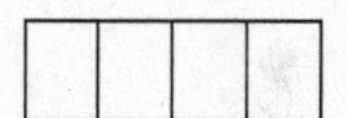

Answer Key

1. **a)** $2, -7$ **b)** $\frac{2}{3}, -\frac{5}{2}$ **c)** $0, 10$ **d)** $0, -2$
e) ± 11 **f)** $\pm\frac{10}{3}$ **g)** $\pm\frac{5}{6}$ **h)** $0, \frac{9}{4}$ **i)** ± 7

2. **a)** $1, 2$ **b)** $-10, -3$ **c)** $-5, 3$ **d)** $\frac{1}{3}, 3$ **e)** $-5, \frac{7}{2}$ **f)** $-5, 3$

3. **a)** $-\frac{7}{2}, 1$ **b)** $-\frac{1}{3}, \frac{3}{2}$ **c)** $-8, 4$ **d)** $-2, \frac{7}{2}$ **e)** $1, 2$ **f)** $-1, 6$

4. **a)** $-\frac{1}{3}, \frac{7}{2}$ **b)** $-\frac{7}{2}, \frac{3}{2}$ **5.** **a)** $x^2 + 17x$ cm^2 **b)** 3

6. 12 **7.** **a)** $x^2 + 8x - 345 = 0$ **b)** 23 mm

8. C **9.** | 0 | . | 8 | 3 | **10.** | 3 | 1 | | |

Factoring and Applications Lesson #6:
Solving Radical Equations Using Factoring - Part One

Restrictions on Values for the Variable in a Radical Expression

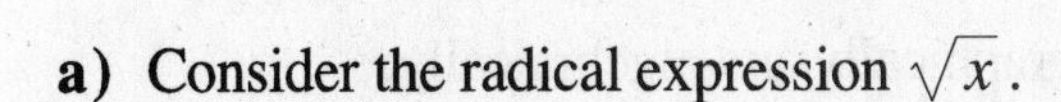

a) Consider the radical expression $\sqrt{x}$.

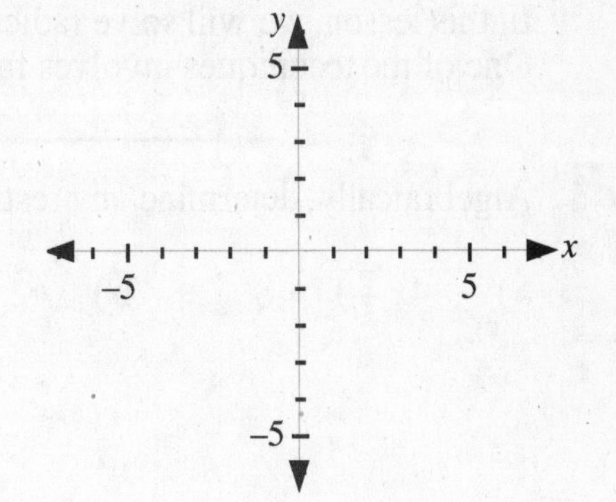

i) On the grid, sketch the graph of $y = \sqrt{x}$.

ii) State the domain of the graph of $y = \sqrt{x}$.

iii) For what values of x is the radical expression $\sqrt{x}$ defined?

b) Consider the radical expression $\sqrt{x-2}$.

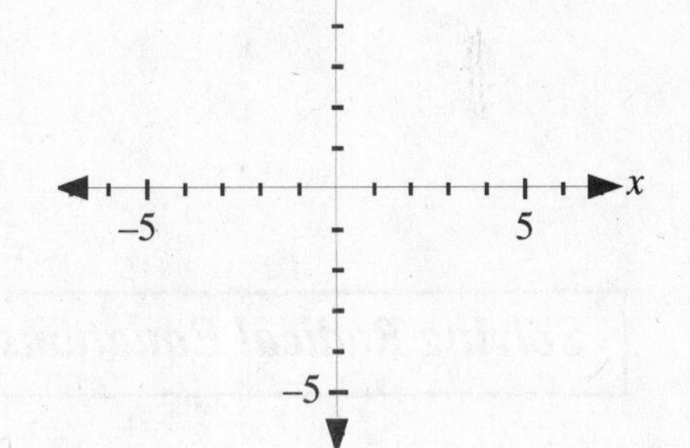

i) On the grid, sketch the graph of $y = \sqrt{x-2}$.

ii) State the domain of the graph of $y = \sqrt{x-2}$.

iii) For the radical expression $\sqrt{x-2}$, state the restrictions on x.

iv) Explain how to determine the restrictions algebraically.

c) Consider the radical expression $\sqrt{3-2x}$.

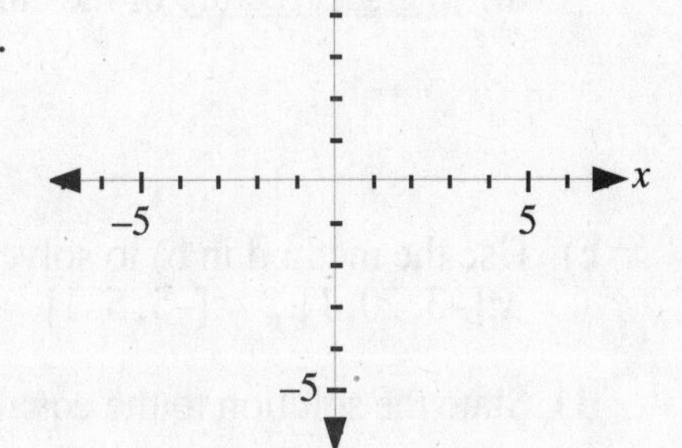

i) On the grid, sketch the graph of $y = \sqrt{3-2x}$.

ii) State the restrictions of the variable in the radical expression $\sqrt{3-2x}$.

iii) Determine the restrictions algebraically.

Radical Equations

A radical equation is an equation which contains a radical. A value of the variable which satisfies the equation is called a **root** of the equation.

In this lesson, we will solve radical equations graphically and algebraically. One of the techniques involves factoring quadratic equations.

Class Ex. #1

Algebraically, determine any restrictions on values for the variable in these radical equations..

a) $\sqrt{4x+1} = 8$ **b)** $\sqrt{2-5x} - 7 = 0$ **c)** $\sqrt{x-2} - \sqrt{x-4} = 1$

d) $\sqrt{x+2} + \sqrt{3-x} = 2.8$ **e)** $3\sqrt{2x-7} - \sqrt{24-5x} = 2$

Solving Radical Equations Graphically

Class Ex. #2

Consider the radical equation $\sqrt{x+1} = 4$.

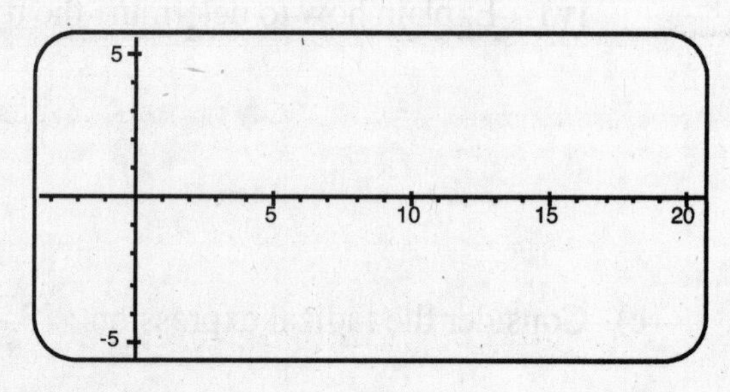

a) State the values of x for which the radical equation is defined.

b) Explain how to use a graphing calculator to find the solution to the equation by using the intersect feature of the calculator.

c) Use the method in b) to solve the radical equation $\sqrt{x+1} = 4$. Use a window $x{:}[-3, 20, 1]$ $y{:}[-5, 5, 1]$ and label the displayed graphs on the grid above.

d) State the solution to the equation.

e) Verify the solution algebraically.

Complete Assignment Questions #1 - #4

Investigation 1 Solving Radical Equations Algebraically

Complete the following steps to solve the following radical equation and verify the solution.

$$\sqrt{x+1} = 4$$

Step 1: Square both sides: $\left(\sqrt{x+1}\right)^2 = (4)^2$

Step 2: Solve the equation:

Step 3: Verify the solution:

The method of solving a radical equation by squaring both sides of the equation needs to studied in more detail. Consider the following example.

Investigation 2 Solving Radical Equations Algebraically

a) Complete the following steps to determine the roots of the radical equation $3 + \sqrt{x-1} = x$ and verify the solution.

$$3 + \sqrt{x-1} = x$$

Step 1: Isolate the radical term : $\sqrt{x-1} = x - 3$

Step 2: Square both sides : $\left(\sqrt{x-1}\right)^2 = (x-3)^2$

Step 3: Solve the equation :

Step 4: Verify the solution :

b) Confirm the above result by solving the equation graphically.

In Investigation #2, one of the solutions can be verified but the other solution cannot be verified. Can you explain why solving a radical equation by squaring both sides of the equation can lead to an invalid solution? The answer is provided in the section below.

Extraneous Roots

The process used in solving Investigation #2 led to an answer which is not one of the roots of the original radical equation or of the radical equation in step 1. It is, however, a root of the non-radical equation in step 2 formed by squaring the original equation.

This is because the process of solving a radical equation is based on squaring both sides of the equation. If two quantities are equal, then their squares are equal. The converse, however, is not necessarily true. Two quantities which have squares that are equal are not necessarily equal quantities, e.g. $(-3)^2 = (3)^2$ but $-3 \neq 3$,

In general, the process of squaring may lead to an answer which does not satisfy the original equation. This type of an answer is called an **extraneous solution** or **extraneous root.**

For this reason, it is always necessary to verify the solution to a radical equation solved algebraically.

Solving Radical Equations Algebraically

Use the following method to solve radical equations algebraically.

Step 1: Isolate the radical term.
If there are two radical terms, isolate the more complex term.

Step 2: Square both sides of the equation.

Step 3: If the resulting equation contains a radical term, repeat steps 1 and 2.
Solve the resulting equation.

Step 4: Verify all answers because the squaring in step 2 may result in **extraneous roots.**

Solve the following radical equations.

a) $\sqrt{x+3} = \sqrt{3x-5}$ **b)** $\sqrt{x-3} = \sqrt{3x-5}$

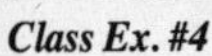

Solve the following radical equation.

$\sqrt{x} + \sqrt{x-3} = 5$

Complete Assignment Question #5 - #11

Assignment

1. Algebraically, determine any restrictions on values of the variable in these radical equations.

a) $\sqrt{3x-9} = 5$ **b)** $\sqrt{2+x} + 13 = 0$ **c)** $\sqrt{1-x} - \sqrt{4-x} = -1$

d) $\sqrt{2x+9} + \sqrt{1-2x} = 4$ **e)** $\sqrt{7x-2} = \sqrt{7-6x}$

2. Consider the equation $\sqrt{x} = \sqrt{33 - 3x}$.

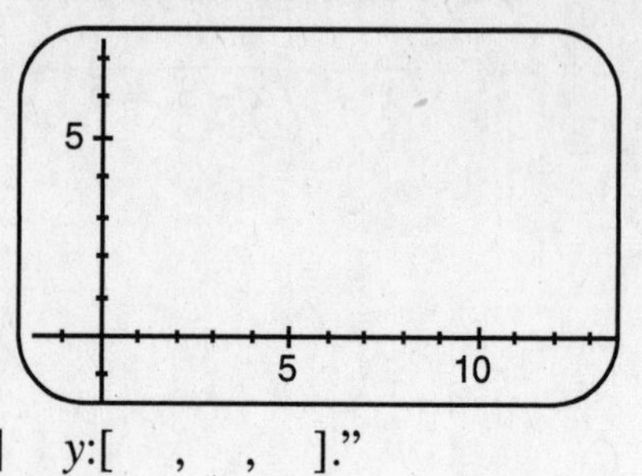

a) Determine the values of x for which the radical equation is defined.

b) Complete the following statement.
"The grid provided shows the window x:[, ,] y:[, ,]."

c) Solve the equation graphically, giving the root(s) to the nearest hundredth. Sketch and label the displayed graphs on the grid.

d) Verify the solution algebraically.

3. Describe how to solve the radical equation $\sqrt{6x + 4} = 3x - 1$ using the intersection feature of the calculator. State the solution of the equation to the nearest tenth.

4. For each of the following radical equations:

i) Determine the values of the variable for which the radical equation is defined.

ii) Solve the radical equation graphically. If the solution is not rational, answer to the nearest hundredth. Sketch and label your calculator graph(s) on the grid.

a) $\sqrt{3x - 7} = x - 5$

b) $\sqrt{x + 5} - 2\sqrt{x} = 2$

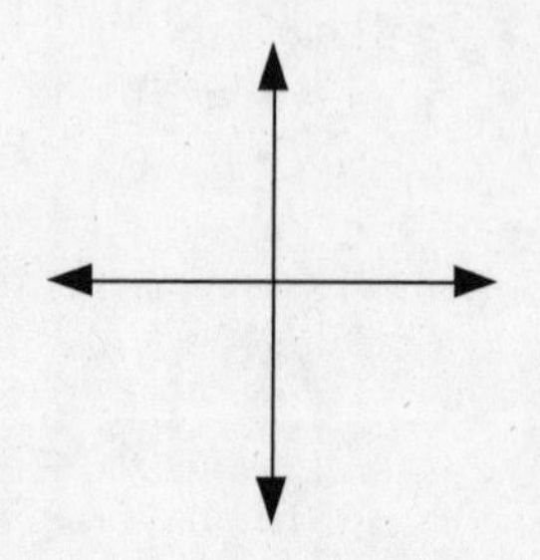

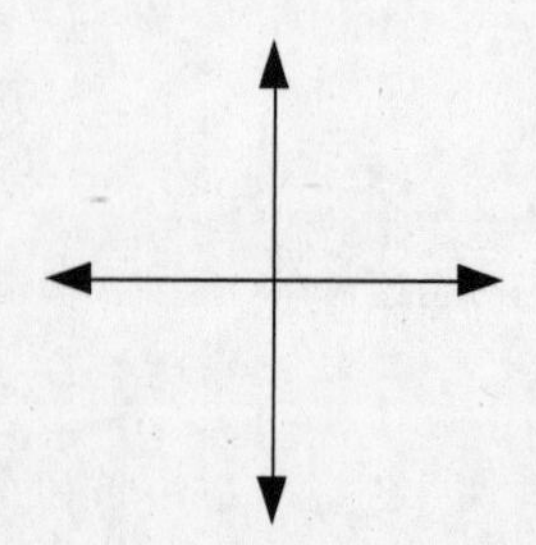

c) $\sqrt{2(1-5x)} - 3 = 0$

d) $\sqrt{3-p} = 1 + \sqrt{2p+5}$

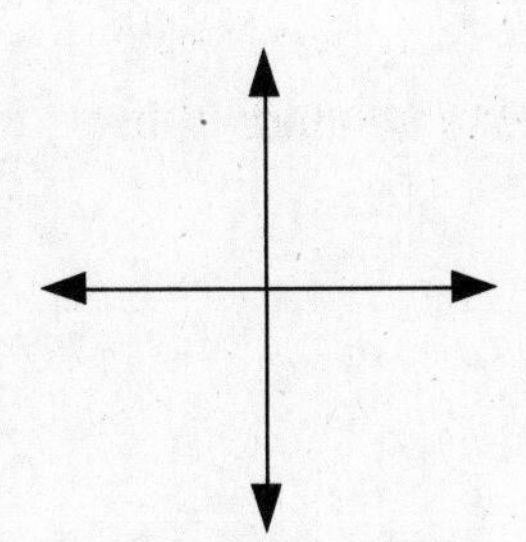

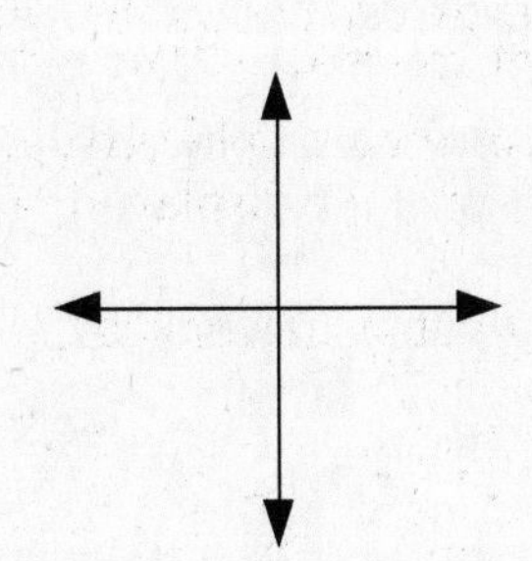

5. Solve the following radical equations algebraically.

a) $\sqrt{x-7} = 8$

b) $\sqrt{2y+3} = 4$

c) $\sqrt{\dfrac{3x-2}{5}} = 6$

d) $4 + \sqrt{x-2} = x$

6. Algebraically determine the solution to the following radical equations.

a) $\sqrt{19a+6} - 2a = 3$

b) $x = 2\sqrt{2x-4}$

Use the following information to answer Question #7.

The time it takes for a pendulum to swing back and forth (the period) depends on the length of the pendulum. The formula $T = 2\pi\sqrt{\dfrac{L}{g}}$ is used to determine the period (in seconds) of a pendulum of length L metres. g is the acceleration due to gravity ($g = 9.81$ m/s^2).

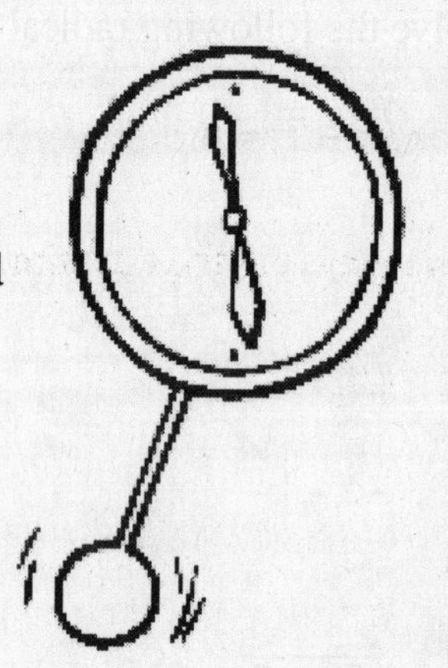

7. a) Determine the period, to the nearest 0.01 seconds, of a pendulum of length 0.5 metres.

b) Determine, to the nearest centimetre, the length of a pendulum whose period is 1 second.

8. Solve the following radical equations.

a) $3 - \sqrt{3x+4} = 4$ **b)** $2\sqrt{21x^2 + 50x} = 8$

Multiple Choice

9. When solving the equation $x - 3 = \sqrt{x-1}$, the extraneous root is

A. -2
B. 2
C. -5
D. 5

10. The solution to the radical equation $\sqrt{x+3} = \sqrt{x^2 - 17}$ is

A. $x = -4$ only
B. $x = 5$ only
C. $x = -4, 5$
D. $x = -5, 4$

Numerical Response **11.** When the solution to the radical equation $6\sqrt{x-2} = 4\sqrt{x+8}$ is verified, the value of each side of the equation, to the nearest tenth, is _____ .

(Record your answer in the numerical response box from left to right.)

Answer Key

1. a) $x \geq 3, x \in R$ **b)** $x \geq -2, x \in R$ **c)** $x \leq 1, x \in R$

d) $-\frac{9}{2} \leq x \leq \frac{1}{2}, x \in R$ **e)** $\frac{2}{7} \leq x \leq \frac{7}{6}, x \in R$

2. a) $0 \leq x \leq 11, x \in R$ **b)** x:[−1, 13, 1], y:[−1, 7, 1] **c)** 8.25

d) LS = $\sqrt{8.25}$, RS = $\sqrt{33 - 3(8.25)} = \sqrt{8.25}$, LS = RS

3. • Graph $Y_1 = \sqrt{6x + 4}$ • Graph $Y_2 = -3x + 1$
• Find the x-coordinate(s) of the point(s) of intersection using the intersect feature of the calculator.
• Solution is $x = 1.5$

4. a) $x \geq \frac{7}{3}, x \in R$. 9.70 **b)** $x \geq 0, x \in R$. 0.01

c) $x \leq \frac{1}{5}, x \in R$. $-\frac{7}{10}$ **d)** $-\frac{5}{2} \leq p \leq 3, p \in R$. −1.79

5. a) 71 **b)** $\frac{13}{2}$ **c)** $\frac{182}{3}$ **d)** 6 **6. a)** $\frac{3}{4}$ or 1 **b)** 4

7. a) 1.42 seconds **b)** 25 cm **8. a)** no solution **b)** $-\frac{8}{3}$ or $\frac{2}{7}$

9. B **10.** B **11.**

1	7	.	0

Factoring and Applications Lesson #7:
Solving Radical Equations Using Factoring - Part Two

Solving More Complex Radical Equations

Billy was given the radical equation $\sqrt{3a+4} - \sqrt{a+1} = 3$ to solve. Billy solved the equation incorrectly. His work is shown.

$$\sqrt{3a+4} - \sqrt{a+1} = 3$$

$$\sqrt{3a+4} = 3 + \sqrt{a+1}$$

$$(\sqrt{3a+4})^2 = (3 + \sqrt{a+1})^2$$

$$3a + 4 = 9 + a + 1$$

$$2a = 6$$

$$a = 3$$

a) Explain where Billy made his error.

b) Show the correct work.

When the square root of two less than a number is subtracted from the square root of five more than twice a number, the result is three.

a) Write a radical equation to represent this information.

b) Solve the equation to determine the number.

Complete Assignment Questions #1 - #7

Assignment

1. For each of the following radical equations:

i) Determine the values of the variable for which the radical equation is defined.

ii) Solve the radical equation algebraically.

a) $\sqrt{x} + 5 = \sqrt{2x + 1}$

b) $\sqrt{x} + \sqrt{x - 4} = 4$

2. Algebraically determine the solution to the following radical equations.

a) $\sqrt{2t+1} - 5 = -\sqrt{t}$

b) $\sqrt{2a} = \sqrt{5a+9} - 3$

3. Consider the two rectangles shown.

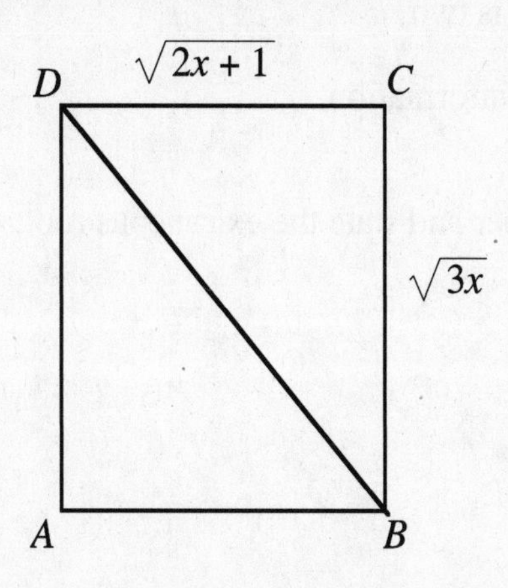

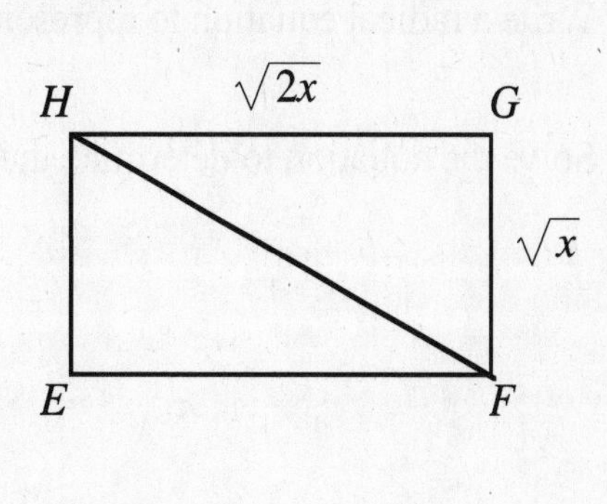

a) Determine the exact length of diagonal *BD*.

b) Determine the exact length of diagonal *FH*.

c) If *BD* is 1 unit longer than *FH*, determine the length and width of each rectangle.

4. When the square root of one more than a number is subtracted from the square root of six less than double the number, the result is two.

a) Write a radical equation to represent this information.

b) Solve the equation to determine the number and state the extraneous root.

5. A number, n, is non-negative. The difference between the square root of nine more than five times the number and the square root of twice the number is three.

a) Write a radical equation to represent this information.

b) Solve the equation to determine all possible values of the number.

6. Algebracially solve and verify the following radical equations.

a) $\sqrt{x+11} - \sqrt{x-9} = 2$

b) $\sqrt{x+3} + 2 = \sqrt{x+11}$

c) $\sqrt{4p+5} = 2 + \sqrt{2p-1}$

d) $\sqrt{3-a} - 3 = -\sqrt{2a+3}$

Numerical Response

7. Jasmine uses an algebraic procedure to determine the solution to the equation $2\sqrt{x} - \sqrt{x+4} = 3$. The solution, to the nearest tenth, is ____ .

(Record your answer in the numerical response box from left to right.)

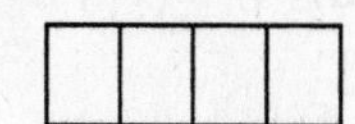

Algebraically determine the roots of the equation $\sqrt{x+3} + \sqrt{x+8} = \sqrt{5x+20}$.

Answer Key

1. a) i) $\{x \mid x \geq 0, x \in R\}$ **ii)** 144 **b) i)** $\{x \mid x \geq 4, x \in R\}$ **ii)** $\frac{25}{4}$

2. a) 4 **b)** 0, 8

3. a) $\sqrt{5x+1}$ **b)** $\sqrt{3x}$ **c)** rectangle *ABCD* has dimensions $\sqrt{7}$ by 3
rectangle *EFGH* has dimensions $\sqrt{6}$ by $\sqrt{3}$

4. a) $\sqrt{2n-6} - \sqrt{n+1} = 2$ **b)** The number is 35 and the extraneous root is 3.

5. a) $\sqrt{5n+9} - \sqrt{2n} = 3$ **b)** 0 or 8

6. a) $x = 25$ **b)** $x = -2$ **c)** $p = 1, 5$ **d)** $a = -1, 3$

7.

1	2	.	4

Group Work −3, 1

Factoring and Applications Lesson #8:
Practice Test

1. One factor of $4x^2 - 25y^2$ is

A. $4x - 25y$ **B.** $4x - 5y$

C. $2x - 25y$ **D.** $2x - 5y$

2. One factor of $6x^2 - 5x - 4$ is

A. $2x - 1$ **B.** $3x - 4$

C. $6x - 1$ **D.** $3x + 4$

3. When factored, the trinomials $x^2 - 8xy + 15y^2$ and $x^2 - 2xy - 15y^2$ have one binomial factor in common. This factor is

A. $x - 5y$ **B.** $x + 3y$

C. $x - 3y$ **D.** $x + 5y$

1. The expression $15x^2 + 14x - 8$ can be written in the form $(ax - b)(cx + d)$ where $a, b, c,$ and d are all positive integers.

Write the value of a in the first box. Write the value of b in the second box.
Write the value of c in the third box. Write the value of d in the fourth box.

(Record your answer in the numerical response box from left to right.)

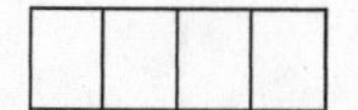

2. Consider the trinomial $4a^2 + kab + 49b^2$, where k is a natural number.
In order for $4a^2 + kab + 49b^2$ to represent a perfect square trinomial, the value of k must be _____.

(Record your answer in the numerical response box from left to right.)

4. Which of the following is a factor of $4x^2 - 144y^2$?

A. $2x + 72y$

B. $2x - 36y$

C. $x + 6y$

D. $x - 18y$

5. Which of the following is not a factor of $a^4 - 13a^2 + 36$?

A. $a + 9$

B. $a - 2$

C. $a + 2$

D. $a - 3$

6. The equation $25x^2 - 9 = 0$ is satisfied by

A. $x = \frac{5}{3}$ only **B.** $x = \frac{3}{5}$ only

C. $x = \pm\frac{5}{3}$ **D.** $x = \pm\frac{3}{5}$

7. Consider the following expressions:

 # 1 : $4x^2 - 36xy + 81y^2$ **# 2** : $10x^2 + 43xy - 9y^2$ **# 3** : $8x^4y^2 - 162x^2y^4$

Which of the these expressions has $2x + 9y$ as one of its factors?

A. # **2** only **B.** # **3** only **C.** # **1** and # **2** only **D.** # **2** and # **3** only

8. The solution to the equation $6x^2 - 18x = 0$ is

A. $x = 3$ only

B. $x = -3$ only

C. $x = 0, 3$

D. $x = -3, 0$

9. The roots of the equation $1 + 4x - 21x^2 = 0$ are

A. $-\frac{1}{3}, \frac{1}{7}$

B. $-\frac{1}{7}, \frac{1}{3}$

C. $-3, 7$

D. $-7, 3$

10. The factored form of $p^2 - (q - r)^2$ is

A. $(p - q - r)(p + q + r)$

B. $(p - q - r)(p + q - r)$

C. $(p - q + r)(p + q - r)$

D. $(p - q + r)(p + q + r)$

Use the following information to answer the next question.

Consider the right-angled triangle shown in which the length of each side is a whole number.

$2x + 1$

x

$x + 7$

Numerical Response 3. The length of the hypotenuse is _____ .

(Record your answer in the numerical response box from left to right.)

11. Which one of the following is a factor of $4(3x+1)^2 - 9(x+2)^2$?

A. $3x - 14$

B. $3x + 8$

C. $9x + 8$

D. $21x + 22$

Use the following information to answer the next question.

Chantelle is asked to factor the expression $4x^2 - 16xy + 16y^2$. Part of her work is shown below.

$4x^2 - 16xy + 16y^2$	$= (2x - 4y)(2x - 4y)$	Line 1
	$= (2x - 4y)^2$	Line 2
	$= 2(x - 2y)^2$	Line 3

12. **A.** Answer A if her work is correct.

B. Answer B if her first mathematical error is in Line 1.

C. Answer C if her first mathematical error is in Line 2.

D. Answer D if her first mathematical error is in Line 3.

4. The expression $8(2a+3)^2 + 14(2a+3) + 3$ can be written in factored form as $(4a+K)(8a+L)$ The value of the product KL is _____.

(Record your answer in the numerical response box from left to right.)

13. The extraneous root in the radical equation $x - 3 = \sqrt{30 - 2x}$ is

A. 7

B. 3

C. −3

D. −7

14. The equation $12t^2 + 17t - 5 = 0$ is satisfied by $t = a$ and by $t = -b$, where $a, b > 0$. The value of a is

A. $\frac{1}{4}$

B. $\frac{3}{5}$

C. $\frac{5}{3}$

D. 4

Use the following information to answer the next two questions.

Consider the radical equation shown.

$$\sqrt{2 + x} = 10 - \sqrt{x}$$

15. All the restrictions on the value of the variable are

A. $x \geq 0$ **B.** $x \geq -2$

C. $x \geq 0$ and $x \leq 2$ **D.** $x \geq 2$

5. The solution to the equation, to the nearest whole number, is
(Record your answer in the numerical response box from left to right.)

Written Response - 5 marks

1. Consider the radical equation $\sqrt{a-1} + \sqrt{3a-5} = 2$.

- Determine the restrictions on the value of the variable a.

- Explain why, in the process of solving this radical equation algebraically, an extraneous root may appear.

- Algebraically, determine the root(s) of the radical equation.

Answer Key

1. D	2. B	3. A	4. C	5. A	6. D	7. D	8. C
9. B	10. C	11. C	12. D	13. C	14. A	15. A	

Numerical Response

1. | 5 | 2 | 3 | 4 |
2. | 2 | 8 | | |
3. | 1 | 7 | | |
4. | 1 | 1 | 7 | |
5. | 2 | 4 | | |

Written Response

1. • $a \geq \frac{5}{3}$
   - The solution process involves squaring both sides of the equation and solving. However, if the squares of two quantities are equal, it does not necessarily mean that the two quantities are equal. An extraneous root may appear.
   - $a = 2$

Quadratic Functions and Equations Lesson #1:
Connecting Zeros, Roots, and x-intercepts

Function and Function Notation

Recall the following information from previous math courses:

Function
A functional relation, or **function**, is a special type of relation in which each element of the domain is related to exactly one element of the range. If any element of the domain is related to more than one element of the range, then the relation is not a function.

Function Notation
Under a function, f, the image of an element x in the domain is denoted by $f(x)$, which is read "f of x".

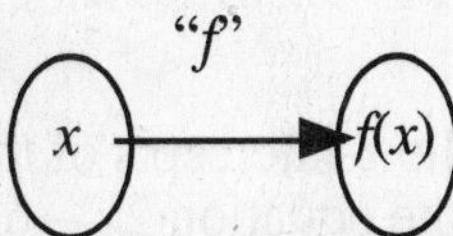

Consider a function f defined by the formula $f(x) = 4x - 8$.
The notation $f(x) = 4x - 8$ is called **function notation**.

We can show that, under the function f, the image of 5 is 12. We write $f(5) = 12$.

function notation	equation of graph of function
$f(x) = 4x - 8$	$y = 4x - 8$
$f(5) = 4(5) - 8$	$y = 4(5) - 8$
$f(5) = 12$	$y = 12$

We can also show that, under the function f, the image of 2 is 0. We write $f(2) = 0$.

function notation	equation of graph of function
$f(x) = 4x - 8$	$y = 4x - 8$
$f(2) = 4(2) - 8$	$y = 4(2) - 8$
$f(2) = 0$	$y = 0$

We can say:
"The zero of the function $f(x) = 4x - 8$ is 2." "The root of the equation $y = 4x - 8$ is 2."

Zero(s) of a Function

A **zero of a function** is a value of the independent variable which makes the value of the function equal to zero. Zero(s) of a function can be found by solving the equation $f(x) = 0$.

Class Ex. #1

Find the zero of the function f where $f(x) = 7x - 21$.

Investigation #1 *Connecting Roots, x-intercepts, and Zeros in a Linear Relation*

a) The graph of $y = 2x - 6$ is shown. Determine the x-intercept of the graph algebraically and graphically.

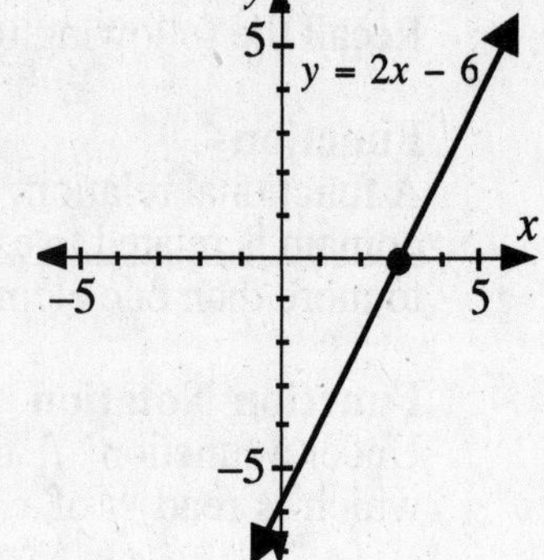

b) Determine the root of the equation $2x - 6 = 0$

c) State the connection between the x-intercepts of the graph of $y = 2x - 6$ and the roots of the equation $2x - 6 = 0$.

d) Consider the function $f(x) = 2x - 6$. What is the zero of the function?

e) What is the connection between the x-intercepts of the graph of $y = 2x - 6$, the roots of the equation $2x - 6 = 0$, and the zero of the function $f(x) = 2x - 6$?

Investigation #2 — *Connecting Roots, x-intercepts, and Zeros in a Quadratic Relation*

a) Jacques is determining the roots of the equation $x^2 - x - 6 = 0$.
He wrote the equation in factored form and used the Zero Product Law to determine the roots of the equation.

Complete his work to solve for x.

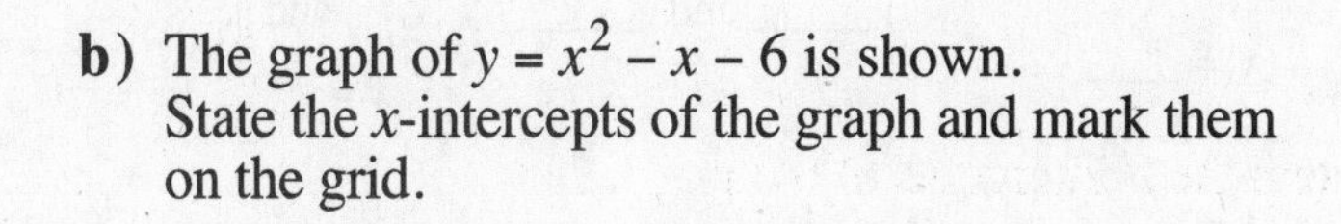

b) The graph of $y = x^2 - x - 6$ is shown.
State the x-intercepts of the graph and mark them on the grid.

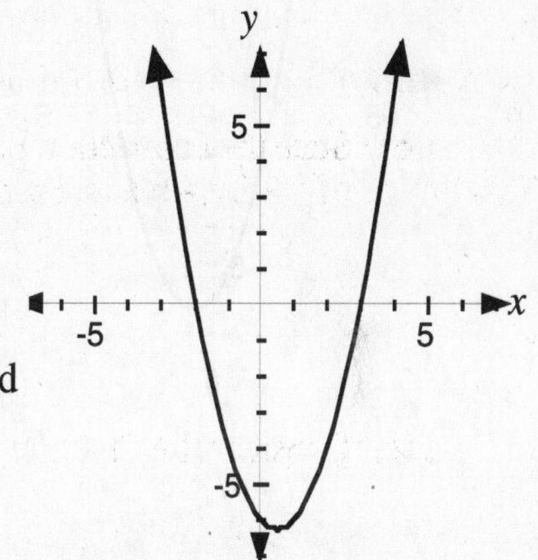

c) i) State the connection between the ***x*-intercepts** of the graph of $y = x^2 - x - 6$ and the **roots** of the equation $x^2 - x - 6 = 0$.

ii) Explain the connection between the **factors** of $x^2 - x - 6$ and the **roots** of the equation $x^2 - x - 6 = 0$.

d) Consider the function $g(x) = x^2 - x - 6$. Determine the zeros of the function.

e) State the connection between:

- the ***x*-intercepts** of the graph of $y = x^2 - x - 6$
- the **roots** of the equation $x^2 - x - 6 = 0$, and
- the **zeros** of the function $g(x) = x^2 - x - 6$

a) Fill in the blanks in the following statement regarding the function with equation $y = f(x)$.

"The ________ of the function, the __________ of the graph of the function, and the __________ of the corresponding equation $y = 0$, are the ________ numbers."

b) The graph of $f(x) = x^2 - x - 6$ is shown. Fill in the blanks.

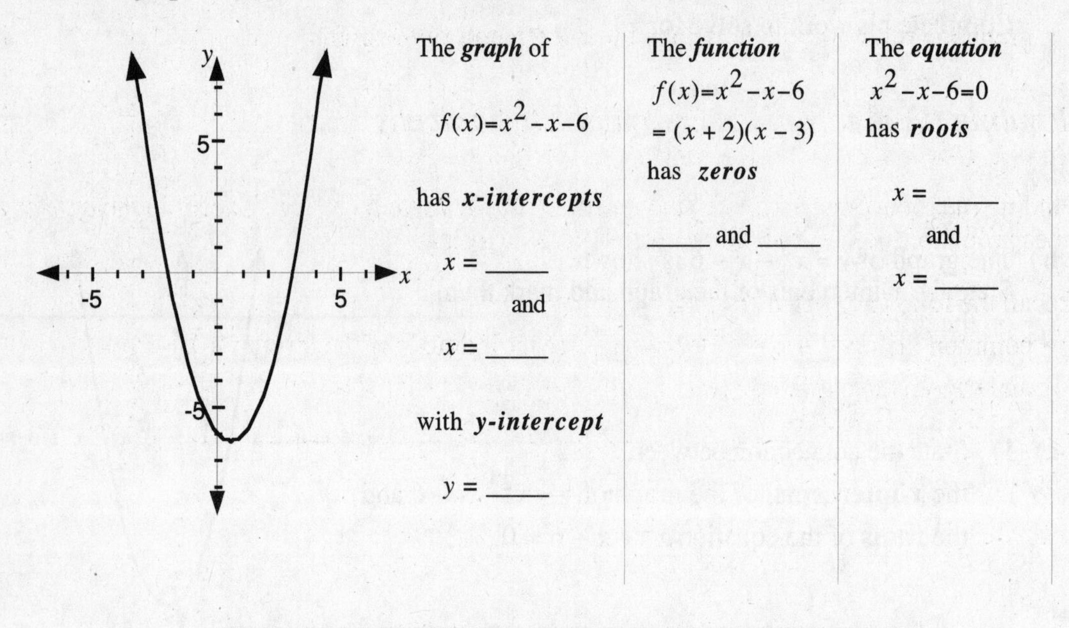

y
5
-5
-5
5
x
The *graph* of
$f(x)=x^2-x-6$
has ***x-intercepts***
$x =$ ____
and
$x =$ ____
with ***y-intercept***
$y =$ ____
The *function*
$f(x)=x^2-x-6$
$= (x + 2)(x - 3)$
has ***zeros***
____ and ____
The *equation*
$x^2-x-6=0$
has ***roots***
$x =$ ____
and
$x =$ ____

Consider the equation $2x^2 - 7x + 3 = 0$.

a) Describe how the **zero feature** of a graphing calculator can be used to determine the roots of the equation.

b) Use a graphing calculator to determine the roots of the equation and sketch the graph on the grid provided.

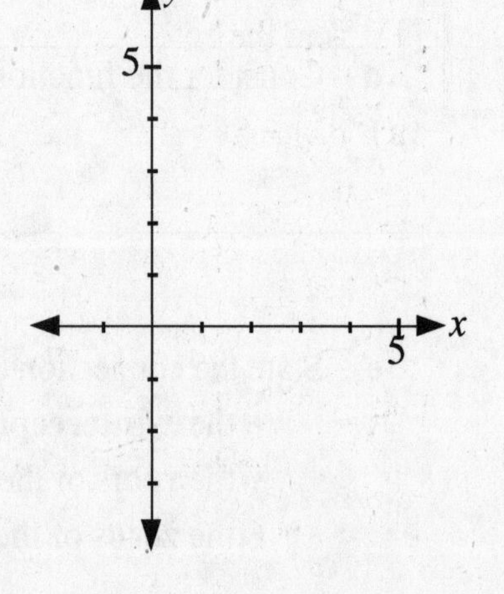

c) Use the x-intercepts of the graph of $y = 2x^2 - 7x + 3$ to factor the expression $2x^2 - 7x + 3$.

d) What are the zeros of the function $f(x) = 2x^2 - 7x + 3$?

Finding Zeros of a Function

To find the zeros of a function, $f(x)$, either:

- substitute zero for $f(x)$ and find the roots of the resulting equation

or

- graph the function and determine the x-intercepts of the graph.

Finding the Roots of an Equation Algebraically

Finding the roots of a single variable equation may involve factoring. Except in the case of a linear equation, set the equation to zero before factoring.

Recall the following techniques for factoring:

- common factors, difference of two squares, trinomials of the form $x^2 + bx + c = 0$, and trinomials of the form $ax^2 + bx + c = 0$.

Find the roots of the following equations:

a) $x^2 + 8x = 33$ **b)** $6(4x + 5)(x - 3) = 0$ **c)** $2x^2 - 8 = 0$

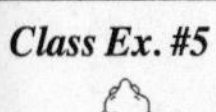

For the following functions:

i) find the zeros **ii)** find the y-intercept of the graph of the function

a) $f(x) = 5x^2 + 15x - 20$ **b)** $f(x) = 3x^2 - 11x + 10$ **c)** $g(x) = 2x(2x + 1)$

For each of the following functions, use a graphing calculator to:

- sketch the graph of the function
- find the zeros of the function as exact values
- write the function in factored form

a) $f(x) = 3x^2 + 4x - 7$

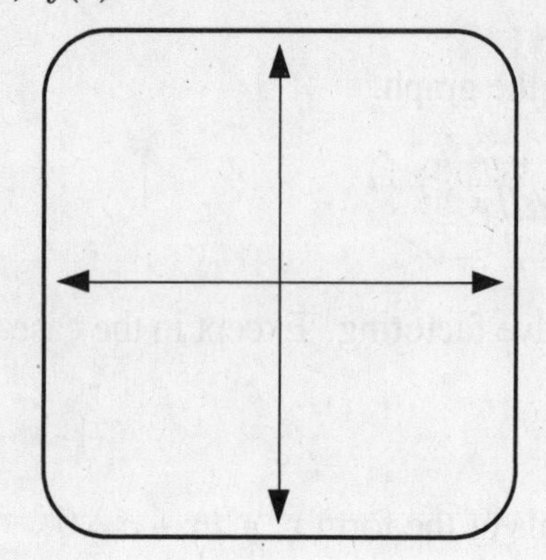

b) $g(x) = 4x^3 - 7x^2 - 4x + 7$

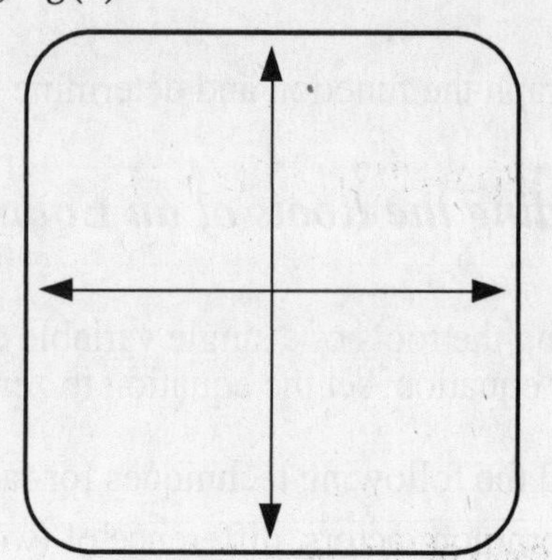

Complete Assignment Questions #1 - #11

Assignment

1. The graph of a function, f, is shown. The x and y-intercepts of the graph are integers.

a) State the x and y-intercepts of the graph.

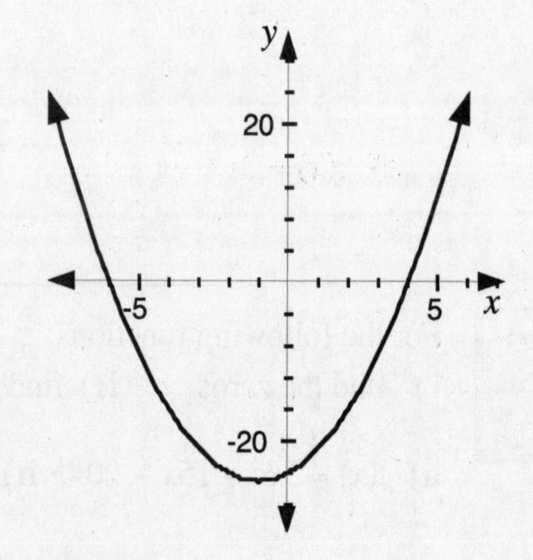

b) State the zeros of the function f.

2. Find the roots of the following equations.

a) $2x(x + 3) = 0$

b) $2x^2 - 10x + 12 = 0$

c) $x^3 + 8x^2 = 20x$

d) $4x^2 + 4x - 3 = 0$

3. Find the zeros of the following functions.

a) $f(x) = \frac{x}{3} + 5$

b) $g(x) = 25x^2 - 64$

c) $P(x) = 3(2x - 5)(x + 1)$

d) $P(x) = x(x - 3)(2x + 1)$

4. In each of the following:

i) determine the zeros of the function
ii) determine the y-intercept of the graph of the function

a) $f(x) = 5x^2 - 35x$

b) $f(x) = 3x(x^2 - 49)$

c) $f(x) = 2x^2 - x - 15$

d) $P(x) = 8x^2 + 14x - 15$

5. Use a graphing calculator to find the zeros (as exact values) of the following functions.

a) $f(x) = 18x^2 - 5x - 7$

b) $g(x) = 3x^3 - 11x^2 + 6x$

6. In each case, the graph of a function with $y = f(x)$ is shown. The x and y-intercepts of the graph are integers. Determine:

- the zeros of the function
- the y-intercept of the graph of the function
- the equation of the function in factored form

a)

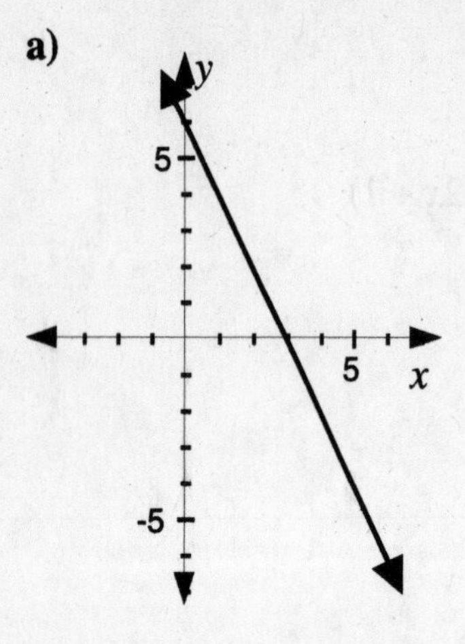

b)

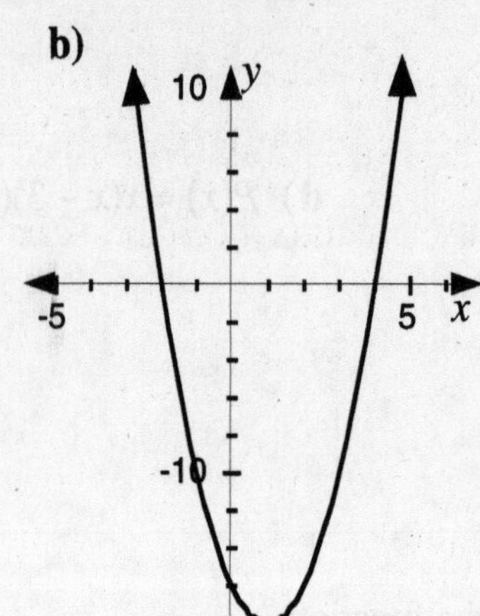

c)

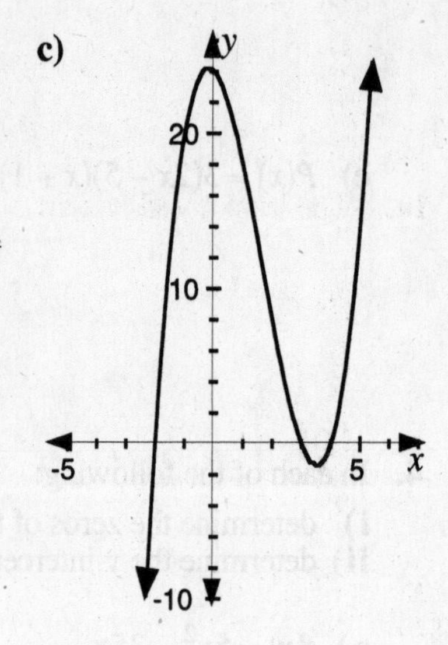

7. Use a graphing calculator to write the equation in factored form.

a) $y = 2x^2 - 3x - 9$ **b)** $y = 5x^3 - 7x^2 - 21x - 9$

Multiple Choice

8. The zeros of the function $f(x) = 2(x - 3)(4x + 7)$ are:

A. $3, -\frac{7}{4}$ **B.** $-3, \frac{7}{4}$

C. $0, 3, -\frac{7}{4}$ **D.** $2, 3, -\frac{7}{4}$

9. The roots of the equation $3x(x + 1) = 6$ are

A. $0, -1$
B. $2, 5$
C. $2, -1$
D. $-2, 1$

10. The least possible zero of the function $f(x) = 2x^3 - 7x^2 + 3x$ is

A. 0
B. $\frac{1}{2}$
C. 3
D. -3

11. The y-intercept of the graph of the function $f(x) = (x + 4)(3 - 2x)(x + 1)$, to the nearest whole number, is _____ .
(Record your answer in the numerical response box from left to right.)

Answer Key

1. a) x-intercepts are $-6, 4$ and y-intercept is -24. **b)** $-6, 4$

2. a) $-3, 0$ **b)** $2, 3$ **c)** $-10, 0, 2$ **d)** $-\frac{3}{2}, \frac{1}{2}$

3. a) -15 **b)** $-\frac{8}{5}, \frac{8}{5}$ **c)** $-1, \frac{5}{2}$ **d)** $-\frac{1}{2}, 0, 3$

4. a) i) $0, 7$ **ii)** 0 **b) i)** $-7, 0, 7$ **ii)** 0
c) i) $-\frac{5}{2}, 3$ **ii)** -15 **d) i)** $-\frac{5}{2}, \frac{3}{4}$ **ii)** -15

5. a) $-\frac{1}{2}, \frac{7}{9}$ **b)** $0, \frac{2}{3}, 3$

6. a) zero: 3
y-intercept: 6
$f(x) = -2(x - 3)$

b) zeros: $-2, 4$
y-intercept: -16
$f(x) = 2(x + 2)(x - 4)$

c) zeros: $-2, 3, 4$
y-intercept: 24
$f(x) = (x + 2)(x - 3)(x - 4)$

7. a) $y = (2x + 3)(x - 3)$ **b)** $y = (5x + 3)(x - 3)(x + 1)$

8. A **9.** D **10.** A **11.**

1	2		

Quadratic Functions and Equations Lesson #2:
Analyzing Quadratic Functions - Part One

Quadratic Function

A **quadratic function** is a function which can be written in the form

$$f(x) = ax^2 + bx + c, \text{ where } a, b, c \in R, \text{ and } a \neq 0$$

or in equation form as

$$y = ax^2 + bx + c, \text{ where } a, b, c \in R, \text{ and } a \neq 0$$

Quadratic Equation

A **quadratic equation** is an equation which can be written in the form

$$ax^2 + bx + c = 0, \text{ where } a, b, c \in R, \text{ and } a \neq 0.$$

The roots of the quadratic equation $ax^2 + bx + c = 0$ are the zeros of the related quadratic function $f(x) = ax^2 + bx + c$.

General and Standard Forms

A quadratic function can be written in **general** or **standard** form.

General Form: $f(x) = ax^2 + bx + c$, **or** $y = ax^2 + bx + c$, where $a, b, c \in R$, and $a \neq 0$.

Standard Form: $f(x) = a(x - p)^2 + q$, **or** $y = a(x - p)^2 + q$, where $a, p, q \in R$, and $a \neq 0$.

In this unit we will study both the general form and standard form, beginning with the standard form in this lesson.

Analyzing the Graph of the Function with Equation $y = x^2$

- Graph the function with equation $y = x^2$ by completing the table of values. Join the points with a smooth curve.
  The graph of this function is called a parabola.

x	−3	−2	−1	0	1	2	3
y							

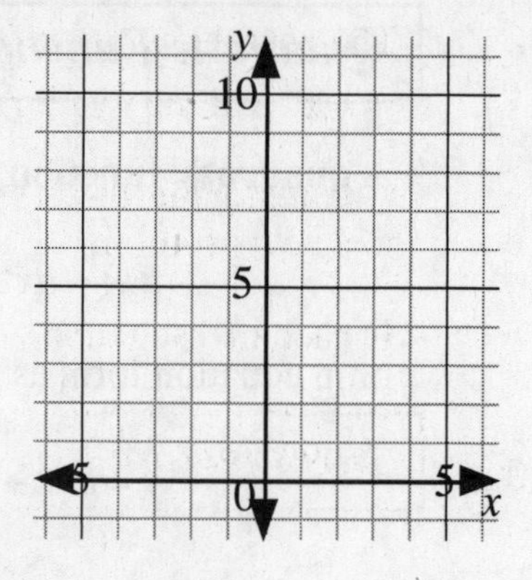

- The **axis of symmetry** is the "mirror" line which splits the parabola in half.
  State the equation of the axis of symmetry for this parabola.

- The **vertex** of a parabola is where the axis of symmetry intersects the parabola.
  The vertex can represent a minimum point or maximum point depending on whether the parabola opens up or down.

  Label the vertex (V) on the graph and state its coordinates.

- The maximum or minimum **value** of a quadratic function occurs at the vertex and is represented by the y-coordinate of the vertex. Complete the following:

  The ______________ value of the function with equation $y = x^2$ is ____ .

- State the domain and range of the function with equation $y = x^2, x \in R$.
  Domain: ______________________ Range: ______________________

The following investigations can be completed as a class lesson or as an individual assignment. The process used in these explorations will be further developed in grade 12 mathematics.

Analyzing the Function with Equation $y = a(x - p)^2 + q, \; a = 1$

The next three investigations help us explore some general **transformations** on the graph of $y = x^2$ and the relationship they have to the standard form $y = a(x - p)^2 + q$ where $a = 1$.

A **transformation** is an operation which moves (or maps) a figure from an original position to a new position.

In each investigation, use a graphing calculator to sketch the equations.

Investigation #1 — Analyzing the Graph of $y = x^2 + q$

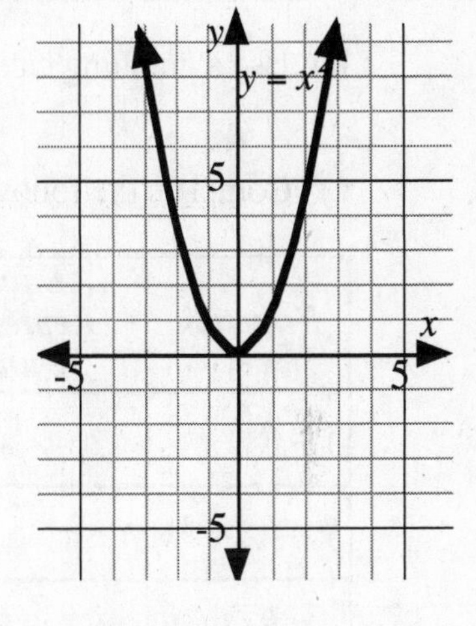

The graph of $y = f(x) = x^2$ is shown.

a) Write an equation which represents each of the following:

- $y = f(x) + 3$
- $y = f(x) - 3$

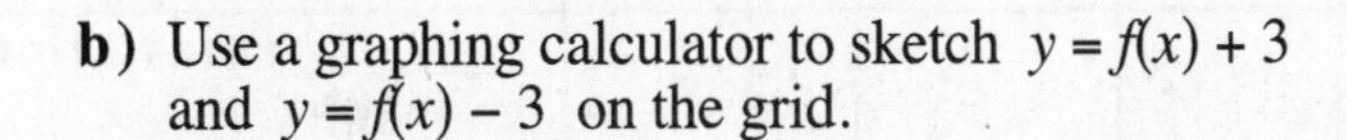

b) Use a graphing calculator to sketch $y = f(x) + 3$ and $y = f(x) - 3$ on the grid.

c) Complete the following chart.

Function	*Equation Representing Function*	*Vertex*	*Max/Min Value*	*Equation of Axis of Symmetry*	*Description of Transformation*
$y = f(x)$	$y = x^2$	(0, 0)	min, 0	$x = 0$	no transformation
$y = f(x) + 3$					________ translation ____ units ____
$y = f(x) - 3$					
$y = f(x) + q$					

d) What is the effect of the **parameter** q on the graph of $y = x^2 + q$?

e) Compared to the graph of $y = x^2$, the graph of $y = x^2 + q$ results in

a ________________ translation (or shift) of q units.

If $q > 0$, the parabola moves _______. If $q < 0$, the parabola moves _______.

Investigation #2 Analyzing the Graph of $y = (x - p)^2$

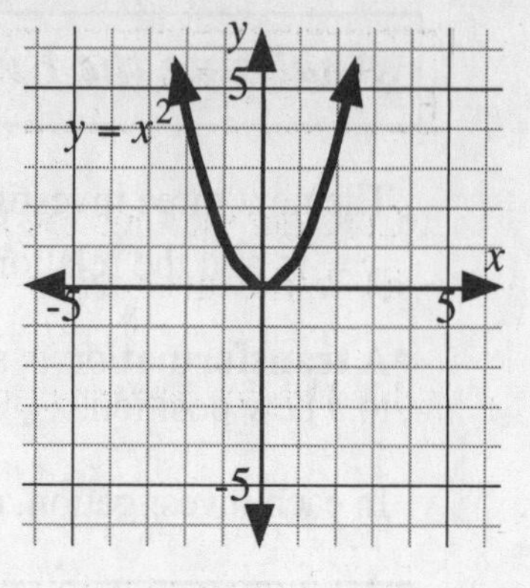

The graph of $y = f(x) = x^2$ is shown.

a) Write an equation which represents each of the following:

• $y = f(x + 3)$ • $y = f(x - 3)$

b) Use a graphing calculator to sketch $y = f(x + 3)$ and $y = f(x - 3)$ on the grid.

c) Complete the following chart.

Function	*Equation Representing Function*	*Vertex*	*Max/Min Value*	*Equation of Axis of Symmetry*	*Description of Transformation*
$y = f(x)$	$y = x^2$	(0, 0)	min, 0	$x = 0$	no transformation
$y = f(x + 3)$					____ translation ____ units ____
$y = f(x - 3)$					
$y = f(x - p)$					

d) What is the effect of the **parameter** p on the graph of $y = (x - p)^2$?

e) Compared to the graph of $y = x^2$, the graph of $y = (x - p)^2$ results in a ________________ translation (shift) of p units.

If $p > 0$, the parabola moves _______. If $p < 0$, the parabola moves _______.

Investigation #3 — Analyzing the Graph of $y = (x - p)^2 + q$

Consider the function $f(x) = x^2$.

a) Write an equation which represents $f(x + 2) - 4$.

b) Predict the transformations on $y = x^2$ in a). Use a graphing calculator to verify the results.

c) Complete the following chart.

Function	*Equation Representing Function*	*Vertex*	*Max/Min Value*	*Equation of Axis of Symmetry*	*Description of Transformation*
$y = f(x)$	$y = x^2$	(0, 0)	min, 0	$x = 0$	no transformation
$y = f(x + 2) - 4$					
$y = f(x - p) + q$					

Class Ex. #1

Describe how the graphs of the following functions relate to the graph of $y = x^2$.

a) $y = (x + 10)^2$ **b)** $y = x^2 + 4$ **c)** $y + 8 = (x - 5)^2$

Class Ex. #2

The following transformations are applied to the graph of $y = x^2$. Write the equation of the image function for each.

a) a horizontal translation of 5 units right

b) a translation of 6 units down and 4 units left

Class Ex. #3

Write the coordinates of the image of the point (3, 9) on the graph $y = x^2$ when a translation of two units up and seven units right is applied.

Complete Assignment Questions #1 - #10

Assignment

1. Describe how the graphs of the following functions relate to the graph of $y = x^2$.

a) $y = (x + 5)^2$ **b)** $y = x^2 - 7$ **c)** $y - 8 = x^2$

d) $y = 5 + (x - 2)^2$ **e)** $y + 7 = (x + 1)^2 - 10$ **f)** $y = (x - a)^2 - b$

2. Consider the graph of the function $f(x) = (x - 2)^2 + 3$.

a) Without using a graphing calculator, sketch the graph on the grid.

b) State the coordinate of the vertex.

c) State the maximum or minimum value of the function.

d) State the domain and range of the function.

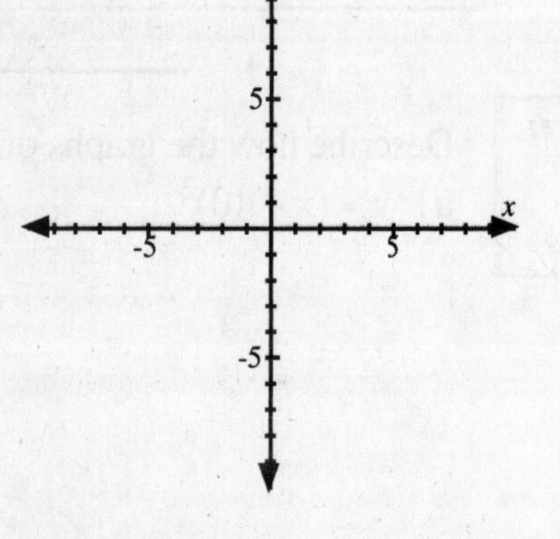

3. The following transformations are applied to the graph of $y = x^2$. Write the equation of the image function for each.

a) a horizontal translation of 7 units right **b)** a vertical translation of 2 units down

c) a translation 3 units left and 8 units up **d)** a translation c units down and d units right

4. Write the coordinates of the image of the point $(-2, 4)$ on the graph $y = x^2$ when each of the following transformations is applied:

a) a horizontal translation of 2 units to the left

b) a translation of 3 units up and 11 units right

5. Complete the following table.

Function	$y = x^2 + 5$	$y = (x+3)^2 - 4$	$y + 9 = (x-6)^2 + 1$	$y - w = (x+r)^2$
Coordinates of Vertex				
Max/Min Value				
Eqn. of Axis of Symmetry				
Domain				
Range				

6. After a combination of a horizontal and a vertical translation, the graph of $y = x^2$ has an image graph with a vertex at $(2, -6)$. Describe the translations.

Use the following information to answer questions #7 and #8.

- The graph of a quadratic function is shown.
- The four points marked have integer coordinates.

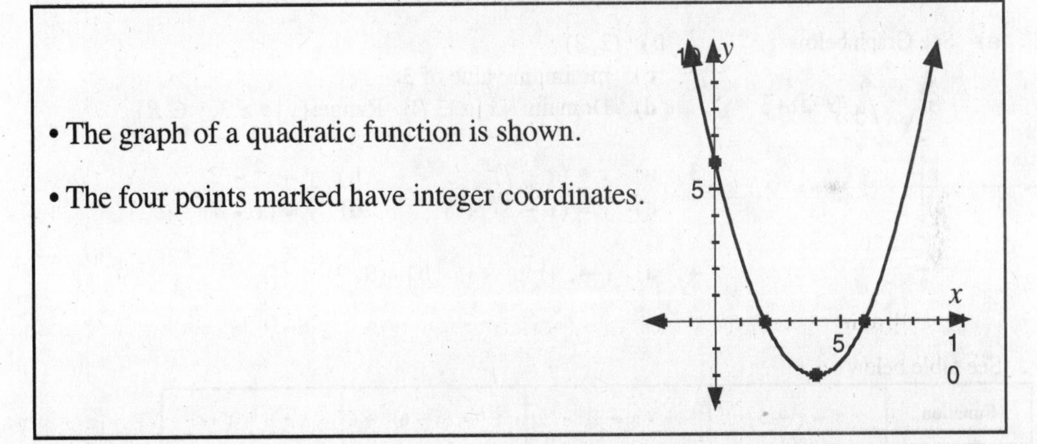

Multiple Choice **7.** The domain and range, respectively, of the function are

A. $x \in R$ and $y \in R$
B. $x \geq -2$ and $y \in R$
C. $x \in R$ and $y \geq -2$
D. $2 \leq x \leq 6$ and $y \geq -2$

Numerical Response **8.** The sum of the x and y-intercepts is _____ .
(Record your answer in the numerical response box from left to right.)

Multiple Choice

9. Which of the following transformations shifts the graph of $y = x^2$ to the graph of $y + a = (x - b)^2$?

A. a units right and b units down **B.** b units right and a units down

C. b units up and a units right. **D.** a units down and b units left

10. The function defined by the equation $y = x^2$ is transformed to $y = (x + 2)^2 + 4$. If the point $(2, 4)$ lies on the graph of $y = x^2$, which of the following points must lie on the graph of $y = (x + 2)^2 + 4$?

A. $(0, 0)$
B. $(4, 0)$
C. $(4, 8)$
D. $(0, 8)$

Answer Key

1. a) horizontal translation 5 units left **b)** vertical translation 7 units down
c) vertical translation 8 units up **d)** translation 2 units right and 5 units up
e) translation 1 unit left and 17 units down **f)** translation a units right and b units down

2. a) See Graph below

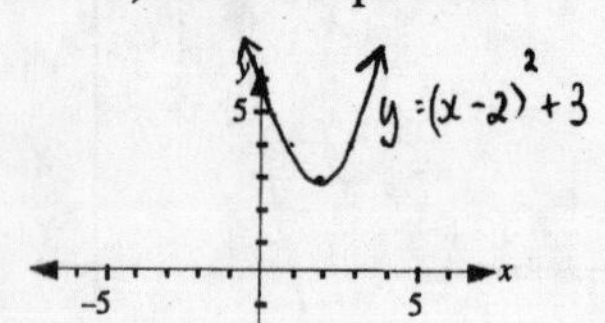

b) $(2, 3)$
c) minimum value of 3
d) Domain: $\{x \mid x \in R\}$ Range: $\{y \mid y \geq 3, y \in R\}$

3. a) $y = (x - 7)^2$ **b)** $y = x^2 - 2$
c) $y = (x + 3)^2 + 8$ **d)** $y = (x - d)^2 - c$

4. a) $(-4, 4)$ **b)** $(9, 7)$

5. See table below

Function	$y = x^2 + 5$	$y = (x + 3)^2 -$	$y + 9 = (x - 6)^2 + 1$	$y - w = (x + r)^2$
Coordinates of Vertex	$(0, 5)$	$(-3, -4)$	$(6, -8)$	$(-r, w)$
Max/Min Value	min, 5	min, -4	min, -8	min, w
Eqn. of Axis of Symmetry	$x = 0$	$x = -3$	$x = 6$	$x = -r$
Domain	$\{x \mid x \in \Re\}$	$\{x \mid x \in \Re\}$	$\{x \mid x \in \Re\}$	$\{x \mid x \in \Re\}$
Range	$\{y \mid y \geq 5, y \in \Re\}$	$\{y \mid y \geq -4, y \in \Re\}$	$\{y \mid y \geq -8, y \in \Re\}$	$\{y \mid y \geq w, y \in \Re\}$

6. horizontal translation 2 units right, vertical translation 6 units down.

7. C **8.** | 1 | 4 | | | **9.** B **10.** D

Quadratic Functions and Equations Lesson #3:
Analyzing Quadratic Functions - Part Two

In the last lesson we analyzed the graph of $y = (x - p)^2 + q$ and discovered transformations associated with the parameters p and q. In this lesson we investigate the effect of the parameter a on the graph of $y = a(x - p)^2 + q$. The following investigations can be completed as a class lesson or as an individual assignment.

Analyzing the Graph of $y = a(x - p)^2, a > 0$

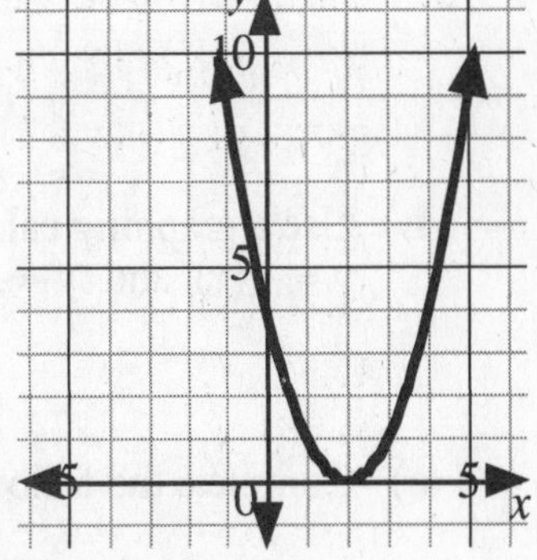

The graph of $y = f(x) = (x - 2)^2$ is shown.

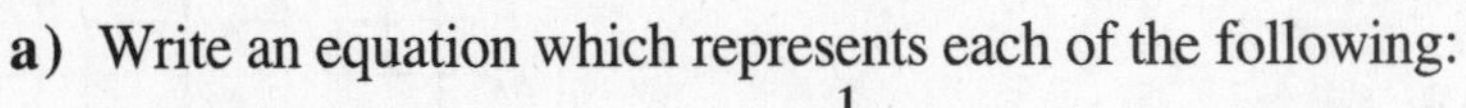

a) Write an equation which represents each of the following:

- $y = 2f(x)$
- $y = \frac{1}{2}f(x)$

b) Use a graphing calculator to sketch $y = 2f(x)$ and $y = \frac{1}{2}f(x)$ on the grid.

c) Complete the following by circling the correct choice and filling in the blank.

- Compared to the graph of $y = f(x)$, the number 2 in the graph of $y = 2f(x)$ results in a vertical *expansion / compression* by a factor of _____ .
- The y intercept of the graph of $y = 2f(x)$ is ____________ the y-intercept of the graph of $y = f(x)$.

d) Complete the following by circling the correct choice and filling in the blank.

- Compared to the graph of $y = f(x)$, the number $\frac{1}{2}$ in the graph of $y = \frac{1}{2}f(x)$ results in a vertical *expansion / compression* by a factor of _____ .
- The y intercept of the graph of $y = \frac{1}{2}f(x)$ is ____________ the y-intercept of the graph of $y = f(x)$.

- In mathematics, the general name given to an expansion <u>or</u> a compression is a **stretch**.
- A vertical stretch is "anchored" by the x-axis, i.e. the x-coordinate of every point on the original graph will not change and the y-coordinate of every point is multiplied by a factor of a.
- In some texts a compression is called a contraction.

e) Describe the effect of the **parameter** a on the graph of $y = a(x - p)^2$ where $a > 0$.

f) Compared to the graph of $y = x^2$, the graph of $y = ax^2$ results in a vertical stretch of factor _____ about the x-axis.
If $a > 1$, the parabola undergoes a vertical expansion.
If $0 < a < 1$, the parabola undergoes a vertical compression.

Analyzing the Graph of $y = ax^2, a < 0$

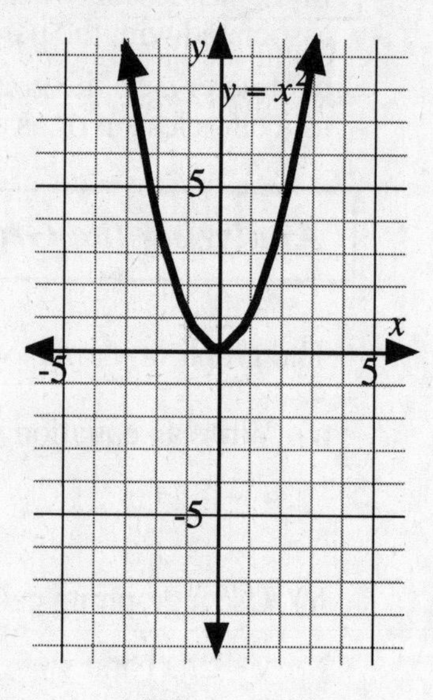

The graph of $y = f(x) = x^2$ is shown.

a) Write an equation which represents:

- $y = -f(x)$
- $y = -2f(x)$

b) Use a graphing calculator to sketch $y = -f(x)$ and $y = -2f(x)$.

c) Complete the following chart. The first row is done.

Function	*Equation Representing Function*	*Vertex*	*Max/Min Value*	*Equation of Axis of Symmetry*	*Description of Transformation*
$y = f(x)$	$y = x^2$	(0, 0)	min, 0	x = 0	no transformation
$y = -f(x)$					
$y = -2f(x)$					
$y = af(x)$, where $a < 0$					

d) How does the graph of $y = -x^2$ compare to the graph of $y = x^2$?

e) Compared to the graph of $y = x^2$, the graph of $y = ax^2, a < 0$ results in a

____________ in the ____________ and a ____________ stretch by a factor

of _____ about the x-axis .

Transformations Associated with the Parameters of $y = a(x - p)^2 + q$

Compared to the graph of $y = x^2$, the following transformations are associated with the parameters of $y = a(x - p)^2 + q$:

a indicates a vertical stretch about the x-axis.

- If $a > 1$ there is an expansion.
- If $0 < a < 1$ there is a compression.
- If $a < 0$, there is also a reflection in the x-axis.

p indicates a horizontal translation.
- If $p > 0$, the parabola moves p units right.
- If $p < 0$, the parabola moves p units left.

q indicates a vertical translation.
- If $q > 0$, the parabola moves q units up.
- If $q < 0$, the parabola moves q units down.

(p, q) are the coordinates of the vertex.

$x = p$ is the equation of the axis of symmetry.

Consider the function $f(x) = 2(x + 4)^2 - 3$.

a) State the transformations applied to the graph of $y = x^2$ which would result in the graph of $y = 2(x + 4)^2 - 3$.

b) Marika and Curtis were discussing how to graph this function without using a graphing calculator. Marika suggested doing the stretch followed by the translation. Curtis suggested doing the translation followed by the stretch.

- Complete the grids below to show the graphs obtained by each student.
- Use a graphing calculator to determine which student is correct.

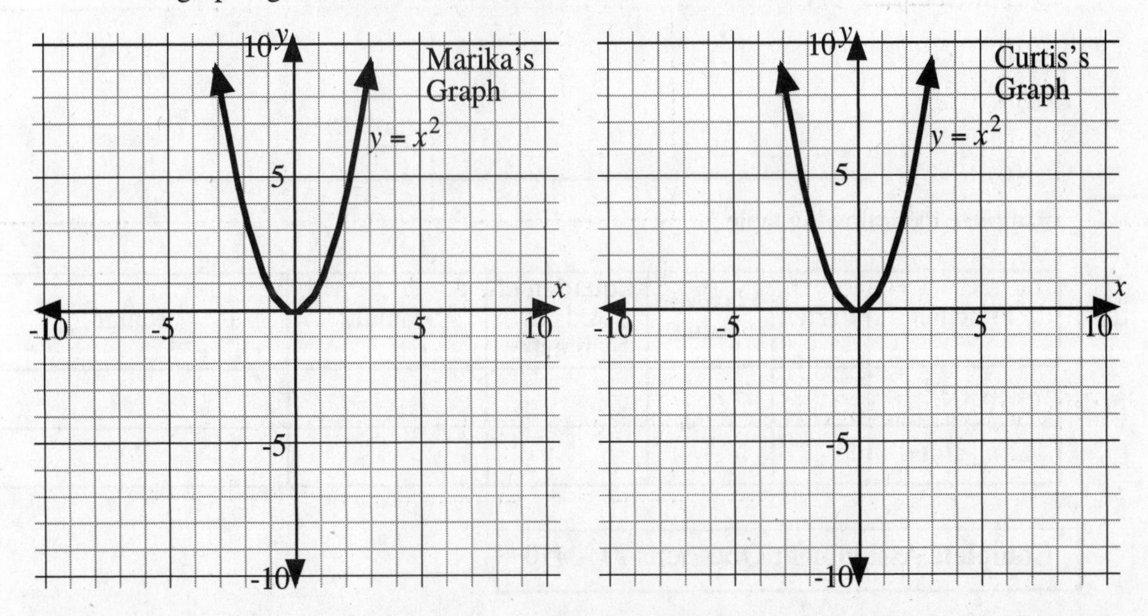

Unless otherwise indicated, use the following order to describe how to transform from one graph to another.

1. Stretches
2. Reflections
3. Translations

Describe how the graphs of the following functions relate to the graph of $y = x^2$.

a) $y = -\frac{1}{4}x^2$ **b)** $\frac{1}{3}y = (x + 6)^2$

The following three transformations are applied, in order, to the graph of $y = x^2$: a reflection in the x-axis, a vertical stretch by a factor of $\frac{1}{3}$ about the x-axis, and a translation 7 units right. At the end of the three transformations, the point $(1, t)$ is on the resulting graph.

a) Find the equation of the image function after each transformation.

b) State the coordinates of the vertex of the final graph.

c) Find the value of t.

Complete the following table.

Function	Vertex	Max/Min Value	Equation of Axis of Symmetry	Domain	Range
$y = -(x + 3)^2 - 4$					
$y = 3(x - 9)^2$					

Complete Assignment Questions #1 - #10

Assignment

1. Describe how the graphs of the following functions relate to the graph of $y = x^2$.

a) $y = -3x^2$

b) $y = x^2 - 15$

c) $y = -\frac{2}{3}(x + 4)^2 - 1$

d) $2y = (x - 8)^2 + 12$

2. The following transformations are applied to the graph of $y = x^2$ in the order given. Write the equation of the image function for each.

a) A reflection in the x-axis and a vertical stretch by a factor of 4 about the x-axis.

b) A vertical stretch by a factor of $\frac{3}{5}$ about the x-axis, and a translation of 5 units down.

c) A vertical stretch by a factor of 8 about the x-axis, a reflection in the x-axis, a vertical translation of 3 units up, and a horizontal translation 9 units left.

d) A vertical stretch by a factor of c about the x-axis, a reflection in the x-axis, and a translation of e units right and f units down.

3. Complete the following table.

Function	Vertex	Max/Min Value	Equation of Axis of Symmetry	Domain	Range
$y = 3x^2$					
$y = 2x^2 + 1$					
$y = -(x + 7)^2$					
$y - 10 = (x + 5)^2$					
$y + 3 = -3(x - 1)^2 + 2$					

4. The following transformations are applied, **in order**, to the graph of $y = x^2$:
- a reflection in the x-axis
- a vertical stretch of factor 3 about the x-axis
- a translation of 5 units right and 2 units down

a) Find the equation of the image function after <u>each</u> transformation.

b) At the end of all the transformations, the point $(4, y)$ is on the final graph of the parabola. Find the y-coordinate for the final graph when $x = 4$.

5. The graph of $f(x) = x^2$ undergoes a series of transformations.

a) State the transformations applied to the graph of $f(x) = x^2$ which would result in the graph of $f(x) = -\frac{1}{2}(x-2)^2 + 1$.

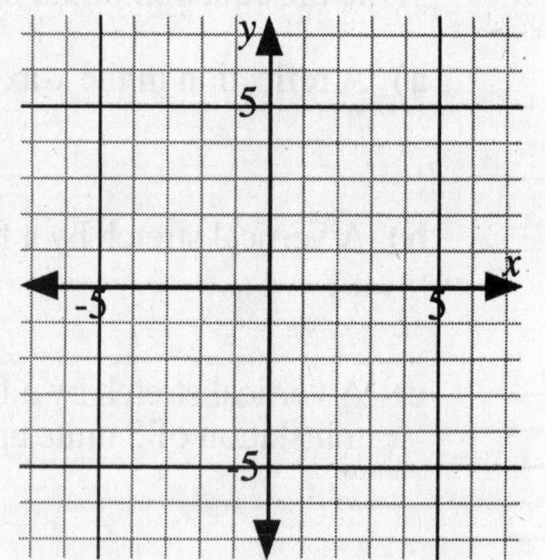

b) Without using a graphing calculator, sketch the graph of $f(x) = -\frac{1}{2}(x-2)^2 + 1$.

c) Verify using a graphing calculator.

6. Write the coordinates of the image of the point $(-3, 9)$ on the graph $y = x^2$ when each of the following transformations are applied:

a) a reflection in the x-axis, followed by a vertical translation of 4 units up

b) a vertical stretch by a factor of $\frac{1}{3}$ about the x-axis

7. Write the equation of a quadratic function which is the image of $y = x^2$ after a vertical stretch about the x-axis by the given factor of a, and after a translation which results in the given vertex.

a) $a = 3$, vertex $(4, -1)$

b) $a = \frac{1}{2}$, vertex $(-3, 2)$

c) $a = -4$, vertex $(0, 5)$

d) $a = -\frac{1}{3}$, vertex $(-6, -3)$

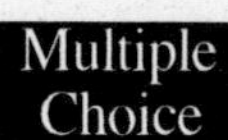

8. The quadratic function $f(x) = x^2$ is transformed to $f(x) = -\frac{1}{2}(x + 3)^2 + 1$.

The point $(1, 1)$ on the graph of $y = x^2$ is transformed to which point on the graph of $y = -\frac{1}{2}(x + 3)^2 + 1$?

A. $\left(-2, \frac{1}{2}\right)$

B. $\left(-2, \frac{3}{2}\right)$

C. $(-2, -1)$

D. $\left(\frac{5}{2}, 2\right)$

9. The diagram shows the graphs of four quadratic functions.

In the first box, write the number corresponding to the graph of $y = \frac{1}{2}(x - 5)^2 - 3$.

In the second box, write the number corresponding to the graph of $y = -3(x + 4)^2 + 2$.

In the third box, write the number corresponding to the graph of $y = (x - 3)^2 + 4$.

In the last box, write the number corresponding to the graph of $y + 3 = -\frac{1}{4}(x - 5)^2$.

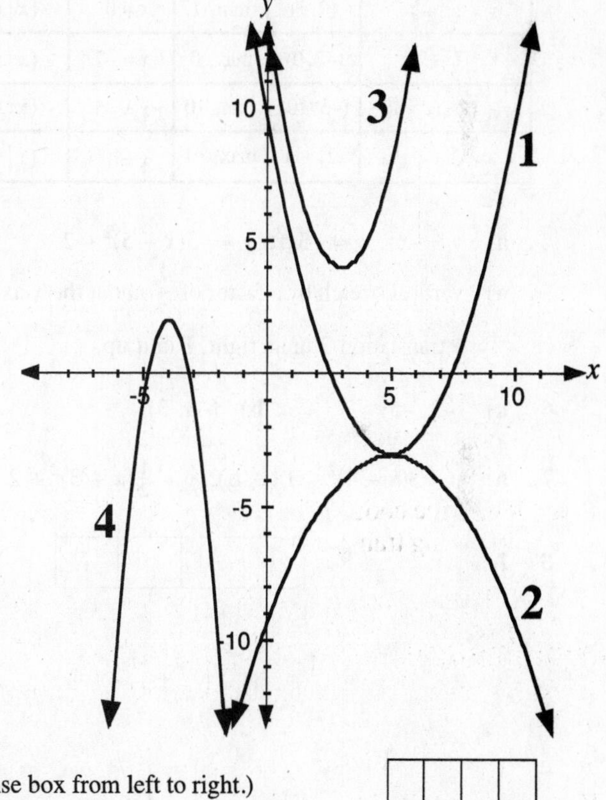

(Record your answer in the numerical response box from left to right.)

10. The following transformations are applied, in order, to the graph of $y = x^2$:

- a vertical stretch of factor 2 about the x-axis
- a reflection in the x-axis
- a vertical translation of 12 units up

At the end of all the transformations, the point $(2, y)$ is on the final graph of the parabola. The value of y, to the nearest tenth, is _____ .

(Record your answer in the numerical response box from left to right.)

Answer Key

1. **a)** vertical stretch by a factor of 3 about the x-axis and a reflection in the x-axis

b) vertical translation 15 units down

c) vertical stretch by a factor of $\frac{2}{3}$ about the x-axis, a reflection in the x-axis, a translation 4 units left, 1 unit down.

d) vertical stretch by a factor of $\frac{1}{2}$ about the x-axis, and a translation 8 units right, 6 units up.

2. **a)** $y = -4x^2$ **b)** $y = \frac{3}{5}x^2 - 5$ **c)** $y = -8(x + 9)^2 + 3$ **d)** $y = -c(x - e)^2 - f$

3.

Function	Vertex	Max/Min Value	Equation of Axis of Symmetry	Domain	Range
$y = 3x^2$	(0, 0)	min, 0	$x = 0$	$\{x \mid x \in \Re\}$	$\{y \mid y \geq 0, y \in \Re\}$
$y = 2x^2 + 1$	(0, 1)	min, 1	$x = 0$	$\{x \mid x \in \Re\}$	$\{y \mid y \geq 1, y \in \Re\}$
$y = -(x+7)^2$	(–7, 0)	max, 0	$x = -7$	$\{x \mid x \in \Re\}$	$\{y \mid y \leq 0, y \in \Re\}$
$y - 10 = (x + 5)^2$	(–5, 10)	min, 10	$x = -5$	$\{x \mid x \in \Re\}$	$\{y \mid y \geq 10, y \in \Re\}$
$y + 3 = -3(x - 1)^2 + 2$	(1, –1)	max, –1	$x = 1$	$\{x \mid x \in \Re\}$	$\{y \mid y \leq -1, y \in \Re\}$

4. **a)** $y = -x^2$, $y = -3x^2$, $y = -3(x - 5)^2 - 2$ **b)** –5

5. **a)** vertical stretch by a factor of $\frac{1}{2}$ about the x-axis, a reflection in the x-axis, a translation 2 units right, 1 unit up.

6. **a)** (–3, –5) **b)** (–3, 3)

7. **a)** $y = 3(x - 4)^2 - 1$ **b)** $y = \frac{1}{2}(x + 3)^2 + 2$ **c)** $y = -4x^2 + 5$ **d)** $y = -\frac{1}{3}(x + 6)^2 - 3$

8. A

9.

1	4	3	2

10.

4	.	0	

Quadratic Functions and Equations Lesson #4: Equations and Intercepts from the Vertex and a Point

In the last lesson, we analyzed the graphs of quadratic functions with equations in standard form $y = a(x - p)^2 + q$. In this lesson, we determine the equation of a quadratic function from the graph. To do this we need the vertex of the parabola and a point on it. We will also learn how to find intercepts from the standard form of the equation.

Determining the Equation from the Vertex and a Point

The following procedure will enable us to write quadratic functions in standard form if we are given the coordinates of the vertex and of another point on the parabola.

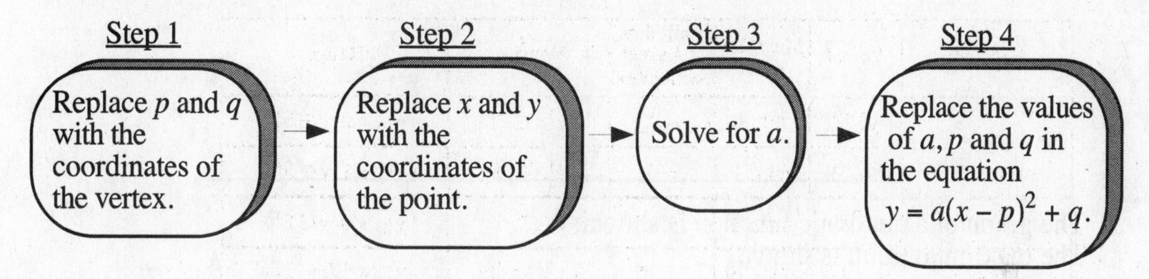

Step 1
Replace p and q with the coordinates of the vertex.
Step 2
Replace x and y with the coordinates of the point.
Step 3
Solve for a.
Step 4
Replace the values of a, p and q in the equation $y = a(x - p)^2 + q$.

Class Ex. #1

The graph of a quadratic function has vertex (–2, 8) and passes through the point (–1, 7).

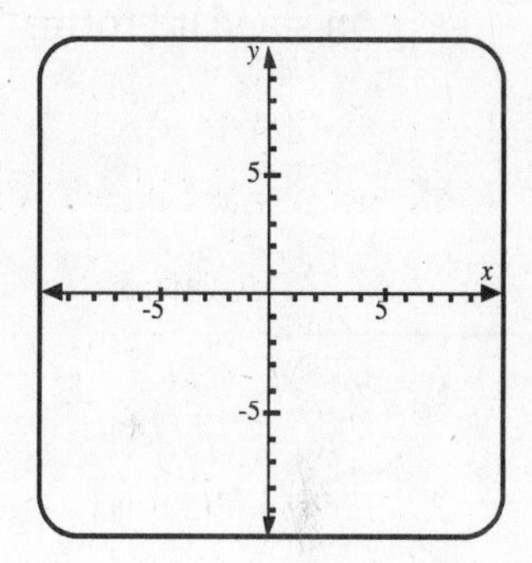

a) Find the equation of the function in standard form $y = a(x - p)^2 + q$.

b) Rewrite the equation in general form $y = ax^2 + bx + c$.

c) Use a graphing calculator to sketch the graph and determine the x and y-intercepts of the graph of the function. Answer to the nearest hundredth if necessary.

Finding Intercepts from the Standard Form

We can use the equation of a quadratic function written in standard form to algebraically determine the x- and y-intercepts of the graph of the function.

Determine, as exact values, the x and y-intercepts of the graph of the function $f(x) = 3(x - 1)^2 - 9$.

The graph of a quadratic function is shown.
The maximum point is shown.

a) Find the equation of the function in standard form.

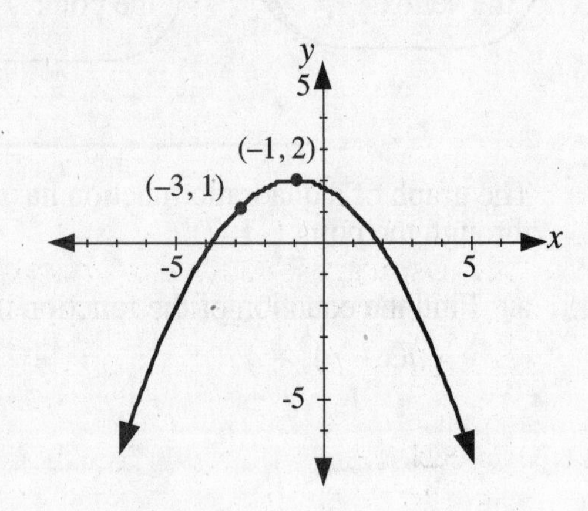

b) Find, algebraically, the x-intercepts and y-intercepts of the graph. Answer both as exact values and to the nearest hundredth.

c) State the domain, range and equation of the axis of symmetry.

Complete Assignment Questions #1 - #12

Assignment

1. The graph of a quadratic function has vertex $(3, -4)$ and passes through the point $(4, 1)$.

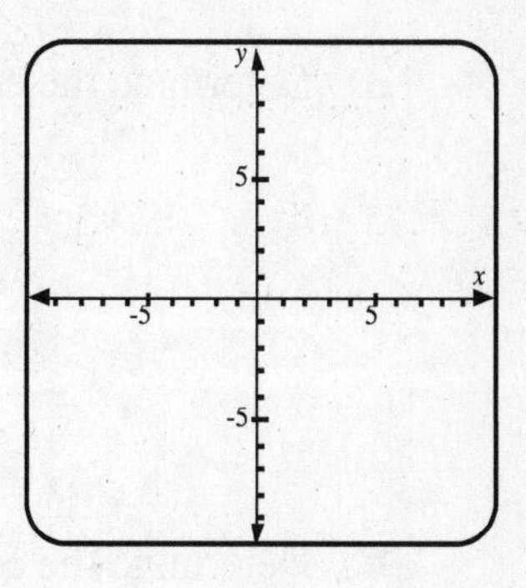

a) Find the equation of the function in standard form.

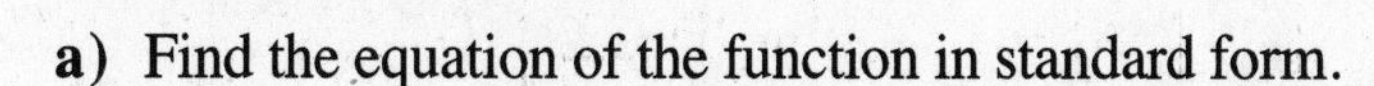

b) Rewrite the equation in general form.

c) Use a graphing calculator to sketch the graph and determine the x and y-intercepts of the graph of the function. Answer to the nearest hundredth if necessary.

2. In each case, write an equation in standard form for the parabola with the given vertex and passing through the given point.

a) vertex $(7, -6)$, point $(9, -4)$

b) vertex $(-2, 5)$, point $(-4, 21)$

c) vertex $(-1, 0)$, point $(-5, -12)$

d) vertex $(3, -8)$, y-intercept is 10

3. The graph of a quadratic function has a vertex at $\left(\frac{5}{3}, 1\right)$ and one x-intercept is $\frac{2}{3}$.

a) Determine the equation of the function in standard form.

b) Determine the equation of the function in general form.

c) State the other x-intercept.

d) State the domain and range of the function.

e) State the equation of the axis of symmetry of the graph.

4. Determine, as exact values, the x and y-intercepts of the graph of the following functions.

a) $f(x) = (x - 4)^2 - 16$

b) $f(x) = -3(x + 2)^2 + 3$

c) $f(x) = 2(x - 6)^2 - 6$

d) $f(x) = -\frac{1}{4}(x + 1)^2 + 5$

5. Write an equation of the form $y = a(x - p)^2 + q$ for each parabola.

a)

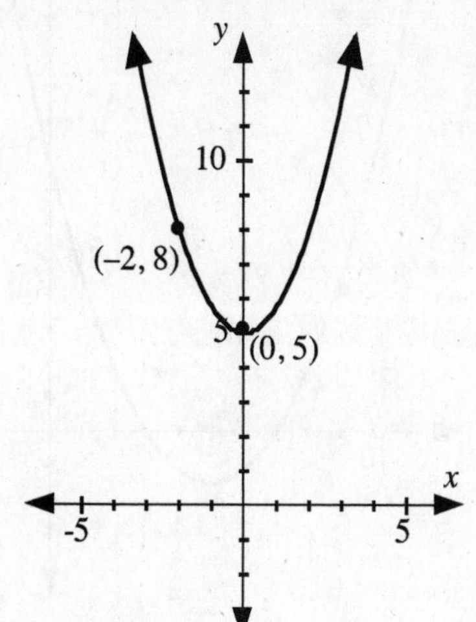

b)

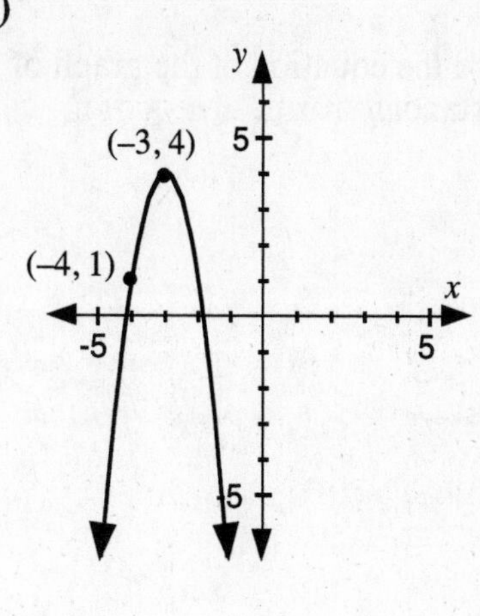

6. A function of the form $p(x) = ax^2 + q$ has two x-intercepts, one of which is 9. Determine the other x-intercept and explain how you arrived at your answer.

7. The parabola with equation $y = a(x - 2)^2 + q$ passes through the points $(-2, 5)$ and $(4, -1)$. Determine the coordinates of the vertex of the parabola.

8. The graph of the function with equation $y = a(x + 5)^2 + q$ passes through the points $(-6, 2)$ and $(-3, 20)$.

Determine whether the function has a maximum or minimum value and state the value.

9. The graph of a quadratic function is shown. The equation of the axis of symmetry is $x = -5$.

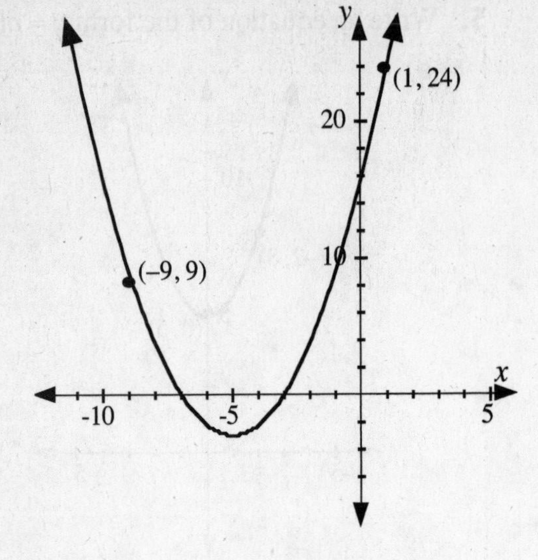

a) Find the equation of the graph of the function in standard form.

b) Find, algebraically, the x-and y-intercepts of the graph.

c) State the domain and range.

Multiple Choice

10. The parabola with equation $y = a(x - p)^2 + q$ has a maximum value of 8. The line $x = 2$ is the axis of symmetry of the parabola. If the graph passes through the origin, then the value of a is

A. 2

B. $\frac{1}{32}$

C. -2

D. $-\frac{1}{32}$

11. The graph of the function $g(x) = -2(x-3)^2 + q$ passes through the point $(-5, -2)$. The value of q, to the nearest whole number, is _____ .
(Record your answer in the numerical response box from left to right.)

12. The graph of a function of the form $f(x) = a(x+2)^2 - 7$ has two x-intercepts, one of which is -6.5. The other x-intercept, to the nearest tenth , is _____ .
(Record your answer in the numerical response box from left to right.)

Answer Key

1. **a)** $y = 5(x-3)^2 - 4$ **b)** $y = 5x^2 - 30x + 41$ **c)** x-intercepts are 2.11, 3.89
y-intercept is 41

2. **a)** $y = \frac{1}{2}(x-7)^2 - 6$ **b)** $y = 4(x+2)^2 + 5$ **c)** $y = -\frac{3}{4}(x+1)^2$ **d)** $y = 2(x-3)^2 - 8$

3. **a)** $y = -\left(x - \frac{5}{3}\right)^2 + 1$ **b)** $y = -x^2 + \frac{10}{3}x - \frac{16}{9}$ **c)** $\frac{8}{3}$
d) Domain: $\{x \mid x \in R\}$, Range: $\{y \mid y \leq 1, y \in R\}$ **e)** axis of symmetry $x = \frac{5}{3}$

4. **a)** x - intercepts 0 and 8
y -intercept 0
b) x - intercepts -3 and -1
y -intercept -9
c) x - intercepts $6 + \sqrt{3}$ and $6 - \sqrt{3}$
y -intercept 66
d) x - intercepts $-1 + 2\sqrt{5}$ and $-1 - 2\sqrt{5}$
y -intercept $\frac{19}{4}$

5. **a)** $y = \frac{3}{4}x^2 + 5$ **b)** $y = -3(x+3)^2 + 4$

6. The vertex of the parabola is on the y-axis so the x-intercepts are an equal distance on either side of $x = 0$. If one x-intercept is 9, the other must be -9.

7. $(2, -3)$ **8.** minimum value of -4

9. **a)** $y = \frac{3}{4}(x+5)^2 - 3$ **b)** x-intercepts are -7 and -3, y-intercept $\frac{63}{4}$
c) Domain: $\{x \mid x \in R\}$, Range: $\{y \mid y \geq -3, y \in R\}$

10. C

11.

1	2	6	

12.

2	.	5	

Quadratic Functions and Equations Lesson #5: Converting from General Form to Standard Form by Completing the Square

Review

The **general form** of a quadratic function has the equation $y = ax^2 + bx + c$.

The **standard form** of a quadratic function has the equation $y = a(x - p)^2 + q$.

Writing a function in standard form enables us to analyze the function more easily e.g. we can determine the vertex, axis of symmetry and maximum / minimum value of the function.

Completing the Square

$(x + 4)^2$, $(x - 5)^2$ etc are examples of **perfect squares.**

a) Expand the following perfect squares.

$(x + 4)^2 = (x + 4)(x + 4) =$ ____________ $(x + 7)^2 = (x + 7)(x + 7) =$ ____________

$(x - 5)^2 = (x - 5)(x - 5) =$ ____________ $(x - 1)^2 = (x - 1)(x - 1) =$ ____________

$(x + a)^2 =$ ____________ $(x - a)^2 =$ ____________

b) Factor the following expressions into perfect squares.

$x^2 + 6x + 9 =$ ____________ $x^2 + 12x + 36 =$ ____________

$x^2 - 4x + 4 =$ ____________ $x^2 - 16x + 64 =$ ____________

c) Add an appropriate constant so that the following expressions can be written as perfect squares.

$x^2 + 2x +$ __ $=$ _______ $x^2 + 18x +$ __ $=$ _______

$x^2 - 3x +$ __ $=$ _______ $x^2 - \frac{1}{4}x +$ __ $=$ _______

The process of adding a constant term to a quadratic expression to make it a perfect square is called **completing the square**.

To complete the square of $x^2 + bx$, add $\left(\frac{1}{2}\text{coefficient of } x\right)^2$ i.e. $\left(\frac{1}{2}b\right)^2$ to give $\left(x + \frac{1}{2}b\right)^2$.

Writing $f(x) = x^2 + bx + c$ in Standard Form by Completing the Square

Use the following process to convert a function of the form $f(x) = x^2 + bx + c$ into standard form.

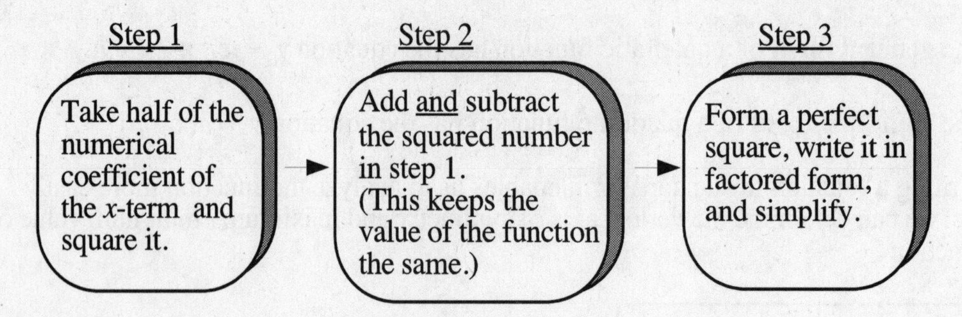

Step 1
Take half of the numerical coefficient of the x-term and square it.
Step 2
Add and subtract the squared number in step 1. (This keeps the value of the function the same.)
Step 3
Form a perfect square, write it in factored form, and simplify.

Express $y = x^2 + 10x + 16$ in completed square form. Use a graphing calculator to verify that both equations are represented by identical graphs.

A function f is defined by $f(x) = x^2 - 9x - 20$. Determine the minimum value of f by writing the function in standard form.

Complete Assignment Questions #1 - #4

Writing $f(x) = ax^2 + bx + c$ in Standard Form by Completing the Square

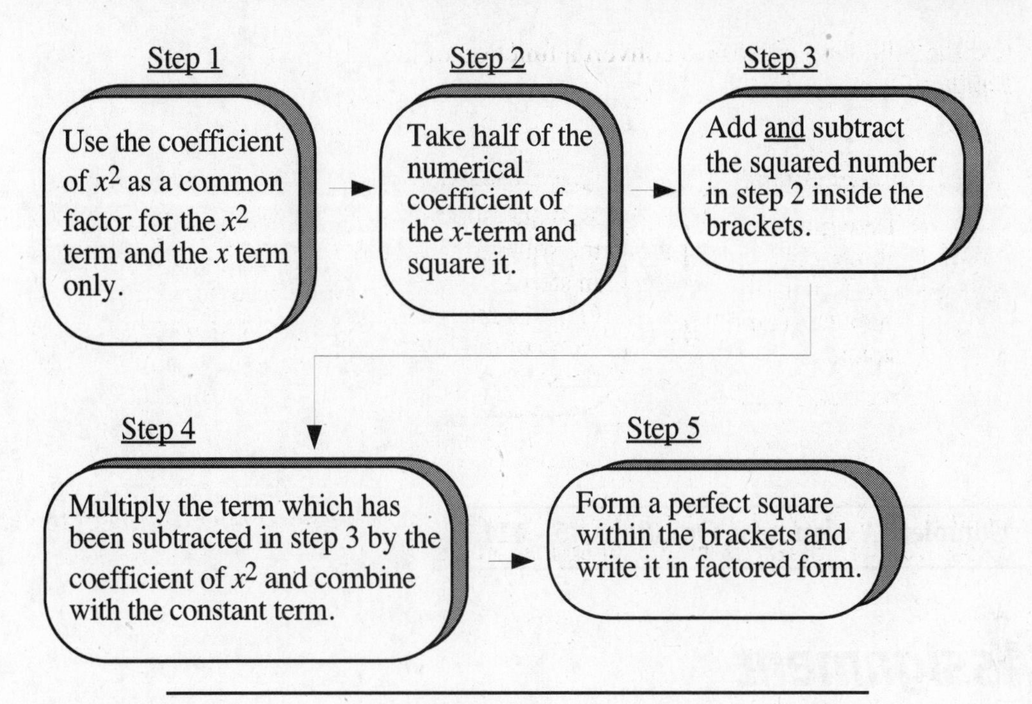

Step 1
Use the coefficient of x^2 as a common factor for the x^2 term and the x term only.
Step 2
Take half of the numerical coefficient of the x-term and square it.
Step 3
Add and subtract the squared number in step 2 inside the brackets.
Step 4
Multiply the term which has been subtracted in step 3 by the coefficient of x^2 and combine with the constant term.
Step 5
Form a perfect square within the brackets and write it in factored form.

Convert $f(x) = 3x^2 - 18x + 20$ to standard form by completing the square. Determine whether the graph of the function f has a maximum or minimum value and state the value.

Convert $y = 7 + 10x - 2x^2$ to standard form by completing the square. In what direction does the parabola open? What are the coordinates of the vertex of the parabola?

Express $f(x) = 3x^2 - 12x - 8$ in completed square form and use this form to determine the zeros of the function. Answer to the nearest hundredth.

Complete Assignment Questions #5 - #11

Assignment

1. What number must be added to each to make a perfect square?

a) $x^2 + 8x$ **b)** $x^2 - 24x$ **c)** $x^2 + 40x$ **d)** $x^2 - x$ **e)** $x^2 + \frac{1}{2}x$ **f)** $x^2 - \frac{2}{3}x$

2. Complete the square in each part.

a) $x^2 + 6x + \_\_ = (x + \_\_)^2$ **b)** $x^2 - 20x + \_\_ = (x \quad \_\_)^2$

c) $x^2 + 5x + \_\_ = (x \quad \_\_)^2$ **d)** $x^2 - 9x + \_\_ = (x \quad \_\_)^2$

e) $x^2 + 0.6x + \_\_ = (x \quad \_\_)^2$ **f)** $x^2 - \frac{3}{4}x + \_\_ = (x \quad \_\_)^2$

3. Express the following in completed square form.

a) $y = x^2 + 10x + 3$ **b)** $y = x^2 - 4x - 21$ **c)** $y = x^2 + 14x - 2$

d) $f(x) = x^2 + 9x + 22$ **e)** $g(x) = x^2 - x + 1$ **f)** $h(x) = x^2 + bx + c$

4. Express $f(x) = x^2 - 14x - 40$ in completed square form. Hence state the coordinates of the vertex and the equation of the axis of symmetry of the graph of the function.

5. Express the following in completed square form.

a) $f(x) = 2x^2 + 12x + 5$ **b)** $y = 3x^2 - 18x - 19$ **c)** $P(x) = 2x^2 + 14x - 11$

d) $y = -x^2 + 10x + 20$ **e)** $y = -4x^2 - 8x + 7$ **f)** $f(x) = -x^2 + bx + c$

g) $g(x) = 11x - x^2$ **h)** $y = 5x^2 - 20x + m$ **i)** $y = -3x^2 + 12x - 11$

6. Write the function $f(x) = ax^2 + bx + c$ in completed square form.

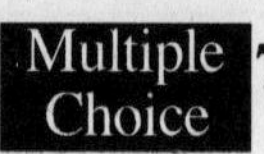

7. When $y = 2x^2 + 5x + 10$ is converted to the form $y = a(x - p)^2 + q$, the value of q is

A. -2.5
B. 3.75
C. 6.875
D. 8.4375

8. The x-coordinate of the vertex of the graph of the function $f(x) = bx - 4x^2$ is

A. $\dfrac{b}{4}$
B. $\dfrac{b}{8}$
C. $\dfrac{b}{16}$
D. $\dfrac{b^2}{16}$

9. A high school student was asked to arrange the equation $y = -3x^2 - 6x - 5$ in the form $y = a(x - p)^2 + q$ by completing the square. The student's procedure is shown:

Step I: $y = -3(x^2 + 2x \qquad) - 5$
Step II: $y = -3(x^2 + 2x + 1 - 1) - 5$
Step III: $y = -3(x + 1)^2 - 5 - 1$
Step IV: $y = -3(x + 1)^2 - 6$

The student made an error in

A. Step I
B. Step II
C. Step III
D. Step IV

10. The x-intercepts of the graph of the function $f(x) = x^2 - 8x - 4$ are

A. $2 \pm 4\sqrt{5}$
B. $4 \pm \sqrt{5}$
C. $4 \pm 2\sqrt{5}$
D. $-4 \pm 2\sqrt{5}$

Numerical Response

11. The maximum value, to the nearest tenth, of the function $g(x) = -5x^2 + 10x + 12$ is _____

(Record your answer in the numerical response box from left to right.)

Answer Key

1. a) 16 **b)** 144 **c)** 400 **d)** $\frac{1}{4}$ **e)** $\frac{1}{16}$ **f)** $\frac{1}{9}$

2. a) $x^2 + 6x + 9 = (x + 3)^2$ **b)** $x^2 - 20x + 100 = (x - 10)^2$ **c)** $x^2 + 5x + \frac{25}{4} = \left(x + \frac{5}{2}\right)^2$

d) $x^2 - 9x + \frac{81}{4} = \left(x - \frac{9}{2}\right)^2$ **e)** $x^2 + 0.6 + 0.09 = (x + 0.3)^2$ **f)** $x^2 - \frac{3}{4}x + \frac{9}{64} = \left(x - \frac{3}{8}\right)^2$

3. a) $y = (x + 5)^2 - 22$ **b)** $y = (x - 2)^2 - 25$ **c)** $y = (x + 7)^2 - 51$

d) $f(x) = \left(x + \frac{9}{2}\right)^2 + \frac{7}{4}$ **e)** $g(x) = \left(x - \frac{1}{2}\right)^2 + \frac{3}{4}$ **f)** $g(x) = \left(x + \frac{b}{2}\right)^2 + c - \frac{b^2}{4}$

4. $(7, -89)$, $x = 7$

5. a) $f(x) = 2(x + 3)^2 - 13$ **b)** $y = 3(x - 3)^2 - 46$ **c)** $P(x) = 2\left(x + \frac{7}{2}\right)^2 - \frac{71}{2}$

d) $y = -(x - 5)^2 + 45$ **e)** $y = -4(x + 1)^2 + 11$ **f)** $f(x) = -\left(x - \frac{b}{2}\right)^2 + c + \frac{b^2}{4}$

g) $g(x) = -\left(x - \frac{11}{2}\right)^2 + \frac{121}{4}$ **h)** $y = 5(x - 2)^2 + m - 20$ **i)** $y = -3(x - 2)^2 + 1$

6. $f(x) = a\left(x + \frac{b}{2a}\right)^2 + \frac{4ac - b^2}{4a}$

7. C **8.** B **9.** C **10.** C **11.**

1	7	.	0

Quadratic Functions and Equations Lesson #6:
Roots of Quadratic Equations - The Quadratic Formula

Review ***Roots of Quadratic Equations by Inspection and by Decomposition***

A quadratic equation is an equation of the form $ax^2 + bx + c = 0$.

a) Find the roots of the equation $x^2 + 7x - 18 = 0$ by inspection.

b) Find the roots of the equation $6x^2 - x - 12 = 0$ by decomposition.

c) Is it possible to solve the quadratic equation $2x^2 - 8x + 5 = 0$ by either of the above methods? Explain.

Developing the Quadratic Formula

In the review on the previous page, we were unable to solve the equation $2x^2 - 8x + 5 = 0$ by inspection or decomposition. Another method is required.
There are two further algebraic methods which can be used - **completing the square** and the **quadratic formula**. We will solve the equation $2x^2 - 8x + 5 = 0$ by completing the square and use this technique to develop the quadratic formula.

Solve the following equations by completing the square.

a) $2x^2 - 8x + 5 = 0$ **b)** $ax^2 + bx + c = 0$

The solution to Class Ex. #1b) is a formula which can be used to solve any quadratic equation of the form $ax^2 + bx + c = 0$. The formula is known as the **quadratic formula**.

Solving a quadratic equation by completing the square is rarely used as the quadratic formula is usually a more efficient method.

The Quadratic Formula

The quadratic equation $ax^2 + bx + c = 0, a \neq 0$ has the roots

$$x = \frac{-b \pm \sqrt{b^2 - 4ac}}{2a}$$

Find the roots of the following equations using the quadratic formula.
Give answers as exact values in simplest form and to the nearest tenth.

a) $x^2 + 2x - 1 = 0$ **b)** $4x^2 - 12x + 3 = 0$ **c)** $4x^2 = 3(4x + 5)$

Find the zeros of the quadratic function $f(x) = -3x^2 + 4x + 1$.
Give answers as exact values in simplest form and to the nearest hundredth.

Complete Assignment Questions #1 - #9

Assignment

1. Solve the equation $x^2 - 3x - 10 = 0$ by using:

a) inspection

b) the quadratic formula

2. Solve the equation $4x^2 - 11x - 3 = 0$ by using:

a) decomposition

b) the quadratic formula

3. Find the exact roots of the equation $6x^2 + 5x + 1 = 0$ by using:

a) graphing

b) the quadratic formula

4. Find the roots of the following quadratic equations (to the nearest tenth) using the quadratic formula.

a) $2x^2 + x - 4 = 0$ **b)** $2x^2 - 3x - 4 = 0$ **c)** $10t^2 = 7t + 1$

5. Solve the following quadratic equations (as exact values) using the quadratic formula.

a) $x^2 - 10x - 15 = 0$ **b)** $x^2 + 6x + 17 = 0$ **c)** $3x^2 - 12x + 11 = 0$

6. Find the zeros of the following quadratic functions.
Give answers as exact values in simplest form and to the nearest hundredth.

a) $f(x) = x^2 + 20x + 15$ **b)** $f(x) = 5x^2 + 12x - 5$

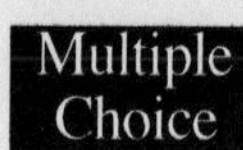

7. The roots of the quadratic equation $dx^2 + ex + f = 0$ are

A. $x = \dfrac{e \pm \sqrt{e^2 - 4df}}{2d}$ **B.** $x = \dfrac{-e \pm \sqrt{e^2 - 4df}}{2d}$

C. $x = \dfrac{e \pm \sqrt{e^2 + 4df}}{2d}$ **D.** $x = \dfrac{-e \pm \sqrt{e^2 + 4df}}{2d}$

8. The zeros of the quadratic function $f(x) = 6x^2 + 2x - 1$ are

A. $\dfrac{-1 \pm \sqrt{14}}{6}$

B. $\dfrac{-1 \pm 2\sqrt{7}}{6}$

C. $\dfrac{-1 \pm \sqrt{7}}{6}$

D. $\dfrac{-2 \pm \sqrt{7}}{6}$

9. The quadratic equation $2x^2 + 15x + p = 0$ has a root of $-\dfrac{1}{2}$ when p has the whole number value of _____ .

(Record your answer in the numerical response box from left to right.)

Answer Key

1. a) $-2, 5$ **b)** $-2, 5$ **2. a)** $-\dfrac{1}{4}, 3$ **b)** $-\dfrac{1}{4}, 3$

3. a) $-\dfrac{1}{3}, -\dfrac{1}{2}$ **b)** $-\dfrac{1}{3}, -\dfrac{1}{2}$ **4. a)** $-1.7, 1.2$ **b)** $-0.9, 2.4$ **c)** $-0.1, 0.8$

5. a) $5 \pm 2\sqrt{10}$ **b)** no solution **c)** $\dfrac{6 \pm \sqrt{3}}{3}$

6. a) $-10 \pm \sqrt{85}$ $-0.78, -19.22$ **b)** $\dfrac{-6 \pm \sqrt{61}}{5}$ $-2.76, 0.36$

7. B **8.** C **9.** 7

Quadratic Functions and Equations Lesson #7:
Roots of Quadratic Equations - The Discriminant

Review

Find the roots of the quadratic equation $x^2 - 8x + 12 = 0$ by each of the following methods:

i) by graphing

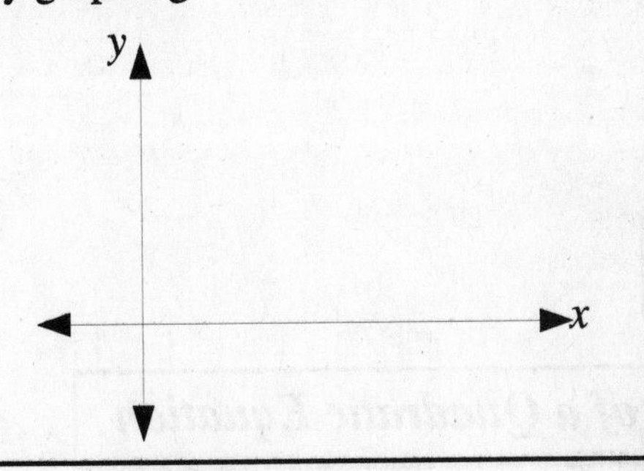

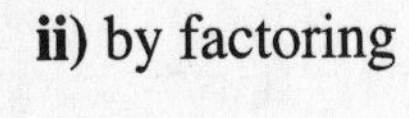

ii) by factoring

iii) by completing the square

iv) by the quadratic formula

Discuss when each of the following methods might be appropriate or not appropriate for solving a quadratic equation.

- by factoring using inspection or decomposition

- by quadratic formula

- by completing the square

- by graphing

Form a quadratic equation and solve. $\frac{2}{a^2} + \frac{3}{a} = -1, \; a \neq 0$

Complete Assignment Questions #1 - #3

Investigating the Nature of the Roots of a Quadratic Equation

Insert the missing values.

Equation #1

$x^2 - 6x + 5 = 0$

$x = \frac{-b \pm \sqrt{b^2 - 4ac}}{2a}$

$x = \frac{6 \pm \sqrt{\quad}}{2}$

$= \frac{6 \pm \sqrt{\quad}}{2}$

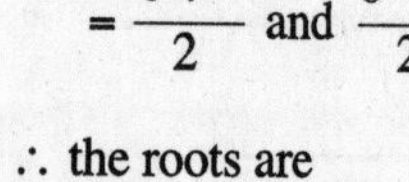

$= \frac{6 +}{2}$ and $\frac{6 -}{2}$

∴ the roots are

$x =$ and $x =$

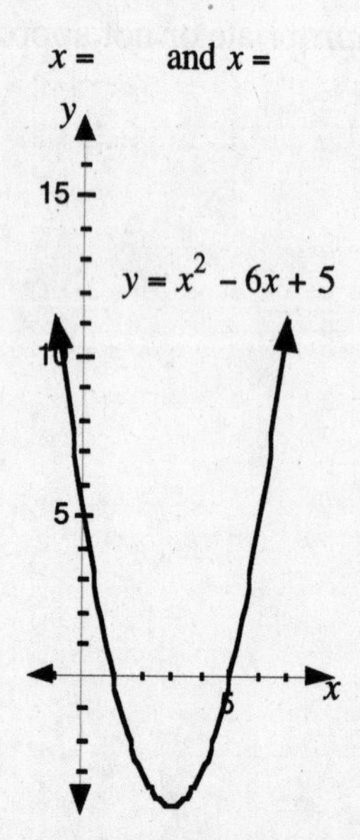

Equation #2

$x^2 - 6x + 9 = 0$

$x = \frac{-b \pm \sqrt{b^2 - 4ac}}{2a}$

$x = \frac{6 \pm \sqrt{\quad}}{2}$

$= \frac{6 \pm \sqrt{\quad}}{2}$

$= \frac{6 +}{2}$ and $\frac{6 -}{2}$

∴ the roots are

$x =$ and $x =$

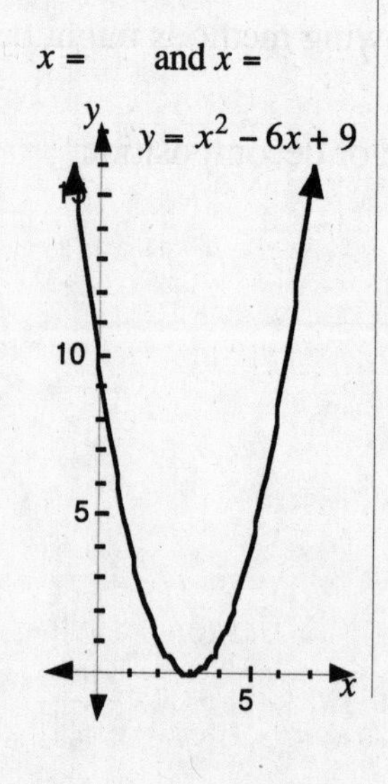

Equation #3

$x^2 - 6x + 13 = 0$

$x = \frac{-b \pm \sqrt{b^2 - 4ac}}{2a}$

$x = \frac{6 \pm \sqrt{\quad}}{2}$

$= \frac{6 \pm \sqrt{\quad}}{2}$

∴ the roots are

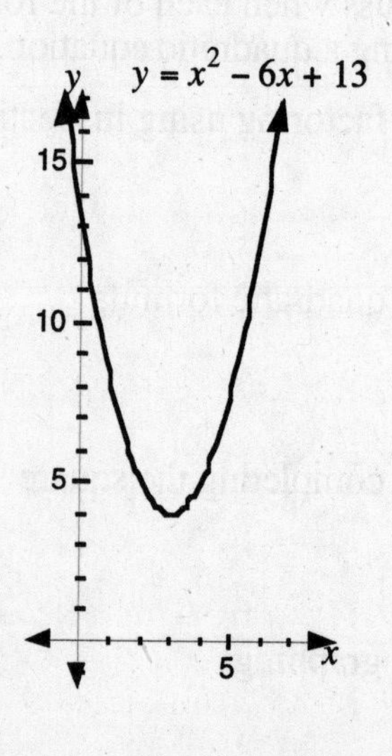

The Nature of the Roots of a Quadratic Equation

The roots of a quadratic equation are represented by the x-intercepts of the graph of the corresponding quadratic function.

The roots of a quadratic equation can be **equal or unequal** and **real or non-real**.

Consider the graphs from the previous page.

- In graph 1 the roots of the equation $x^2 - 6x + 5 = 0$ are real and unequal (distinct).
- In graph 2 the roots of the equation $x^2 - 6x + 9 = 0$ are real and equal.
- In graph 3 the roots of the equation $x^2 - 6x + 13 = 0$ are non-real.

The Discriminant

The nature of the roots of a quadratic equation can be determined without actually solving the equation or drawing its graph.

The number $b^2 - 4ac$, which appears under the radical symbol in the quadratic formula, can be used to discriminate between the different types of roots and is called the **discriminant**.

$$\text{discriminant} = b^2 - 4ac$$

a) Complete the table using the calculations from the investigation on the previous page.

Equation	Roots	Nature of Roots	$b^2 - 4ac$
$x^2 - 6x + 5 = 0$			
$x^2 - 6x + 9 = 0$			
$x^2 - 6x + 13 = 0$			

b) Complete the following:

- If the discriminant $b^2 - 4ac = 0$, then the roots are __________ and __________ .
- If the discriminant $b^2 - 4ac > 0$, then the roots are __________ and __________ .
- If the discriminant $b^2 - 4ac < 0$, then the roots are __________ .

Determine the nature of the roots of the following equations without solving or graphing.

a) $6x^2 - x - 1 = 0$ **b)** $x^2 + 16 = 8x$ **c)** $5x^2 + 2x + 1 = 0$.

Determine for what value(s) of m the quadratic equation $x^2 - 8x + m$ has:

a) real and distinct roots **b)** real and equal roots **c)** non-real roots

a) State a condition for $b^2 - 4ac$ so that the equation $ax^2 + bx + c = 0$ has real roots.

b) Given that the equation $ax^2 + bx + c = 0$ has real roots, state a condition for $b^2 - 4ac$ so that the roots are: **i)** rational, **ii)** irrational.

c) Show that the roots of the equation $(m - 2)x^2 - (3m - 2)x + 2m = 0$ are always real and rational.

Complete Assignment Questions #4 - #12

Assignment

1. Form a quadratic equation and solve. Answer to the nearest tenth.

a) $x + \frac{1}{x} = 3,\ x \neq 0$

b) $(2x - 1)(3x + 2) = (x + 3)(2x + 1)$

2. Form a quadratic equation and solve. Give answers as exact values in simplest form

a) $\frac{4}{x^2} + \frac{2}{x} = 3$

b) $3x(x - 4) = 8$

c) $3(x - 1)(x + 2) - (x^2 + 3) = 0$

3. Find a quadratic equation in simplest form which is equivalent to the given equation, but has integral coefficients. Hence find the roots of the given equation to the nearest tenth.

a) $1.4x^2 - 2.8x = 1.8$

b) $\frac{x^2}{2} - x - \frac{5}{4} = 0$

4. Find the value of the discriminant in each of the following equations.

a) $x^2 + x + 9 = 0$ **b)** $3x^2 - 18x + 27 = 0$

5. Determine the nature of the roots of the following equations without solving or graphing.

a) $2x^2 + 4x + 8 = 0$ **b)** $9x^2 - 24x + 16 = 0$ **c)** $-2x^2 - x + 3 = 0$

d) $-2(x + 3)^2 + 40 = 0$ **e)** $x^2 + 10 + 3x = 0$ **f)** $4x^2 + 4x + 1 = 0$

6. a) Determine for what value(s) of d the quadratic equation $5x^2 - 10x + d = 0$ has:

i) real and distinct roots **ii)** real and equal roots **iii)** non-real roots

b) Determine an integer value for d such that the equation has rational, non-zero roots.

7. For what values of n does each equation have real roots?

a) $nx^2 - 2x + 1 = 0$

b) $2x^2 + 20x + n = 0$

8. For what values of a does the equation $ax^2 + (2a - 3)x + a = 0$ have non-real roots?

9. Show that the roots of the equation $x(x - 3) = k^2 - 2, k \in R$, are always real.

Use the following information for questions #10 and #11

Rosa was analyzing the following four functions:

I. $f(x) = x^2 - x - 11$ **II.** $f(x) = 2x^2 - x + 3$

III. $f(x) = (3x - 1)(x - 2)(x + 3)$ **IV.** $f(x) = 4x^2 - 12x + 9$

Multiple Choice

10. Which of these functions is a quadratic function with real and equal zeros?

A. I
B. II
C. III
D. IV

11. Which of these functions is a quadratic function with no real zeros?

A. I
B. II
C. III
D. IV

12. The discriminant for the quadratic equation $3x^2 - 8 - 7x = 0$ is _____ .

(Record your answer in the numerical response box from left to right.)

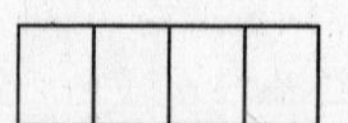

Answer Key

1. a) 0.4, 2.6 **b)** –0.6, 2.1

2. a) $\frac{1 \pm \sqrt{13}}{3}$ **b)** $\frac{6 \pm 2\sqrt{15}}{3}$ **c)** $-3, \frac{3}{2}$

3. a) $7x^2 - 14x - 9 = 0$, –0.5, 2.5 **b)** $2x^2 - 4x - 5 = 0$, –0.9, 2.9

4. a) –35 **b)** 0

5. a) non-real **b)** real and equal **c)** real and unequal
d) real and unequal **e)** non-real **f)** real and equal

6. a) i) $d < 5$ **ii)** $d = 5$ **iii)** $d > 5$ **b)** $d = -15$ or -40 or -75, etc.

7. a) $n \leq 1$ **b)** $n \leq 50$ **8.** $a > \frac{3}{4}$

9. $b^2 - 4ac = 1 + 4k^2$ which is always positive. **10.** D **11.** B

12.

1	4	5	

Quadratic Functions and Equations Lesson #8:
Applications of Quadratic Functions - A Graphical Approach

Using A Graphing Calculator to Find Maximum or Minimum Values

1. Enter the equation of the function into [Y_1] and press [GRAPH].

2. Access the CALC feature by entering [2nd] then [TRACE].

3. Select "minimum" or "maximum".

4. On the bottom left hand side of the screen the calculator will ask for a left bound. Select a value on the left side of the max/min point and press [ENTER].

5. On the bottom left hand side of the screen the calculator will ask for a right bound. Select a value on the right side of the max/min point and press [ENTER].

6. On the bottom left hand side of the screen the calculator will ask for a guess. Press [ENTER]. The *y* **value** will be the max/min answer.

The height, h, in metres above the ground, of a projectile at any time, t, in seconds, after the launch is defined by the function $h(t) = -4t^2 + 48t + 3$.

Use a graphing calculator to answer the following:

a) Sketch the relevant part of the parabola on the grid.

b) Find the height of the projectile 3 seconds after the launch.

c) Find the maximum height reached by the projectile.

d) How many seconds after the launch is the maximum height reached?

e) What was the height of the projectile at the launch?

f) Determine when the projectile hit the ground to the nearest tenth of a second.

Last season, a struggling hockey club had only 7 200 season ticket holders. The owner of the hockey club has decided to raise the price of a package of season tickets for the new season to generate more revenue. The existing cost of a package of season tickets is \$1 400. Before raising the price of a package of season tickets, he hired a market research company to gather data on the proposed increase. The research company reported that for every \$25 increase in price, approximately 100 season ticket holders would not renew their season tickets.

If the price increase is to be a multiple of \$25, use the following procedure to determine what price would maximize the revenue from season tickets.

a) Let x be the number of \$25 increases from the current price of a season ticket. Write expressions in x for the cost of a package of season tickets and the potential number of season ticket holders.

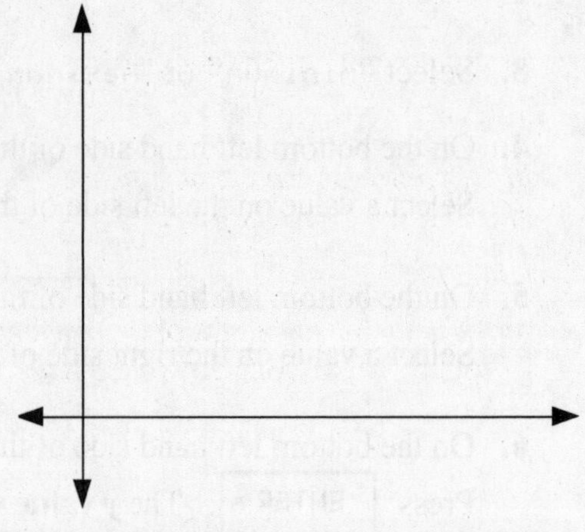

b) Use the results of a) to generate an expression which represents the revenue obtained.

c) Determine the price of a package of season tickets which would generate maximum revenue.

d) How many season ticket holders would there be if this plan was implemented?

e) How much more revenue would be generated if the plan in c) was implemented?

Complete Assignment Questions #1 - #7

Assignment

1. A football punted during a high school football game followed the path of a parabola. The path can be modelled by the function

$$d(t) = -5t^2 + 15t + 1, \; t \geq 0$$

where t is the number of seconds which have elapsed since the football was punted, and $d(t)$ is the number of metres above the ground after t seconds.

a) Sketch the graph on the grid.

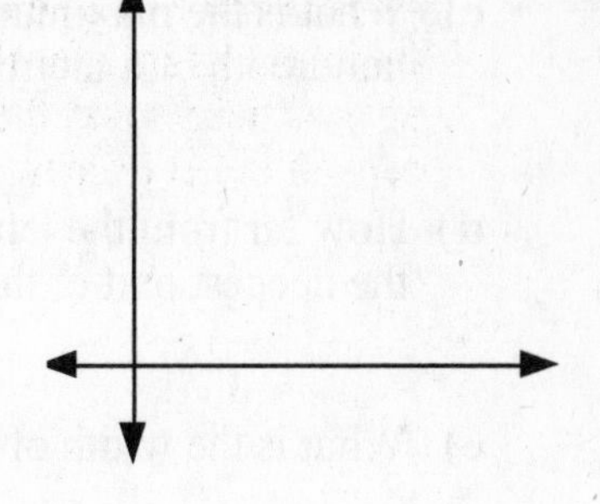

In the following questions, answer to the nearest hundredth of a unit where necessary.

b) What was the height of the football above the ground as the punter made contact with the football?

c) What was the height of the football above the ground 1 second after contact?

d) What is the maximum height reached by the football?
What relation does this have to the vertex of the parabola?

e) How many seconds had elapsed when the football reached its maximum height?
What relation does this have to the vertex?

f) The punt was not fielded by the opposition and the football hit the ground.
How many seconds did it take for the football to hit the ground?

g) The original domain was given as $t \geq 0$.
Write a more accurate domain for the function which describes the path of the football.

2. The cross section of a river, from one bank to the other, can be represented by the function

$$d(w) = \frac{1}{14}w^2 - \frac{5}{7}w$$

where $d(w)$ is the depth, in metres, of the river w metres from the left edge of the river bank.

a) Sketch the graph of the cross section of the river using a graphing calculator.

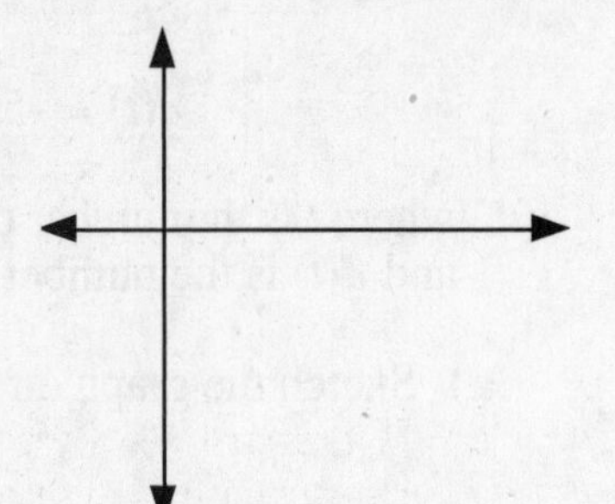

b) Determine the depth of the river 3 metres from the left edge.

c) What is the maximum depth of the river, to the nearest hundredth of a metre?

d) How far from the left edge of the river, to the nearest tenth of a metre, is the deepest part of the river?

e) What is the width of the river to the nearest tenth of a metre?

3. Recall the following information from Class Ex. #2 on page 348.

The hockey club had 7 200 season ticket holders who each paid $1 400 for a package of season tickets. The owner had suggested raising the price to generate more revenue, but knew that the number of season ticket holders would be reduced.

The general manager suggested that more revenue might be obtained by decreasing the price and thus attracting more fans to buy a package of season tickets. The research company, that the owner hired to explore the general manager's suggestion, reported that for every $50 decrease in price, approximately 400 new season ticket holders would be generated.

a) If the price decrease is to be a multiple of $50, determine the following:

i) the price of a package of season tickets which would generate maximum revenue

ii) the number of season ticket holders which would be generated

iii) the revenue which would be generated if the plan in a) was implemented

b) What advice would you give the owner in regards to the direction he should take to obtain maximum revenue?

4. The cost of car insurance depends on many factors, one of which is the age of the driver. Insurance companies know that younger drivers under the age of 25 and older drivers over the age of 70 are statistically more likely to have accidents than drivers between the ages of 25 and 70. The following data shows the number of accidents, per million kilometres driven, by drivers of a particular age.

Age (x)	18	30	45	60	75
Number of Accidents (y)	5.2	3.1	2.2	2.8	4.7

a) If x represents the age of drivers and y represents the number of accidents per million kilometres driven, plot the data on a Cartesian plane, and join the points with a smooth curve.

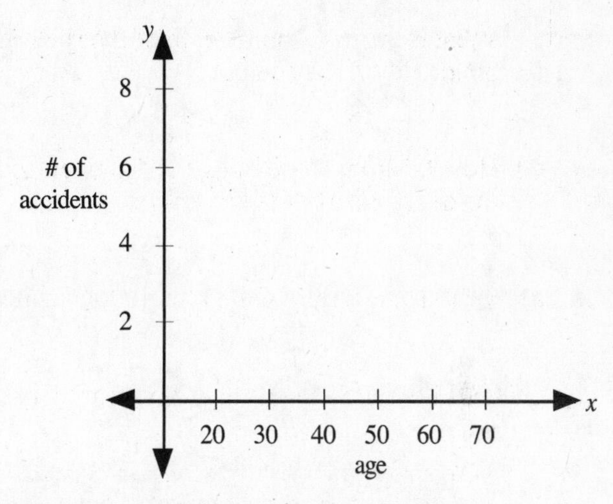

b) The data looks like it could be modelled by a quadratic function with equation $y = ax^2 + bx + c$. Using the technique of quadratic regression (which is taught in a higher level math course), a teacher determines that the equation which best models the data is

$$y = 0.0034x^2 - 0.3232x + 9.8505$$

Use the above model to determine what age, to the nearest year, results in the lowest number of accidents per million kilometres?

c) Determine the lowest number of accidents per million kilometres. Answer to the nearest tenth.

d) Based on this model, who is more likely to have an accident - a 17 year old student or a 78 year old senior?

5. Luigi owns a potato farm in southern Alberta. Each year he faces a dilemma as to when to harvest his crop of potatoes. He know that if he harvests early, the price will be high but his yield will be low and if he harvests late, the price will be low but the yield will be high.

From past experience, he knows that if he harvests on July 15, he can expect approximately 2000 kg of potatoes which he could sell at $0.60 per kg.

For each week he waits after July 15, he can expect an extra 400 kg of potatoes, but the price will reduce by $0.05 per kg.

When should he harvest his crop for maximum revenue?

Use the following information to answer questions #6 and #7.

Researchers predict that the world population will peak sometime during the 21st century before starting to decline. In the year 2000, the world population was approximately 6 100 000 000 (or 6.1 billion).

The following model has been suggested as an approximate relationship between the number of years, x, since the year 2000 and the world population, y.

The equation of the relationship is $y = -595\,000x^2 + 83\,000\,000x + 6\,100\,000\,000$

Numerical Response

6. The world population is expected to peak in the year _____ .

(Record your answer in the numerical response box from left to right.)

7. The maximum population, to the nearest tenth of a billion, is expected to be _____ .

(Record your answer in the numerical response box from left to right.)

Answer Key

1. b) 1 metre **c)** 11 metres **d)** 12.25 metres. It is the y-coordinate of the vertex.
e) 1.50 seconds. It is the x-coordinate of the vertex. **f)** 3.07 seconds **g)** $0 \le t \le 3.07$

2. b) 1.5 metres **c)** 1.79 metres **d)** 5.0 metres **e)** 10.0 metres

3. a) i) $1,150.00 **ii))** 9 200 **iii)** $10,580 000
b) It would be better to reduce the price to $1,150 than to increase the price to $1,600.

4. b) 48 years **c)** 2.2 accidents per million km **d)** both are about equally likely (17 year old is slightly more likely).

5. $3\frac{1}{2}$ weeks after July 15. **6.** | 2 | 0 | 6 | 9 | **7.** | 9 | . | 0 | |

Quadratic Functions and Equations Lesson #9:
Applications of Quadratic Functions - An Algebraic Approach

Review

The standard form of quadratic functions is useful to solve, analyze, and interpret problems whose graphical model is parabolic in shape. Complete the following statements for the standard form equation of a parabola $y = a(x - p)^2 + q$.

a) The coordinates of the vertex are ________ .

b) When a__0, the maximum value is ___ .   When a__0, the minimum value is ___ .

c) The equation of the axis of symmetry is ________ .

Maximum/Minimum Applications

In this lesson, all the questions are intended to be completed algebraically.

Consider the following information taken from Lesson 8, page 347, Class Ex. #1.

"The height, h, in metres above the ground, of a projectile at any time, t, in seconds, after the launch is defined by the function $h(t) = -4t^2 + 48t + 3$."

a) Complete the square to write h in standard form.

b) Find the height of the projectile 3 seconds after the launch.

c) Find the maximum height reached by the projectile.

d) How many seconds after the launch is the maximum height reached?

e) What was the height of the projectile at the launch?

f) Determine when the projectile hits the ground to the nearest tenth of a second.

g) Compare the answers from b) - f) with those on page 347.

A rancher has 300 m of fencing with which to form a rectangular corral (an enclosure for confining livestock), one of whose sides is an existing wall which does not require fencing.

a) If two of the sides of the rectangle are each x metres in length, show that the area of the corral can be expressed in the form $A(x) = 300x - 2x^2$.

b) Use the method of completing the square to determine the maximum area possible.

c) State the dimensions of the rectangle which gives the maximum area.

Ashley was asked by her Math teacher to find two numbers which differ by 8 and whose product is a minimum.

a) If x represents the smaller number, write a quadratic expression in x for the product of the two numbers.

b) Write the product in completed square form.

c) Determine the numbers and the minimum product.

Complete Assignment Questions #1 - #9

Extension: The Vertex Formula

The coordinates of the vertex of the graph of a quadratic function $f(x) = ax^2 + bx + c$ can be found by completing the square as follows:

$$f(x) = ax^2 + bx + c$$

$$= a\left(x^2 + \frac{b}{a}x\right) + c$$

$$= a\left(x^2 + \frac{b}{a}x + \frac{b^2}{4a^2} - \frac{b^2}{4a^2}\right) + c$$

$$= a\left(x^2 + \frac{b}{a}x + \frac{b^2}{4a^2}\right) + c - \frac{b^2}{4a}$$

$$= a\left(x + \frac{b}{2a}\right)^2 + \frac{4ac - b^2}{4a}$$

Vertex $= \left(\frac{-b}{2a}, \frac{4ac - b^2}{4a}\right)$

Maximum / Minimum value $= \frac{4ac - b^2}{4a}$

Use an appropriate procedure to determine the coordinates of the vertex of the graph of each of the following functions. State the maximum or minimum value of each function.

a) $f(x) = 2(x + 5)^2 + 8$

b) $P(x) = -2x^2 + 12x - 13$

Complete Assignment Question #10

Assignment

In this assignment, all the questions are intended to be completed algebraically.

1. At a local golf course, on the par 3, eighth hole, Linda used a seven iron to reach the green. Her golf ball followed the path of a parabola, approximated by the function

$$h(t) = -5t^2 + 25t + 0.05$$

where t is the number of seconds which have elapsed since Linda hit the ball,
and $h(t)$ is the height, in metres, of the ball above the ground after t seconds.

a) Write the function in standard form.

b) Find the height of the golf ball 2 seconds after the ball is hit.

c) Find the maximum height reached by the golf ball.

d) How many seconds did it take for the golf ball to reach its maximum height?

e) How high, in centimetres, did Linda tee up her golf ball before she hit it?

f) How long, to the nearest tenth of a second, did it take for the golf ball to hit the ground?

2. The sum of a number, x, and its reciprocal, is $\frac{29}{10}$. Form an equation and find the original number.

3. The perimeter of a rectangular plot of land is 84 metres and its area is 320 metres^2. If the length of the plot is represented by x metres, form a quadratic equation in x, and solve it to find the length and width of the plot.

4. The paved walkway from the main school building to the Physical Education block at a school is "L" shaped, with the total distance being 180 metres. A student, taking a short cut diagonally across the grass, shortens the distance to 130 m.

a) Draw a sketch to illustrate this information.

b) If one of the "L" shaped sides has a length of x metres, state the length of the other "L" shaped side in terms of x.

c) Use the Pythagorean Theorem to write a quadratic equation in x. Solve the equation to determine the length of the two legs of the paved walkway. Answer to the nearest tenth of a metre.

5. A stone is thrown vertically upward at a speed of 22 m/s. Its height, h metres, after t seconds, is given approximately by the function $h(t) = 22t - 5t^2$.
Use this formula to find, to the nearest tenth of a second, when the stone is 15 metres up and explain the double answer.

Multiple Choice

6. Two numbers have a difference of 20. When the squares of the numbers are added together, the result is a minimum. The larger of the two numbers is

A. 0

B. 10

C. 20

D. 30

7. A springboard diver's height, in metres, above the water, is given by the formula

$$h(t) = -5t^2 + 8t + 4$$

where t is the number of seconds which have elapsed since the start of the dive,
and $h(t)$ is the height, in metres, of the diver above the water after t seconds.

The time taken, to the nearest tenth of a second, for the diver to enter the water is _____ .

(Record your answer in the numerical response box from left to right.)

8. One positive integer is 3 greater than 4 times another positive integer.
If the product of the two integers is 76, then the sum of the two integers is _____ .

(Record your answer in the numerical response box from left to right.)

9. A whole number is multiplied by 5 and added to 3 times its reciprocal to give a sum of 16.
The number is _____ .

(Record your answer in the numerical response box from left to right.)

10. Use the vertex formula to determine the coordinates of the vertex of the graph of each of the following functions. State the maximum or minimum value of each function.

a) $f(x) = 5x^2 + 3x - 2$ **b)** $f(x) = -3x^2 - 7x - 1$ **c)** $f(x) = x^2 + 9x + 4$

Answer Key

1. **a)** $h(t) = -5(t - 2.5)^2 + 31.3$ **b)** 30.05 metres **c)** 31.3 metres
d) 2.5 seconds **e)** 5 cm **f)** 5.0 seconds

2. $\frac{2}{5}$ or $\frac{5}{2}$

3. length = 32 metres, width = 10 metres

4. **b)** $(180 - x)$ metres **c)** $2x^2 - 360x + 15500 = 0$, 108.7m and 71.3m

5. 0.8 seconds and 3.6 seconds. There are two answers as the stone goes up and then comes down.

6. B

7.

2	.	0	

8.

2	3		

9.

3			

10. **a)** vertex $\left(-\frac{3}{10}, -\frac{49}{20}\right)$ minimum value is $-\frac{49}{20}$ **b)** vertex $\left(-\frac{7}{6}, \frac{37}{12}\right)$ maximum value is $\frac{37}{12}$
c) vertex $\left(-\frac{9}{2}, -\frac{65}{4}\right)$ minimum value is $-\frac{65}{4}$

Quadratic Functions and Equations Lesson #10: Practice Test

1. Which one of the following statements is false?

A. The zeros of the function $f(x) = x^2 + 4x - 5$ are the roots of the equation $x^2 + 4x - 5 = 0$.

B. The x-intercepts of the graph of the function with equation $y = x^2 + 5x + 6$ are the factors of the expression $x^2 + 5x + 6$.

C. If $x = 3$ is a root of the equation $f(x) = 0$, then $x - 3$ is a factor of $f(x)$.

D. If $x + 7$ is a factor of the function with equation $y = f(x)$, then -7 is an x-intercept of the graph of the function.

2. The zeros of the function $f(x) = 3(x - 5)(3x + 2)$ are:

A. $5, -\frac{2}{3}$ **B.** $-5, \frac{2}{3}$ **C.** $0, 5, -\frac{2}{3}$ **D.** $3, 5, -\frac{2}{3}$

3. The graph of the function $f(x) = (x - a)^2 - b$ is a parabola. Which of the following is a correct statement about the graph?

A. There is a maximum point at $(-a, -b)$. **B.** There is a maximum point at $(a, -b)$.

C. There is a minimum point at $(-a, b)$. **D.** There is a minimum point at $(a, -b)$.

4. The range of the function $f(x) = -2(x - 1)^2 + 8$ is all real numbers such that

A. $y \geq 8$ **B.** $y \leq 8$

C. $y \geq 1$ **D.** $y \leq 1$

5. The coordinates of the vertex of the graph of the function $g(x) = x^2 - 4x + 11$ are

A. $(2, 15)$

B. $(2, 7)$

C. $(4, -5)$

D. $(4, 11)$

6. The graph of $y = x^2$ is translated 4 units left. The equation of the transformed graph is

A. $y = x^2 + 4$ **B.** $y = x^2 - 4$ **C.** $y = (x + 4)^2$ **D.** $y = (x - 4)^2$

7. The graph of $y = x^2$ undergoes two transformations to form the graph of $y = 4(x - 5)^2$. Which of the following is one of these transformations?

A. a horizontal translation 5 units left
B. a vertical translation 4 units up
C. a vertical stretch by a factor of 4 about the x-axis
D. a vertical stretch by a factor of 5 about the x-axis

Numerical Response

1. The graph of $y = (x - 5)^2 + b$ passes through the point $(3, 24)$. The value of b is _____.

(Record your answer in the numerical response box from left to right.)

Numerical Response

2. The quadratic function $f(x) = x^2 - 12x + 41$ can be written in standard form $f(x) = (x - a)^2 + b$.

Write the value of a in the first box. Write the value of b in the second box.

(Record your answer in the numerical response box from left to right.)

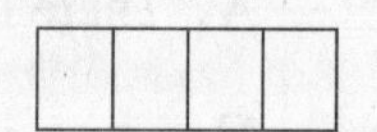

8. The quadratic function $f(x) = x^2$ is transformed to $g(x) = -\frac{2}{3}(x + 3)^2 + 6$. The point $(6, 36)$ on the graph of f is transformed to which point on the graph of g?

A. $(3, -30)$

B. $(3, -28)$

C. $(3, -18)$

D. $(-6, 42)$

9. The graph of a quadratic function has x-intercepts at m and at $5m$ and a y-intercept of n. The equation of the axis of symmetry of the graph is

A. $x = \frac{m+n}{2}$ **B.** $x = \frac{6m+n}{3}$

C. $x = 3m$ **D.** $x = 6m$

Use the following information to answer questions #10 and #11.

The graph of the quadratic function $f(x) = ax^2 + bx + c$ has vertex $(3, 7)$ and passes through the point $(2, 11)$.

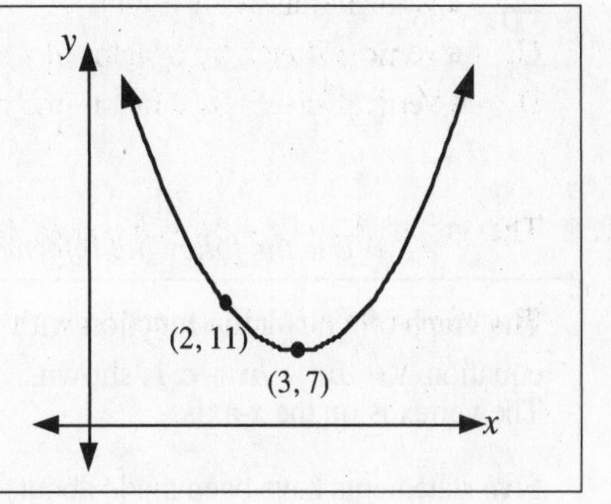

10. The value of a is

A. -4

B. 4

C. -18

D. 18

11. The value of $b^2 - 4ac$ is

A. positive **B.** negative

C. zero **D.** unable to be determined

Numerical Response

3. Bailey used the quadratic formula to determine the positive root of the equation $2a^2 - 25a = 80$. To the nearest tenth, this root is _____ .

(Record your answer in the numerical response box from left to right.)

12. The roots of the equation $4x^2 + 4x - 5 = 0$ can be written in the form $x = \dfrac{-1 \pm \sqrt{A}}{2}$.
The value of A is

A. 6

B. 12

C. 24

D. 96

Use the following information to answer the next question.

The graph of a quadratic function with equation $y = ax^2 + bx + c$ is shown.
The vertex is on the x-axis.

Five statements have been made about the information from the graph.

Statement 1: The discriminant of $ax^2 + bx + c$ is zero.

Statement 2: The discriminant of $ax^2 + bx + c$ is positive.

Statement 3: The discriminant of $ax^2 + bx + c$ is negative.

Statement 4: The value of a is positive.

Statement 5: The value of a is negative.

Numerical Response

4. Only two of the five statements are correct.

Write the number of the first correct statement in the first box.

Write the number of the second correct statement in the second box.

(Record your answer in the numerical response box from left to right.)

13. When $y = 2x^2 - 7x + 6$ is converted to the form $y = a(x - p)^2 + q$, the value of q is

A. $-\frac{1}{8}$

B. $-\frac{37}{2}$

C. $\frac{47}{16}$

D. $\frac{97}{8}$

14. The roots of the equation $2x^2 - 7x - 5 = 0$ are

A. $\frac{7 \pm \sqrt{89}}{2}$

B. $\frac{-7 \pm \sqrt{89}}{4}$

C. $\frac{7 \pm \sqrt{9}}{4}$

D. $\frac{7 \pm \sqrt{89}}{4}$

15. The shortest side of a right angled triangle is 7 cm less than the second shortest side. The sum of the squares of these two sides is equal to 289 cm^2. The perimeter of the triangle, in cm, is

A. 15

B. 23

C. 40

D. none of the above

Use the following information to answer the next question.

The diagram shows a photograph measuring 8 inches by 6 inches surrounded by a mat. The mat has the same width on all sides of the photograph.

The photograph and mat are put into a glass photo frame which just covers the outside of the mat.

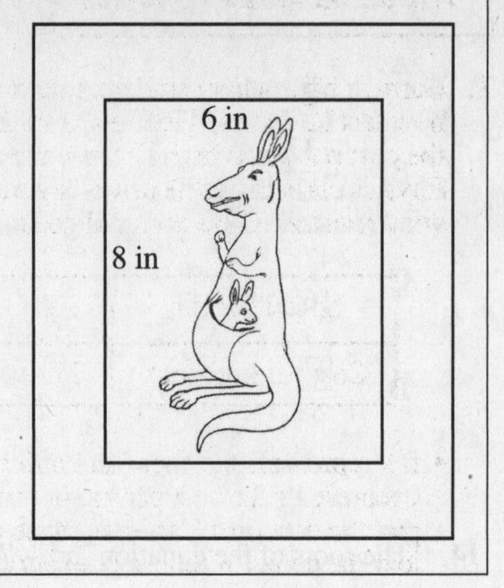

Numerical Response

5. If the area of the glass surface is 120 square inches, determine the width of the mat to the nearest tenth of an inch.

(Record your answer in the numerical response box from left to right.)

Written Response - 5 marks

1. Barry, a high school student, found that driving a truck can be a costly venture depending on how fast he drives. He knew from his Mechanics class that if he drives his truck too slowly, the cost per km is high because the engine does not run efficiently. He also knows from Physics class that if he drives his truck too fast, the cost per km is also high because of high wind resistance. He accumulated the following data.

Speed (km/hr)	30	50	65	100	120
Cost per kilometre	27.4¢	19.4¢	16.0¢	16.9¢	22.9¢

- If x represents the speed in km/h and y represents the cost per km in cents, plot the data on a Cartesian plane and join the points with a smooth curve.

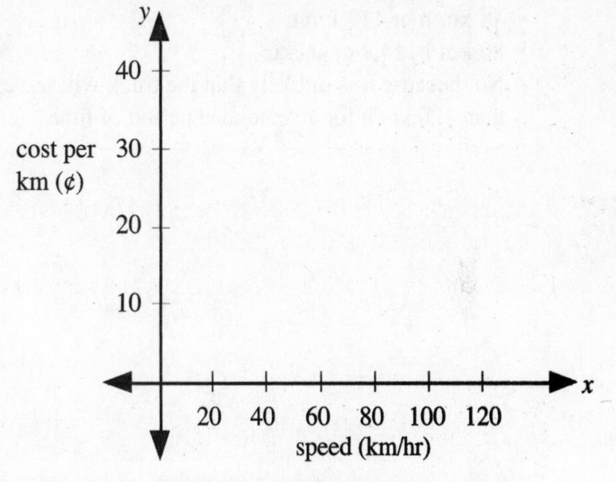

- Looking at the graph, Barry thought that the data could be modelled by a quadratic function with equation $y = ax^2 + bx + c$.
  He used the technique of quadratic regression to determine the equation $y = 0.005x^2 - 0.801x + 46.928$ as the best model for the data.

  Using the model above, determine the cost per km, to the nearest tenth of a cent, at a speed of 70 km/h.

- Determine the speed, to the nearest km/h, if the cost is 20 cents per km.

- Which speed, to the nearest km/h, results in the lowest cost per kilometre? What is this cost to the nearest tenth of a cent?

- Does it make sense to extend the parabola to the left or right of the data points?

Answer Key

Multiple Choice

1. B	**2.** A	**3.** D	**4.** B	**5.** B	**6.** C	**7.** C	**8.** C
9. C	**10.** B	**11.** B	**12.** A	**13.** A	**14.** D	**15.** C	

Numerical Response

1. | 2 | 0 | | |

2. | 6 | 5 | | |

3. | 1 | 5 | . | 1 |

4. | 1 | 5 | | |

5. | 2 | . | 0 | |

Written Response

1.
- Graph
- 15.4 cents/km
- 48 km/h or 112 km/h
- 80 km/h, 14.8 cents/km
- No, because it is unlikely that the truck will travel at speeds less then 30 km/h or speeds greater than 120 km/h for an extended period of time.

Rational Expressions and Equations Lesson #1:
Simplifying Rational Expressions - Part One

Rational Expressions

In previous courses we have learned that the quotient of two integers $\left(\text{eg. } \frac{4}{7}\right)$ is a **rational number**.

Similarly, the quotient of two polynomials $\left(\text{eg. } \frac{x+7}{x+8}\right)$ is called a **rational expression**.

A single variable **rational expression** is an algebraic fraction in one variable in which the numerator and denominator are both polynomials $\left(\text{eg. } \frac{x-3}{x^2+1}, \frac{7}{2y+5}\right)$.

In this unit, we will learn how to add, subtract, multiply and divide rational expressions. We will also learn how to solve problems involving rational equations.

The key to success in operating with rational expressions in this unit lies in our ability to factor polynomials.

Recall the following methods for factoring polynomial expressions:

i) greatest common factor

ii) difference of squares

iii) factoring trinomials by inspection

iv) factoring trinomials by decomposition

v) grouping

Investigating Equivalent Forms of a Rational Expression

Consider the rational expressions

$\dfrac{2x+2}{x^2+3x+2}$ and $\dfrac{2}{x+2}$.

a) Complete the table.

Value of x	Value of $\dfrac{2x+2}{x^2+3x+2}$	Value of $\dfrac{2}{x+2}$
0		
1		
2		
3		
4		

b) What can we say about the values of the rational expressions $\dfrac{2x+2}{x^2+3x+2}$ and $\dfrac{2}{x+2}$ when x is replaced by 0, 1, 2, 3, or 4?

c) The expressions $\dfrac{2x+2}{x^2+3x+2}$ and $\dfrac{2}{x+2}$ are known as **equivalent forms** of a rational expression. To explain why they are equivalent, read the following procedure and complete after step ii).

i) Write the numerator, $2x + 2$, and the denominator, $x^2 + 3x + 2$ in factored form.

ii) Reduce the rational expression by dividing out a common factor, called **cancelling factors**, and show that $\dfrac{2x+2}{x^2+3x+2}$ can be reduced to $\dfrac{2}{x+2}$.

Complete:

$$\frac{2x+2}{x^2+3x+2} = \frac{2(\quad + \quad)}{(\qquad)(\qquad)} =$$

- When $\dfrac{2x+2}{x^2+3x+2}$ is written in the form $\dfrac{2}{x+2}$, it is said to be in **lowest terms** or **simplest form**.

- $\dfrac{2}{x+2}$ cannot be further reduced by cancelling terms. **The two 2's cannot** be reduced.

i.e. $\dfrac{2}{x+2}$ is **NOT** equivalent to $\dfrac{1}{x+1}$ (Replace x by any permissible value to verify this.)

- **To reduce fractions we cancel factors, not terms.**

Investigating Nonpermissible Values

a) Complete the table.

Write the value as **not defined** if the value cannot be calculated.

Value of x	Value of $\frac{2x+2}{x^2+3x+2}$	Value of $\frac{2}{x+2}$
0		
−1		
−2		
−3		

b) For which value(s) of x is the expression $\frac{2x+2}{x^2+3x+2}$ not defined?

c) For which value(s) of x is the expression $\frac{2}{x+2}$ not defined?

d) Why do the values in b) and c) result in the expressions not being defined?

Values of the variable which result in the value of a rational expression not being defined are called **nonpermissible values.** These values are known as the **restrictions** on the variable.

Nonpermissible values are values of the variable which make the denominator equal to zero.

Note that although $\frac{2x+2}{x^2+3x+2}$ and $\frac{2}{x+2}$ are equivalent forms of a rational expression, they have <u>different restrictions</u> on the value of x.

The restrictions must be determined before dividing out common factors.

Be aware that nonpermissible values are present each time we divide by an expression containing a variable.

A rational expression is in **simplest form** if its numerator and denominator have **no** common factor other than 1.

Express in simplest form, stating the nonpermissible values of the variable.

a) $\dfrac{12x^2}{2x}$ **b)** $\dfrac{(a+1)(a-6)}{(a+7)(a+1)}$ **c)** $\dfrac{y+4}{y^2-y-20}$ **d)** $\dfrac{x^2+11x+28}{x^2-49}$

Complete Assignment Questions #1 - #8

Assignment

1. Determine the nonpermissible values of the variable.

a) $\dfrac{6}{8x-7}$ **b)** $\dfrac{y}{10y+20}$ **c)** $\dfrac{5a}{5-a}$ **d)** $\dfrac{a^2+7a+12}{(a+4)(a+5)}$ **e)** $\dfrac{12y^2-2}{y}$

f) $\dfrac{1+16x^2}{1-16x^2}$ **g)** $\dfrac{40p^3-4}{8q^3}$ **h)** $\dfrac{3}{x^2+13x+12}$ **i)** $\dfrac{d}{d^2-8d+16}$

2. Express in simplest form, stating the nonpermissible values of the variable.

a) $\dfrac{4ab}{16a}$ **b)** $\dfrac{25x^3y^4}{5y^9}$ **c)** $\dfrac{(a+3)(a-8)}{(a+1)(a-8)}$ **d)** $\dfrac{(x+7)(x-2)}{x(x-2)(x+14)}$

3. Express in simplest form, stating the nonpermissible values of the variable.

a) $\dfrac{y+9}{y^2-81}$ **b)** $\dfrac{25y^2-36}{5y+6}$ **c)** $\dfrac{64-9p^2}{(8-3p)(3+8p)}$ **d)** $\dfrac{x^2-100}{(x+10)^2}$

4. The area of a soccer field is represented by $a^2 - 12a + 32$ square metres.

a) Find a simplified expression for the length of the field if the width can be represented by $a - 8$ metres.

b) Calculate the area of the field if $a = 90$.

5. Reduce to lowest terms, stating the restrictions on the variable.

a) $\dfrac{(t+3)^2}{(t+1)(t+3)}$ **b)** $\dfrac{x^2-1}{x^2+2x+1}$ **c)** $\dfrac{e^2+2e-35}{e^2+14e+49}$ **d)** $\dfrac{m^2-2m-15}{m^2+12m+27}$

e) $\dfrac{y^2+4y}{y^2-16}$ **f)** $\dfrac{x^2+9x-22}{x^2+12x+11}$ **g)** $\dfrac{a^2+11a+10}{a^2+8a-20}$ **h)** $\dfrac{p^2+5p+6}{p^2-4}$

Multiple Choice

6. $\dfrac{(x-y)^2}{x^2-y^2}$ is equivalent to

A. 0 **B.** 1

C. $\left(\dfrac{1}{x}-\dfrac{1}{y}\right)^2$ **D.** $\dfrac{x-y}{x+y}$

7. In the rational expression $\dfrac{a-3}{a(a+7)}$, the nonpermissible value(s) of a are

A. 3, −7 **B.** 0, 3, −7
C. 0, −7 **D.** −7

8. The rational expressions $\dfrac{x^2+13x+40}{x^2-13x+40}$ and $\dfrac{64+x^2}{64-x^2}$ have one nonpermissible value in common. The nonpermissible value is_____.

(Record your answer in the numerical response box from left to right.)

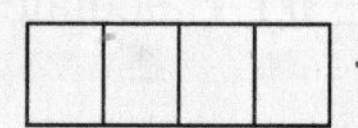

Answer Key

1. a) $x \neq \frac{7}{8}$ **b)** $y \neq -2$ **c)** $a \neq 5$ **d)** $a \neq -5, -4$ **e)** $y \neq 0$

f) $x \neq \pm\frac{1}{4}$ **g)** $q \neq 0$ **h)** $x \neq -12, -1$ **i)** $d \neq 4$

2. a) $\frac{b}{4}$. $a \neq 0$ **b)** $\frac{5x^3}{y^5}, y \neq 0$ **c)** $\frac{a+3}{a+1}, a \neq -1, 8$ **d)** $\frac{x+7}{x(x+14)}, x \neq -14, 0, 2$

3. a) $\frac{1}{y-9}, y \neq \pm 9$ **b)** $5y-6, y \neq -\frac{6}{5}$ **c)** $\frac{8+3p}{3+8p}, p \neq -\frac{3}{8}, \frac{8}{3}$ **d)** $\frac{x-10}{x+10}, x \neq -10$

4. a) $a-4$ metres **b)** 7052 square metres

5. a) $\frac{t+3}{t+1}$, $t \neq -1, -3$ **b)** $\frac{x-1}{x+1}, x \neq -1$ **c)** $\frac{e-5}{e+7}, e \neq -7$ **d)** $\frac{m-5}{m+9}, m \neq -9, -3$

e) $\frac{y}{y-4}, y \neq \pm 4$ **f)** $\frac{x-2}{x+1}, x \neq -11, -1$ **g)** $\frac{a+1}{a-2}, a \neq -10, 2$ **h)** $\frac{p+3}{p-2}, p \neq \pm 2$

6. D **7.** C **8.** 8

Rational Expressions and Equations Lesson #2:
Simplifying Rational Expressions Part Two

In this lesson, we extend the method of simplifying rational expression to more complex examples.

Recall that when we divide by an expression containing a variable, there are restrictions on the value which can be replaced for the variable.
These are called nonpermissible values of the variable.

Recall also that reducing rational expressions involves **cancelling factors** and **not terms**.

Class Ex. #1

Reduce to lowest terms, stating the restrictions on the variable.

a) $\dfrac{4t^3 - 9t}{2t^2 - 3t}$ **b)** $\dfrac{2x^2 + 5x - 3}{2x^2 + x - 1}$ **c)** $\dfrac{a^2 + 2a - 8}{a^4 - 20a^2 + 64}$

Class Ex. #2

Express in simplest form, stating the values of the variable for which the expression is not defined.

a) $\dfrac{c-4}{4-c}$ **b)** $\dfrac{2p^3 - 4p^2}{16 - 8p}$ **c)** $\dfrac{1 - 4x^2}{6x^2 - 5x - 4}$

The area (in m^2) of a rectangular field can be represented by the expression $12a^2 + 25a - 7$, and the length (in m) of the field can be represented by $3a + 7$.

a) Write and simplify a rational expression which represents the width of the field.

b) If the perimeter of the field is 54 metres, determine the value of a.

c) The field has to be treated with fertilizer at a cost of \$2.40 per square metre. Calculate the cost of the treatment.

Simplify, where possible, and state the nonpermissible values for x in terms of y.

a) $\dfrac{x+y}{x-y}$ **b)** $\dfrac{x+5y}{x^2-25y^2}$ **c)** $\dfrac{6(x+y)^2}{3x^4-3y^4}$

Complete Assignment Questions #1 - #10

Assignment

1. Reduce to lowest terms, stating the restrictions on the variable.

a) $\dfrac{5a^3 - 15a^2}{30a}$ **b)** $\dfrac{7x}{7x - 21}$ **c)** $\dfrac{6a - 3}{8a - 4}$

d) $-\dfrac{4a - 12}{a - 3}$ **e)** $-\dfrac{a^2}{a^2 + a}$ **f)** $\dfrac{3t^2 - 75}{(t + 3)(t - 5)}$

g) $\dfrac{2 - r}{r - 2}$ **h)** $-\dfrac{9a^2 - 1}{1 - 3a}$ **i)** $\dfrac{2b^2 - 18b}{b(b - 9)^2}$

2. Express in simplest form, stating the values of the variable for which the expression is not defined.

a) $\dfrac{t^2 + 4t + 4}{2t^2 + 10t + 12}$ **b)** $\dfrac{2x^2 + 5x - 3}{4x - 2}$ **c)** $\dfrac{2y^2 - 3y - 2}{2y^2 - y - 6}$

3. Express in simplest form, stating the values of the variable for which the expression is not defined.

a) $\dfrac{3t^2 - 5t - 12}{2t^2 - 6t}$ **b)** $\dfrac{32 - 2a^2}{2a^2 + 4a - 16}$ **c)** $\dfrac{4 - 4x^2}{8x^3 + 8x^2 - 16x}$

4. Express in simplest form, stating the restrictions on the variable

a) $\dfrac{2 - x - x^2}{x^4 - 5x^2 + 4}$ **b)** $\dfrac{16x^4 - y^4}{8x^3 + 4x^2y + 2xy^2 + y^3}$

5. A rectangular prism has a length of p cm and a width and height that are each 2 cm less than the length.

a) Write an expression in terms of p for the surface area of the prism, and express the surface area in simplest factored form.

b) The rectangular prism has two square faces. Write an expression in simplest factored form which represents the total length of the edges which make up these two squares.

c) If the ratio of the surface area in a) to the edge length in b) is 10:1, find the volume of the prism.

6. Simplify, where possible, and state the nonpermissible values for x in terms of y.

a) $\dfrac{x+y}{4x+4y}$ b) $\dfrac{4x^2-y^2}{y-2x}$ c) $\dfrac{3x+12y}{x^2-16y^2}$

7. Consider the rectangle shown.

a) Write and simplify an expression for the length of the rectangle.

area
$24x^3 - 54x^2 - 15x$

$6x^2 - 15x$

b) Determine the perimeter of the rectangle if $x = 2\sqrt{2}$ cm. Give the answer in simplest radical form.

8. Write a rational expression in x with a numerator of 1 and a denominator written as an integral polynomial so that the nonpermissible values are

a) $x \neq 2, 3$ **b)** $x \neq -2, 0$ **c)** $x \neq -\frac{3}{4}, \frac{1}{3}$ **d)** $x \neq \pm 2, 0$

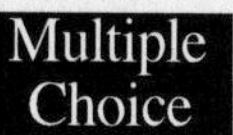

9. With appropriate restrictions, the simplified form of $\dfrac{x^2 - 121}{3x^2 + 29x - 44}$ is

A. $\dfrac{x - 11}{3x - 4}$

B. $\dfrac{x - 11}{3x + 4}$

C. $\dfrac{x + 11}{3x - 4}$

D. $\dfrac{x + 11}{3x + 4}$

10. If the rational expression $\dfrac{8a^2 + 22a + k}{2a^2 - 11a - 21}$, where k is a constant, reduces to $\dfrac{4a + 5}{a - 7}$, then the value of k, to the nearest whole number, is _____.

(Record your answer in the numerical response box from left to right.)

Answer Key

1. a) $\dfrac{a(a-3)}{6}, a \neq 0$ **b)** $\dfrac{x}{x-3}, x \neq 3$ **c)** $\dfrac{3}{4}, a \neq \dfrac{1}{2}$ **d)** $-4, a \neq 3$ **e)** $-\dfrac{a}{a+1}, a \neq -1, 0$

f) $\dfrac{3(t+5)}{t+3}, t \neq -3, 5$ **g)** $-1, r \neq 2$ **h)** $3a+1, a \neq \dfrac{1}{3}$ **i)** $\dfrac{2}{b-9}, b \neq 0, 9$

2. a) $\dfrac{t+2}{2(t+3)}, t \neq -3, -2$ **b)** $\dfrac{x+3}{2}, x \neq \dfrac{1}{2}$ **c)** $\dfrac{2y+1}{2y+3}, y \neq -\dfrac{3}{2}, 2$

3. a) $\dfrac{3t+4}{2t}, t \neq 0, 3$ **b)** $\dfrac{4-a}{a-2}, a \neq -4, 2$ **c)** $\dfrac{-1-x}{2x(x+2)}, x \neq -2, 0, 1$

4. a) $-\dfrac{1}{(x+1)(x-2)}, x \neq \pm 2, \pm 1$ **b)** $2x-y, x \neq -\dfrac{1}{2}y$

5. a) $2(3p-2)(p-2)$ cm^2 **b)** $8(p-2)$ cm **c)** 2016 cm^3 $(p = 14)$

6. a) $\dfrac{1}{4}, x \neq -y$ **b)** $-2x-y, x \neq \dfrac{1}{2}y$ **c)** $\dfrac{3}{x-4y}, x \neq \pm 4y$

7. a) $4x+1$ **b)** $98 - 44\sqrt{2}$ cm

8. a) $\dfrac{1}{x^2-5x+6}$ **b)** $\dfrac{1}{x^2+2x}$ **c)** $\dfrac{1}{12x^2+5x-3}$ **d)** $\dfrac{1}{x^3-4x}$

9. A **10.**

1	5		

Rational Expressions and Equations Lesson #3:
Addition and Subtraction of Rational Expressions
Part One

Review *Addition and Subtraction of Rational Numbers*

Recall these steps for adding or subtracting rational numbers.

1. Determine the lowest common denominator (LCD) for the rational numbers.

2. Express each rational number as an equivalent rational number with the LCD as the denominator.

3. Combine the rational numbers by adding/subtracting numerators.

4. Reduce to lowest terms, if possible.

Class Ex. #1

Add or subtract as indicated.

a) $\frac{2}{3} + \frac{2}{5}$ **b)** $\frac{5}{6} - \frac{1}{4}$ **c)** $\frac{7}{8} - \frac{2}{3} + \frac{5}{12}$

Addition/Subtraction of Single Variable Rational Expressions

The method for adding and subtracting of rational expressions is identical to the method described for addition and subtraction of rational numbers. Recall that when we deal with rational expressions with a variable in the denominator, there are restrictions on the variable.

Addition/Subtraction with Non-Variable Denominators

Class Ex. #2

Simplify.

a) $\frac{3x}{4} + \frac{x}{5} - \frac{7x}{10}$ **b)** $\frac{3a-1}{3} + \frac{4a+5}{6}$ **c)** $\frac{8y-3}{8} - \frac{2y+1}{3}$

Simplify. **a)** $\dfrac{7x+3}{2} + 3x - \dfrac{x-3}{8}$ **b)** $4 - \dfrac{y-4}{9} - \dfrac{5-3y}{3}$

Complete Assignment Questions #1 - #3

Addition/Subtraction with Common Denominators

Simplify. Express answers in lowest terms, and indicate nonpermissible values.

a) $\dfrac{2}{x} + \dfrac{7}{x} - \dfrac{1}{x}$ **b)** $\dfrac{5a+3}{2a} + \dfrac{a-6}{2a}$ **c)** $\dfrac{3y}{3y-1} - \dfrac{1}{3y-1}$ **d)** $\dfrac{4x+10}{x+3} - \dfrac{2x+4}{x+3}$

Addition/Subtraction with Different Monomial Denominators

Simplify. Express answers in lowest terms, and state any restrictions on the variables.

a) $\dfrac{5}{3p} + \dfrac{2}{7p}$ **b)** $\dfrac{1}{3y} + \dfrac{6}{5}$ **c)** $\dfrac{2x-5}{6x} - \dfrac{3x-2}{3x}$ **d)** $\dfrac{a+7}{2a^2} - \dfrac{3}{5a}$

Complete Assignment Questions #4 - #6

Addition/Subtraction with Different Monomial/Binomial Denominators

In this section, we will add or subtract rational expressions with monomial or binomial denominators with no factor in common.

Simplify. Express answers in lowest terms, and indicate nonpermissible values.

a) $\frac{x-9}{2x} + \frac{3x}{x-4}$ **b)** $\frac{4}{2y+5} - \frac{1}{y-3}$ **c)** $\frac{2x+1}{x-5} - \frac{x-4}{x+1}$

Perform the indicated operation. State the nonpermissible values.

$\frac{3}{x+2} - \frac{2}{x+1} + \frac{1}{x}$

Complete Assignment Questions #7 - #12

Assignment

1. Add or subtract as indicated.

a) $\frac{5}{8}+\frac{3}{4}$ **b)** $\frac{4}{7}-\frac{2}{5}$ **c)** $\frac{7}{9}-\frac{1}{3}+2$ **d)** $\frac{3}{2}-\frac{4}{3}+\frac{5}{4}$

2. Simplify.

a) $\frac{4x}{5}+\frac{3x}{10}-\frac{2x}{3}$ **b)** $\frac{c}{2}-\frac{c+2}{6}$ **c)** $\frac{a+2}{3}+\frac{a-3}{5}$

d) $\frac{t-2}{4}-\frac{t-3}{5}$ **e)** $\frac{2y-3}{4}-\frac{y+4}{7}$ **f)** $\frac{2x-3}{3}-\frac{5-2x}{9}$

3. Simplify.

a) $\frac{x}{4}+\frac{x+3}{6}+\frac{3x}{2}$ **b)** $\frac{4-2p}{3}+\frac{7-3p}{4}-\frac{p}{5}$ **c)** $\frac{6x+3}{5}-\frac{2x+1}{2}-\frac{x-3}{10}$

d) $2 - \frac{y-5}{5} + \frac{6y}{7}$ **e)** $\frac{3a+4}{12} + \frac{5-4a}{18} - 1$ **f)** $\frac{t}{7} - t - \frac{t-3}{3}$

4. Simplify. Express answers in lowest terms, and indicate nonpermissible values.

a) $\frac{2}{y} + \frac{3}{y} + \frac{4}{y}$ **b)** $\frac{1}{2x} + \frac{3}{2x} - \frac{5}{2x}$ **c)** $\frac{7y}{3y+8} - \frac{4y}{3y+8}$

d) $\frac{a+2}{a^2} - \frac{2-a}{a^2}$ **e)** $\frac{4b+1}{b+3} - \frac{2b-5}{3+b}$ **f)** $\frac{15x}{4(3x+5)} + \frac{25}{4(3x+5)}$

5. Simplify. Express answers in lowest terms, and state any restrictions on the variables.

a) $\frac{1}{4x} + \frac{1}{2}$ **b)** $\frac{1}{3a} - \frac{1}{4a}$ **c)** $\frac{1}{3t} + \frac{1}{4t} + \frac{1}{5t}$ **d)** $\frac{1}{2t} - \frac{2}{3t} - \frac{3}{4t}$

e) $\frac{6}{5x} + \frac{2}{3x}$ **f)** $\frac{7}{5p} - \frac{5}{7p}$ **g)** $\frac{2}{x} - \frac{3}{2x} + \frac{4}{3x} - \frac{5}{4x}$ **h)** $\frac{3}{x} + 1$

6. Simplify. Express answers in lowest terms, and state any restrictions on the variables.

a) $\frac{9}{2x} + \frac{1}{x^2}$ **b)** $\frac{3}{4a^2} - \frac{5}{3a}$ **c)** $\frac{8}{3b^2} + \frac{7}{b^3}$ **d)** $\frac{4}{3c^2} - \frac{5}{2c^3} + \frac{6}{c^4}$

7. Simplify. Express answers in lowest terms, and indicate nonpermissible values.

a) $\frac{1}{a+1} + \frac{1}{a-1}$ **b)** $\frac{2}{b+3} + \frac{3}{b+2}$ **c)** $\frac{5}{x+2} - \frac{2}{x+5}$

d) $\frac{4}{x-3} + \frac{6}{x-1}$ **e)** $\frac{3}{y+2} - \frac{1}{y-7}$ **f)** $\frac{5t}{2t+1} - \frac{3t}{4t+1}$

8. Simplify.

a) $\frac{x-5}{3} + \frac{4x}{x-2}$ **b)** $\frac{p-1}{p+2} + \frac{p+2}{p+3}$ **c)** $\frac{2x-1}{x+2} - \frac{x+2}{2x-1}$

d) $\dfrac{2}{2x-3}+\dfrac{3}{3x-2}+\dfrac{4}{4x-1}$

e) $\dfrac{2}{t}-\dfrac{t+3}{t+2}-\dfrac{t+4}{t+3}$

Multiple Choice

9. $\dfrac{a}{a+2}+\dfrac{2}{a+2}$, $a \neq -2$, is equal to

A. $\dfrac{2a}{a+2}$ **B.** $\dfrac{a^2}{a+2}$

C. 1 **D.** $a+2$

10. For all $t \neq \pm 1$, the reduced form of $\dfrac{t+1}{t-1}-\dfrac{t-1}{t+1}$ is

A. 1 **B.** $\dfrac{2}{t^2-1}$

C. $\dfrac{2t}{t^2-1}$ **D.** $\dfrac{4t}{t^2-1}$

11. A rectangle has length $\dfrac{1}{x}$ cm and width $\dfrac{1}{x+1}$ cm.
The perimeter of the rectangle (in cm) is

A. $\dfrac{4}{4x+2}$ **B.** $\dfrac{4x+2}{x(x+1)}$

C. $\dfrac{2x+1}{x(x+1)}$ **D.** $\dfrac{1}{x(x+1)}$

12. For some whole number k, the reduced form of $\dfrac{x-k}{2x} + \dfrac{x+1}{4x}$ is $\dfrac{3x-5}{4x}$.
The value of k is _____.

(Record your answer in the numerical response box from left to right.)

Answer Key

1. a) $\dfrac{11}{8}$ b) $\dfrac{6}{35}$ c) $\dfrac{22}{9}$ d) $\dfrac{17}{12}$

2. a) $\dfrac{13x}{30}$ b) $\dfrac{c-1}{3}$ c) $\dfrac{8a+1}{15}$ d) $\dfrac{t+2}{20}$ e) $\dfrac{10y-37}{28}$ f) $\dfrac{8x-14}{9}$

3. a) $\dfrac{23x+6}{12}$ b) $\dfrac{185-97p}{60}$ c) $\dfrac{x+4}{10}$ d) $\dfrac{23y+105}{35}$ e) $\dfrac{a-14}{36}$ f) $\dfrac{21-25t}{21}$

4. a) $\dfrac{9}{y}, y \neq 0$ b) $-\dfrac{1}{2x}, x \neq 0$ c) $\dfrac{3y}{3y+8}, y \neq -\dfrac{8}{3}$ d) $\dfrac{2}{a}, a \neq 0$ e) $2, b \neq -3$ f) $\dfrac{5}{4}, x \neq -\dfrac{5}{3}$

5. a) $\dfrac{1+2x}{4x}, x \neq 0$ b) $\dfrac{1}{12a}, a \neq 0$ c) $\dfrac{47}{60t}, t \neq 0$ d) $-\dfrac{11}{12t}, t \neq 0$
e) $\dfrac{28}{15x}, x \neq 0$ f) $\dfrac{24}{35p}, p \neq 0$ g) $\dfrac{7}{12x}, x \neq 0$ h) $\dfrac{3+x}{x}, x \neq 0$

6. a) $\dfrac{9x+2}{2x^2}, x \neq 0$ b) $\dfrac{9-20a}{12a^2}, a \neq 0$ c) $\dfrac{8b+21}{3b^3}, b \neq 0$ d) $\dfrac{8c^2-15c+36}{6c^4}, c \neq 0$

7. a) $\dfrac{2a}{(a-1)(a+1)}, a \neq \pm 1$ b) $\dfrac{5b+13}{(b+3)(b+2)}, b \neq -3, -2$ c) $\dfrac{3x+21}{(x+2)(x+5)}, x \neq -5, -2$
d) $\dfrac{10x-22}{(x-3)(x-1)}, x \neq 1, 3$ e) $\dfrac{2y-23}{(y+2)(y-7)}, y \neq -2, 7$ f) $\dfrac{14t^2+2t}{(2t+1)(4t+1)}, t \neq -\dfrac{1}{2}, -\dfrac{1}{4}$

8. a) $\dfrac{x^2+5x+10}{3(x-2)}, x \neq 2$ b) $\dfrac{2p^2+6p+1}{(p+2)(p+3)}, p \neq -3, -2$ c) $\dfrac{3x^2-8x-3}{(x+2)(2x-1)}, x \neq -2, \dfrac{1}{2}$

d) $\dfrac{72x^2-116x+37}{(2x-3)(3x-2)(4x-1)}, x \neq \dfrac{1}{4}, \dfrac{2}{3}, \dfrac{3}{2}$ e) $\dfrac{-2t^3-10t^2-7t+12}{t(t+2)(t+3)}, t \neq -3, -2, 0$

9. C **10.** D **11.** B **12.**

3			

Rational Expressions and Equations Lesson #4: Addition and Subtraction of Rational Expressions Part Two

Denominators with Factors in Common

In this lesson we will add/subtract rational expressions where the denominators are different but have a common monomial or binomial factor.

It is important to factor the denominators in the rational expressions (if possible) **before** beginning to add or subtract.

Class Ex. #1

Perform the indicated operations. Express final answers in lowest terms, and indicate the nonpermissible values.

a) $\dfrac{3}{5x} - \dfrac{3}{10x}$ **b)** $\dfrac{4}{5x+5} + \dfrac{3}{2x+2}$ **c)** $\dfrac{1}{x^2} - \dfrac{1}{x^2+2x}$

Class Ex. #2

Simplify, stating restrictions on the value of x. $\dfrac{5}{(x+1)(x-2)} + \dfrac{2}{(x+4)(x-2)}$

Simplify $\dfrac{4}{p^2 - 1} + \dfrac{2}{p + 1}$. State the nonpermissible values for p.

Notice that in Class Example #3, the numerator of the answer had a factor in common with the denominator. This resulted in a further reduction which simplified the answer.
We must always check to see that our answers are in fully-reduced form.

Complete Assignment Questions #1 - #2

Trinomial Denominators

Simplify: **a)** $\dfrac{2}{x + 1} - \dfrac{x - 1}{x^2 - 2x - 3}$ **b)** $\dfrac{1}{y^2 - 3y + 2} + \dfrac{3}{y^2 + y - 2}$

Simplify $\dfrac{x^2 - 3x + 2}{x^2 - 5x + 4} - \dfrac{x^2 + 10x + 24}{x^2 + 8x + 12}$.

Show that $\dfrac{2a + 7}{a^2 + 7a + 12} + \dfrac{2a}{9 - a^2}$ can be reduced to $\dfrac{-7}{(a + 4)(a - 3)}$.

Complete Assignment Questions #3 - #11

Assignment

1. Perform the indicated operations. Express final answers in lowest terms, and indicate the nonpermissible values.

a) $\dfrac{1}{a} - \dfrac{1}{6a}$ **b)** $\dfrac{2}{5x - 15} + \dfrac{3}{2x - 6}$ **c)** $\dfrac{3}{4x + 2} - \dfrac{1}{6x + 3}$

d) $\dfrac{1}{x^2 - 3x} - \dfrac{1}{x}$ **e)** $\dfrac{y}{8 - 6y} + \dfrac{2y}{20 - 15y}$ **f)** $\dfrac{4}{b} - \dfrac{1}{b^3 - b}$

2. Perform the indicated operations. Express final answers in lowest terms, and indicate the nonpermissible values.

a) $\dfrac{1}{(x-1)(x-2)} - \dfrac{1}{(x-2)(x-3)}$ **b)** $\dfrac{4}{a(a+4)} + \dfrac{3}{a(a-3)}$

c) $\dfrac{7}{(x-2)(x+5)} - \dfrac{8}{(x+5)(x-3)}$ **d)** $\dfrac{2}{x(x-1)(x+1)} - \dfrac{1}{x(x-1)(x+2)}$

3. Simplify.

a) $\dfrac{1}{x^2 + 2x + 1} - \dfrac{1}{x + 1}$ **b)** $\dfrac{1}{y + 2} - \dfrac{1}{y^2 - 4}$ **c)** $\dfrac{2}{t^2 - 1} + \dfrac{1}{t + 1}$

4. Perform the indicated operations. Express final answers in lowest terms, and indicate the nonpermissible values.

a) $\dfrac{1}{x^2 - x - 2} - \dfrac{1}{x^2 + 4x + 3}$ **b)** $\dfrac{3}{t^2 - 7t + 10} - \dfrac{2}{t^2 - 6t + 8}$

c) $\dfrac{2x}{x^2 - 3x - 88} - \dfrac{2x - 1}{x^2 - 10x - 11}$

d) $\dfrac{12y}{y^2 - 8y - 20} - \dfrac{7y}{y^2 - 13y + 30}$

5. Simplify, stating the nonpermissible values.

a) $\dfrac{2x + 3}{5x - 25} + \dfrac{x - 4}{20 - 9x + x^2}$

b) $\dfrac{4x}{2x^2 - 5x - 3} - \dfrac{1 - 2x}{9 - x^2}$

6. Simplify, stating the restrictions on x.

a) $\dfrac{x^2 - x - 12}{x^2 - 8x + 16} - \dfrac{x^2 + 5x - 14}{x^2 + 10x + 21}$

b) $\dfrac{2x^2 - x - 3}{2x^2 + 7x - 15} + \dfrac{x^2 + 16x + 63}{x^2 + 12x + 35}$

c) $\dfrac{x^2 - 9}{x^2 - x - 12} - \dfrac{x^2 - 5x - 14}{x^2 - 4x - 21}$

d) $\dfrac{4x^2 - 4x - 3}{4x^2 - 1} - \dfrac{x^2 - 4x - 96}{x^2 + 4x - 32}$

7. Simplify.

a) $\dfrac{2}{2a+3} + \dfrac{8}{4a^2+4a-3}$

b) $\dfrac{2}{6b^2-5b-4} - \dfrac{3}{9b^2-16}$

8. A helicopter left Calgary and travelled 135 km west into the Rocky Mountains at an average speed of $2x^2 + 3x$ km/h. The return journey was at an average speed of $4x^2 - 9$ km/h.

a) Write and simplify an expression for the total flying time in hours.

b) If the value of x is 6, determine the total flying time.

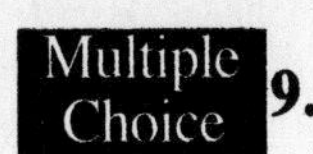

9. For all $x \neq \pm 6$, the sum $\dfrac{3}{x^2 - 36} + \dfrac{2}{x - 6}$ is equal to

A. $\dfrac{5x + 12}{x^2 - 36}$

B. $\dfrac{5x - 12}{(x - 6)^2}$

C. $\dfrac{2x - 9}{x^2 - 36}$

D. $\dfrac{2x + 15}{x^2 - 36}$

10. A simplified form of $\dfrac{3}{x - 7} - \dfrac{5}{7 - x}$, $x \neq 7$, is

A. $\dfrac{8}{x - 7}$ **B.** $\dfrac{-2}{x - 7}$

C. $\dfrac{8}{7 - x}$ **D.** $\dfrac{-2}{7 - x}$

11. When simplified, the difference $\dfrac{5}{x^2 - 7x + 12} - \dfrac{3}{x^2 - x - 12}$ can be written in the form $\dfrac{Ax + B}{(x - 4)(x - 3)(x + 3)}$, where A and B are integers.

The value of $B - A$ is _____.

(Record your answer in the numerical response box from left to right.)

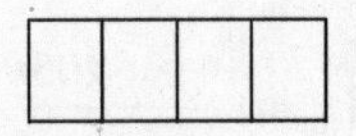

Answer Key

1. **a)** $\dfrac{5}{6a}, a \neq 0$ **b)** $\dfrac{19}{10(x-3)}, x \neq 3$ **c)** $\dfrac{7}{6(2x+1)}, x \neq -\dfrac{1}{2}$

d) $\dfrac{4-x}{x(x-3)}, x \neq 0, 3$ **e)** $\dfrac{9y}{10(4-3y)}, y \neq \dfrac{4}{3}$ **f)** $\dfrac{4b^2-5}{b(b-1)(b+1)}, b \neq 0, \pm 1$

2. **a)** $-\dfrac{2}{(x-1)(x-2)(x-3)}, x \neq 1, 2, 3$ **b)** $\dfrac{7}{(a+4)(a-3)}, a \neq -4, 0, 3$

c) $-\dfrac{1}{(x-2)(x-3)}, x \neq -5, 2, 3$ **d)** $\dfrac{x+3}{x(x-1)(x+1)(x+2)}, x \neq -2, \pm 1, 0$

3. **a)** $-\dfrac{x}{(x+1)^2}, x \neq -1$ **b)** $\dfrac{y-3}{(y+2)(y-2)}, y \neq \pm 2$ **c)** $\dfrac{1}{t-1}, t \neq \pm 1$

4. **a)** $\dfrac{5}{(x-2)(x+1)(x+3)}, x \neq -3, -1, 2$ **b)** $\dfrac{1}{(t-5)(t-4)}, t \neq 2, 4, 5$

c) $\dfrac{8-13x}{(x-11)(x+8)(x+1)}, x \neq -8, -1, 11$ **d)** $\dfrac{5y}{(y+2)(y-3)}, y \neq -2, 3, 10$

5. **a)** $\dfrac{2x+8}{5(x-5)}, x \neq 4, 5$ **b)** $\dfrac{12x+1}{(2x+1)(x-3)(x+3)}, x \neq -\dfrac{1}{2}, \pm 3$

6. **a)** $\dfrac{12x+1}{(x-4)(x+3)}, x \neq -7, -3, 4$ **b)** $2, x \neq -7, -5, \dfrac{3}{2}$

c) $\dfrac{2x-1}{(x-4)(x+3)}, x \neq -3, 4, 7$ **d)** $\dfrac{14x}{(2x-1)(x-4)}, x \neq -8, \pm\dfrac{1}{2}, 4$

7. **a)** $\dfrac{2}{2a-1}, a \neq -\dfrac{3}{2}, \dfrac{1}{2}$ **b)** $\dfrac{5}{(3b-4)(2b+1)(3b+4)}, b \neq -\dfrac{1}{2}, \pm\dfrac{4}{3}$

8. **a)** $\dfrac{405x-405}{x(2x+3)(2x-3)}, x \neq 0, \pm\dfrac{3}{2}$ **b)** 2.5 h

9. D **10.** A **11.**

2	2		

Rational Expressions and Equations Lesson #5:
Multiplication of Rational Expressions

Review *Multiplication of Rational Numbers*

Recall these steps for multiplying rational numbers.

1. Consider the factors of the numerator and of the denominator.
2. If there are factors common to the numerator and the denominator, reduce by dividing out the common factors.
3. Multiply all the numerators together and multiply all the denominators together.

   Note that steps 2 and 3 may be interchanged.

Multiply: **a)** $\frac{7}{10} \times \frac{1}{5}$ **b)** $\frac{9}{10} \times \frac{5}{6}$

Review *Multiplication of Monomials*

The above method can be extended to multiplication of monomials containing variables.

Simplify. State the restrictions on the variables.

a) $\frac{12xy}{4z} \times \frac{3xz^2}{y}$ **b)** $\frac{5a^2b^2c^4}{14b^2cd} \times \frac{35b}{40a^3c}$

Multiplication of Single Variable Rational Expressions

The method for multiplication of rational expressions is similar to the method described for multiplication of rational numbers. The first step is usually to factor the numerator and denominator of each rational expression.

Simplify. State the restrictions on the variable.

a) $\frac{(x+1)}{(x-2)(x+3)} \times \frac{2(x+3)}{x(x+1)}$ **b)** $\frac{4x+16}{14x-7} \times \frac{2x-1}{(x+4)^2}$

Simplify $\dfrac{2m^3 - 4m^2}{3m^2 - 9m} \times \dfrac{m^2 - m - 6}{m^2 - 4}$. State the restrictions on the variable.

Simplify $\left(\dfrac{a^2 + 8a + 15}{6a^2 + 21a + 9}\right)\left(\dfrac{a - 4a^3}{2a^2 + 9a - 5}\right)$. State the nonpermissible values.

Complete Assignment Questions #1 - #8

Assignment

1. Simplify. State the restrictions on the variables.

a) $\dfrac{8a^2b^2c}{12abc^2} \times \dfrac{12a^2c}{6bc}$

b) $\dfrac{9x^4y^3}{12x^5} \times \dfrac{48x^2y^3}{14y} \times \dfrac{6x}{27y^4}$

2. Simplify. State the restrictions on the variable.

a) $\dfrac{15a^2(a-1)}{8(2a+3)} \times \dfrac{10(2a+3)}{3a}$

b) $\dfrac{7x(x+2)(x-3)}{21(x-7)(x+7)} \times \dfrac{(x+7)^2(x-7)}{2x(x-3)}$

c) $\dfrac{6y-30}{(y-1)} \times \dfrac{5y-5}{3y^2-15y}$

d) $\dfrac{10x+2}{5x-1} \times \dfrac{x-1}{35x+7}$

3. Simplify. State the nonpermissible values.

a) $\dfrac{x^2-9}{6x+24} \times \dfrac{10x+40}{x(x+3)}$

b) $\dfrac{4a^2-1}{4a^2-16} \times \dfrac{2-a}{2a-1}$

c) $\dfrac{x^2+5x+6}{3x} \times \dfrac{6x}{x^2+9x+14}$

d) $\dfrac{2y^3-4y^2}{3y^2-9y} \times \dfrac{y^2-y-6}{y^2-4}$

4. Simplify. State the nonpermissible values.

a) $\left(\dfrac{x^2 - 3x + 2}{x^2 + 3x - 4}\right)\left(\dfrac{x^2 + 9x + 20}{x^2 + x - 6}\right)$

b) $\left(\dfrac{3t^2 + 3t - 6}{2t^2 - 2t - 4}\right)\left(\dfrac{4t^2 + 4t - 24}{3t^2 + 6t - 9}\right)$

c) $\dfrac{x^2 - 6x}{x^2 + 5x} \times \dfrac{x^2 + 7x + 10}{18 - 3x}$

d) $\dfrac{a^2 - 6a + 8}{2a^2 - 8a} \times \dfrac{a^2 - a}{8a^2 + 28} \times \dfrac{12a^2 + 42}{2a}$

5. Consider the rectangle shown.

Width: $\dfrac{20x}{x^3 - 2x^2}$

Length: $\dfrac{x^2 - 4x + 4}{5x}$

a) Write and simplify an expression for the area of the rectangle.

b) Calculate the *exact* area if $x = 4\sqrt{5}$ cm.

6. Simplify.

a) $\dfrac{2x^2 - 8y^2}{12x + 6y} \times \dfrac{18x^2 + 9xy}{6x + 12y}$

b) $\dfrac{p^2 + 2pq - 15q^2}{3p^2 - 33pq + 84q^2} \times \dfrac{12q^2 + qp - p^2}{2p^2 + 16pq + 30q^2}$

Multiple Choice

7. For all $x \neq 1, \pm \frac{7}{3}$, $\dfrac{(3x-7)^3}{3x^2 - 10x + 7} \times \dfrac{4 - 4x}{9x^2 - 49}$ reduces to

A. -4

B. $\dfrac{4(3x+7)}{3x-7}$

C. $\dfrac{4(3x-7)}{(3x+7)}$

D. $-\dfrac{4(3x-7)}{3x+7}$

Numerical Response

8. For the appropriate restrictions, the product $\left(\frac{12x-24}{3x^2-12}\right)\left(\frac{6x^2+30x+36}{2x+6}\right)$ reduces to a whole number, k. The value of k is ____.

(Record your answer in the numerical response box from left to right.)

Answer Key

1. a) $\frac{4a^3}{3c}$, $a \neq 0, b \neq 0, c \neq 0$ **b)** $\frac{4x^2y}{7}$, $x \neq 0, y \neq 0$

2. a) $\frac{25a(a-1)}{4}$, $a \neq -\frac{3}{2}, 0$ **b)** $\frac{(x+2)(x+7)}{6}$, $x \neq 0, 3, \pm 7$

c) $\frac{10}{y}$, $y \neq 0, 1, 5$ **d)** $\frac{2(x-1)}{7(5x-1)}$, $x \neq \pm\frac{1}{5}$

3. a) $\frac{5(x-3)}{3x}$, $x \neq -4, -3, 0$ **b)** $\frac{-2a-1}{4(a+2)}$, $a \neq \pm 2, \frac{1}{2}$

c) $\frac{2(x+3)}{x+7}$, $x \neq -7, -2, 0$ **d)** $\frac{2y}{3}$, $y \neq \pm 2, 0, 3$

4. a) $\frac{x+5}{x+3}$, $x \neq -4, -3, 1, 2$ **b)** $\frac{2(t+2)}{t+1}$, $t \neq -3, \pm 1, 2$

c) $\frac{-x-2}{3}$, $x \neq -5, 0, 6$ **d)** $\frac{3(a-1)(a-2)}{8a}$, $a \neq 0, 4$

5. a) $\frac{4(x-2)}{x^2}$ **b)** $\frac{2\sqrt{5}-1}{10}$ cm^2

6. a) $\frac{x(x-2y)}{2}$, $x \neq -\frac{1}{2}y, -2y$ **b)** $\frac{3q-p}{6(p-7q)}$, $p \neq -5q, -3q, 4q, 7q$

7. D **8.**

1	2		

Rational Expressions and Equations Lesson #6: Division of Rational Expressions

Review *Division of Rational Numbers*

Recall that the procedure for dividing by a rational number is to multiply by the reciprocal of the rational number.

Divide: **a)** $\frac{7}{10} \div \frac{3}{14}$ **b)** $\frac{6}{5} \div \frac{9}{10} \times \frac{1}{20}$ **c)** $\frac{6}{5} \div \left(\frac{9}{10} \times \frac{1}{20}\right)$

Review *Division of Monomials*

The above method can be extended to division of monomials containing variables. Remember to invert the divisor and multiply.

Simplify. At this stage, do not state the restrictions on the variables.

a) $\frac{16a}{9b^2} \div \frac{32a^2}{15b}$ **b)** $\frac{-5xy^3}{7xz^3} \times \frac{2z}{15x} \div \frac{10x^2y^2}{-21z^4}$

Nonpermissible Values in Division of Rational Expressions

Consider the division $\frac{a}{b} \div \frac{c}{d}$, where a, b, c and d are variables.

For the rational expression $\frac{a}{b}$, the nonpermissible value is ______.

For the rational expression $\frac{c}{d}$, the nonpermissible value is ______.

The first step in simplifying $\frac{a}{b} \div \frac{c}{d}$ is to invert the divisor and multiply to obtain $\frac{a}{b} \times \frac{d}{c}$.

This introduces another nonpermissible value ________.

For a division of the type $\frac{a}{b} \div \frac{c}{d}$, we need to consider nonpermissible values at b, c and d.

Any variable which appears in the denominator at **any** stage in the simplification should be considered for nonpermissible values.

State the restrictions on the variables in Class Example 2.

a) $\dfrac{16a}{9b^2} \div \dfrac{32a^2}{15b}$ **b)** $\dfrac{-5xy^3}{7xz^3} \times \dfrac{2z}{15x} \div \dfrac{10x^2y^2}{-21z^2}$

Division of Single Variable Rational Expressions

The method for division of rational expressions is similar to the method described for division of rational numbers. The first step is usually to invert the divisor and multiply. Then follow the procedure for multiplication of rational expressions. Nonpermissible values occur when a variable is present in the denominator at any stage in the simplification.

Simplify. State the restrictions on the variable.

a) $\dfrac{(x+1)}{(x-2)(x+3)} \div \dfrac{2(x+1)}{x(x+3)}$ **b)** $\dfrac{\dfrac{4x+12}{3x+12}}{\dfrac{3x^2+9x}{(x+4)^2}}$

Perform the indicated operations for each of the following expressions.
Express final answers in lowest terms, and identify the nonpermissible values.

a) $\dfrac{4x^2 - 12x}{x^2 - 9} \div \dfrac{7x^3 + 7x^2}{x^2 + 4x + 3}$

b) $\dfrac{20m^2 + 30m}{9 - 4m^2} \div \left(\dfrac{11m^3 - 11m}{2m^2 - m - 3} \times \dfrac{2m + 3}{m - 1}\right)$

Simplify $\dfrac{\dfrac{10}{a} - \dfrac{12}{2a + 1}}{\dfrac{5}{a} + 4}$. State the restrictions on the value of a.

Complete Assignment Questions #1 - #10

Assignment

1. Simplify. State the restrictions on the variables.

a) $\dfrac{3a^2bc}{10bc^2} \div \dfrac{12a^2b^2c}{6bc}$

b) $\dfrac{8x^2y^3}{-9x^3y} \div \dfrac{-15x^2y}{14y^3} \div \dfrac{7x}{-6xy^4}$

c) $\dfrac{\dfrac{2xy}{5x^2y^2}}{\dfrac{10x^2y}{15y}}$

d) $\dfrac{-5m^3n}{2p} \div \left(\dfrac{8p^3}{10m} \div \dfrac{4p}{15n}\right)$

2. Simplify. State the nonpermissible values.

a) $\dfrac{(3x+5)^2}{x^2-49} \div \dfrac{(3x+5)(x+1)}{x-7}$

b) $\dfrac{4y+20}{5y-20} \div \dfrac{2y^2-50}{y^2-16}$

c) $\dfrac{(p-6)(p+2)}{p(p+1)} \div \dfrac{36-p^2}{p^2+p}$

d) $\dfrac{\dfrac{a^2-81}{9a}}{(a-9)^2}$

3. Simplify.

a) $\dfrac{a^2-3a-10}{a^2-5a+6} \div \dfrac{a^2+a-30}{a^2+4a-12}$

b) $\dfrac{x^2+13x+36}{x^2-4} \div \dfrac{x^2-6x-40}{x^2-8x-20}$

c) $\dfrac{\dfrac{y^3+4y^2-32y}{y^2-64}}{y-4}$

d) $\dfrac{x^2+14x+49}{\dfrac{x^2+5x-14}{x^2-2x}}$

4. Simplify.

a) $\dfrac{2a^2 - 3a - 9}{8a^2 + 14a + 3} \div \dfrac{3a^2 - 7a - 6}{8a^2 + 14a + 3}$

b) $\dfrac{x^4 - 5x^2y^2 + 4y^4}{x^2 + 3xy + 2y^2} \div \dfrac{x^2 - 4xy + 4y^2}{5x - 10y}$

5. The rectangle shown has length $5x^2 + 10x$ cm and width $16x - 4$ cm. The triangle has base $4x^2 + 7x - 2$ cm and height $10x$ cm.

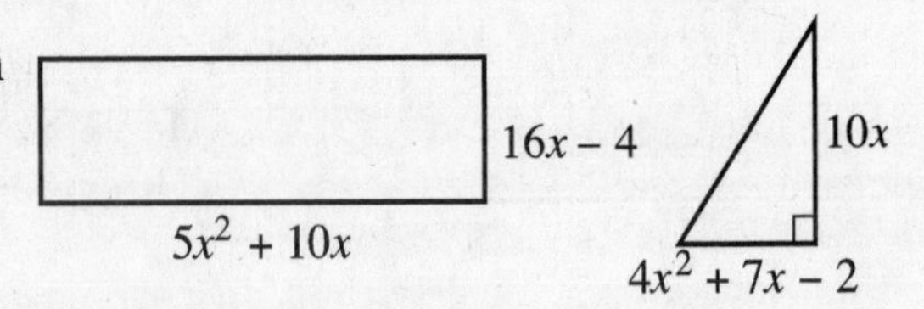

Write and simplify an expression that represents the ratio of the area of the rectangle to the area of the triangle.

6. Simplify.

a) $\dfrac{5-\dfrac{1}{a}}{5+\dfrac{1}{a}}$ b) $\dfrac{8+\dfrac{4}{x}}{4-\dfrac{1}{x^2}}$ c) $\dfrac{\dfrac{3}{p^2}-\dfrac{1}{p^2-4}}{1-\dfrac{6}{p^2}}$

7. Simplify. State the nonpermissible values.

a) $\dfrac{a-1}{a+4} \div \dfrac{a^2+6a+5}{a^2-1} \times \dfrac{a^2+3a-4}{a^2-2a+1}$ b) $\dfrac{a-1}{a+4} \div \left(\dfrac{a^2+6a+5}{a^2-1} \times \dfrac{a^2+3a-4}{a^2-2a+1}\right)$

8. Simplify $\left(\dfrac{x}{x+1} \times \dfrac{3}{3-x}\right) - \left(\dfrac{1}{x+1} \div \dfrac{2}{x-3}\right)$.

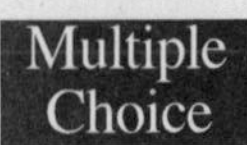

9. Consider the division $\dfrac{a^2 - a - 12}{a^2 - 4a + 4} \div \dfrac{a^2 - 10a + 24}{a^2 - a - 2}$. The number of nonpermissible values is

A. 2
B. 3
C. 4
D. more than 4

Numerical Response

10. When simplified, the complex fraction $\dfrac{\dfrac{10x^2 - x - 3}{2x^2 - 5x - 3}}{\dfrac{5x - 3}{2x^2 - 18}}$ reduces to a linear expression of the form $Ax + B$. The value of $A + B$ is _____.

(Record your answer in the numerical response box from left to right.)

Answer Key

1. a) $\dfrac{3}{20bc}$, a ≠ 0, b ≠ 0, c ≠ 0   **b)** $-\dfrac{32y^8}{45x^3}, x \neq 0, y \neq 0$ **c)** $\dfrac{3}{5x^3y}, x \neq 0, y \neq 0$

d) $-\dfrac{5m^4}{6p^3}, m \neq 0, n \neq 0, p \neq 0$ **2. a)** $\dfrac{3x + 5}{(x + 7)(x + 1)}, x \neq \pm 7, -\dfrac{5}{3}, -1$

2. b) $\dfrac{2y + 8}{5(y - 5)}, y \neq \pm 5, \pm 4$ **c)** $\dfrac{-p - 2}{p + 6}, p \neq \pm 6, -1, 0$ **d)** $\dfrac{a + 9}{9a(a - 9)}, a \neq 9, 0$

3. a) $\dfrac{a + 2}{a - 3}, a \neq -6, 2, 3, 5$ **b)** $\dfrac{x + 9}{x - 2}, x \neq \pm 2, -4, 10$

c) $\dfrac{y}{y - 8}, y \neq \pm 8, 4$ **d)** $x(x + 7), x \neq -7, 0, 2$

4. a) $\dfrac{2a + 3}{3a + 2}, a \neq -\dfrac{3}{2}, -\dfrac{2}{3}, -\dfrac{1}{4}, 3$ **b)** $5(x - y),\ x \neq \pm 2y, -y$

5. 4 to 1   **6. a)** $\dfrac{5a - 1}{5a + 1}, a \neq 0, -\dfrac{1}{5}$ **b)** $\dfrac{4x}{2x - 1}, x \neq \pm\dfrac{1}{2}, 0$ **c)** $\dfrac{2}{p^2 - 4}, p \neq \pm 2, \pm\sqrt{6}, 0$

7. a) $\dfrac{a - 1}{a + 5}, a \neq -5, -4, \pm 1$ **b)** $\dfrac{(a - 1)^3}{(a + 4)^2(a + 5)}, a \neq -5, -4, \pm 1$

8. $\dfrac{x^2 + 9}{2(x + 1)(3 - x)}, x \neq -1, 3$ **9.** C   **10.** 8

Rational Expressions and Equations Lesson #7:
Rational Equations Part One

Rational Equation

A rational equation is an equation in which at least one of the terms is a rational expression with a variable in the denominator.

Solving Rational Equations Using A Graphing Calculator

Intersection Method

To solve the equation $\frac{3}{x+1} + \frac{1}{x-1} = 2$ by the intersection method, use the following procedure.

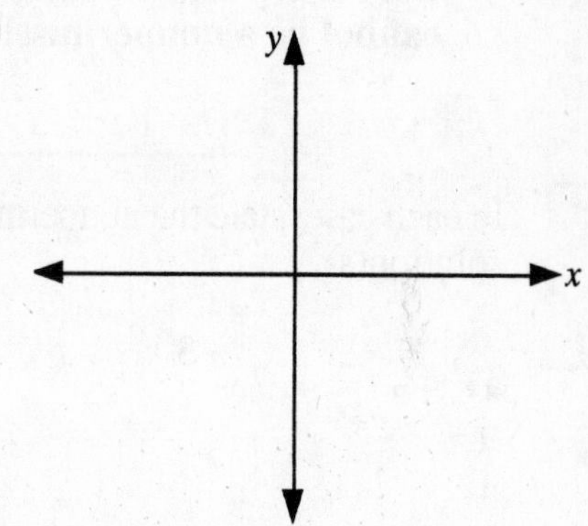

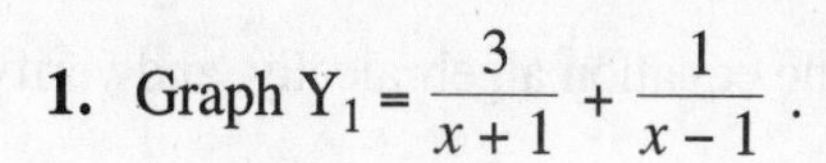

1. Graph $Y_1 = \frac{3}{x+1} + \frac{1}{x-1}$.

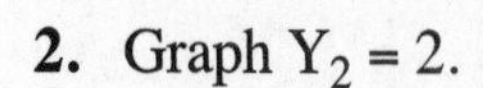

2. Graph $Y_2 = 2$.

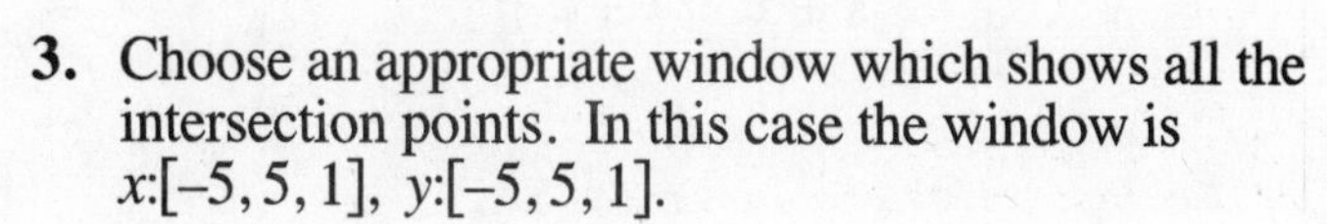

3. Choose an appropriate window which shows all the intersection points. In this case the window is $x:[-5, 5, 1]$, $y:[-5, 5, 1]$.

4. Find the x-coordinate(s) of the point(s) of intersection using the `intersect` feature of the calculator.

x-intercept Method

To solve the equation $\frac{3}{x+1} + \frac{1}{x-1} = 2$ by the x-intercept method, use the following procedure.

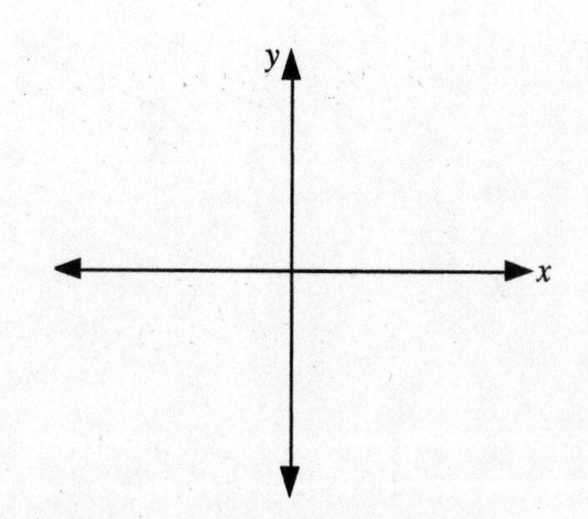

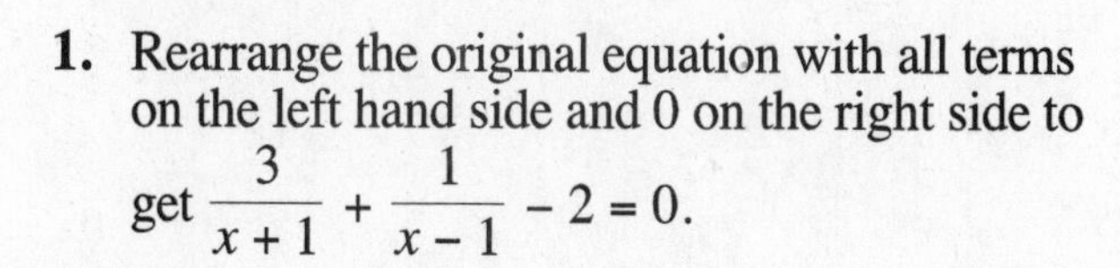

1. Rearrange the original equation with all terms on the left hand side and 0 on the right side to get $\frac{3}{x+1} + \frac{1}{x-1} - 2 = 0$.

2. Graph $Y_1 = \frac{3}{x+1} + \frac{1}{x-1} - 2$.

3. Choose an appropriate window which shows all the x-intercepts of the graph.

4. Use the `zero` feature of the calculator to find the x-intercept(s).

Complete Assignment Question #1

Solving Simple Rational Equations Algebraically

The following strategies should be considered when solving rational equations algebraically:

1. If the equation consists of a single rational expression on each side, use cross-multiplication to simplify the equation.

2. If the rational equation has more than one term, on either side, consider multiplying each term in the equation by the lowest common multiple of the denominators.

3. Use previously learned skills for solving linear or quadratic equations.

4. Always be aware there are domain restrictions when dealing with rational functions, and check your solutions accordingly, i.e. when verifying solutions note that the solution **cannot be a nonpermissible value** since this would result in division by zero.

In each case, state the nonpermissible value(s), solve the equation algebraically, and verify the solution(s).

a) $4 + \frac{2}{x} = 7 + \frac{3}{x}$

b) $\frac{5}{x+1} = \frac{2}{x+2}$

State the nonpermissible value(s), and solve the equation algebraically.

a) $\dfrac{4x-2}{2x+3}=\dfrac{6x-1}{3x+5}$ **b)** $\dfrac{5t-2}{t+1}-\dfrac{2t-1}{t-3}=3$

Solve the equation $\dfrac{1}{x-4}+\dfrac{2}{x+4}=\dfrac{5}{x^2-16}$.

Complete Assignment Questions #2 - #7

Assignment

1. Solve the following rational equations using a graphing calculator, using either the intersect method or the x-intercept method. State a suitable window, and answer to the nearest hundredth where necessary.

a) $\dfrac{2}{x-4} + \dfrac{6}{x+2} = \dfrac{1}{2}$

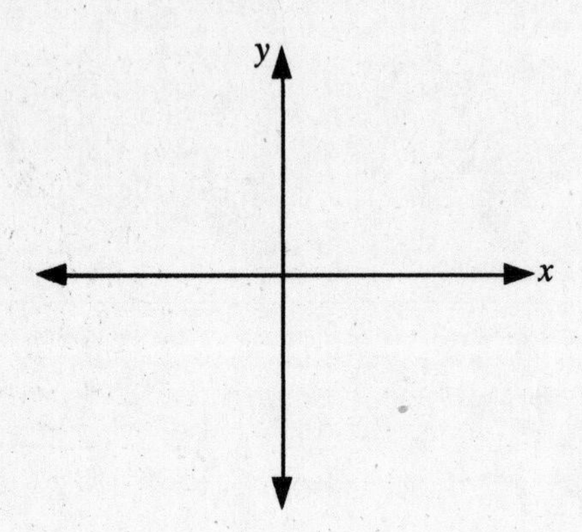

b) $\dfrac{8}{x} - 5 = \dfrac{x}{2}$

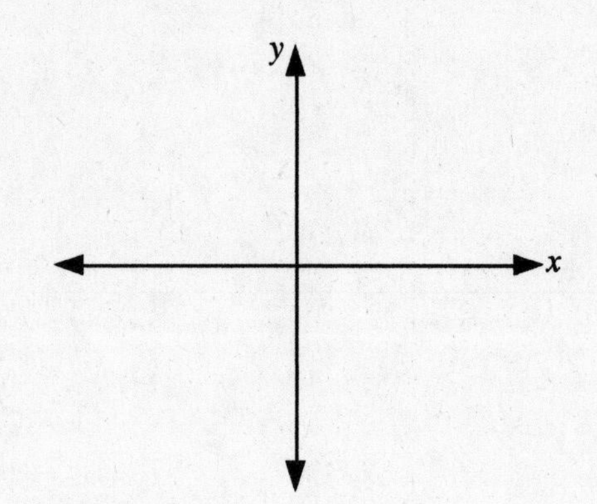

c) $\dfrac{x+3}{x+1} = \dfrac{x+7}{5x+1}$

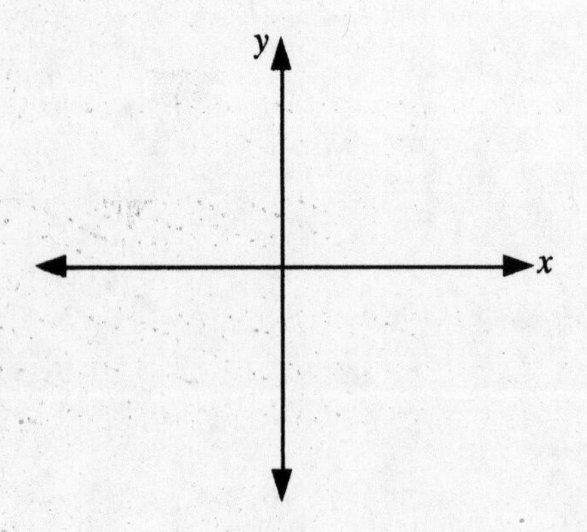

d) $\dfrac{x}{x+2} + \dfrac{x}{x-2} = \dfrac{16}{x^2-16}$

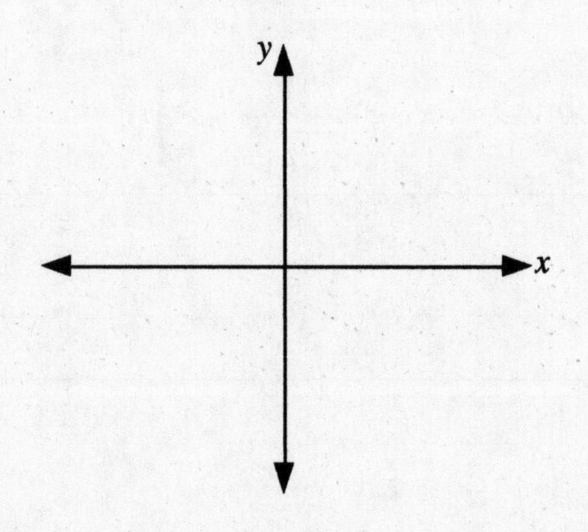

In the remainder of this assignment, a written verification is only required where indicated. All solutions must be checked for nonpermissible values.

2. In each case, state the nonpermissible value(s), solve the equation algebraically, and verify the solution(s).

a) $\frac{6a+3}{2a-3} = \frac{3}{2}$

b) $\frac{2}{m+1} = \frac{8m}{m+1} - 3$

3. Solve.

a) $\frac{5a-3}{a+7} = \frac{5a-14}{a+1}$

b) $\frac{2x+1}{x-3} - \frac{4x-1}{2x-3} = 0$

c) $\dfrac{6y-2}{3y-2} - \dfrac{2y+6}{y+6} = 0$

d) $\dfrac{4a+9}{2a} - \dfrac{3}{4} = 2$

e) $\dfrac{5}{3x-1} + \dfrac{3x}{3x+1} = 1$

f) $\dfrac{8x}{2x+3} - \dfrac{x+3}{x+7} = 3$

4. Solve and verify the equation $\dfrac{1}{x^2-9} = \dfrac{4}{x-3} - \dfrac{2}{x+3}$.

Multiple Choice

5. If $\dfrac{2}{4-y} = 3$, then y equals

A. $\dfrac{5}{2}$

B. $\dfrac{10}{3}$

C. -2

D. $\dfrac{14}{3}$

6. The solution to the rational equation $\frac{4}{x} + \frac{2x}{x-4} - 2 = 0$, to the nearest tenth, is _____.

(Record your answer in the numerical response box from left to right.)

7. The root of the rational equation $\frac{1}{x+3} - \frac{2}{x+7} = \frac{x}{x^2 + 10x + 21}$, to the nearest tenth, is _____.

(Record your answer in the numerical response box from left to right.)

Answer Key

1. a) $x = 2$ or 16 **b)** $x = -11.40$ or 1.40 **c)** $x = -2.41$ or 0.41 **d)** $x = -4.75, -1.19, 1.19,$ or 4.75

2. a) $-\frac{5}{2}$ **b)** 1 **3. a)** 5 **b)** $\frac{2}{3}$ **c)** 0 **d)** 6 **e)** $-\frac{1}{2}$ **f)** -18

4. $x = -\frac{17}{2}$ **5.** B

6.

1	.	3	

7.

0	.	5	

Rational Expressions and Equations Lesson #8:
Rational Equations Part Two

In this lesson, we will solve rational equations which reduce to quadratic equations. We will also consider equations which have no solutions.

Recall the following strategies when solving rational equations algebraically:

1. If the equation consists of a single rational expression on each side, use cross-multiplication to simplify the equation.

2. If the rational equation has more than one term, on either side, consider multiplying each term in the equation by the lowest common multiple of the denominators.

3. Use previously learned skills for solving linear or quadratic equations.

4. Always be aware there are domain restrictions when dealing with rational functions, and check your solutions accordingly, i.e. when verifying solutions, note that the solution **cannot be a nonpermissible value** since this would result in division by zero.

a) In the previous lesson, we solved the equation $\frac{3}{x+1} + \frac{1}{x-1} = 2$ graphically. The solution is $x =$ _____ or $x =$ _____ .

b) Solve the equation $\frac{3}{x+1} + \frac{1}{x-1} = 2$ algebraically.

Consider the rational equation $\dfrac{x^2 - 5x - 6}{x + 1} = 2$.

a) Solve the following rational equation by cross multiplication.

b) Explain why one of the solutions to the quadratic equation formed in a) does not satisfy the original equation.

State the nonpermissible value(s), solve the equation algebraically, and verify the solution(s).

a) $x + \dfrac{2}{x} = 3$

b) $\dfrac{x}{x^2 - 4} = \dfrac{2}{x + 2}$

An Equation with No Solution

Show that the equation $\dfrac{8x+10}{x-3} - 4 = \dfrac{10x+4}{x-3}$ has no solution.

Complete Assignment Questions #1 - #7

Assignment

In this assignment, a written verification is only required where indicated.
All solutions must be checked for nonpermissible values.

1. In each case, state the nonpermissible value(s), solve the equation algebraically, and verify the solution(s).

a) $\dfrac{4}{x+2} = 3$

b) $\dfrac{3}{2x-1} = \dfrac{4}{x+7}$

2. In each case, state the nonpermissible value(s), solve the equation algebraically, and verify the solution(s).

a) $\dfrac{x+3}{x^2+4x+3}=1$

b) $\dfrac{30}{x^2-25}=\dfrac{3}{x-5}-\dfrac{2}{x+5}$

3. Solve the following equations algebraically.

a) $\dfrac{x-1}{x+1}=\dfrac{2x}{15}$

b) $\dfrac{4x}{3x+4}-\dfrac{10}{x+6}=0$

4. Determine the roots of the following equations algebraically.

a) $\dfrac{4x+3}{2x-1} - 2 = \dfrac{6x+2}{2x-1}$

b) $\dfrac{2}{x} + \dfrac{1}{6-x} = 1$

5. Determine the roots of the equation $\dfrac{8}{x} - 5 = \dfrac{x}{2}$ in simplest radical form.

Multiple Choice

6. The solution to the equation $\frac{7}{a+6} - \frac{3}{a} = \frac{4}{a+6}$ is

A. $a = 18$
B. $a = -6$
C. $a = 0$
D. no solution

Numerical Response

7. The roots of the rational equation $\frac{x+3}{2x+1} = \frac{x+7}{5x+1}$ are $x = a$ and $x = -b$, where $a, b > 0$.

The value of $\frac{a}{b}$, to the nearest hundredth, is _____.

(Record your answer in the numerical response box from left to right.)

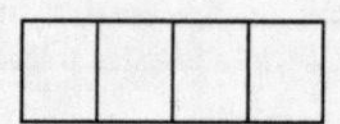

Answer Key

1. a) $x = -\frac{2}{3}$ **b)** $x = 5$ **2. a)** $x = 0$ **b)** no solution

3. a) $x = \frac{3}{2}, 5$ **b)** $x = -\frac{5}{2}, 4$ **4. a)** no solution **b)** $x = 3, 4$

5. $x = -5 \pm \sqrt{41}$ **6.** D **7.**

0	.	7	5

Rational Expressions and Equations Lesson #9:
Solving Problems Involving Rational Equations

Guideline for Solving Problems

1. Read the problem carefully, and understand what is being asked.
2. Introduce a variable to represent an unknown quantity (usually the quantity that is being asked for).
3. Write an algebraic equation (in this case a rational equation) to represent the given information.
4. Solve the equation.
5. State the solution to the problem. Check that the solution "makes sense".

Problems Involving Distance, Speed, and Time

Competing in an endurance race, Shannon cycled for 120 km, then swam for 12 km. Her average cycling speed was eight times faster than her average swimming speed. Shannon took nine hours to complete the race.

a) If her average swimming speed is s km/h, use the information above to complete the table.

	Distance	Speed	Time
Cycle			
Swim		s	

b) Calculate her average swimming speed.

St. Andre Students' Council is travelling from Knoxtown to Harperville for the Students' Council National Conference. From the travel budget allowed for the trip, the St. Andre Students' Council has two options. They can leave tonight by bus, or they can save three hours by leaving tomorrow morning and using the express train which travels 25 km/hr faster than the bus.

If the distance between Knoxtown and Harperville is 1500 km, determine how long it would take to travel by express train.

Complete Assignment Questions #1 - #11

Assignment

1. Evan drove 308 km in the same time that Meghan drove 329 km. If Meghan drove on average 6 km/h faster than Evan, calculate her average speed and the time taken for the journey.

2. Erin Airlines has a fleet of airplanes whose average speed is 4 times the average speed of the Derailer passenger train. A Derailer train requires 12 hours more than an Erin airplane to travel a distance of 2000km. Calculate the average speed of each mode of transport.

3. On average, Exante Express trains are 50 km/hr faster than Paral passenger trains. A Paral train requires 60% more time than an Exante train to travel 1800 km from Matsay to Rawindi.

a) Calculate the average speed of each train.

b) Calculate the time it takes each train for the journey.

4. Two consecutive even whole numbers are selected. The difference between the reciprocals of the two numbers is $\frac{1}{60}$. Determine the numbers.

5. Al and Bob, who live in North Vancouver, are Seattle Mariners fans. They regularly drive the 264 km from their home to the ballpark in Seattle. On one particular day, Bob drove to the game. On the return journey Al was able to increase their average speed by 10% and save 18 minutes on the travelling time.

a) Calculate the average speed at which Bob drove to the game.

b) Calculate the time it took Al to drive back from the game.

6. To prevent grounding, a cruise ship anchors 18 km away from a river port. To transport the passengers to the port, the crew uses smaller boats. The smaller boats travel 12 km downstream the same time it takes them to travel 8 km upstream.

a) If the speed of the current is 6 km/hr, write expressions for the speed of the boat travelling upstream and travelling downstream.

b) Calculate the time it takes for the small boats to travel upstream from the cruise ship to the port.

7. Part of a student's midterm Mathematics report card is shown. Before her mother could analyze the report, she spilled some coffee over it and could not read one of the figures.

The student's mother asked her if she could calculate the mark possible for the quiz on radicals. Show how she could calculate the possible mark for the radical quiz if the quizzes are equally weighted.

Quiz	Actual Mark	Total Possible Mark
Polynomials	21	30
Factoring	38	50
Radicals	15	
Exponents	29	40

Average mark for quizzes is 64%

8. A rectangular flower bed at a garden centre has an area of 144 m^2. During a redesign of the garden centre, the dimensions of the rectangular flower bed are altered but the area is unchanged. The width is doubled and the length is decreased by 12m. Calculate the dimensions of the redesigned flower bed.

9. A plane flew from Victoria to Calgary, a flying distance of 1260 km. On the return journey, due to a strong head wind, the average flying speed was 90 km/hr slower than on the outward journey. The time taken for the return journey was 20 minutes more than for the outward journey.

a) Calculate the time taken for the journey from Victoria to Calgary.

b) Calculate the average speed of the journey from Calgary to Victoria.

Use the following information to answer questions 10 and 11.

Kelcie drove from Edmonton Airport to downtown Calgary, a distance of 340 km, in the same time that Nick drove from Calgary Airport to downtown Edmonton, a distance of 360 km. Nick's average speed was 6 km/h faster than Kelcie's average speed.

Multiple Choice

10. If Nick's average speed is denoted by s km/h, then the equation which can be used to determine the value of s is

A. $\frac{340}{s} = \frac{360}{s-6}$

B. $\frac{340}{s} = \frac{360}{s+6}$

C. $\frac{340}{s-6} = \frac{360}{s}$

D. $\frac{340}{s+6} = \frac{360}{s}$

Numerical Response

11. The number of minutes taken for each journey, to the nearest minute, is ____.

(Record your answer in the numerical response box from left to right.)

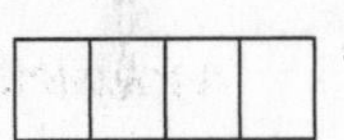

Answer Key

1. 94 km/hr, and 3.5 hours

2. Erin airplane 500 km/h, Derailer train 125 km/h

3. **a)** Paral 83⅓ km/hr; Exante 133⅓ km/hr.
b) Paral 21 hours 36 minutes; Exante 13 hours 30 minutes

4. 10, 12

5. **a)** 80 km/hr **b)** 3 hours

6. **a)** $s - 6$ km/h, $s + 6$ km/h **b)** 45 minutes

7. 40

8. 12m x 12m

9. **a)** 2 hours **b)** 540 km/hr

10. C

11.

2	0	0	

Rational Expressions and Equations Lesson #10: Practice Test

Use the following information to answer the next question.

A student made the following four statements regarding rational expressions:

Statement 1: Values of the variable which result in the rational expression not being defined are called nonpermissible values.

Statement 2: Values of the variable which make the numerator equal to zero are restrictions on the variable.

Statement 3: Nonpermissible values are known as the restrictions on the variable.

Statement 4: Nonpermissible values are values of the variable which make the denominator equal to zero.

1. The statement which is false is

A. Statement 1 **B.** Statement 2
C. Statement 3 **D.** Statement 4

2. When simplified, the rational expression $\dfrac{a^2 + a - 2}{a^2 - 1}$ can be reduced to

A. $\dfrac{a-2}{-1}$ **B.** $\dfrac{a-2}{a-1}$

C. $\dfrac{a+2}{a+1}$ **D.** $\dfrac{a-2}{a+1}$

3. The reduced form of $\dfrac{15 + 2y - y^2}{3y^2 - 16y + 5}$ is

A. $\dfrac{3-y}{3y-1}$

B. $\dfrac{-3-y}{3y+1}$

C. $\dfrac{3+y}{3y-1}$

D. $\dfrac{3+y}{1-3y}$

4. The expression $\dfrac{x^2 + 9xy + 20y^2}{x^2 + 5xy}$ can be reduced to

A. $x + 4y$

B. $1 + 4y$

C. $4y$

D. none of the above

5. The expression $\dfrac{9v^2 - 6v + 1}{12v^2 - 13v + 3}$ can be reduced to

A. $\dfrac{3v - 1}{4v - 3}$

B. $\dfrac{3v + 1}{4v + 3}$

C. $\dfrac{3v - 1}{4v + 3}$

D. $\dfrac{3v + 1}{4v - 3}$

6. The restriction(s) on the variable in the division $\dfrac{x - 5}{x - 2} \div \dfrac{x - 3}{x - 1}$ is/are

A. $x \neq 1$ only

B. $x \neq 1$ and $x \neq 2$ only

C. $x \neq 1, x \neq 2$, and $x \neq 3$ only

D. $x \neq 1, x \neq 2, x \neq 3$, and $x \neq 5$ only

7. Consider the nonpermissible values for the addition $\dfrac{5y}{6y^2 - 7y - 3} + \dfrac{4y - 3}{2y^2 - 15y + 18}$.

The product of the nonpermissible values is

A. -3

B. $-\dfrac{9}{2}$

C. $-\dfrac{4}{3}$

D. 3

8. A simplified form of $\dfrac{4}{x-3} + \dfrac{2}{3-x}$ is

A. $\dfrac{2}{x-3}$

B. $\dfrac{2}{3-x}$

C. $\dfrac{6}{x-3}$

D. $\dfrac{6}{3-x}$

9. If the difference $\dfrac{8}{3a} - \dfrac{2}{a}$ can be written in the form $\dfrac{k}{3a}$, then the value of k is

A. 2

B. 3

C. 4

D. 22

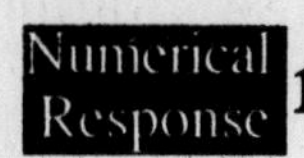

1. When simplified, the difference $\dfrac{4}{x^2-49} - \dfrac{3}{x^2-5x-14}$ can be written in the form $\dfrac{Ax-B}{(x-7)(x+2)(x+C)}$, where A, B, and C are integers.

The value of $A + B + C$ is _____.

(Record your answer in the numerical response box from left to right.)

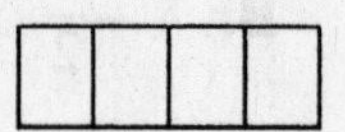

10. $\dfrac{6x}{x^2-8x+16} - \dfrac{2}{x-4}$ can be simplified to

A. $\dfrac{6x-2}{(x-4)^2}$

B. $\dfrac{4x-8}{(x-4)^2}$

C. $\dfrac{4x-4}{(x-4)^2}$

D. $\dfrac{4x+8}{(x-4)^2}$

Use the following information to answer the next question.

A student determines that the dimensions of the door to the conference hall can be written as rational expressions. Expressions for the length and width of the door are shown.

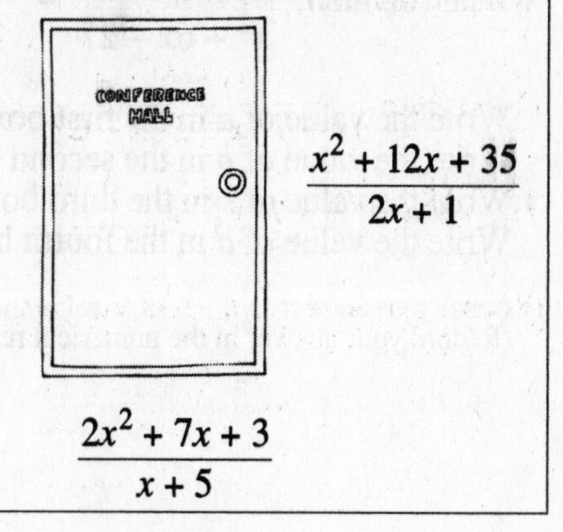

11. The area of the door to the conference hall can be expressed as a quadratic expression $Ax^2 + Bx + C$. The value of $A + B + C$ is

A. 30

B. 31

C. 32

D. 33

12. The product $\left(\frac{2x^3 - 50x}{5x^2 - 30x + 25}\right)\left(\frac{5x - 5x^2}{x^3 + 5x^2}\right)$ can be reduced to an integer n.

The value of n is

A. 2

B. −2

C. 10

D. −10

2. When divided, $\dfrac{16x^2 + 8x + 1}{x^2 + 6x - 27} \div \dfrac{8x^2 + 22x + 5}{2x^2 - x - 15}$ can be written in the form $\dfrac{ax + b}{cx + d}$.

Write the value of a in the first box.
Write the value of b in the second box.
Write the value of c in the third box.
Write the value of d in the fourth box.

(Record your answer in the numerical response box from left to right.)

13. For the appropriate restrictions, the expression $\left(\dfrac{\dfrac{1}{a^2 - 36}}{\dfrac{1}{a - 6}}\right)$ can be written as

A. $a - 6$

B. $a + 6$

C. $\dfrac{1}{a - 6}$

D. $\dfrac{1}{a + 6}$

14. The simplified form of $\left(6 - \frac{2}{x}\right) \div \left(9 - \frac{1}{x^2}\right)$ is

The value of n is

A. $\frac{2}{x + 3}$

B. $\frac{2x}{1 + 3x}$

C. $\frac{2x}{1 - 3x}$

D. $\frac{2}{x(1 + 3x)}$

Numerical Response

3. Two numbers differ by three and their quotient is $\frac{3}{4}$. The larger number is _____ .

(Record your answer in the numerical response box from left to right.)

15. In solving the rational equation $\frac{4x}{3x + 4} - \frac{10}{x + 6} = 0$, an equation which appears is

A. $4x^2 - 6x + 40 = 0$

B. $4x^2 - 6x - 40 = 0$

C. $12x^2 + 6x - 60 = 0$

D. $12x^2 + 6x + 60 = 0$

Numerical Response **4.** The formula $\frac{1}{R} = \frac{1}{R_1} + \frac{1}{R_2}$, concerning resistance in an electrical circuit, is used in Physics. If $R = 3$ ohms and R_1 is 8 ohms more than R_2, the value of R_1 is ____ .

(Record your answer in the numerical response box from left to right.)

Numerical Response **5.** Govinda has a cardiovascular routine where he walks for 3km, runs for $7\frac{1}{2}$ km and then walks for an additional 4 km. He runs $2\frac{1}{2}$ times as fast as he walks, and the total time taken for his routine is 2 hours. His walking speed, to the nearest km/h, is _____ .

(Record your answer in the numerical response box from left to right.)

Written Response - 5 marks

A plane flew from Red Deer to Winnipeg, a flying distance of 1260 km. On the return journey, due to a strong head wind, the plane travelled 1200 km in the same time it took to complete the outward journey. On the outward journey, the plane was able to maintain an average speed 20 km/hr greater than on the return journey.

- If the average speed of the plane from Red Deer to Winnipeg is x km/hr, state an expression for the average speed of the plane from Winnipeg to Red Deer in km/hr.

- Calculate the average speed of the plane from Winnipeg to Red Deer.

- Calculate the total flying time for the round trip.

Answer Key

1. B 2. C 3. D 4. D 5. A 6. C 7. A 8. A
9. A 10. D 11. C 12. B 13. D 14. B 15. B

Numerical Response

1. | 2 | 1 | | |

2. | 4 | 1 | 1 | 9 |

3. | 1 | 2 | | |

4. | 1 | 2 | | |

5. | 5 | | | |

Written Response

1.
- $(x - 20)$ km/hr
- 400 km/h
- 6 hours 9 minutes

Absolute Value Functions and Reciprocal Functions Lesson #1: Absolute Value Functions

The Absolute Value of a Number

The **absolute value** of a real number can be defined as the principal square root of the square of the number.

e.g. the absolute value of 6 = $\sqrt{(6)^2} = \sqrt{36} = 6$

the absolute value of −6 = $\sqrt{(-6)^2} = \sqrt{36} = 6$

For a real number, a, the absolute value of a is written $|a|$. e.g. $|6| = 6$ and $|-6| = 6$.

The absolute value of a real number can be regarded as the distance of the number from zero on a number line.

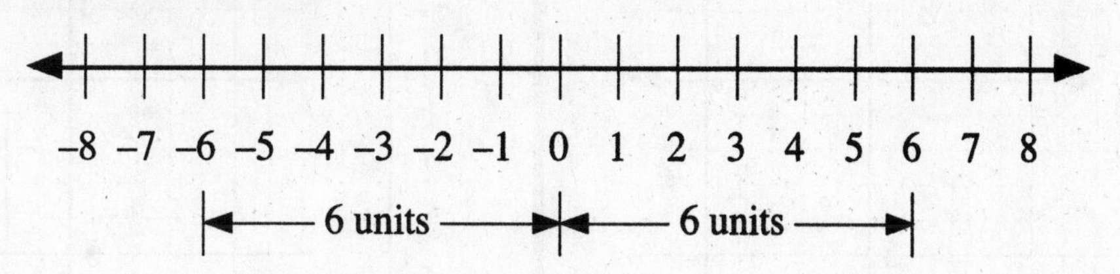

The absolute value of a number will never be negative.

Evaluate:

a) $|3|$ b) $|-3|$ c) $-|8|$ d) $-|-8|$

e) $|-7| + |7|$ f) $|1-5|$ g) $-|-\sqrt{81}|$

Complete Assignment Questions #1 - #3

Investigating the Function $f(x) = |x|$

1. Consider the functions $g(x) = x$, and $h(x) = -x$, whose graphs respectively have equations $y = x$ and $y = -x$.

Sketch and label each graph on the grid below.

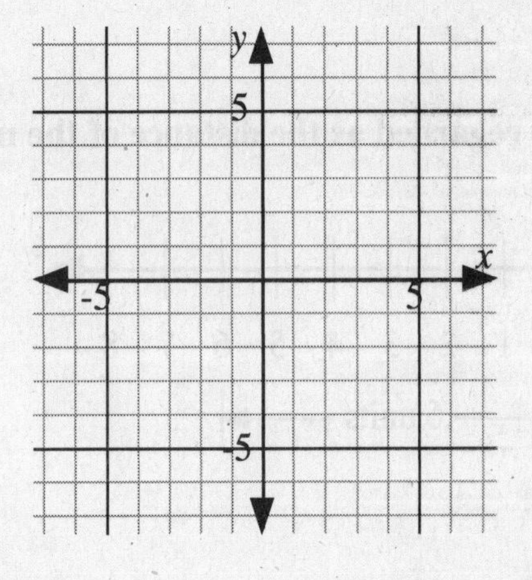

2. Consider the function $f(x) = |x|$, whose graph has the equation $y = |x|$.

a) Complete the table of values.

b) Plot the points on the grid and join the points.

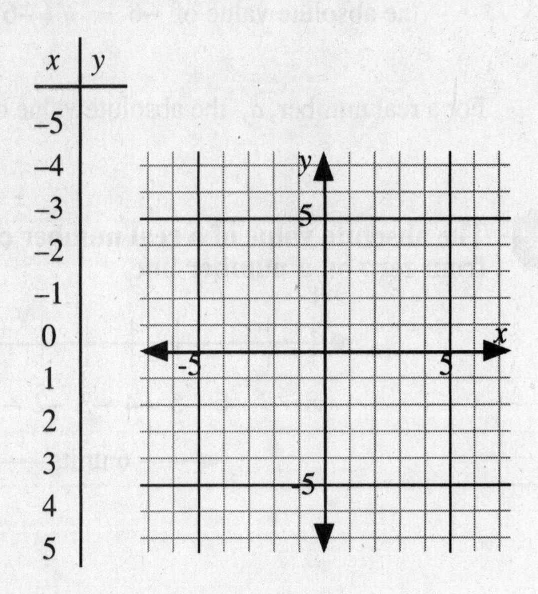

x	y
-5	
-4	
-3	
-2	
-1	
0	
1	
2	
3	
4	
5	

3. Explain the similarities and differences between the graphs on the two grids above.

4. The graph of $y = |x|$ contains two straight lines.

a) State the equation of the line in quadrant 1.

b) State the equation of the line in quadrant 2.

5. We can see from #4 that the equation $y = |x|$ can be written in two **pieces** with different domains for each piece.

Complete the following to write the absolute value function $f(x) = |x|$ as a **piecewise function**;

$$f(x) = \begin{cases} \quad & \text{if } x \geq 0 \\ \quad & \text{if } x < 0 \end{cases}$$

Recall from the definition of the absolute value of a number on the previous page that the absolute value function $f(x) = |x|$ could be written as $f(x) = \sqrt{x^2}$.

Defining The Absolute Value Function $f(x) = |x|$

The absolute value function $f(x) = |x|$ can be defined as:

$$f(x) = |x| = \sqrt{x^2} = \begin{cases} x & \text{if } x \geq 0 \\ -x & \text{if } x < 0 \end{cases}$$

Notice that when x is a positive number, $|x| = x$, and when x is a negative number, $|x| = -x$.

Investigating the Function $f(x) = |x - 3|$

1. Consider the functions $g(x) = x - 3$, and $h(x) = -(x - 3)$, whose graphs respectively have equations $y = x - 3$ and $y = -(x - 3)$.

a) Complete the tables of values.

b) Plot the points on the grid, join the points, and extend the graphs.

x	−4	−3	−2	−1	0	1	2	3	4	5
$y = x - 3$										

x	−4	−3	−2	−1	0	1	2	3	4	5
$y = -(x - 3)$										

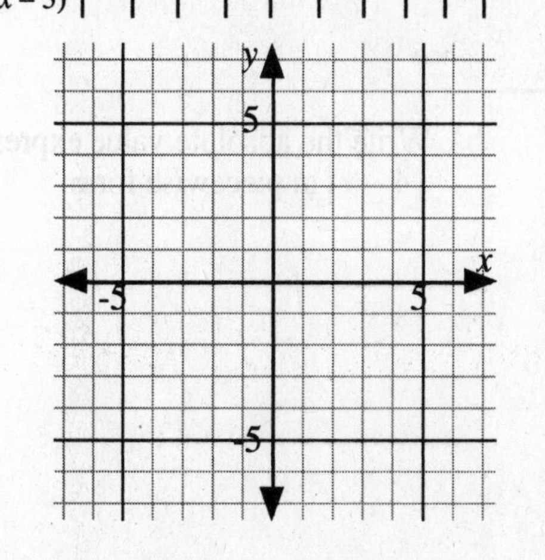

2. Consider the function $f(x) = |x - 3|$, whose graph has the equation $y = |x - 3|$.

a) Complete the table of values.

b) Plot the points on the grid, join the points, and extend the graph.

x	y
−5	
−4	
−3	
−2	
−1	
0	
1	
2	
3	
4	
5	

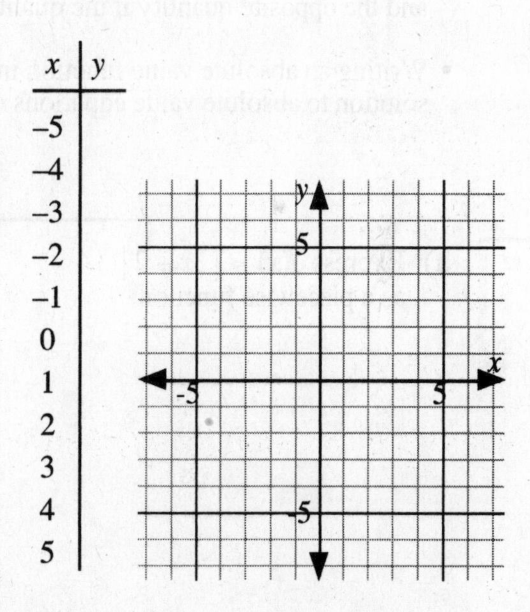

3. The function $f(x) = |x - 3|$ is written below as a piecewise function, but the domain for each piece has been omitted.

Use the graph of $y = |x - 3|$ to determine the domain for each piece, and complete the piecewise function form of $f(x) = |x - 3|$ shown below.

$$f(x) = \begin{cases} x - 3 & \text{if} \\ -(x - 3) & \text{if} \end{cases}$$

4. Explain how the equation of the second piece can be determined from the equation of the first piece.

5. Explain algebraically, without using a graph, how the domain for each piece could be determined.

- Every absolute value function can be defined in pieces.
- The absolute value of a quantity will always be the same quantity if the quantity is positive and the opposite quantity if the quantity is negative.
- Writing an absolute value function in piecewise form is an integral part of determining the solution to absolute value equations or inequalities.

a) Express $f(x) = |3x + 2|$ as a piecewise function.

b) Write the absolute value expression $|4 - x|$ in piecewise form.

Complete Assignment Questions #4 - #11

Assignment

1. Evaluate:

a) $|8|$ **b)** $|-8|$ **c)** $-|7|$ **d)** $-|-7|$

e) $|-2| - |2|$ **f)** $|-23| + |15|$ **g)** $|16 - 25|$ **h)** $|12 - 22| - 11$

2. Evaluate:

a) $|3 - 9|$ **b)** $|3| - |9|$ **c)** $||3| - |9||$ **d)** $-|-\sqrt{81}|$

e) $-|\sqrt[3]{27}|$ **f)** $|-\sqrt[3]{27}|$ **g)** $|\sqrt[3]{-27}|$ **h)** $|-\sqrt[3]{-27}|$

3. Which of the following statements are true and which are false?

a) $|-7| = |7|$ **b)** $|3 - 6| = -3$ **c)** $|2| - |4| = |-2|$ **d)** $||5| - |-32|| = 27$

4. Write the following absolute value functions as piecewise functions.

a) $f(x) = |x|$ **b)** $g(x) = |x + 1|$

c) $f(x) = |x - 2|$ **d)** $g(x) = |3 - x|$

5. Write the following absolute value expressions in piecewise form.

a) $|2x + 1|$ **b)** $|4x - 1|$

c) $|2 + x|$ **d)** $|4 - 2x|$

6. Decide whether each statement is true or false.

a) $|x| = x$ if $x > 0$ **b)** $|x| = -x$ if $x < 0$

7. Given that the absolute value of a number is a positive quantity, explain why "$|x| = -x$ if $x < 0$" is a true statement when it appears that the right hand side of the equation is a negative quantity.

8. Which of the following statements are true and which are false?

a) $|-x| = x$, if $x < 0$ **b)** $|-x| = -x$, if $x \geq 0$

c) $|2x - 1| = 2x - 1$, if $x < \frac{1}{2}$ **d)** $|3x + 4| = -3x - 4$, if $x < -\frac{4}{3}$

e) $|2 - 5x| = 2 - 5x$, if $x \geq \frac{2}{5}$ **f)** $|x - 7| = -x - 7$, if $x < 7$

9. a) Consider the function $g(x) = x^2 - 4$, whose graph has the equation $y = x^2 - 4$.

i) Complete the tables of values.

ii) Plot the points on the grid, join the points, and extend the graph.

x	y
–4	
–3	
–2	
–1	
0	
1	
2	
3	
4	

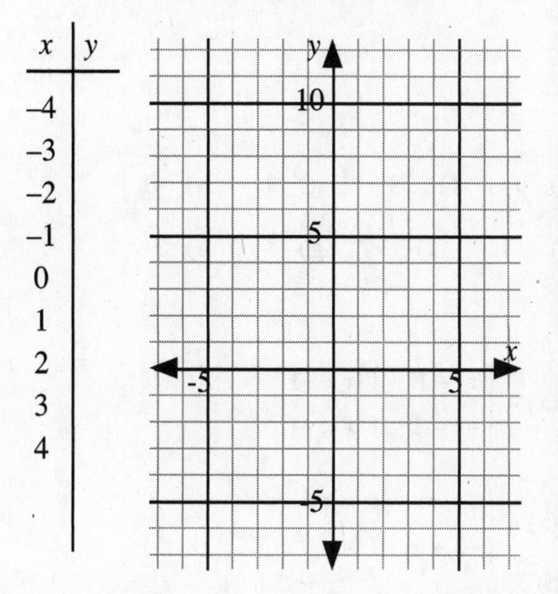

b) Consider the function $f(x) = |x^2 - 4|$, whose graph has the equation $y = |x^2 - 4|$.

i) Complete the table of values.

ii) Plot the points on the grid, join the points, and extend the graph.

x	y
–4	
–3	
–2	
–1	
0	
1	
2	
3	
4	

c) The function $f(x) = |x^2 - 4|$ can be written as a piecewise function in three pieces. Complete the piecewise function for $f(x) = |x^2 - 4|$ shown.

$$f(x) = \begin{cases} \qquad & \text{if} \quad x < -2 \\ \qquad & \text{if} \quad -2 \le x \le 2 \\ \qquad & \text{if} \quad x > 2 \end{cases}$$

d) Write the following absolute value functions as piecewise functions.

i) $f(x) = |x^2 - 25|$ **ii)** $g(x) = |36 - x^2|$

10. Explain why the function $f(x) = |x^2 + 4|$ can be written, without absolute value symbols, as only a single piece.

Multiple Choice

11. Which of the following is false?

A. $|x-9| = x-9$ if $x \geq 9$

B. $|9-x| = 9-x$ if $x < 9$

C. $|9-x^2| = 9-x^2$ if $-3 \leq x \leq 3$

D. $|x^2-9| = x^2-9$ if $-3 \leq x \leq 3$

Answer Key

1. **a)** 8 **b)** 8 **c)** –7 **d)** –7 **e)** 0 **f)** 38 **g)** 9 **h)** –1

2. **a)** 6 **b)** –6 **c)** 6 **d)** –9 **e)** –3 **f)** 3 **g)** 3 **h)** 3

3. **a)** T **b)** F **c)** F **d)** T

4. **a)** $f(x) = \begin{cases} x & \text{if } x \geq 0 \\ -x & \text{if } x < 0 \end{cases}$ **b)** $g(x) = \begin{cases} x+1 & \text{if } x \geq -1 \\ -x-1 & \text{if } x < -1 \end{cases}$

c) $f(x) = \begin{cases} x-2 & \text{if } x \geq 2 \\ -x+2 & \text{if } x < 2 \end{cases}$ **d)** $g(x) = \begin{cases} 3-x & \text{if } x \leq 3 \\ -3+x & \text{if } x > 3 \end{cases}$

5. **a)** $|2x+1| = \begin{cases} 2x+1 & \text{if } x \geq -\frac{1}{2} \\ -2x-1 & \text{if } x < -\frac{1}{2} \end{cases}$ **b)** $|4x-1| = \begin{cases} 4x-1 & \text{if } x \geq \frac{1}{4} \\ -4x+1 & \text{if } x < \frac{1}{4} \end{cases}$

c) $|2+x| = \begin{cases} 2+x & \text{if } x \geq -2 \\ -2-x & \text{if } x < -2 \end{cases}$ **d)** $|4-2x| = \begin{cases} 4-2x & \text{if } x \leq 2 \\ -4+2x & \text{if } x > 2 \end{cases}$

6. **a)** T **b)** T

7. Although $-x$ might appear to be a negative quantity, it is in fact a positive quantity if x is negative.

8. **a)** F **b)** F **c)** F **d)** T **e)** F **f)** F

9. **c)** $f(x) = \begin{cases} x^2-4 & \text{if } x < -2 \\ -x^2+4 & \text{if } -2 \leq x \leq 2 \\ x^2-4 & \text{if } x > 2 \end{cases}$

d) **i)** $f(x) = \begin{cases} x^2-25 & \text{if } x < -5 \\ -x^2+25 & \text{if } -5 \leq x \leq 5 \\ x^2-25 & \text{if } x > 5 \end{cases}$ **ii)** $g(x) = \begin{cases} -36+x^2 & \text{if } x < -6 \\ 36-x^2 & \text{if } -6 \leq x \leq 6 \\ -36+x^2 & \text{if } x > 6 \end{cases}$

10. Since x^2+4 is positive for all values of x, $|x^2+4|$ can be written as x^2+4 for $x \in R$.

11. D

Absolute Value Functions and Reciprocal Functions Lesson #2:
Solving Absolute Value Equations - Part One

Absolute Value Equations

$|2x + 3| = 8$, $|3 + x| = 2x + 1$, $|2x - 3| - |x + 4| = 8$, and $|x^2 - 17| = 8$ are all examples of **absolute value equations**.

In the next two lessons, we will learn how to solve these equations graphically and algebraically.

Solving Absolute Value Equations Using a Graphing Calculator

Intersection Method

To solve the equation $|2x + 3| = 8$ by the intersection method, use the following procedure.

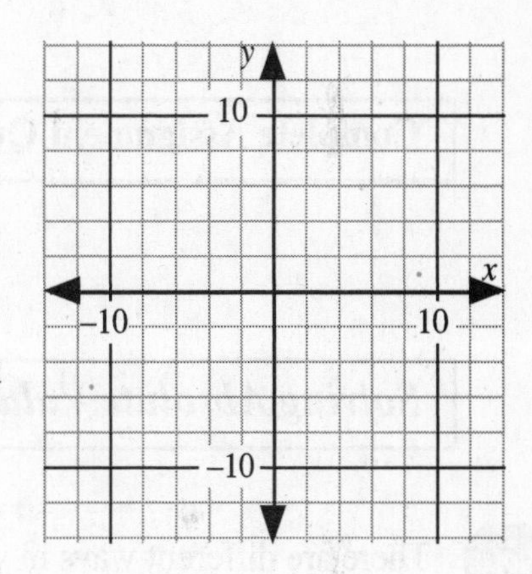

1. Graph $Y_1 = |2x + 3|$.
2. Graph $Y_2 = 8$.
3. Find the x-coordinate(s) of the point(s) of intersection using the `intersect` feature of the calculator.

x-intercept Method

To solve the equation $|2x + 3| = 8$ by the zero method, use the following procedure.

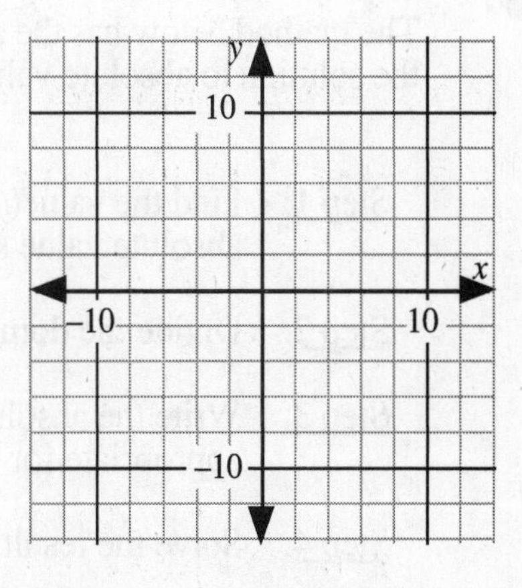

1. Rearrange the original equation with all terms on the left hand side and 0 on the right side to get $|2x + 3| - 8 = 0$.
2. Graph $Y_1 = |2x + 3| - 8$.
3. Use the `zero` feature of the calculator to find the x-intercept(s).

Solve the following absolute value equations by graphing.

a) $|3 + x| = 2x + 1$

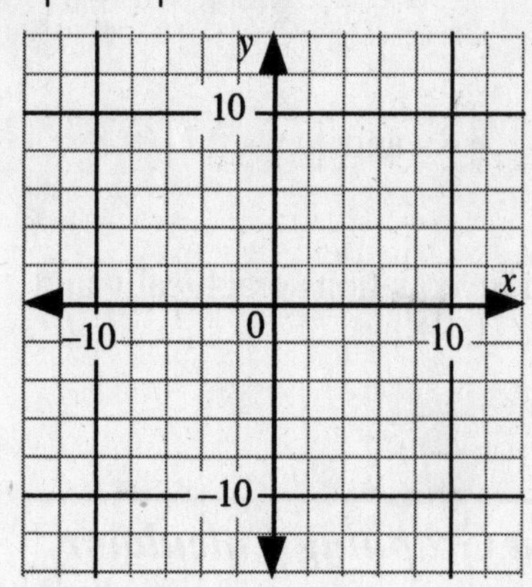

b) $|x^2 - 17| = 8$

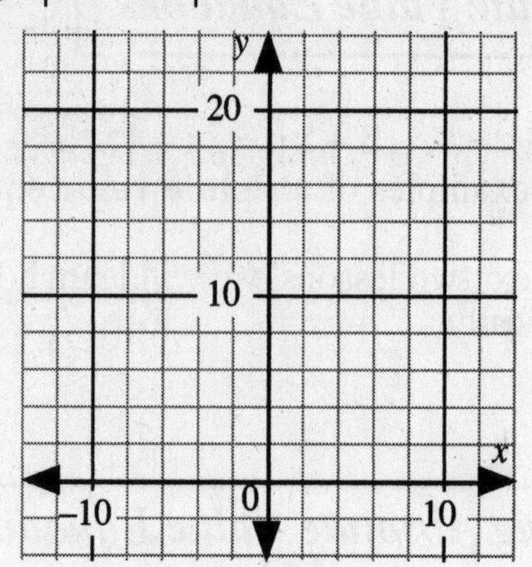

Complete Assignment Question #1 - #3

Solving Absolute Value Equations Algebraically

There are different ways in which to determine algebraically the solution to absolute value equations.

The method below has the advantage that a virtually identical method can be used to determine the solution to absolute value inequalities in calculus and other higher level math courses.

Step 1: Find the value(s) of the variable which will make the expression within the absolute value symbol(s) equal to zero.

Step 2: Divide the domain into smaller subdomains using the value(s) found in Step 1.

Step 3: Write the absolute value expressions in piecewise form, using the piece that is appropriate for each subdomain.

Step 4: Solve the resulting equation in each subdomain.

Step 5: Check that the solution to each equation is in the subdomain, and combine all valid solutions.

Class Ex. #2

Alan has started to solve the equation $|2x + 3| = 8$ using the steps on the previous page. Complete Alan's work and check the solution with the graphical solution on page 457.

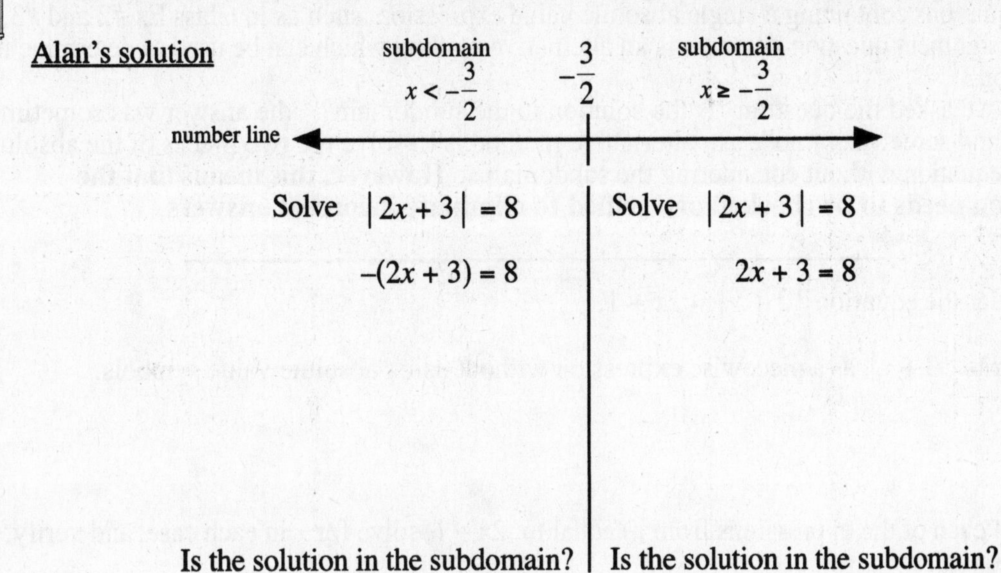

Final solution: $x =$ ________

Class Ex. #3

Haley solved the equation $|3 + x| = 2x + 1$ algebraically.
Complete Haley's work and compare the solution with the one from Class Ex. #1a).

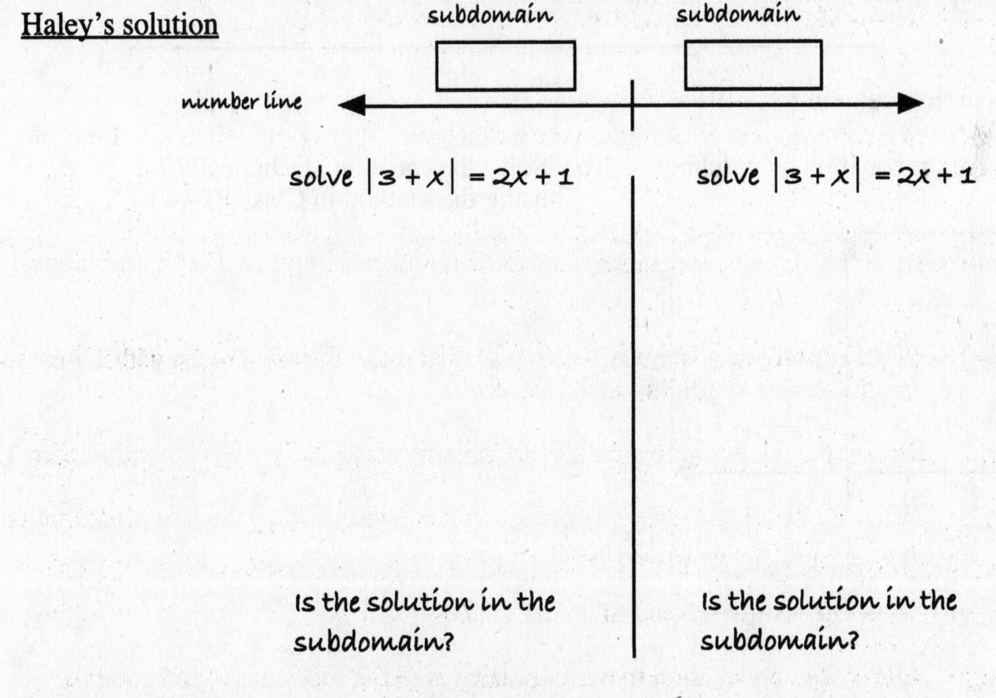

Final solution: $x =$ ________

Complete Assignment Question #4

An Alternative Method for Solving Single Absolute Value Equations

For equations containing a single absolute value expression, such as in Class Ex #2 and #3, and assignment question #4, there is an alternative method which can be used to determine the solution.
When we asked the question "Is the solution in the subdomain?", the answer was sometimes "yes" and sometimes "no". An alternative method is to solve the two pieces of the absolute value equation without considering the subdomains. **However, this means that the solution needs to be checked or verified to eliminate incorrect answers.**

Consider the equation $|3 + x| = 2x + 1$.

a) Write $|3 + x|$ as a piecewise expression without using absolute value symbols.

b) Set each of the expressions from a) equal to $2x + 1$, solve for x in each case, and verify.

c) Compare this method with the method in Class Ex #3.

Consider the equation $|x^2 - 9| = 7$.

a) Solve the equation by graphing.

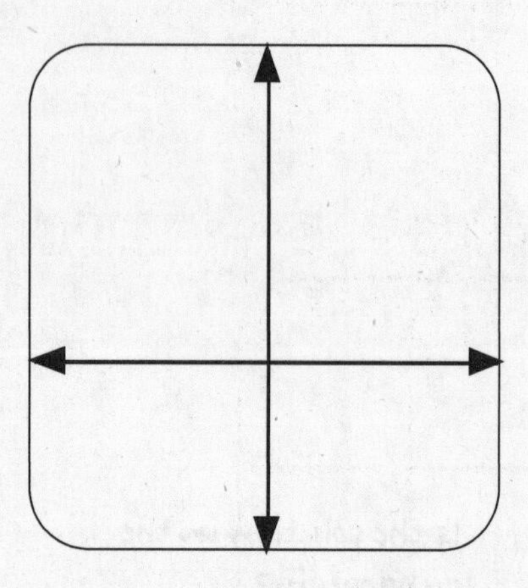

b) Solve the equation algebraically, using the method in Class Ex #4 b).

Complete Assignment Question #5 - #9

Assignment

1. Describe clearly how to use the method of intersection to solve the equation $|x+3| = 4$. State the solution.

2. Describe clearly how to use the x-intercept method to solve the equation $|x-2| = x+1$. State the solution.

3. Solve each of the following equations graphically. Sketch and label each graph.

a) $|x+5| = 0$

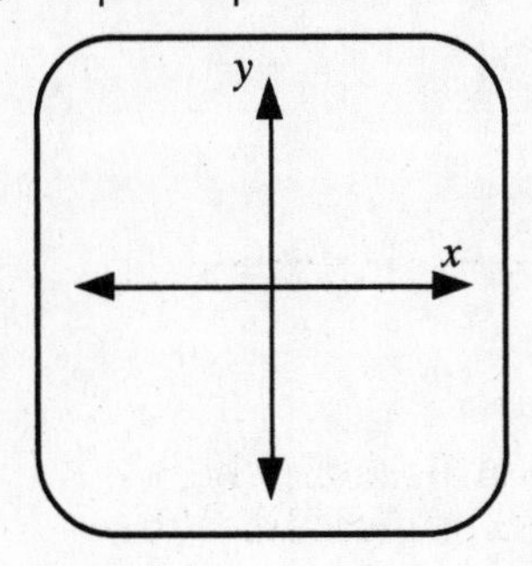

b) $|1-4x| = x+4$

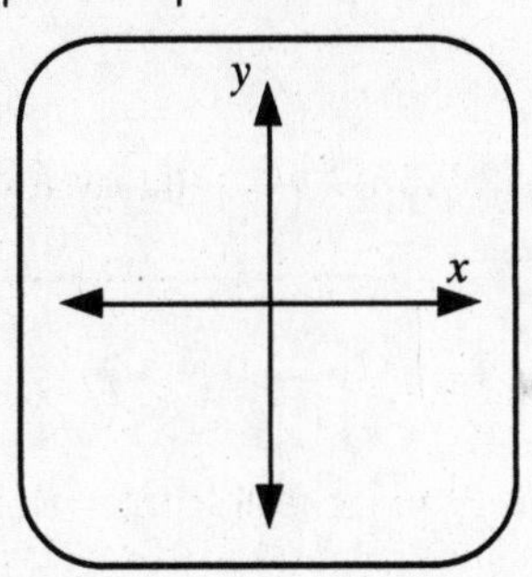

c) $|4-x| = -2x-10$

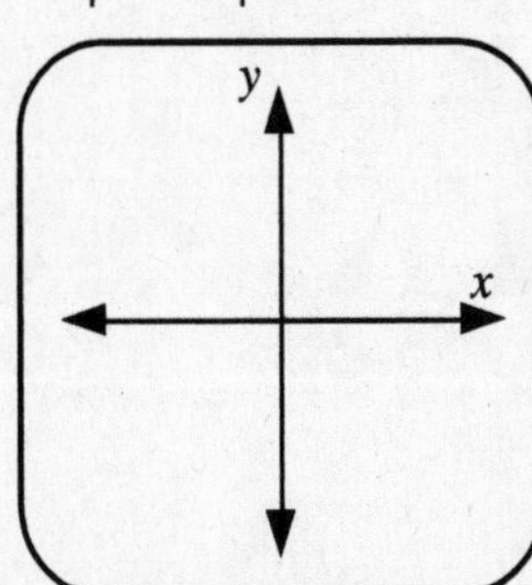

d) $3|x-8| = 2x+7$

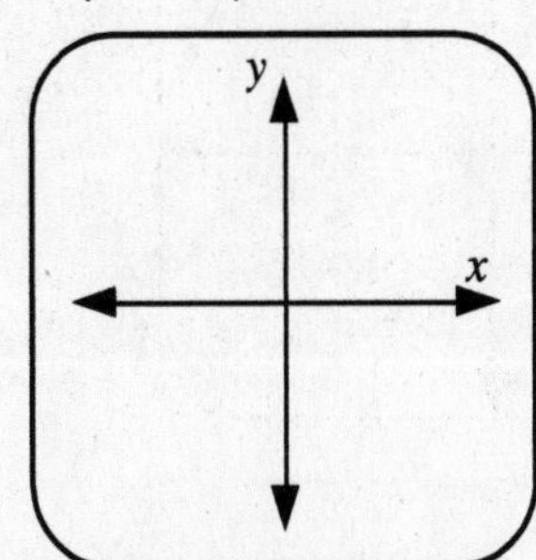

4. Solve each of the following equations algebraically.

a) $|x+5| = 10$

b) $|3x-1| = 4$

c) $|2x+1| = x$

d) $|1-4x| = 6x$

e) $|7x-2| + 6 = 3x$

f) $|4-x| = -2x - 10$

5. Solve the following algebraically.

a) $3|x-8| = 2x+7$

b) $|2x-8| - 2 = 4x$

c) $|x^2-26| = 10$

d) $|x^2+10x+15| = 6$

6. Use a graphing calculator to solve, to the nearest tenth, the following absolute value equations.

a) $|x^2-2x-6| = 4$

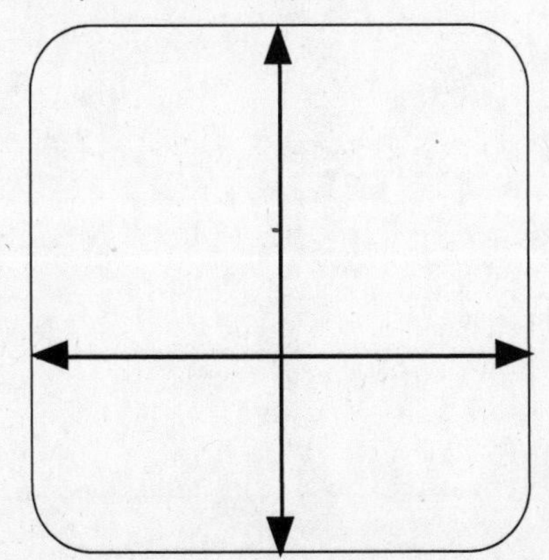

b) $|12+3x-x^2| - 14 = 0$

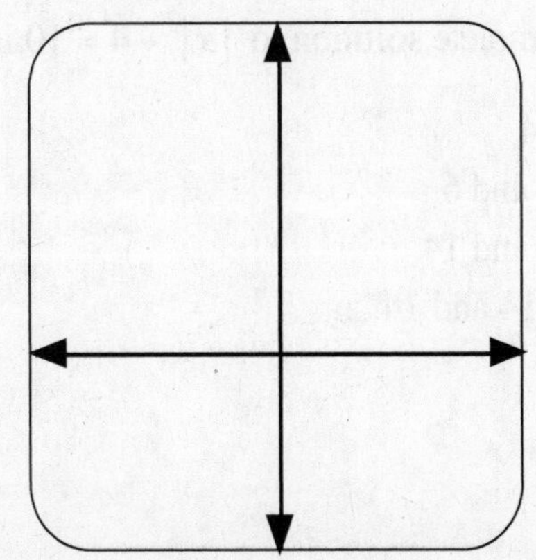

7. Solve the equation $|x^2 - 2x - 6| = 4$ (from #6a) algebraically, using the quadratic formula.

Multiple Choice

8. The complete solution to $|x| - 4 = 10$ is

A. 14
B. 6 and 6
C. 6 and 14
D. -14 and 14

9. Mike solved the equation $|x^2 + 4x - 15| = 6$ algebraically.
He wrote the solutions as $x = a, x = b,$ and $x = c \pm \sqrt{d}$.
The value of $a + b + c + d$ is _____.

(Record your answer in the numerical response box from left to right.)

Some students were trying to solve the equation $|2x + 1| - |x - 2| = 2$.
Develop and explain an algebraic procedure to solve this equation.
Determine the solution to the equation.

Answer Key

1. • Graph $Y_1 = |x + 3|$
   • Graph $Y_2 = 4$
   • Find the x-coordinate(s) of the point(s) of intersection using the intersect feature of the calculator.
   • Solution is $x = -7$ or 1.

2. • Graph $Y_1 = |x - 2| - x - 1$
   • Use the zero feature of the calculator to find the x-intercept(s).
   • Solution is $x = \frac{1}{2}$.

3. a) $x = -5$ b) $x = -\frac{3}{5}$ or $x = \frac{5}{3}$ c) $x = -14$ d) $x = \frac{17}{5}$ or $x = 31$

4. a) -15 or 5 b) -1 or $\frac{5}{3}$ c) no solution
   d) $\frac{1}{10}$ e) no solution f) -14

5. a) $\frac{17}{5}, 31$ b) 1 c) $\pm 4, \pm 6$ d) $-9, -7, -3, -1$

6. a) $-2.3, -0.7, 2.7, 4.3$ b) $-3.8, 1.0, 2.0, 6.8$

7. $1 \pm \sqrt{3}, 1 \pm \sqrt{11}$ 8. D 9.

7			

Group Work
$x = -5, 1$ (The method is covered in the next lesson.)

The following class examples are beyond the scope of this course. We include the method here for students intending to take higher level math courses.

Jefferson and Julia were asked to solve the equation $|2x-3|-|x+4|=8$.
Jefferson solved the equation graphically, and Julia solved the equation algebraically.

a) Solve the equation using Jefferson's method.

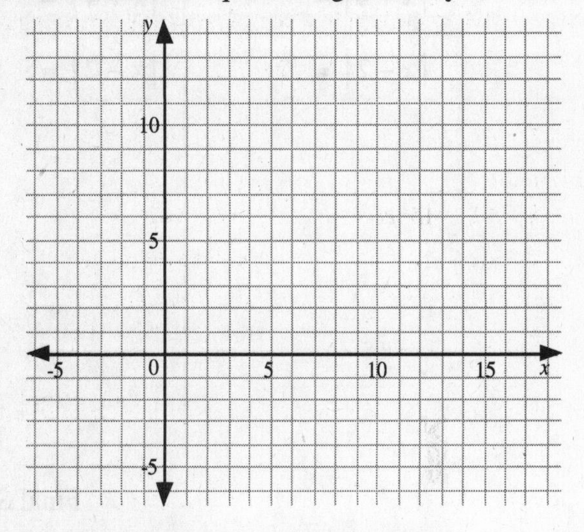

b) Julia has started to solve the equation $|2x-3|-|x+4|=8$ algebraically. Complete Julia's solution below.

number line

$2x-3=0 \Rightarrow x=3/2$

$x+4=0 \Rightarrow x=-4$

Number line marked at -4 and $3/2$.

subdomain $x<-4$	subdomain $-4 \le x \le 3/2$	subdomain $x>3/2$
$\lvert 2x-3\rvert = -2x+3$	$\lvert 2x-3\rvert =$	$\lvert 2x-3\rvert =$
$\lvert x+4\rvert = -x-4$	$\lvert x+4\rvert =$	$\lvert x+4\rvert =$
Solve $\lvert 2x-3\rvert - \lvert x+4\rvert = 8$	Solve $\lvert 2x-3\rvert - \lvert x+4\rvert = 8$	
$-2x+3-(-x-4)=8$		
$-2x+3+x+4=8$		
$-x+7=8$		
$-x=8-7$		
$-x=1$		
$x=-1$		
Is the solution in the subdomain? <u>No</u>		

Final Solution: $x=$ ________

Complete the solution to the equation $|x+4| = |x-2|$.

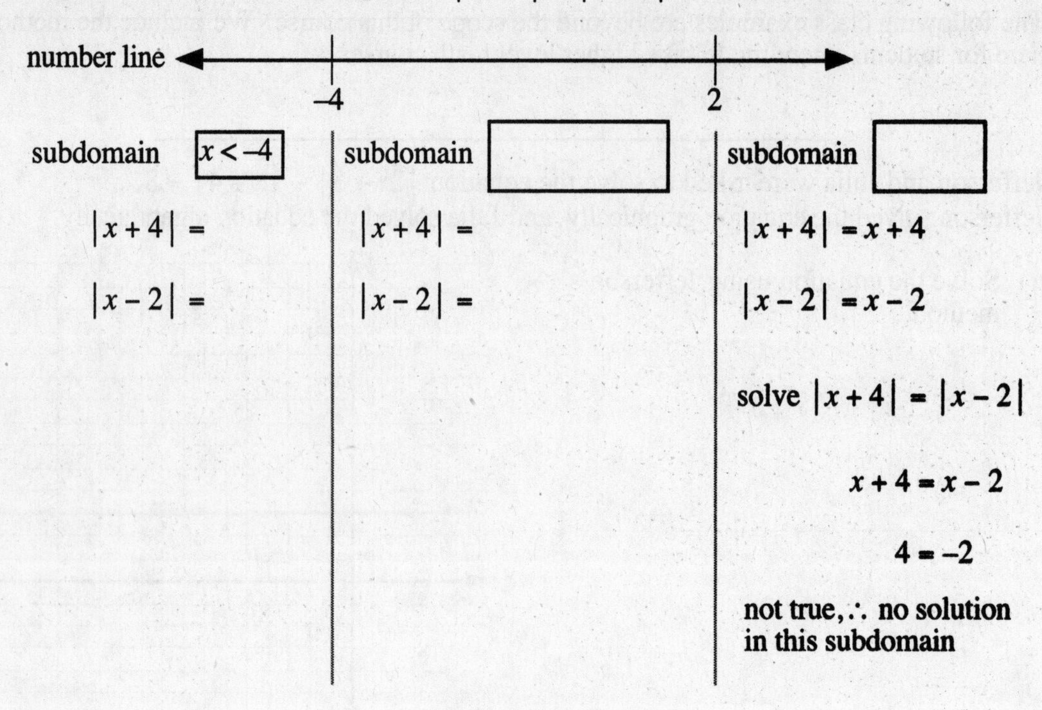

Final Solution $x =$ ________

Complete Assignment Question #1 - #8

Assignment

1. Solve each of the following equations graphically. Sketch and label each graph.

a) $|x+4| = |x-2|$

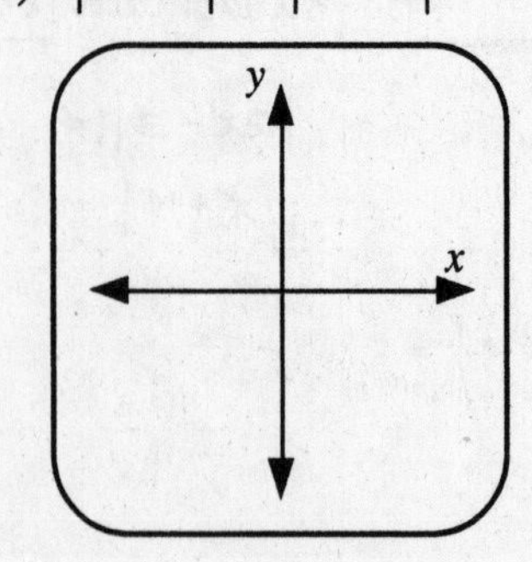

b) $|x+4| - |2x| = 0$

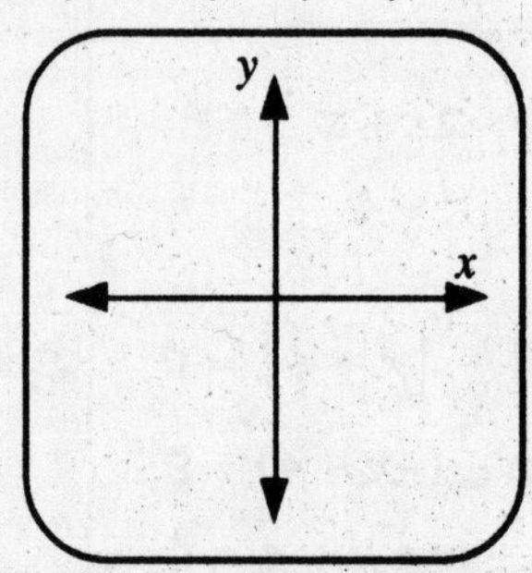

c) $|3x+1| = |x-2|$

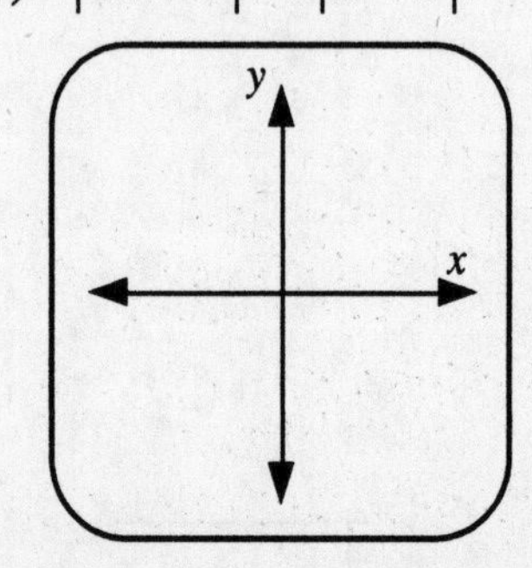

d) $|x^2-4| = x^2-4$

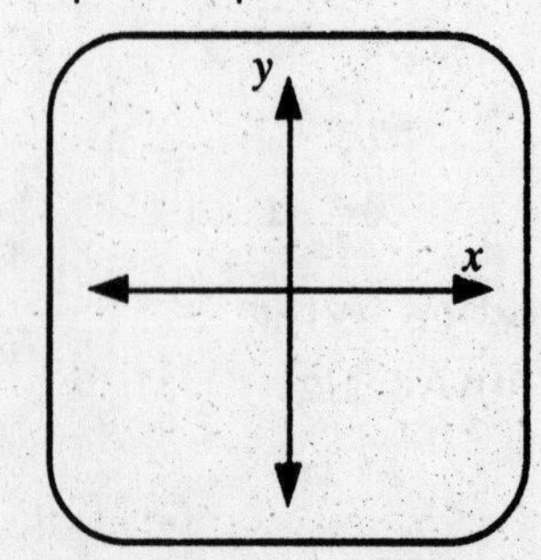

2. Algebraically solve $|4x - 1| = |x - 3|$.

3. Algebraically determine the solution to the equation $|2x + 1| - |x - 2| = 2$.

4. Algebraically determine the solution to the equation $|2x-3| - |2x+5| = 0$.

5. Consider the equation $|3x-2| = |2x+5| + 1$. Algebraically solve for x.

6. Use an algebraic procedure to solve to the equation $|3 - x| - 1 = |4x + 2|$.

Numerical Response

7. To the nearest hundredth, the smallest positive root of the equation $|x^2 + 1| = |x^2 - 8|$ is _____ .

(Record your answer in the numerical response box from left to right.)

8. The positive root, to the nearest hundredth, of the equation $\left|\frac{x}{2} + 3\right| - |2x - 1| = x^2$ is _____ .

(Record your answer in the numerical response box from left to right.)

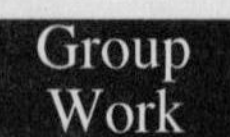

Extend your thinking by applying the skills you have learned in this lesson to solve the following absolute value inequalities.

a) $|5x - 10| < |3x + 9|$

b) $\dfrac{|3x - 6|}{|x + 1|} \geq 2$

Answer Key

1. **a)** $x = -1$ **b)** $x = -\frac{4}{3}, 4$ **c)** $x = -\frac{3}{2}, \frac{1}{4}$ **d)** $x \leq -2$ or $x \geq 2$

2. $x = -\frac{2}{3}, \frac{4}{5}$ **3.** $x = -5, 1$ **4.** $x = -\frac{1}{2}$ **5.** $x = -\frac{4}{5}, 8$ **6.** $x = -\frac{4}{3}, 0$

7.

1	.	8	7

8.

1	.	3	9

Group Work: **a)** $\frac{1}{8} < x < \frac{19}{2}, x \in R$ **b)** $x < -1$ or $-1 < x \leq \frac{4}{5}$ or $x \geq 8$, $x \in R$

(Note that $x = -1$ is a non-permissible value.)

Absolute Value Functions and Reciprocal Functions Lesson #4:
Absolute Value Transformations

Absolute Value Transformations

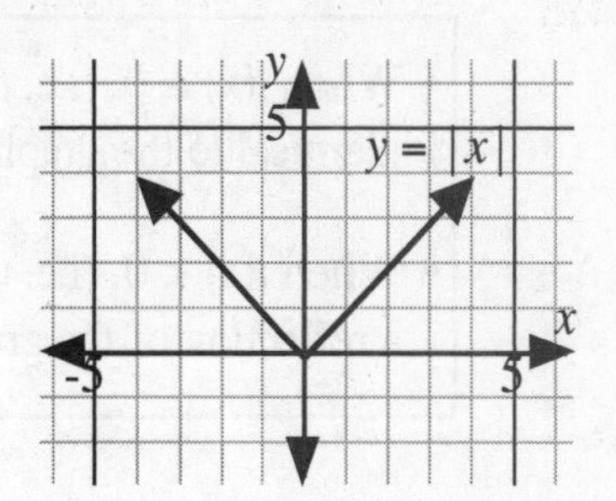

Recall the definition of absolute value.

$$|x| = \begin{cases} x & \text{if } x \geq 0 \\ -x & \text{if } x < 0 \end{cases}$$

An absolute value transformation transforms the graph of $y = f(x)$ to the graph of $y = |f(x)|$.

Investigating the Graphs of y = f(x) and y = |f(x)|

1. A function $f(x)$ has equation $y = x - 1$.

a) Write the equation for $y = |f(x)|$.

b) Complete the table of values for $y = f(x)$ and $y = |f(x)|$.

c) Sketch the graphs of $y = f(x)$ and $y = |f(x)|$ on the same grid.

d) Complete the following statements based on the observations in c).

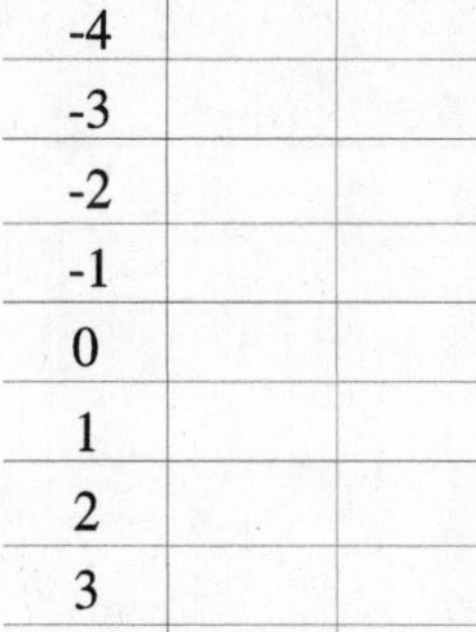

x	$y = f(x)$	$y = \|f(x)\|$
-4		
-3		
-2		
-1		
0		
1		
2		
3		
4		

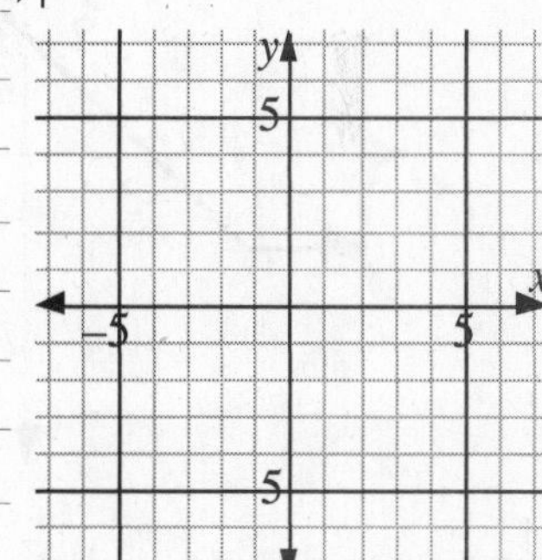

i) When $f(x) \geq 0$, the graph of $y = |f(x)|$ is ______________ to the graph of $y = f(x)$.

ii) When $f(x) < 0$, the graph of $y = |f(x)|$ is a ______________________________ of the graph of $y = f(x)$.

2. The graph of the function $f(x)$ with equation $y = x^2 - 4$ is shown.

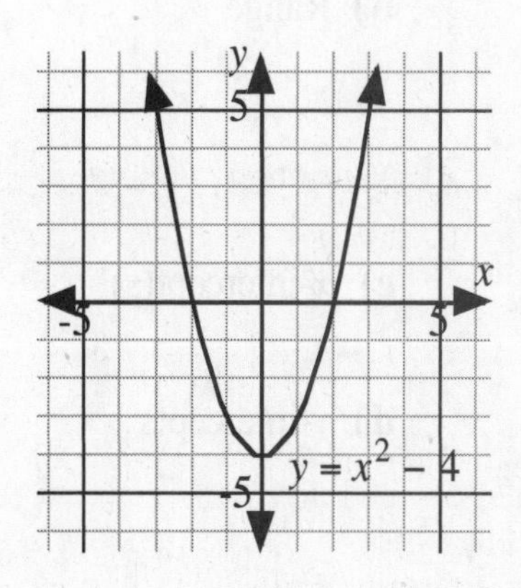

a) Write the equation for $y = |f(x)|$.

b) Use a graphing calculator to sketch $y = |f(x)|$.

c) Do the observations from #1d) also apply in this example?

In general, given the function $y = f(x)$, the graph of $y = |f(x)|$ has the following characteristics:

- When $f(x) \geq 0$, (i.e. the graph of $y = f(x)$ is above the x-axis), the graph of $y = |f(x)|$ is identical to the graph of $y = f(x)$.
- When $f(x) < 0$, (i.e. the graph of $y = f(x)$ is below the x-axis), the graph of $y = |f(x)|$ is a reflection of the graph of $y = f(x)$ in the x-axis.

3. In each case, the graph of $y = f(x)$ is shown. Sketch the graph of $y = |f(x)|$.

a)

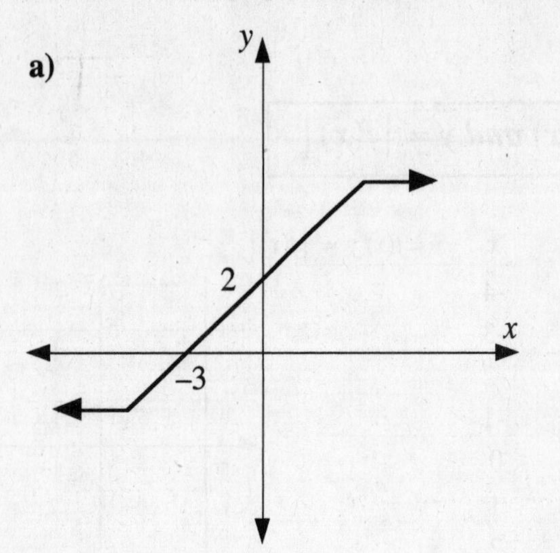

b)

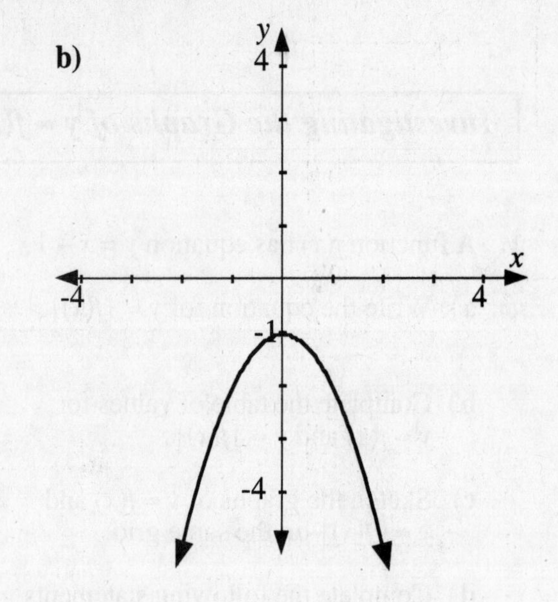

4. Consider all the graphs of $y = f(x)$ and $y = |f(x)|$ from parts 1 to 3 of the investigation. Compare the following aspects of the graphs of $y = f(x)$ and $y = |f(x)|$.

a) Domain

b) Range

c) x-intercept(s)

d) y-intercepts

Complete Assignment Questions #1 - #7

Assignment

1. In each case, the graph of $y = f(x)$ is shown. Sketch the graph of $y = |f(x)|$.

a)

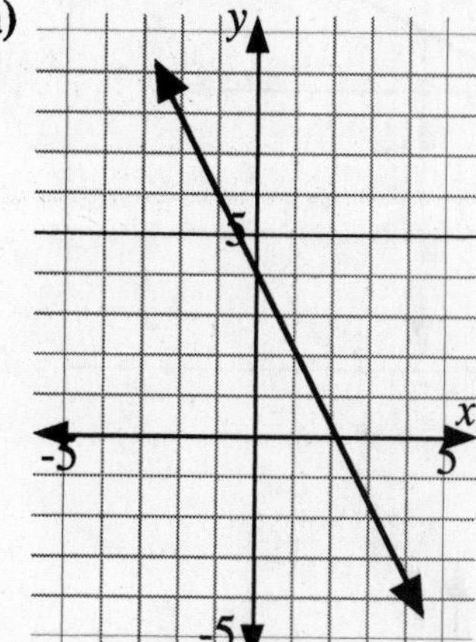

b)

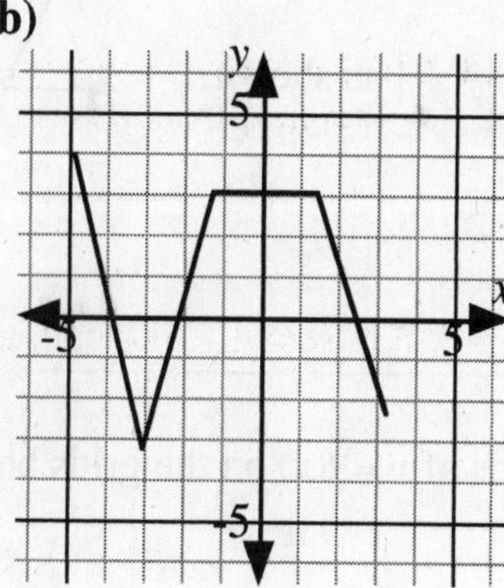

c)

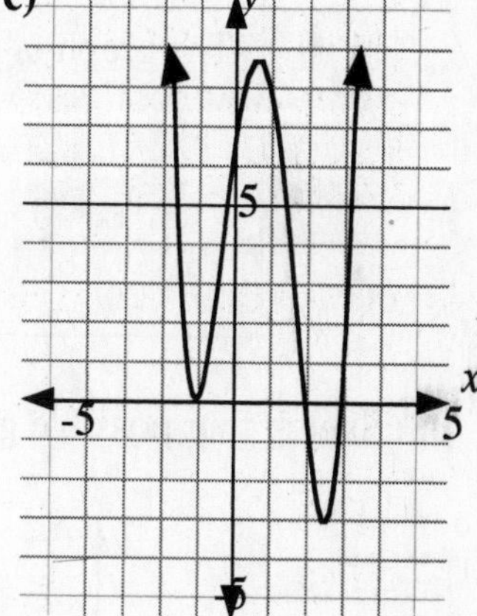

d)

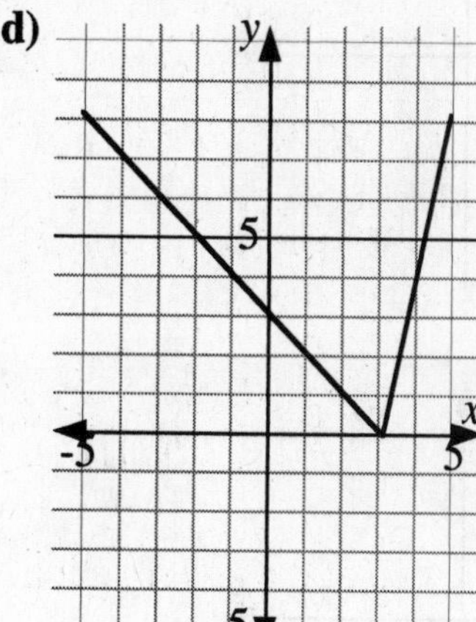

e)

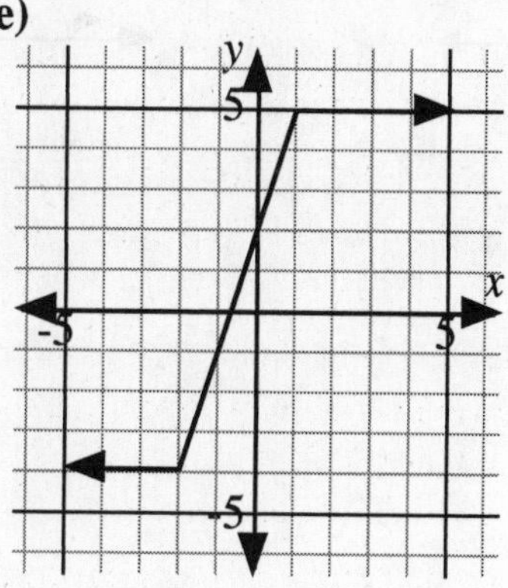

f)

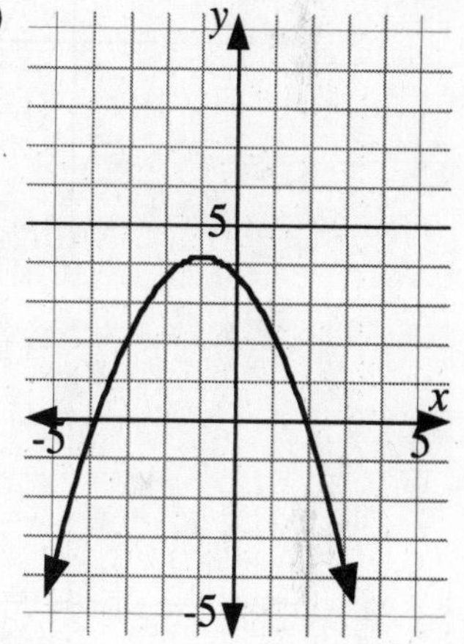

2. Consider a function $y = f(x)$. Explain why the equation $|f(x)| < 0$ has no solution.

Use the following information to answer the next question.

$y = f(x)$ is a continous function with domain $x \in R$.

The graph of $y = |f(x)|$ is shown.

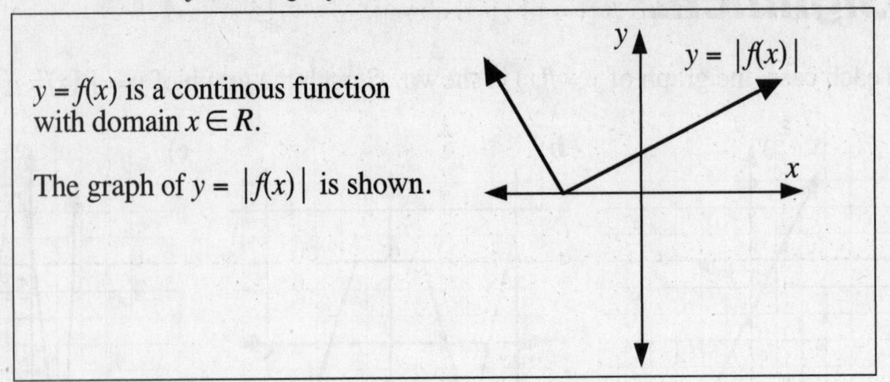

3. Sketch four possible graphs of $y = f(x)$ on the grids below.

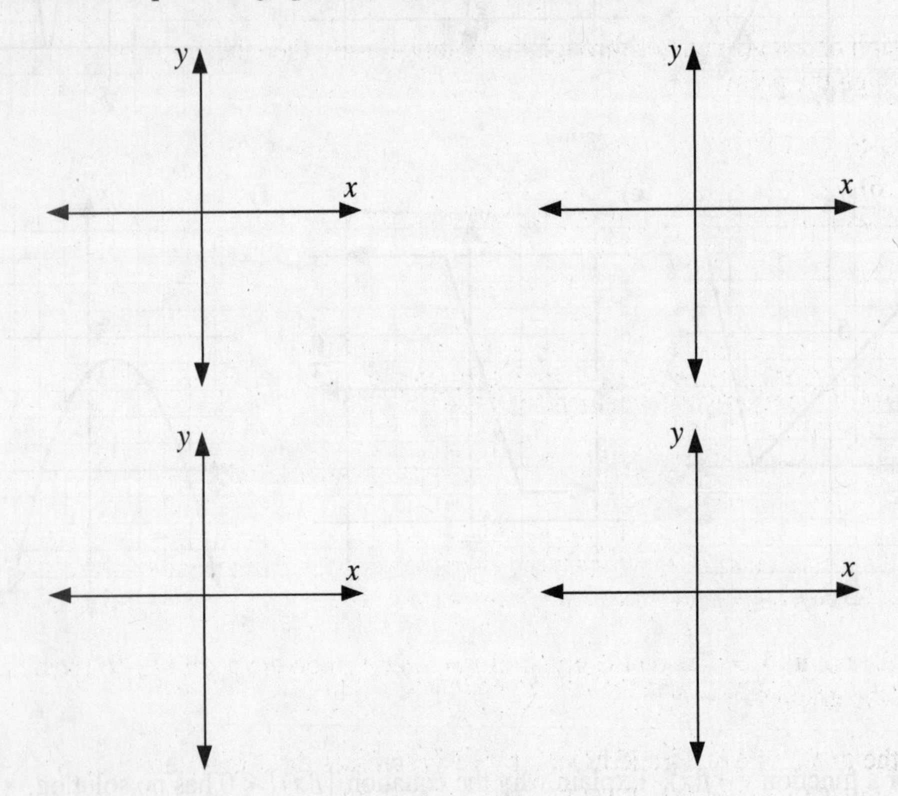

4. The graph of a quadratic function, $g(x)$, has domain $x \in R$, range $y \leq 4$, y-intercept of -5, and x-intercepts 1 and 5.

On the grid provided, sketch the graph of $y = |g(x)|$.

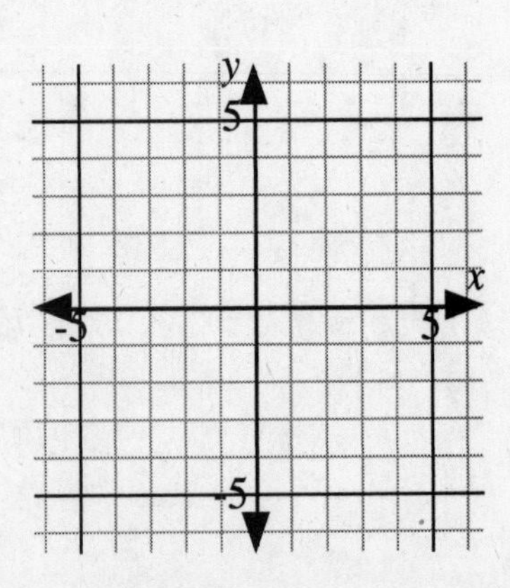

5. Consider a quadratic function $y = f(x)$ with a y-intercept of -2.
Sketch a possible graph of $y = f(x)$ if the range of $y = |f(x)|$ is:

a) $\{y \mid y \geq 0, y \in R\}$ **b)** $\{y \mid y \geq 2, y \in R\}$ **c)** $\{y \mid y \geq 1, y \in R\}$

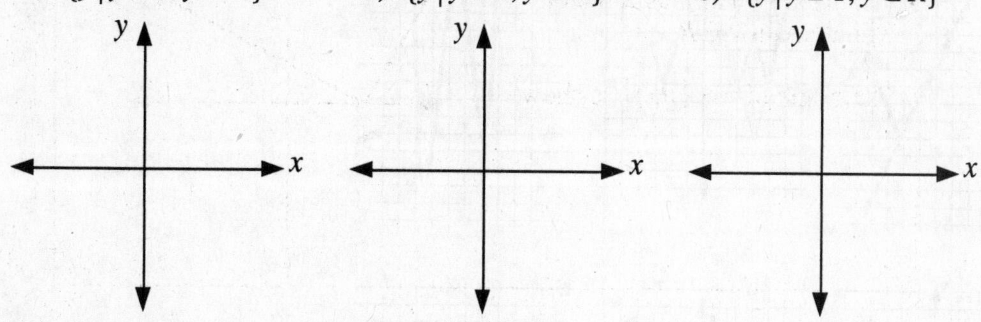

Multiple Choice

6. If the graph of $y = g(x)$ passes through the point $(-3, -6)$, then the graph of $y = |g(x)|$ must pass through the point

A. $(3, -6)$
B. $(3, 6)$
C. $(-3, 6)$
D. $(6, 3)$

7. Which one of the following statements is false?

A. If the y-intercept of the graph of $y = f(x)$ is -8, then the y-intercept of the graph of $y = |f(x)|$ is 8.

B. If the x-intercepts of the graph of $y = g(x)$ are 2 and 7, then the x-intercepts of the graph of $y = |g(x)|$ are 2 and 7.

C. If the point $(4, 9)$ lies on the graph of $y = |h(x)|$, then the point $(4, -9)$ must lie on the graph of $y = h(x)$.

D. If the graph of a quadratic function $y = P(x)$ crosses the x-axis, then the range of $y = |P(x)|$ must be $\{y \mid y \geq 0, y \in R\}$.

Answer Key

1.

a)
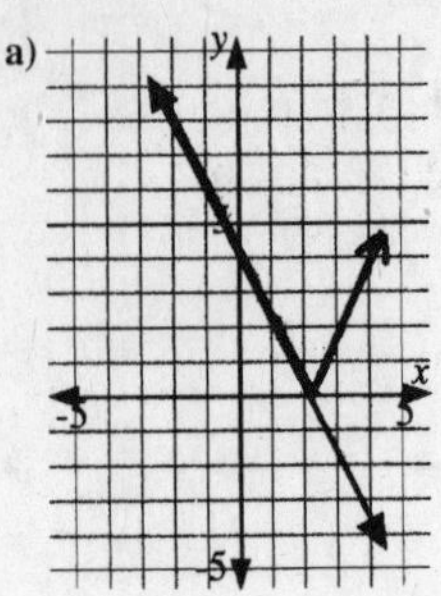

b)

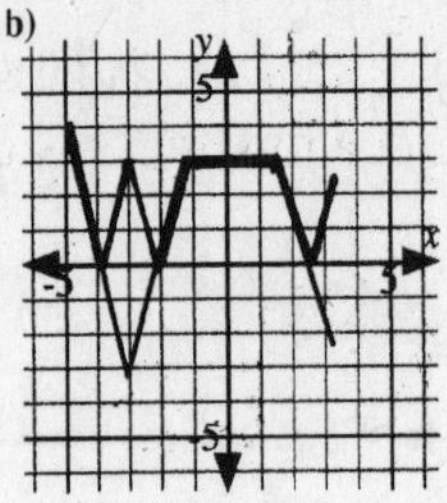

c)
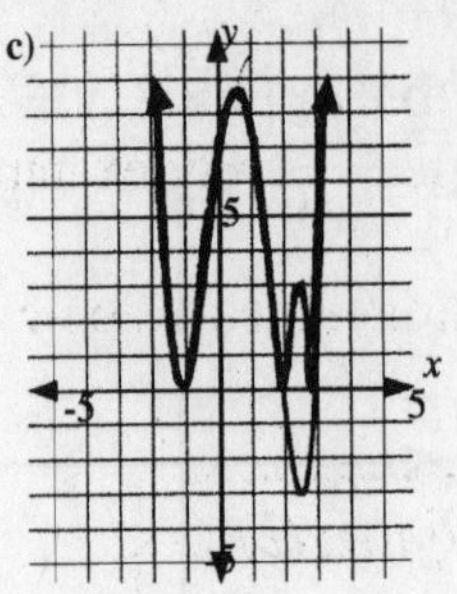

d)

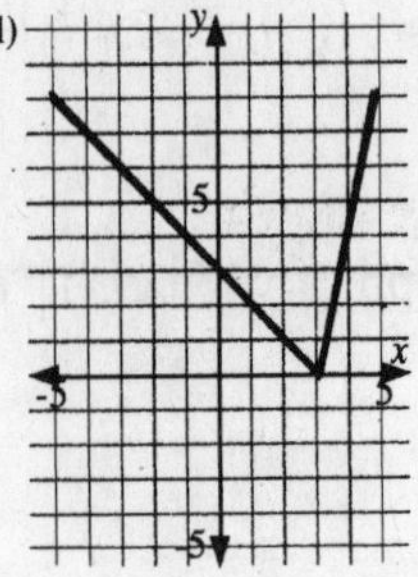

e)
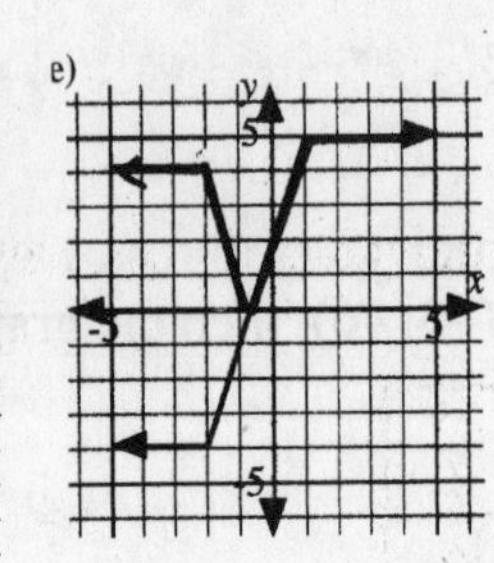

f)
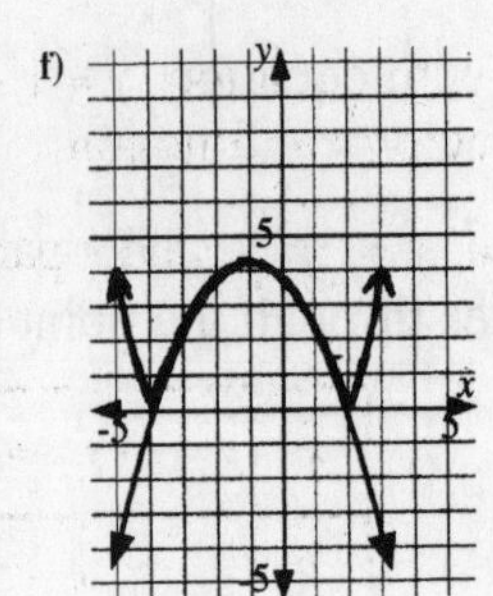

2. The absolute value of a function is non negative for all values of x.
It is not possible for $|f(x)|$ to be less than zero.

3.

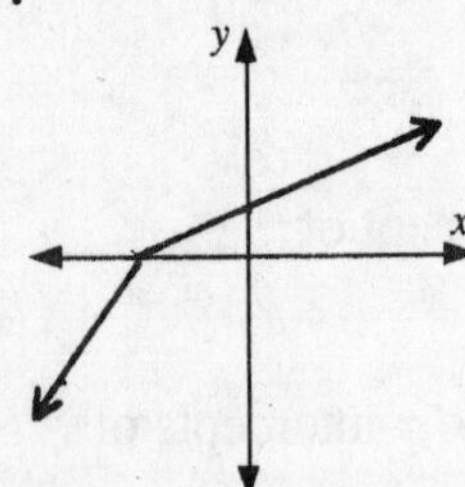

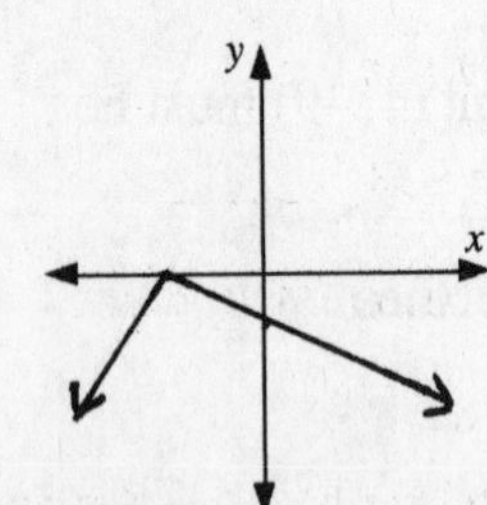

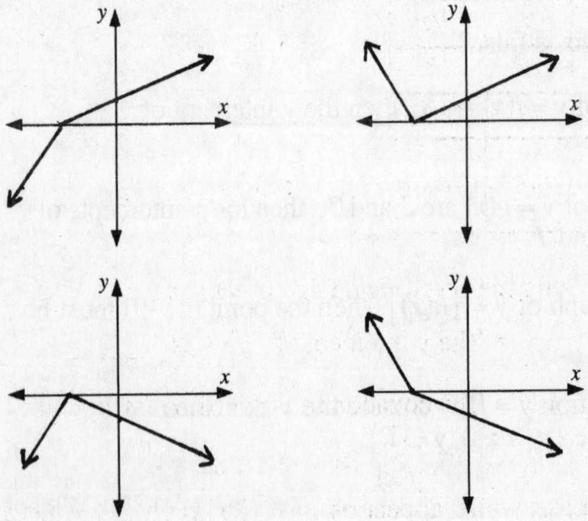

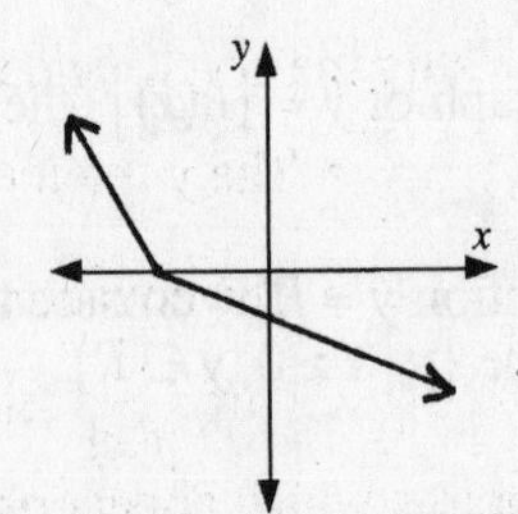

4.

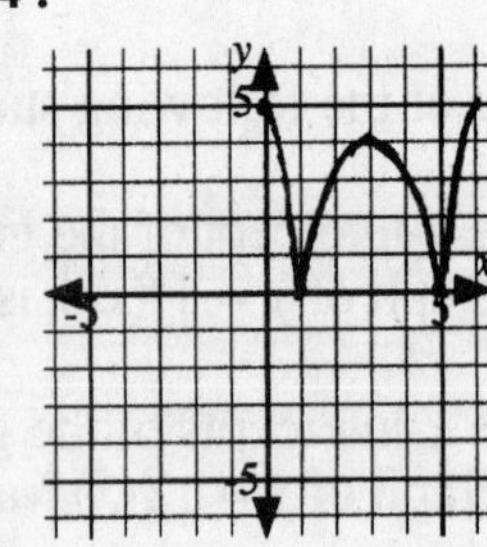

5. a)
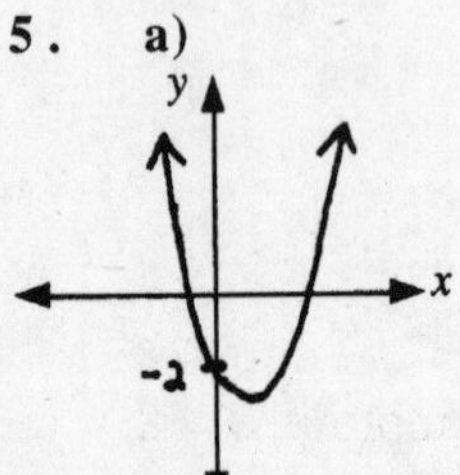

b)
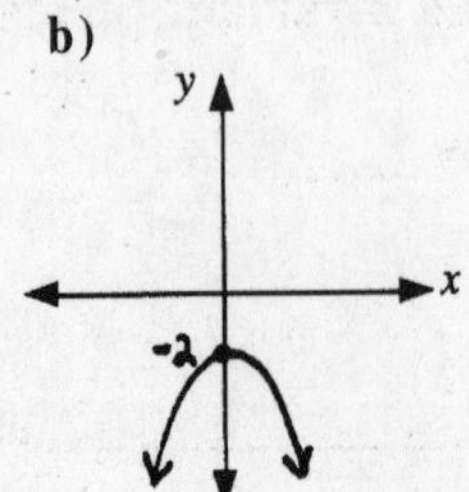

c)
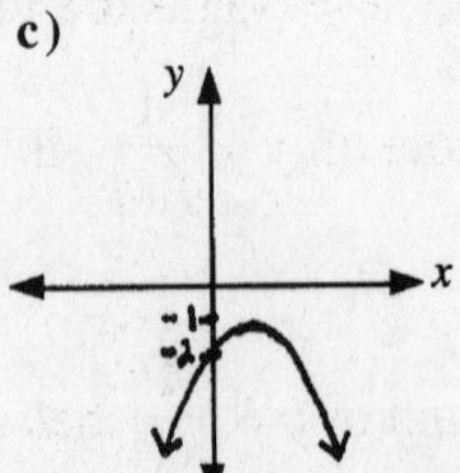

6. C 7. C

Absolute Value Functions and Reciprocal Functions Lesson #5: Reciprocal Functions

Reciprocal Functions

The reciprocal function of $f(x)$ is $\dfrac{1}{f(x)}$. For example, if a function has the equation $y = x^2 - 5$, the reciprocal function has equation $y = \dfrac{1}{x^2 - 5}$.

Exploring a Reciprocal Function

1.a) Consider the function $f(x)$ with equation $y = x + 3$.
Write the equation of the reciprocal function.

b) The graphs of $y = f(x)$ and $y = \dfrac{1}{f(x)}$ and a partial table of values are shown.

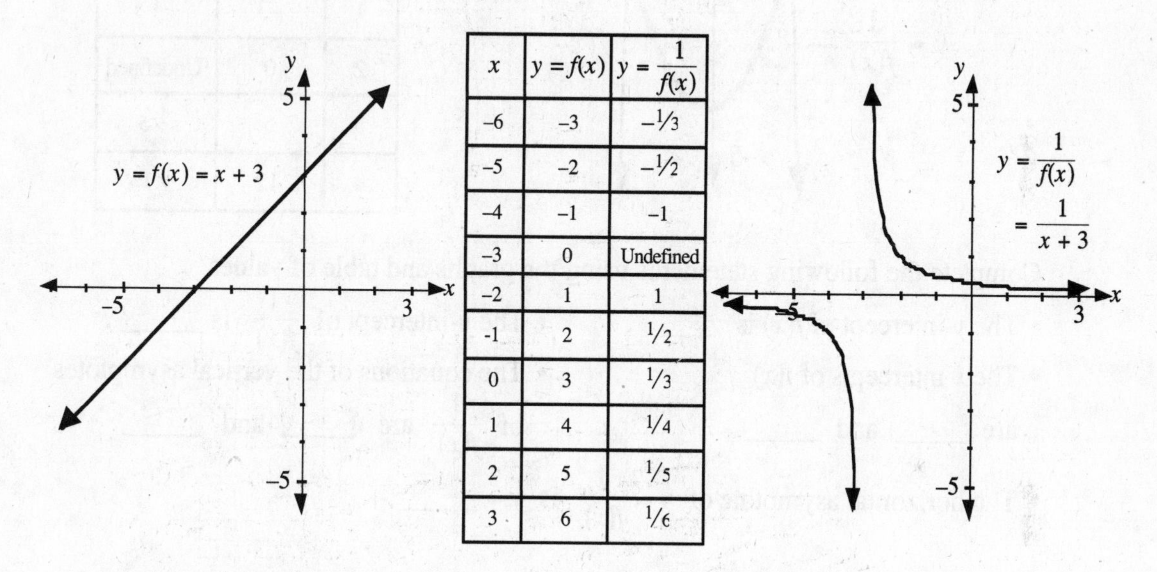

x	$y = f(x)$	$y = \dfrac{1}{f(x)}$
–6	–3	–⅓
–5	–2	–½
–4	–1	–1
–3	0	Undefined
–2	1	1
-1	2	½
0	3	⅓
1	4	¼
2	5	⅕
3	6	⅙

Complete the following statements using the graphs and table of values.

- The y-intercept of $f(x)$ is ______ .
- The y-intercept of $\dfrac{1}{f(x)}$ is ______ .
- The x-intercept of $f(x)$ is ______ .
- The equation of the vertical asymptote of $\dfrac{1}{f(x)}$ is $x =$ ______ .
- State the coordinates of the two points which appear on **both** the graph of $y = f(x)$ and the graph of $y = \dfrac{1}{f(x)}$. These points are called **invariant points**.
- The horizontal asymptote of $y = \dfrac{1}{f(x)}$ is $y =$ ______ .

c) Complete the following:

- When $f(x) = 0$, the graph of $y = \dfrac{1}{f(x)}$ has a ______________ asymptote.
- As $f(x)$ approaches $\pm\,\infty$, (positive or negative infinity), the graph of $y = \dfrac{1}{f(x)}$ approaches closer to the ______________ asymptote.

2.a) Consider the function $f(x)$ with equation $y = x^2 - 4$.
Write the equation of the reciprocal function.

b) The graphs of $y = f(x)$ and $y = \frac{1}{f(x)}$ and a partial table of values are shown.

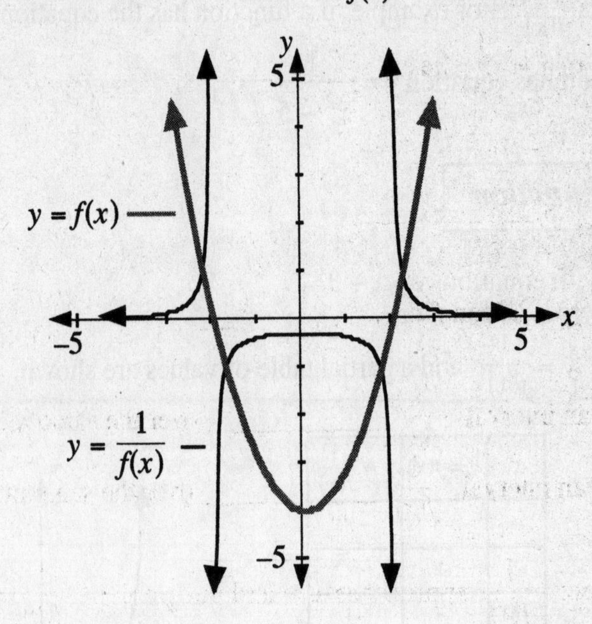

x	$y = f(x)$	$y = \frac{1}{f(x)}$
-4	12	1/12
-3	5	1/5
−2	0	Undefined
−1	−3	−1/3
0	−4	−1/4
1	−3	−1/3
2	0	Undefined
3	5	1/5
4	12	1/12

Complete the following statements using the graphs and table of values.

- The y-intercept of $f(x)$ is _____ .
- The y-intercept of $\frac{1}{f(x)}$ is _____ .
- The x-intercepts of $f(x)$ are _____ and _____ .
- The equations of the vertical asymptotes of $\frac{1}{f(x)}$ are _____ and _____ .
- The horizontal asymptote of $y = \frac{1}{f(x)}$ is $y =$ _____ .

c) In example 1 of the previous page we were able to determine the invariant points of the graphs of $f(x)$ and $\frac{1}{f(x)}$ by using the table of values for $y = \pm 1$. Explain why we can use the lines $y = \pm 1$ to find the invariant points of the graphs of $f(x)$ and $\frac{1}{f(x)}$. Mark these points on the above sketch.

d) Complete the following:

- When $f(x) =$ ____, the graph of $y = \frac{1}{f(x)}$ has vertical asymptotes.
- As $f(x)$ approaches ____________, the graph of $y = \frac{1}{f(x)}$ approaches closer to the horizontal asymptote with equation $y =$ ____ .

Properties of Reciprocal Transformations

Complete the following statements based on the exploration on the previous two pages.

1. • When $f(x) = 0$, the graph of $y = \frac{1}{f(x)}$ has a ____________ ____________ .
   • When $f(x)$ is positive, $\frac{1}{f(x)}$ is ____________ .
   • When $f(x)$ is negative, $\frac{1}{f(x)}$ is ____________ .

2. • When $f(x) = 1$, $\frac{1}{f(x)}$ = ____ . When $f(x) = -1$, $\frac{1}{f(x)}$ = ____ .

3. • When $f(x)$ increases over an interval, $\frac{1}{f(x)}$ ____________ over the same interval.
   • When $f(x)$ decreases over an interval, $\frac{1}{f(x)}$ ____________ over the same interval.

4. • When $f(x)$ approaches zero, $\frac{1}{f(x)}$ approaches $\pm\infty$ and the graph of $\frac{1}{f(x)}$ approaches a ____________ asymptote.
   • When $f(x)$ approaches $\pm\infty$, $\frac{1}{f(x)}$ approaches zero and the graph of $\frac{1}{f(x)}$ approaches a ____________ asymptote.

Suggestions for Sketching the Graph of a Reciprocal Function

1. Zeros of the original function become vertical asymptotes of the reciprocal function.
2. Mark the **invariant points** where $y = 1$ and $y = -1$.
3. The y-intercept of the reciprocal graph is the reciprocal of the y-intercept on the original graph.
4. Points where $y = 2$ on the original graph become points where $y = \frac{1}{2}$ on the reciprocal graph, etc.
5. Complete the reciprocal graph based on the information above.

The graph of $y = f(x)$ is shown.
The x-intercept is 2 and the y-intercept is 3.

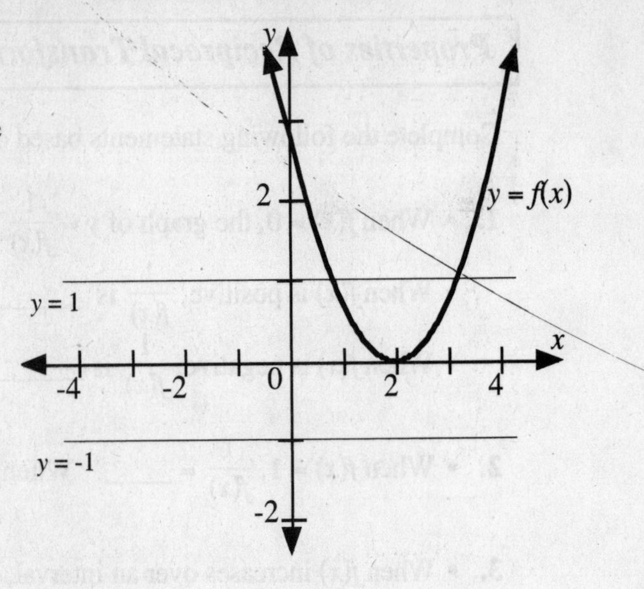

a) Use the suggestions on the previous page to sketch the graph of $y = \dfrac{1}{f(x)}$.
The lines with equations $y = 1$ and $y = -1$ have been provided as a guide.

b) State the y-intercept of the graph of $y = \dfrac{1}{f(x)}$.

c) Given that the graph of $f(x)$ has equation $y = \dfrac{3}{4}(x - 2)^2$, state the equation of $y = \dfrac{1}{f(x)}$.

d) Use a graphing calculator to verify the graph drawn in a).

The graph of the quadratic function $y = f(x)$ is shown.

The x-intercepts of the graph are integers, and the maximum value of f is 2.

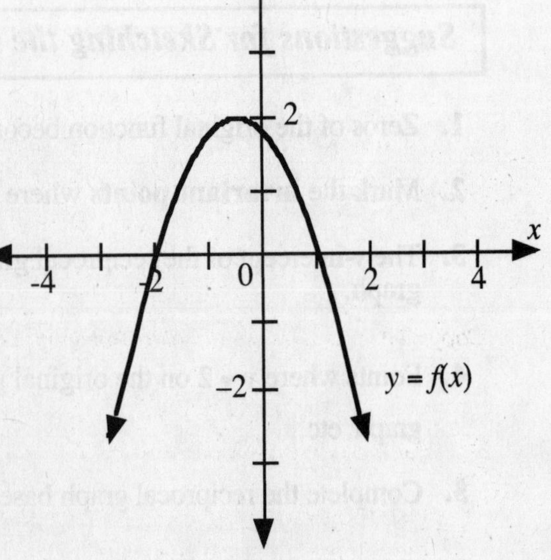

a) Sketch the graph of $y = \dfrac{1}{f(x)}$.

b) State the equations of the asymptotes of the graph of $y = \dfrac{1}{f(x)}$.

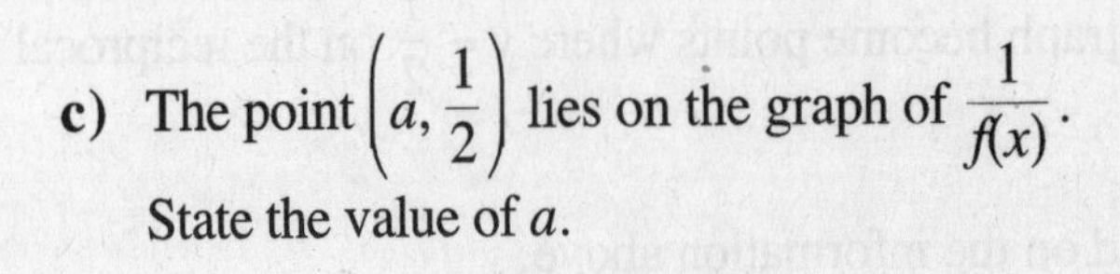

c) The point $\left(a, \dfrac{1}{2}\right)$ lies on the graph of $\dfrac{1}{f(x)}$.

State the value of a.

Complete Assignment Questions #1 - #8

The graph of $g(x) = \dfrac{1}{f(x)}$ is shown.
The maximum point of $g(x)$ is at $(-3, 2)$ and the y-intercept of $g(x)$ is $\dfrac{1}{5}$.

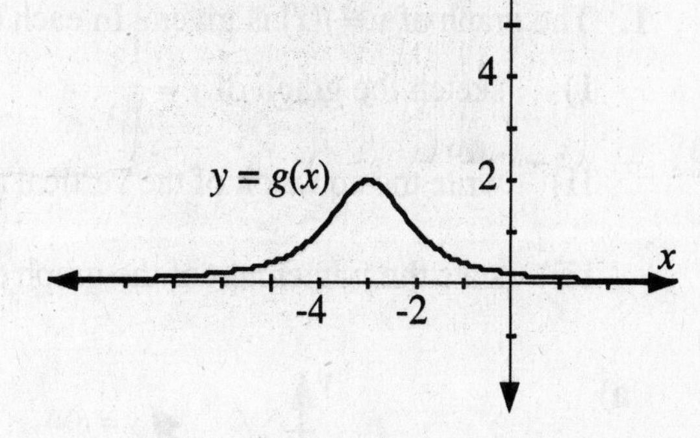

a) Given that $f(x)$ is a quadratic function, sketch the graph of $y = f(x)$ on the grid and state the coordinates of the minimum point.

b) $f(x)$ can be written in the form $y = a(x - p)^2 + q$. Determine the values of $a, p,$ and q.

Complete Assignment Questions #9 - #13

Assignment

1. The graph of $y = f(x)$ is given. In each case:

i) sketch the graph of $y = \dfrac{1}{f(x)}$

ii) write the equation of the vertical asymptote of the graph of $y = \dfrac{1}{f(x)}$

iii) state the y-intercept of the graph of $y = \dfrac{1}{f(x)}$

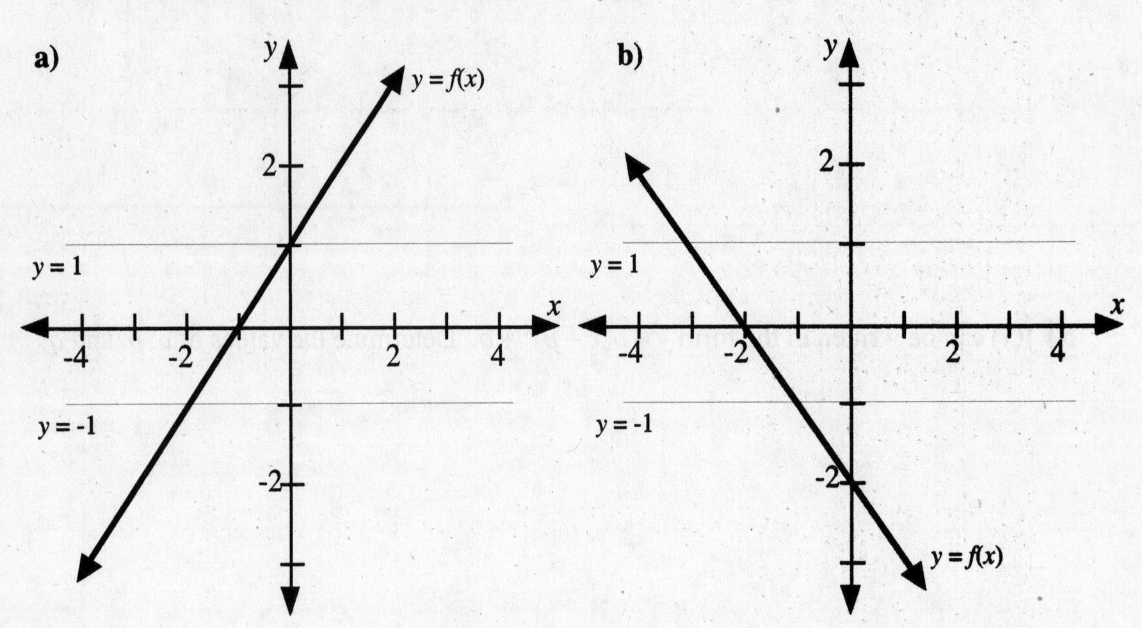

2. The graph of $y = f(x)$ is given. In each case sketch the graph of $y = \dfrac{1}{f(x)}$.

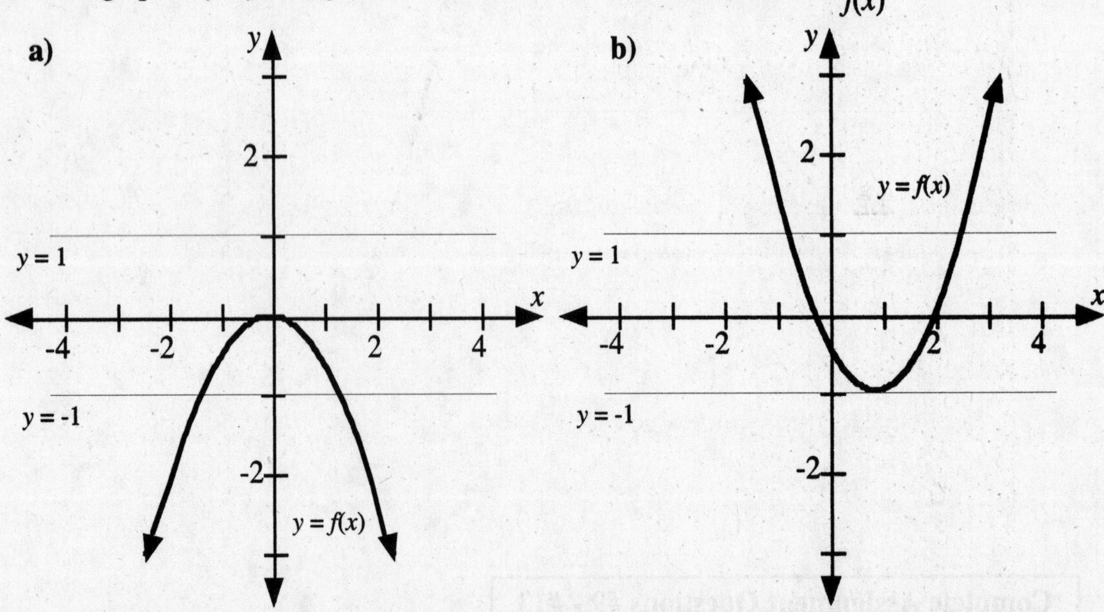

3. The graphs of $y = f(x)$ and $y = g(x)$ are shown. Sketch the graphs of $y = \dfrac{1}{f(x)}$ and $y = \dfrac{1}{g(x)}$ and explain why neither graph has a y-intercept.

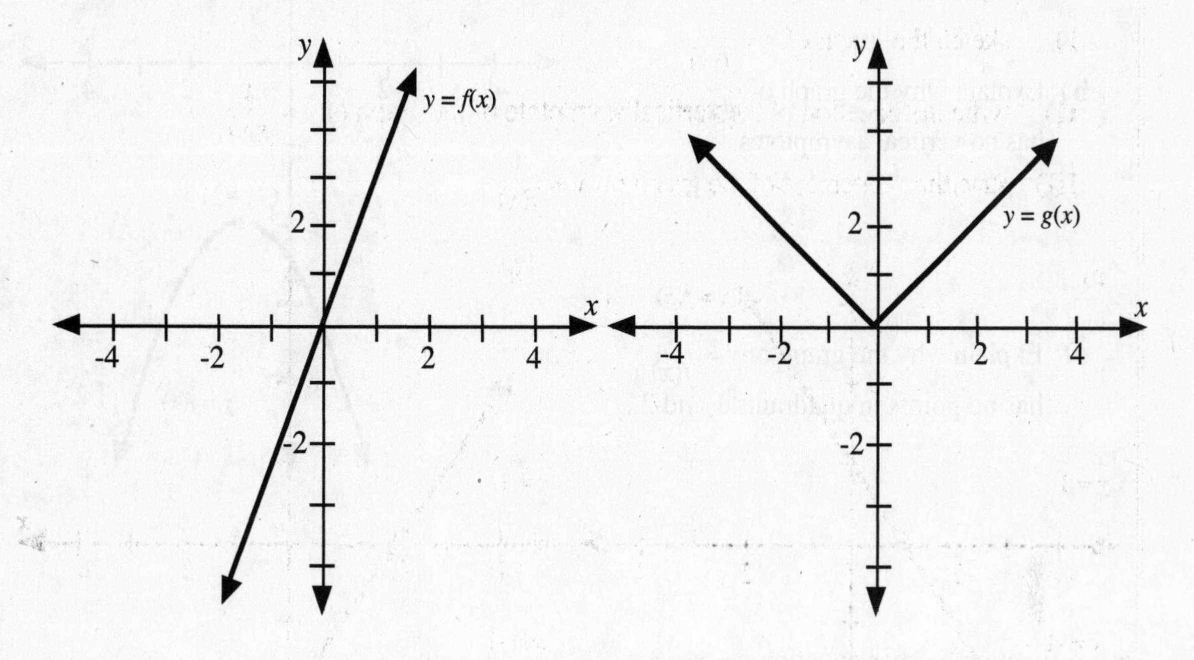

4. The graph of $y = f(x)$ is shown.
The y-intercept of the graph is 2.

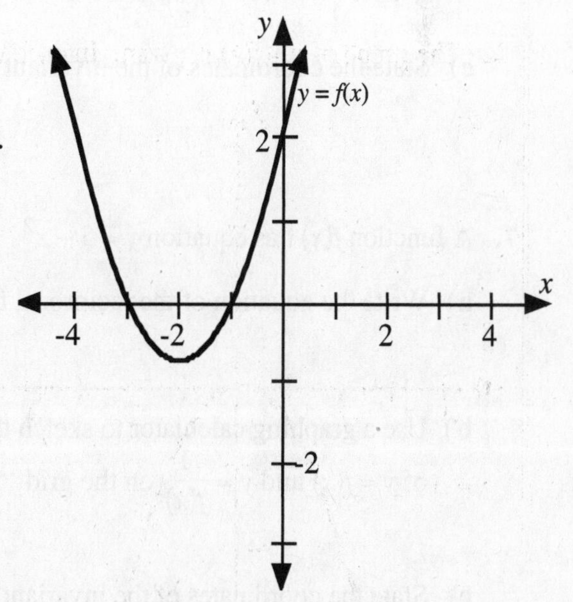

a) State the y-intercept of the graph of $\dfrac{1}{f(x)}$.

b) If the graph of $y = \dfrac{1}{f(x)}$ passes through the point $(-2, -1.25)$, sketch the graph of $\dfrac{1}{f(x)}$ on the grid.

c) Determine the minimum value of f.

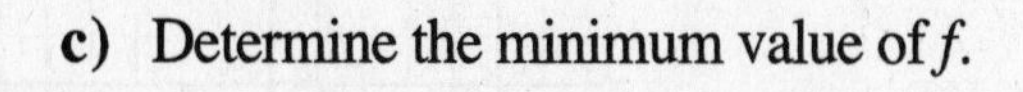

5. a) Use the information given to sketch the graph of $y = \dfrac{1}{f(x)}$.

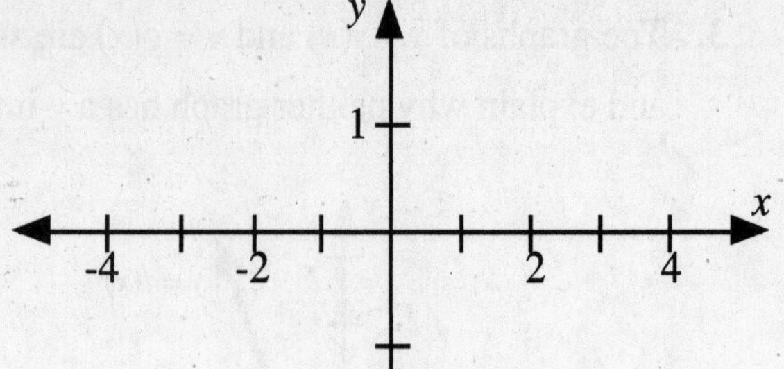

b) Explain why the graph of $\dfrac{1}{f(x)}$ has no vertical asymptotes.

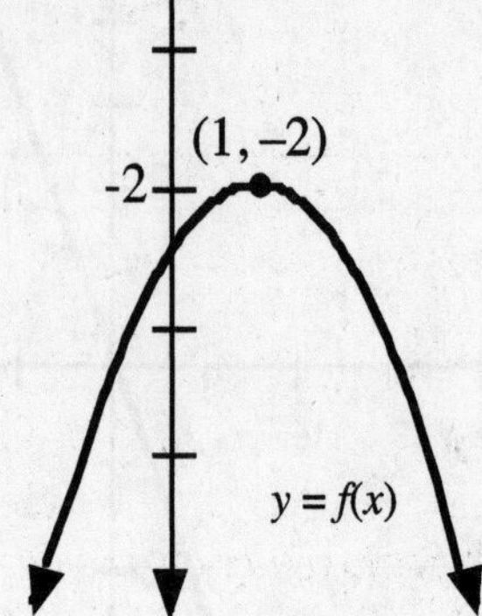

c) Explain why the graph of $y = \dfrac{1}{f(x)}$ has no points in quadrants 1 and 2.

6. A function $f(x)$ has equation $y = x + 3$.

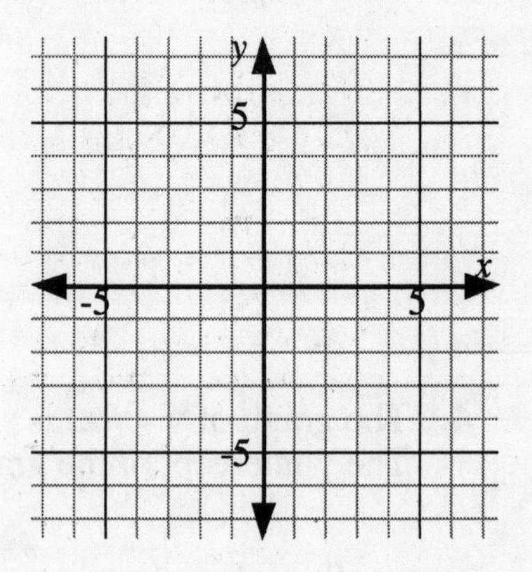

a) Write the equation of the reciprocal function.

b) Use a graphing calculator to sketch the graph of $y = f(x)$ and $y = \dfrac{1}{f(x)}$ on the grid.

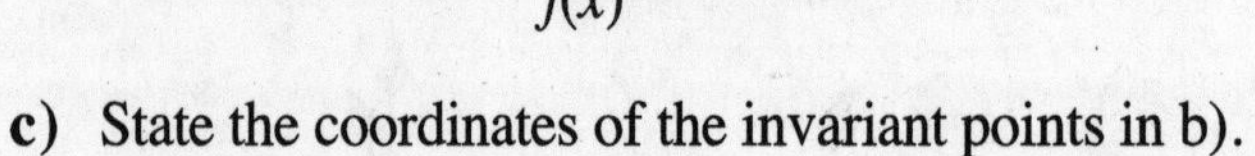

c) State the coordinates of the invariant points in b).

7. A function $f(x)$ has equation $y = 5 - x^2$.

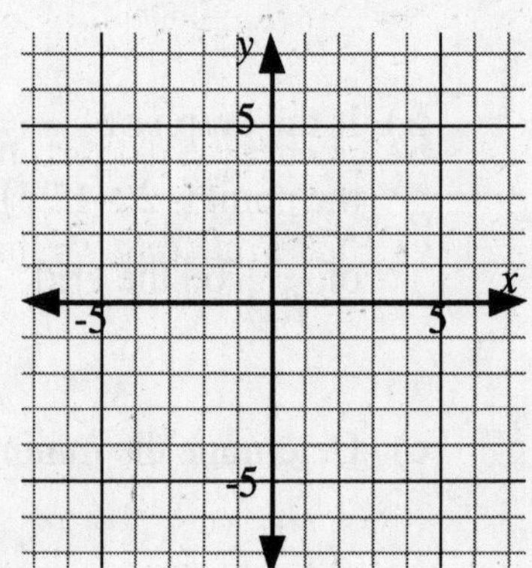

a) Write the equation of the reciprocal function.

b) Use a graphing calculator to sketch the graph of $y = f(x)$ and $y = \dfrac{1}{f(x)}$ on the grid.

c) State the coordinates of the invariant points in quadrant 1.

8. a) Sketch the graphs of:

i) $y = x$ **ii)** $y = \dfrac{1}{x}$

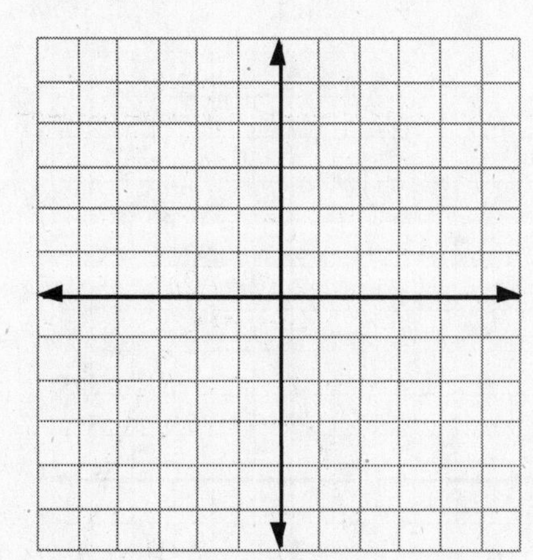

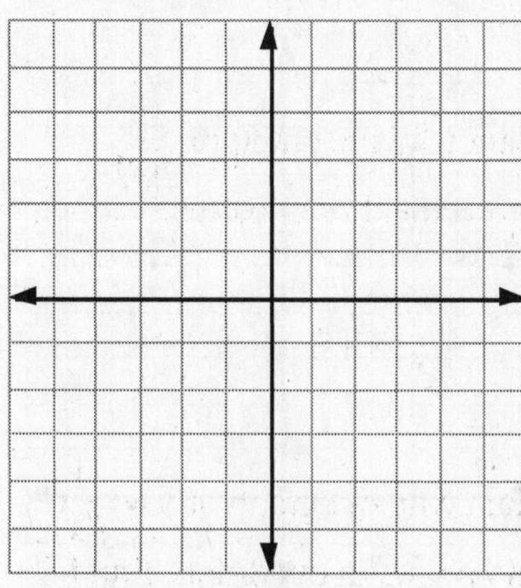

b) State the coordinates of the invariant points on the graphs above.

9. The graph of $g(x) = \dfrac{1}{f(x)}$, where $f(x)$ is a linear function, is shown. The graph of $y = g(x)$ has a y-intercept of 1 and a vertical asymptote with equation $x = -1$.

a) Describe a strategy for sketching the graph of $y = f(x)$ on the grid.

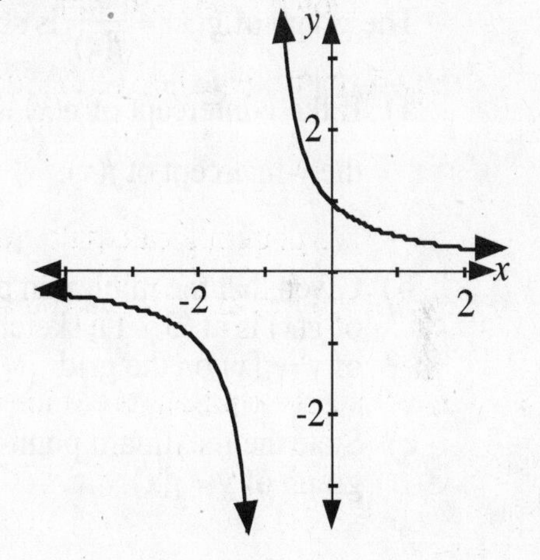

b) Sketch the graph of $y = f(x)$ on the grid.

c) If the function $f(x)$ has equation $y = ax + b$, determine the values of a and b.

10. a) Sketch the graphs of:

i) $y = x^2$ **ii)** $y = \dfrac{1}{x^2}$

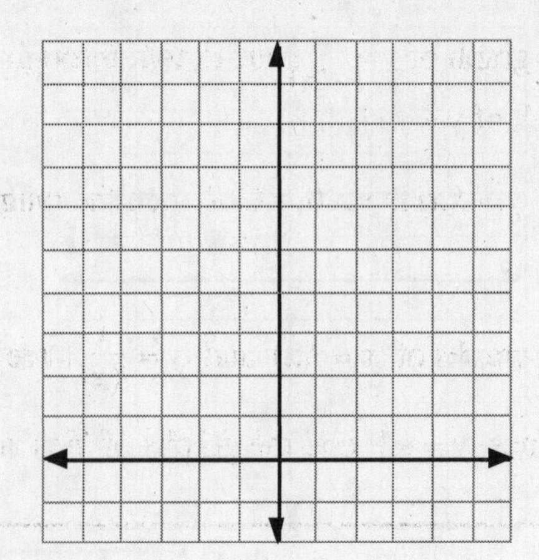

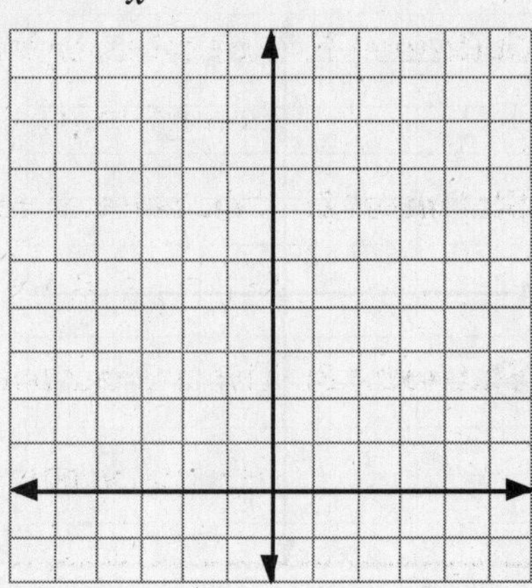

b) State the coordinates of the invariant points on the graphs above.

11. Consider the quadratic function $f(x) = ax^2 + bx + c$.

The graph of $g(x) = \dfrac{1}{f(x)}$ is shown.

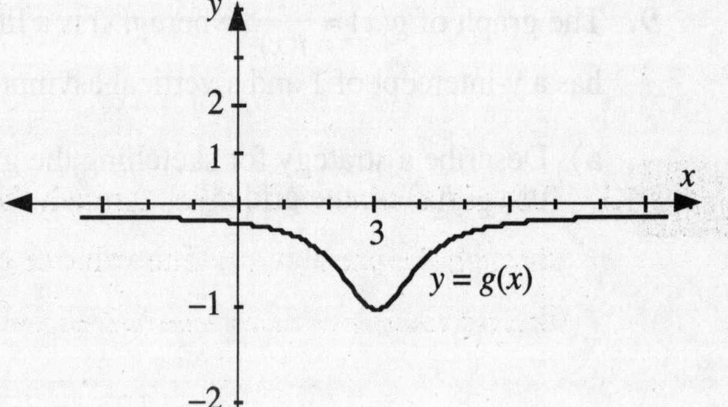

a) If the y-intercept of $g(x)$ is $-\dfrac{1}{3}$, state the y-intercept of $f(x)$.

b) Given that the minimum point of $g(x)$ is at $(3, -1)$, sketch the graph of $y = f(x)$ on the grid.

c) State the maximum point on the graph of $y = f(x)$.

d) Express $f(x)$ in the form $f(x) = a(x - p)^2 + q$.

e) Express $f(x)$ in the form $f(x) = ax^2 + bx + c$.

Use the following information to answer the next question.

A student made the following statements about reciprocal functions.

Statement 1: Vertical asymptotes on the graph of $y = \dfrac{1}{f(x)}$ are drawn through the x-intercepts on the graph of $y = f(x)$.

Statement 2: If the range of the graph of $y = f(x)$ is $y > 0, y \in R$, then the range of $y = \dfrac{1}{f(x)}$ is $y < 0, y \in R$.

Statement 3: The invariant points of the graphs of $y = f(x)$ and $y = \dfrac{1}{f(x)}$ are the intersection points of the lines $y = \pm 1$ and the graphs of $f(x)$ and $\dfrac{1}{f(x)}$.

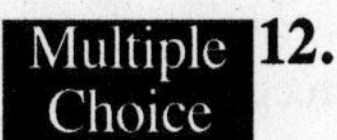

12. Which of the student's statements are true?

A. 1 and 2 only **B.** 1 and 3 only **C.** 2 and 3 only **D.** 1, 2, and 3

13. The graph of $y = f(x)$ passes through the point $(4, 6)$. The graph of $y = \dfrac{1}{f(x)}$ passes through the point $(4, p)$. The value of p to the nearest hundredth is _____ .

(Record your answer in the numerical response box from left to right.)

Answer Key

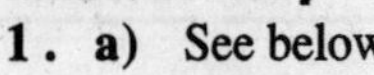

1. a) See below **b)** See below

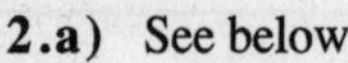

2. a) See below **b)** See below

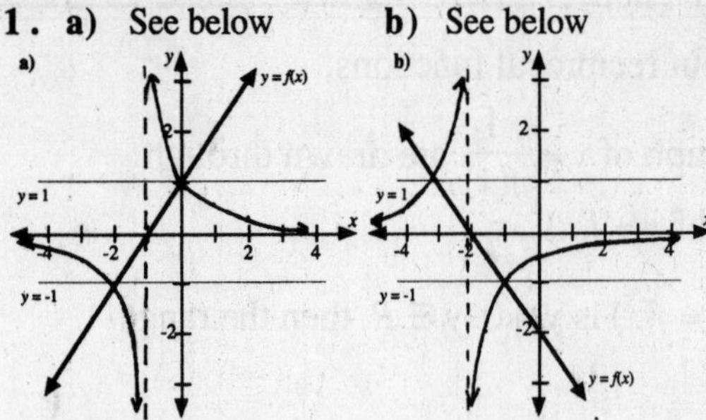

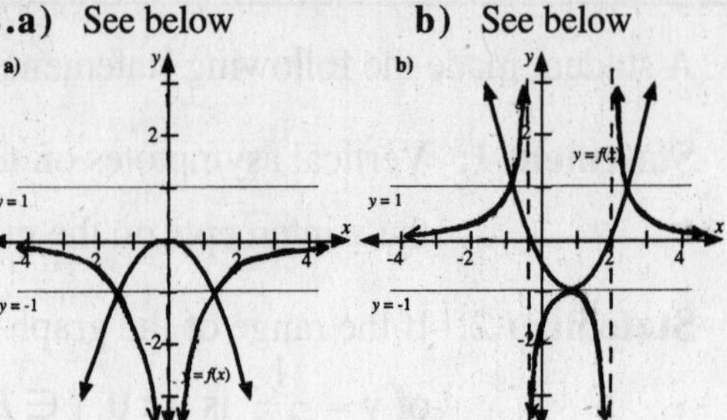

ii) $x = -1$ **iii)** 1 **ii)** $x = -2$ **iii)** $-\frac{1}{2}$

3. See below.

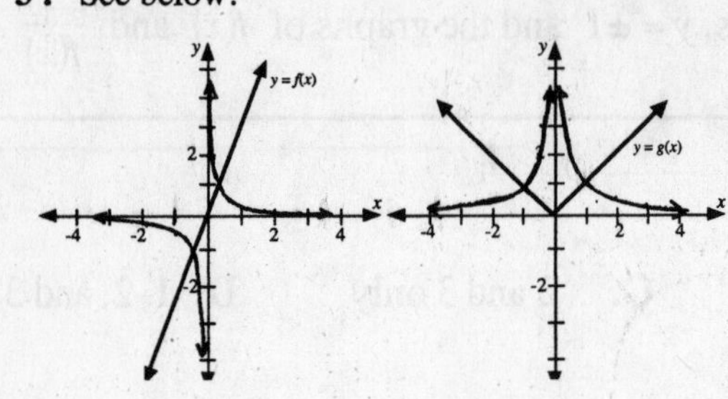

Both $y = f(x)$ and $y = g(x)$ have a y-intercept of 0 and an x-intercept of 0.

The graphs of $y = \dfrac{1}{f(x)}$ and $y = \dfrac{1}{g(x)}$ have asymptotes with equation $x = 0$, and so do not have any y-intercepts.

4. a) $\dfrac{1}{2}$

b) See graph at the right

c) $\left(-2, -\frac{5}{4}\right)$ lies on $y = \frac{1}{f(x)}$ so $\left(-2, -\frac{4}{5}\right)$ lies on $y = f(x)$.

minimum value $f = -\frac{4}{5}$ or -0.8

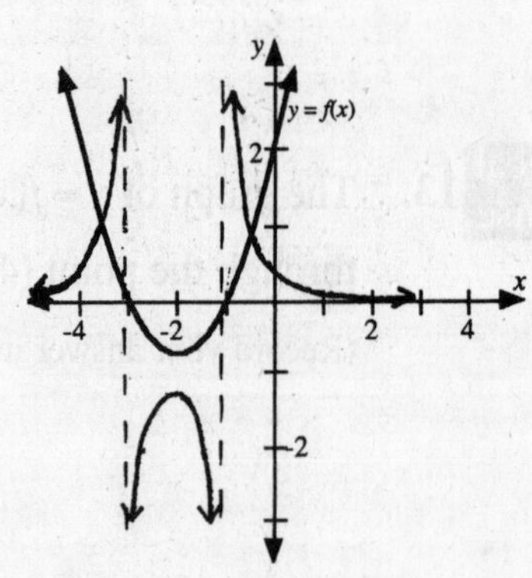

5. a) See graph at the right.

b) The graph of $y = f(x)$ has no x-intercepts, so the graph of $y = f(x)$ has no vertical asymptotes.

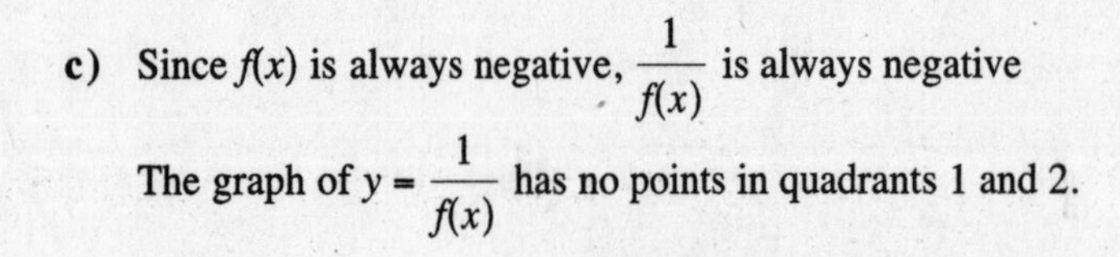

c) Since $f(x)$ is always negative, $\dfrac{1}{f(x)}$ is always negative

The graph of $y = \dfrac{1}{f(x)}$ has no points in quadrants 1 and 2.

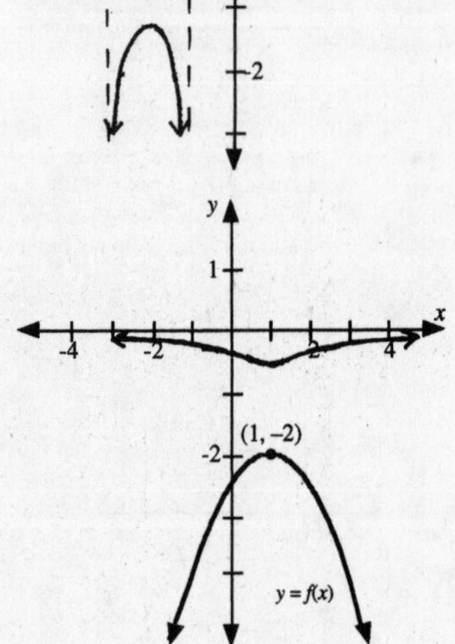

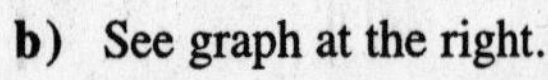

6. a) $y = \dfrac{1}{x + 3}$

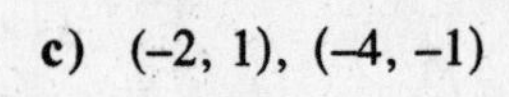

b) See graph at the right.

c) $(-2, 1)$, $(-4, -1)$

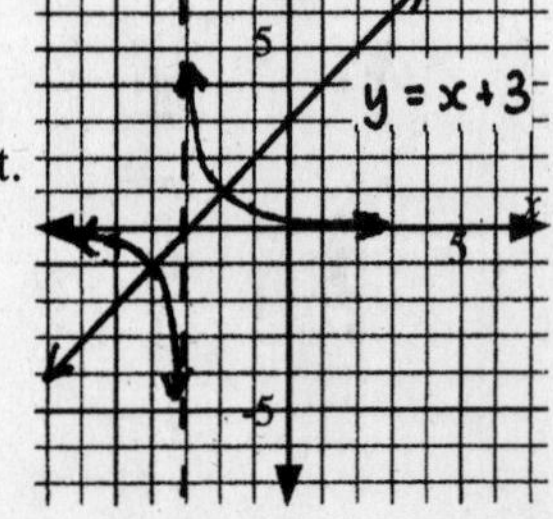

7. a) $y = \dfrac{1}{5 - x^2}$

b) See graph below

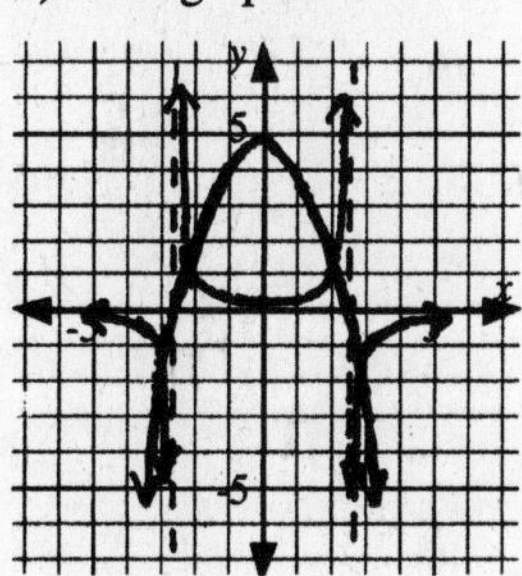

c) (2, 1)

8. a) i) See graph below **ii)** See graph below

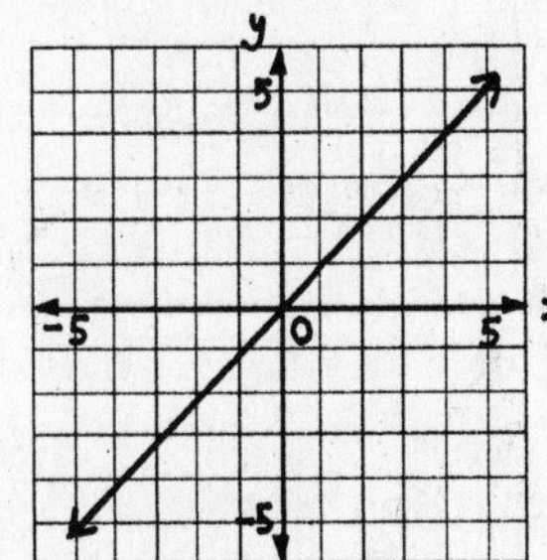

b) For both graphs, the invariant points are (1, 1) and (–1, –1).

9. a) The asymptote of $y = g(x)$ becomes a zero of $y = f(x)$.

b) See graph to the right

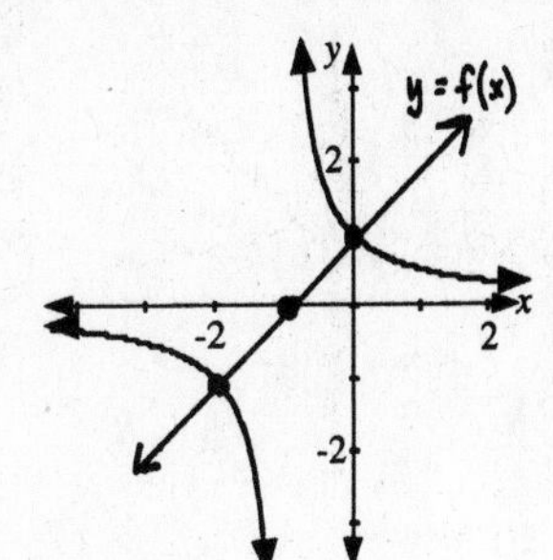

c) Points (0, 1) and (–1, 0).
Slope = 1, so $a = 1$
y-intercept = 1, so $b = 1$
$y = x + 1$.

10. a) i) See graph below **ii)** See graph below

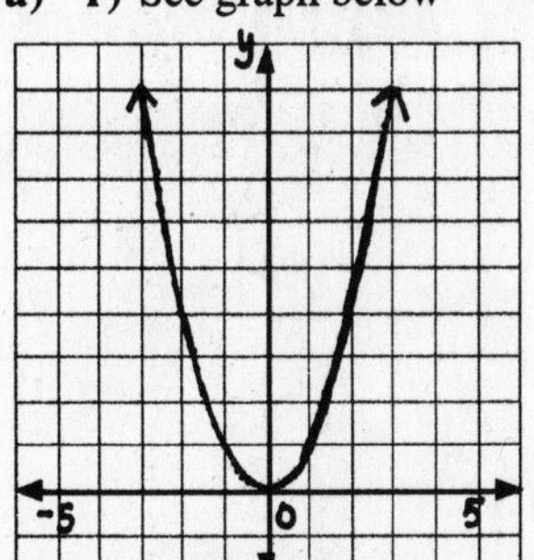

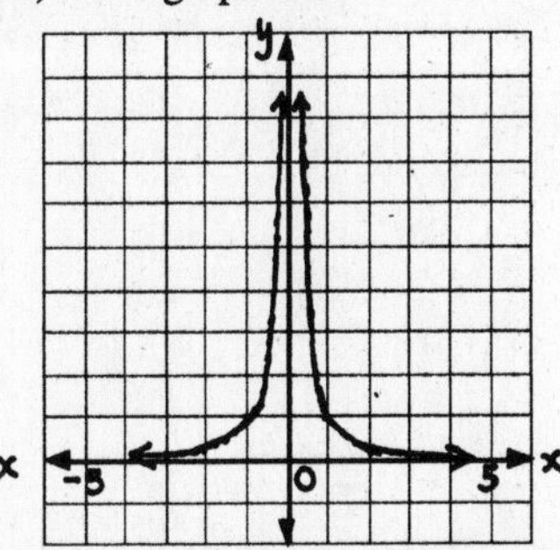

b) For both graphs, the invariant points are (1, 1) and (–1, 1).

11. a) –3

b) See graph at the right.

c) (3, –1)

d) $f(x) = -\dfrac{2}{9}(x - 3)^2 - 1$

e) $f(x) = -\dfrac{2}{9}x^2 + \dfrac{4}{3}x - 3$

12. B **13.**

0	.	1	7

Absolute Value Functions and Reciprocal Functions Lesson #6: Practice Test

Use the following information to answer question #1.

> A student made the following statements:
>
> **Statement 1:** The absolute value of a real number is the principal square root of the square of the number.
>
> **Statement 2:** The absolute value of a real number is the distance of the number from zero on a number line.
>
> **Statement 3:** The absolute value of a real number can never be negative.

1. The statements which are correct are

A. **1** and **2** only **B.** **1** and **3** only
C. **2** and **3** only **D.** **1, 2,** and **3**

2. The absolute value function $g(x) = |5 - x|$ can be written as a piecewise function. The piecewise function which represents $g(x)$ is

A. $g(x) = \begin{cases} 5 - x & \text{if } x \le 5 \\ -x + 5 & \text{if } x > 5 \end{cases}$

B. $g(x) = \begin{cases} 5 - x & \text{if } x \le 5 \\ x + 5 & \text{if } x > 5 \end{cases}$

C. $g(x) = \begin{cases} x - 5 & \text{if } x \le 5 \\ 5 - x & \text{if } x > 5 \end{cases}$

D. $g(x) = \begin{cases} x - 5 & \text{if } x \ge 5 \\ 5 - x & \text{if } x < 5 \end{cases}$

1. The value of $|7| - |-6| + |-\sqrt[3]{-64}|$, is _____ .

(Record your answer in the numerical response box from left to right.)

3. Which one of the following statements is false?

A. $|-2x| = -2x$, if $x < 0$

B. $|6 - 7x| = -6 + 7x$, if $x \geq \frac{6}{7}$

C. $|5 - x| = 5 - x$, if $x \geq 5$

D. $|4x + 3| = 4x + 3$, if $x \geq -\frac{3}{4}$

4. Which of the following is a root of the equation $|3x - 1| = -5$?

A. 2
B. -3
C. $-\frac{4}{3}$
D. There are no roots of the equation $|3x - 1| = -5$.

5. The complete solution to $12 - |x| = 9$ is

A. 3
B. -3
C. 3 and -3
D. none of the above

2. The equation $|x - 2| = x^2 - 5$ has two solutions. Gavin determines the solutions using a graphing calculator. If these solutions are $x = p$ and $x = q$, then the value of $|pq|$, to the nearest tenth, is _____ .

(Record your answer in the numerical response box from left to right.)

6. For which of the following functions is the graph of $y = |f(x)|$ identical to the graph of $y = f(x)$?

A. $f(x) = 2x$ **B.** $f(x) = -2x$

C. $f(x) = 2x^2$ **D.** $f(x) = -2x^2$

7. If the graph of $y = f(x)$ passes through the point $\left(-\frac{1}{2}, -\frac{2}{3}\right)$, then the graph of $y = |f(x)|$ must pass through the point

A. $\left(\frac{1}{2}, \frac{2}{3}\right)$ **B.** $\left(-\frac{1}{2}, \frac{2}{3}\right)$

C. $\left(\frac{1}{2}, -\frac{2}{3}\right)$ **D.** $\left(-\frac{1}{2}, -\frac{2}{3}\right)$

Use the following information to answer the next question.

> Students are solving the equation $|6x - 3| = 4x - 5$.
>
> Quinn solves the equation graphically and correctly determines there is no solution to the equation.
>
> Maddy solves the equation algebraically. In the course of her work, she correctly determines two solutions, both of which must be rejected.

3. One of the solutions which Maddy rejects is a positive number and the other is a negative number. To the nearest tenth, the value of the positive number which Maddy rejects is _____ .

(Record your answer in the numerical response box from left to right.)

8. The roots of the equation $|x^2 + 2x - 10| = 5$ are $-5, 3$, and $-1 \pm \sqrt{N}$. The value of N is

A. 6

B. 8

C. 12

D. 24

Numerical Response

4. To the nearest hundredth, the largest root of the equation $4 - |3x^2 - 5x + 1| = 0$, is _____ .

(Record your answer in the numerical response box from left to right.)

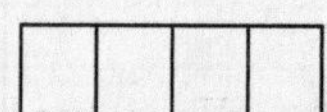

9. Consider a function $f(x)$ which is negative and decreasing on the interval $0 \le x \le 6, x \in R$. Which one of the following statements is true?

A. $|f(x)|$ is increasing on the interval $0 \le x \le 6, x \in R$ and $\frac{1}{f(x)}$ is decreasing on the interval $0 \le x \le 6, x \in R$.

B. $|f(x)|$ is decreasing on the interval $0 \le x \le 6, x \in R$ and $\frac{1}{f(x)}$ is increasing on the interval $0 \le x \le 6, x \in R$.

C. Both $|f(x)|$ and $\frac{1}{f(x)}$ are increasing on the interval $0 \le x \le 6, x \in R$.

D. Both $|f(x)|$ and $\frac{1}{f(x)}$ are decreasing on the interval $0 \le x \le 6, x \in R$.

10. If the graph of $y = g(x)$ passes through the point $\left(-\frac{1}{2}, -\frac{2}{3}\right)$, then the graph of $y = \frac{1}{f(x)}$ must pass through the point

A. $\left(\frac{1}{2}, \frac{2}{3}\right)$ **B.** $\left(-\frac{1}{2}, -\frac{3}{2}\right)$

C. $\left(-2, -\frac{2}{3}\right)$ **D.** $\left(-\frac{1}{2}, \frac{2}{3}\right)$

11. The points $A(4,-1)$, $B(1,4)$, $C(-2,1)$, $D(-1,0)$ lie on the graph of $y = P(x)$. Which one of these points must lie on both the graph of $y = |P(x)|$ and the graph of $y = \frac{1}{P(x)}$?

A. A
B. B
C. C
D. D

12. Which of the following statements is true for all functions?

A. The domain of $\frac{1}{f(x)}$ is the same as the domain of $f(x)$.

B. The domain of $|f(x)|$ is the same as the domain of $f(x)$.

C. The range of $\frac{1}{f(x)}$ is the same as the domain of $f(x)$.

D. The range of $|f(x)|$ is the same as the domain of $f(x)$.

13. The range of $y = f(x)$ is $-7 \leq y \leq 1$. The range of $y = \frac{1}{f(x)}$ is

A. $y \leq -\frac{1}{7}, y \geq 1$

B. $y \leq -7, y \geq 1$

C. $-7 \leq y \leq 1, y \neq 0$

D. $-\frac{1}{7} \leq y \leq 1, y \neq 0$

Use the following information to answer questions #14 and #15.

Consider the function $f(x) = \dfrac{1}{x^2 - x - 6}$.

14. The graph of $f(x)$ has a vertical asymptote with equation

A. $x = 1$ **B.** $x = 2$

C. $x = 3$ **D.** $x = 6$

15. The minimum value of $\dfrac{1}{f(x)}$ is

A. $-\dfrac{25}{4}$ **B.** $-\dfrac{4}{25}$

C. 0.5 **D.** -6

Use the following information to answer the next question.

The partial graph of $g(x) = \dfrac{1}{f(x)}$ is shown.

The maximum point of $g(x)$ is at $(2, 4)$

and the y-intercept of $g(x)$ is 2.

y
y = g(x)
0
x

Numerical Response **5.** Given that $f(x)$ is a quadratic function, the equation of $f(x)$, can be written in the form $y = a(x - p)^2 + q$. The value of $a + p + q$, to the nearest tenth, is _____.

(Record your answer in the numerical response box from left to right.)

Written Response - 5 marks

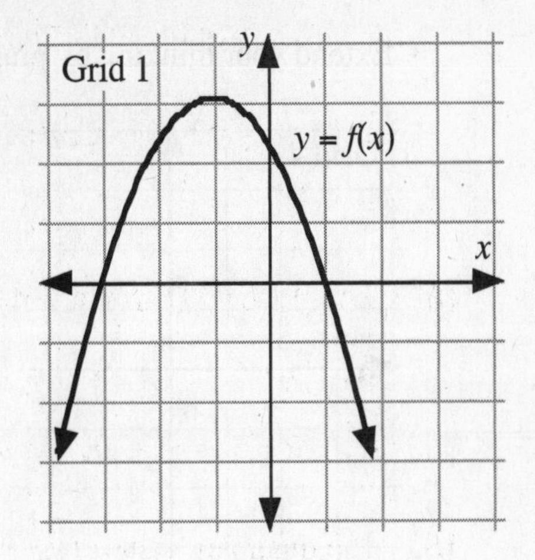

1. Consider the graph of $y = f(x)$ shown on Grid 1.

- Describe a strategy for graphing $y = |f(x)|$.

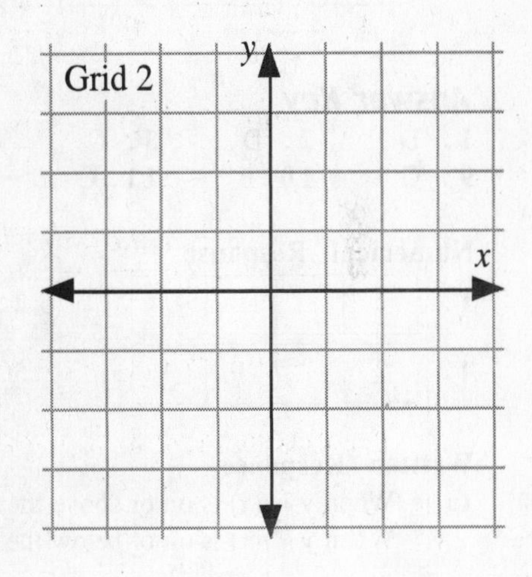

- Sketch the graph of $y = |f(x)|$ on Grid 2.

- Describe a strategy for graphing $y = \frac{1}{f(x)}$.

- Sketch the graph of $y = \frac{1}{f(x)}$ on Grid 3.

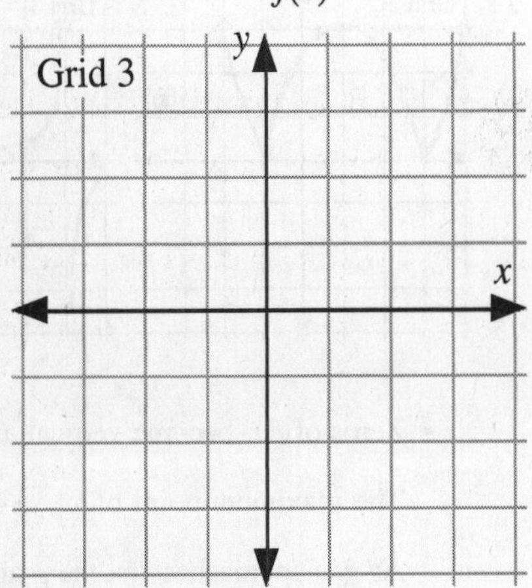

- Extend your thinking by graphing $y = \left|\frac{1}{f(x)}\right|$ and $y = \frac{1}{|f(x)|}$.

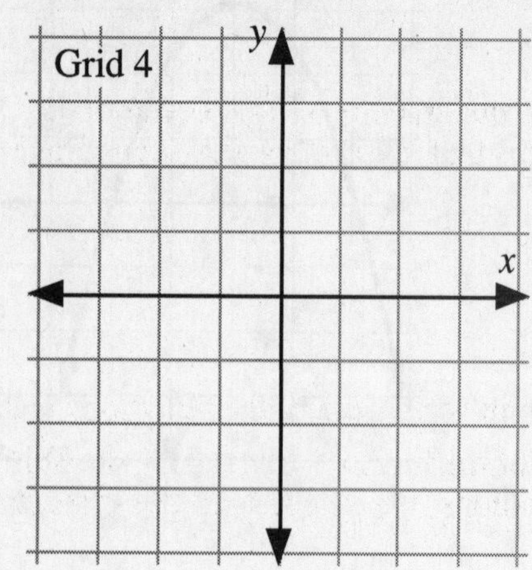

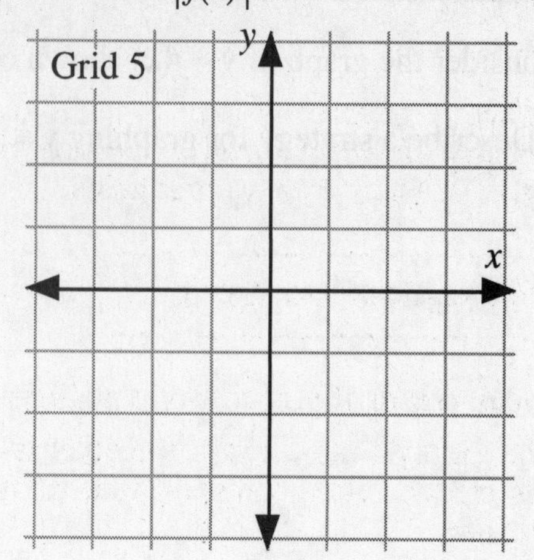

Answer Key

1. D	2. D	3. C	4. D	5. C	6. C	7. B	8. A
9. C	10. B	11. C	12. B	13. A	14. C	15. A	

Numerical Response

1. | 5 | | | |

2. | 7 | . | 4 | |

3. | 0 | . | 8 | |

4. | 2 | . | 1 | 4 |

5. | 2 | . | 3 | |

Written Response

1. • When $y = f(x)$ is on or above the y-axis, the graph of $y = |f(x)|$ is identical.
When $y = f(x)$ is on or below the y-axis, the graph of $y = |f(x)|$ is a reflection in the x-axis.

- See Grid 2 below.

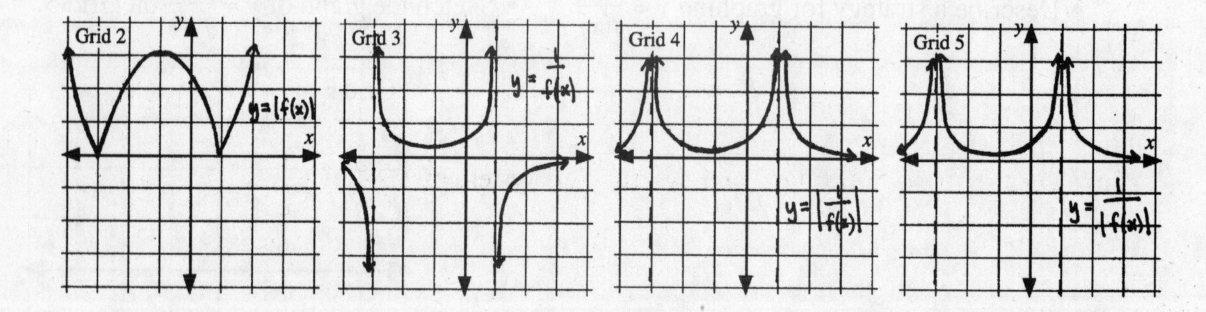

- Zeros of $f(x)$ become vertical asymptotes of $\frac{1}{f(x)}$. The points where $y = \pm 1$ are invariant.

  The maximum point of (x, y) on $f(x)$ becomes a local minimum point $\left(x, \frac{1}{y}\right)$ on $\frac{1}{f(x)}$.

  As $f(x)$ approaches $-\infty$, the graph of $\frac{1}{f(x)}$ approaches the x-axis.
  As $f(x)$ approaches 0, the graph of $\frac{1}{f(x)}$ approaches $\pm\infty$.

- See Grid 3 above.

- See Grids 4 and 5 above.

Linear and Quadratic Systems and Inequalities Lesson #1:
Solving a System of Linear-Quadratic Equations

Overview

In this unit, we solve systems of linear-quadratic and quadratic-quadratic **equations**, graphically and algebraically. We also solve problems that involve linear and quadratic **inequalities** in one or two variables.

Linear-Quadratic Systems

A **linear-quadratic** system of equations is a system in which one of the equations is linear (of the form $y = mx + b$) and the other is quadratic (of the form $y = ax^2 + bx + c$). When we determine the values of x and y that satisfy both equations, we have **solved the system of equations.**

In Calculus class, in order to determine the shaded area in the diagram between the parabola $y = x^2$ and the line $y = x + 6$, it is first of all necessary to determine the points of intersection of the parabola and the line.

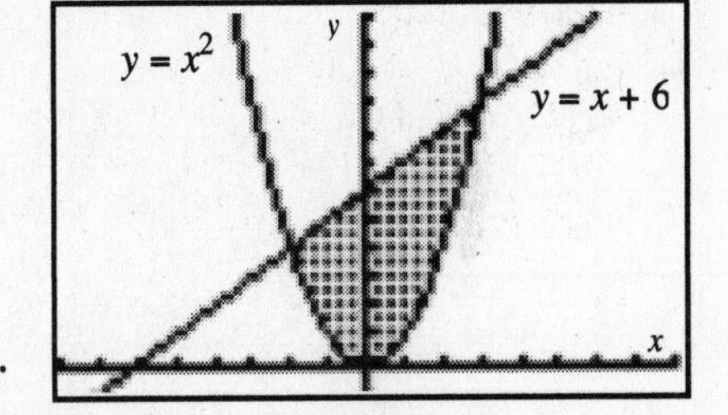

a) Use the intersect feature of a graphing calculator to determine the coordinates of the points of intersection.

b) Use the method of substitution, or the method of elimination, to algebraically determine the coordinates of the points of intersection.

c) Verify that the points in a) and b) satisfy the system of equations.

d) The solution to the linear-quadratic system of equations $\begin{aligned} y &= x^2 \\ y &= x + 6 \end{aligned}$

can be written as

$x =$, $y =$, or $x =$, $y =$, OR (,), (,).

Note that in the graphical method, both the linear and the quadratic equation need to be written in the form "$y =$". When using the method of substitution, the linear equation must be written in the form "$y =$" or "$x =$".

Investigating the Number of Solutions to a Linear-Quadratic System

The graph of $y = x^2 - x - 12$ is shown on the grid.

a) • Algebraically determine the point(s) of intersection of the line $y = 3x$ and the parabola $y = x^2 - x - 12$.

• Sketch the line and plot the point(s) of intersection on the grid.

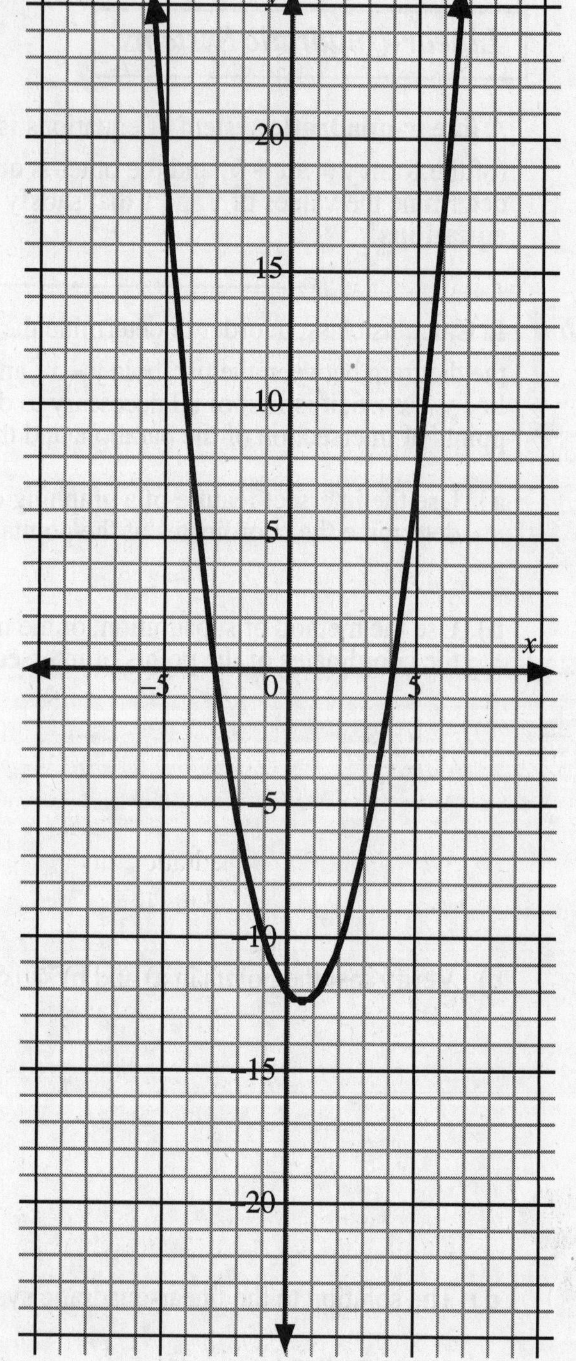

b) Repeat part a) for the line $y = 3x - 16$ and the parabola $y = x^2 - x - 12$.

c) Repeat part a) for the line $y = 3x - 24$.

d) Complete the following statements:

- If the graph of a linear equation and the graph of a quadratic equation intersect at two points, then the linear-quadratic system has _____ solutions.
- If the graph of a linear equation and the graph of a quadratic equation intersect at one point, then the linear-quadratic system has _____ solution.
- If the graph of a linear equation and the graph of a quadratic equation do not intersect, then the linear-quadratic system has _____ solutions.

e) In the process of solving a linear-quadratic system of equations, we end up solving another quadratic equation. The discriminant of the resulting quadratic equation can be used to determine the number of solutions to the linear-quadratic system.

Complete the following statements:

- If the resulting quadratic equation has two distinct roots, then the discriminant is __________ and the linear-quadratic system has _____ solutions.
- If the resulting quadratic equation has two equal roots, then the discriminant is __________ and the linear-quadratic system has _____ solution.
- If the resulting quadratic equation has no real roots, then the discriminant is __________ and the linear-quadratic system has _____ solutions.

- If the resulting quadratic equation does not factor (i.e. the discriminant is not a perfect square), then the quadratic formula can be used to determine the solution(s).
- We say a line is **tangent** to a parabola if there is only one point of intersection, i.e. the line just touches the parabola. See part b) on the previous page.

Complete Assignment Questions #1 - #8

Assignment

1. For each of the following linear-quadratic system of equations:
- solve the system using a graphing technique
- solve the system using an algebraic method
- verify the solution satisfies both equations

a) $y = x^2 - 2$
$y = x$

b) $y = 8x - x^2$
$y = 2x$

c) $y = 2x - 7$
$y = x^2 - 12x + 42$

2. Consider the system of equations $\begin{aligned} y &= x^2 - 3x - 3 \\ y &= x + 1 \end{aligned}$.

a) Graphically determine the solution to the system to the nearest tenth.

b) Algebraically determine the **exact** solution to the system.

3. a) Explain a graphical strategy you could use to show that a particular linear-quadratic system of equations has no solution.

b) Explain an algebraic strategy you could use to show that a particular linear-quadratic system of equations has no solution.

c) Use the strategies in a) and b) to show that the system of equations $\begin{aligned} y &= 2x - 3 \\ y &= 2x^2 + 3x + 9 \end{aligned}$

has no solution.

4. A farmer has 12 m of fencing with which to erect two sides of a rectangular pen, the other two sides being formed by the corner of a walled garden.

a) If the area of the pen is 24 m^2 and the length of one side is x metres, show that $x^2 + 24 = 12x$.

b) Write a system of equations which could be graphed in order to determine the dimensions of the pen. State the dimensions of the pen to the nearest hundredth of a metre.

5. Determine the exact coordinates of the points of intersection of the circle with equation $x^2 + y^2 = 100$ and the line $y = 2x$.

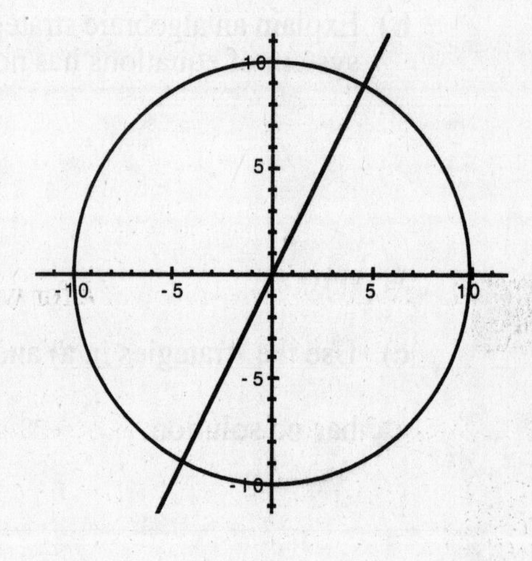

6. The diagram shows the circle with equation $x^2 + y^2 = 25$. Algebraically prove that the line with equation $3x + 4y - 25 = 0$ is tangent to the circle, and determine the point of contact.

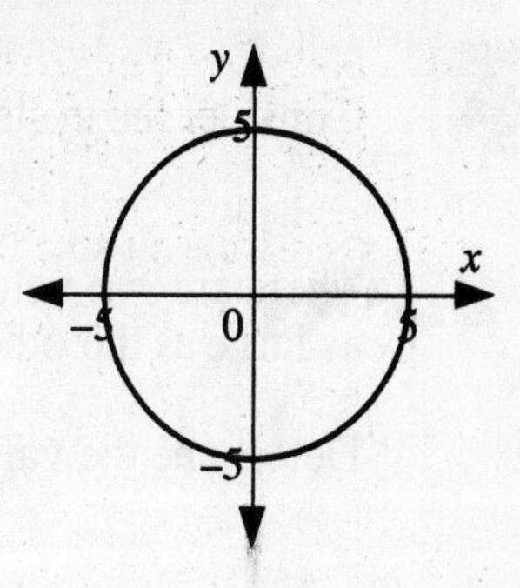

Multiple Choice

7. The x coordinate of the point of intersection of the graphs with equations $y = -3x + 7$ and $y = 4x^2 - 15x + 16$ is

A. -1.5

B. 1.5

C. -2.5

D. 2.5

Numerical Response

8. There are two values of k for which the line $y = kx - 2$ is a tangent to the parabola $y = x^2$. The sum of the squares of these two values of k is _____ .

(Record your answer in the numerical response box from left to right.)

Consider the system of equations $y = 4x^2 - 9x + 20$
$y = 15x + k$

There are two values of x which are solutions to the system, one of which is three times as large as the other.

Determine the value of k and hence the solution to the system.

Answer Key

1. a) $x = -1,\ y = -1$; $x = 2,\ y = 2$ **b)** $x = 0,\ y = 0$; $x = 6,\ y = 12$ **c)** $x = 7,\ y = 7$

2. a) $x = 4.8, y = 5.8$; $x = -0.8, y = 0.2$ **b)** $x = 2 + 2\sqrt{2}\,,\ y = 3 + 2\sqrt{2}$; $x = 2 - 2\sqrt{2}\,,\ y = 3 - 2\sqrt{2}$

3. a) Graph each equation. There will be no points of intersection.
b) Try to solve the system by substitution. The quadratic equation which results will have no solution, i.e. the discriminant will be negative.

4. b) $y = x^2 + 24,\ y = 12x,$ 2.54 m by 9.46 m

5. $\left(2\sqrt{5}\,, 4\sqrt{5}\right), \left(-2\sqrt{5}\,, -4\sqrt{5}\right)$ **6.** (3, 4) **7.** B **8.**

1	6		

Group Work $k = -7,\ x = \frac{3}{2}, \frac{9}{2}$

Linear and Quadratic Systems and Inequalities Lesson #2:
Solving a System of Quadratic-Quadratic Equations

Quadratic-Quadratic Systems

A **quadratic-quadratic** system of equations is a system in which both of the equations are quadratic of the form $y = ax^2 + bx + c$.

Class Ex. #1

Consider the system of equations $\begin{aligned} y &= 6x^2 + 7x - 4 \\ y &= 2x^2 - x + 1 \end{aligned}$.

a) Use an algebraic technique to determine the solution to the system of equations.

b) Sketch the equations on the grid and use a graphing technique to determine the solution to the system. State an appropriate window.

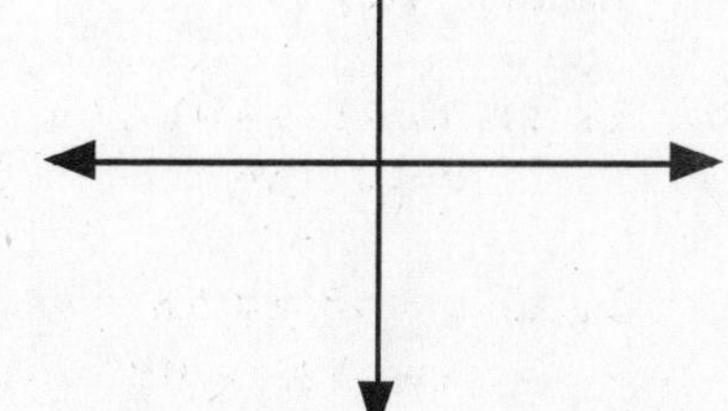

c) Verify that the solution obtained satisfies both equations.

Complete Assignment Questions #1 - #11

Assignment

1. Consider the system of equations $\begin{array}{l} y = x^2 - 4x + 8 \\ y = 2x^2 - 3x + 2 \end{array}$.

a) Use an algebraic technique to determine the solution to the system of equations.

b) Sketch the equations on the grid and use a graphing technique to determine the solution to the system. State an appropriate window.

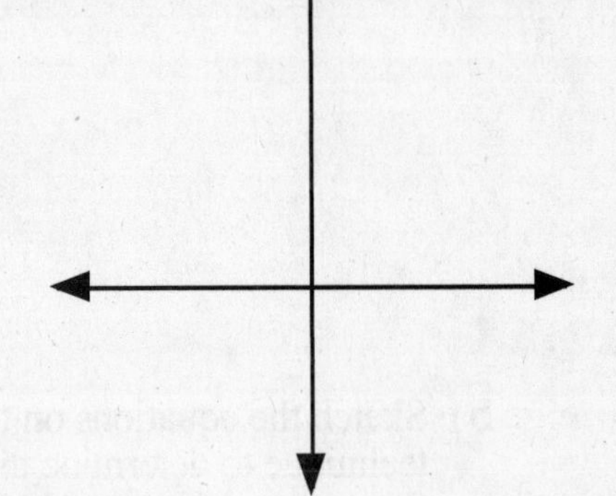

c) Verify that the solution obtained satisfies both equations.

2. Consider a quadratic-quadratic system of equations. Draw a graph of a system illustrating the following:

a) no solution **b)** one solution **c)** two solutions **d)** infinite number of solutions

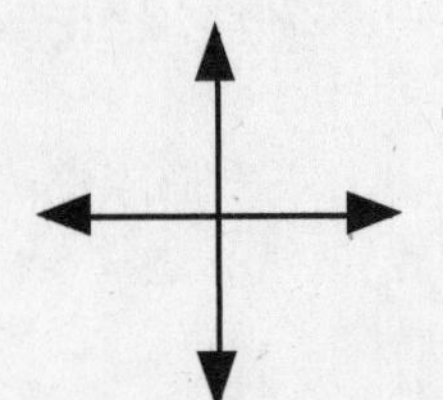
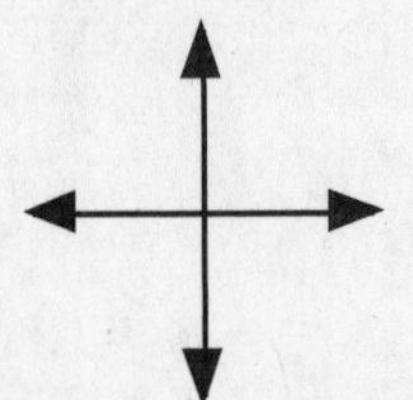
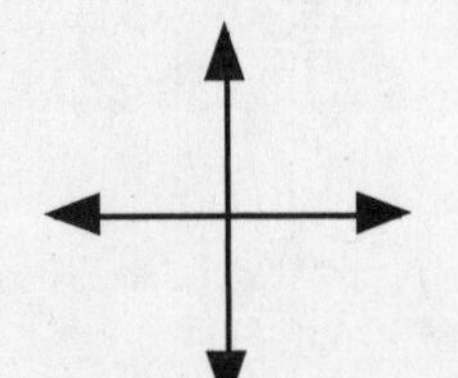
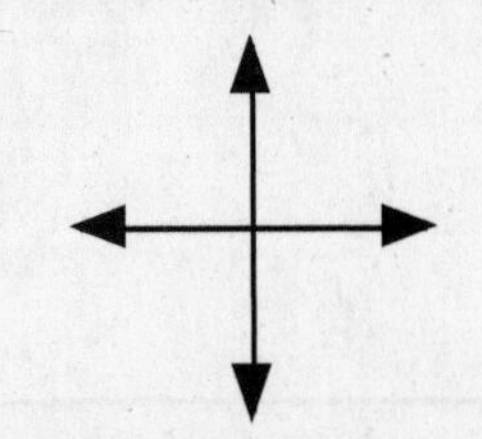

3. For each of the following quadratic-quadratic system of equations:
- solve the system using an algebraic technique
- solve the system using a graphical method
- verify the solution satisfies both equations

a) $y = x^2$
$y = (x - 2)^2$

b) $y = x^2 - 4x + 6$
$y = -x^2 + 4x - 2$

c) $y = 3x^2 - 3x - 8$
$y = 12 - 3x - 2x^2$

4. For each of the following quadratic-quadratic system of equations:

- solve the system using a graphing technique
- solve the system using an algebraic method

a) $y = x^2 + 6x + 9$

$y = 1 - 2x - x^2$

b) $y = \frac{1}{2}x^2 - 20x + 200$

$y = 20 + 7x - \frac{1}{2}x^2$

5. Algebraically determine the coordinates of the points of intersection of the parabolas with equations $y = 3x^2 + 9x - 10$ and $y = x^2 + 2x + 5$.

6. The number of solutions of the system $\begin{array}{l} y = x^2 + 4x - 12 \\ y = 2x^2 - 10x + 12 \end{array}$ is

A. 0

B. 1

C. 2

D. infinite number of solutions

Use the following information to answer questions #7 - #10.

Aaron stands on the roof of a tall building and throws a tennis ball up into the air. On its way down, the ball just misses the roof of the building and falls all the way to the ground.

The height, h metres, of the ball above the ground after t seconds, is given by the quadratic equation in standard form $h = -4.9(t-p)^2 + q$.

After 4 seconds the ball is 102.9 metres above the ground, and after 6 seconds the ball is 44.1 metres above the ground.

7. The height of the building is

A. 44.1 m

B. 102.9 m

C. 122.5 m

D. 135.0 m

8. The maximum height of the ball is

A. 44.1 m

B. 102.9 m

C. 122.5 m

D. 135.0 m

Numerical Response **9.** The number of seconds it takes for the ball to reach its maximum height is _____ .

(Record your answer in the numerical response box from left to right.)

Numerical Response **10.** The number of seconds it takes for the ball to hit the ground is _____ .

(Record your answer in the numerical response box from left to right.)

The following question may be used as a lead-in to the next lesson.

On the grid, shade the region that satisfies the following system of inequalities.

$y \geq x^2 + 2x - 15$, and $y \leq -2x - 1$

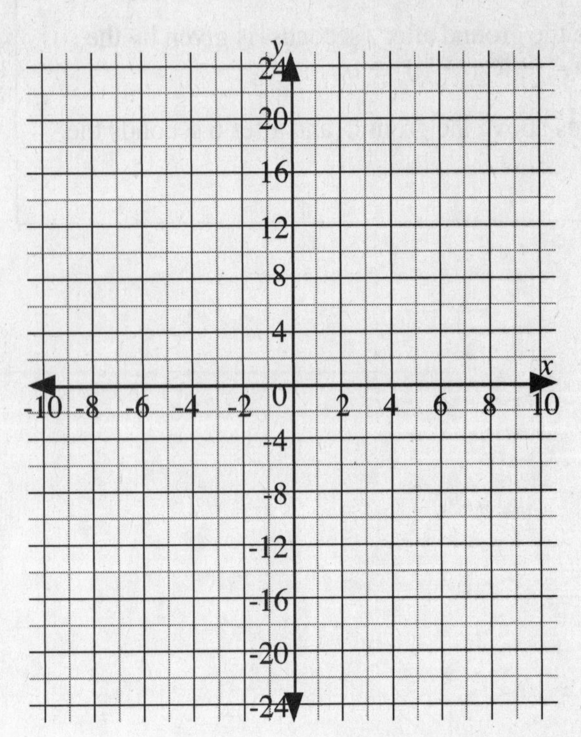

Answer Key

1. a) $x = -3,\ y = 29$, and $x = 2, y = 4$

2.

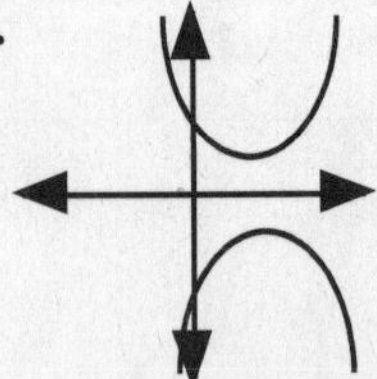

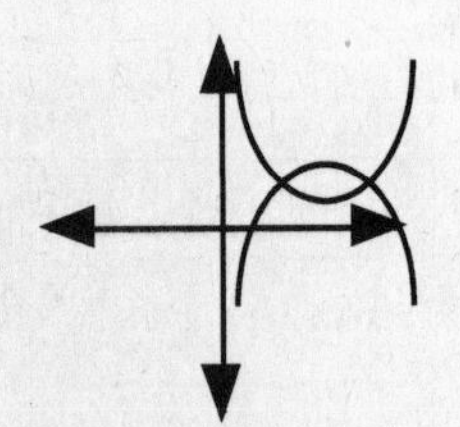

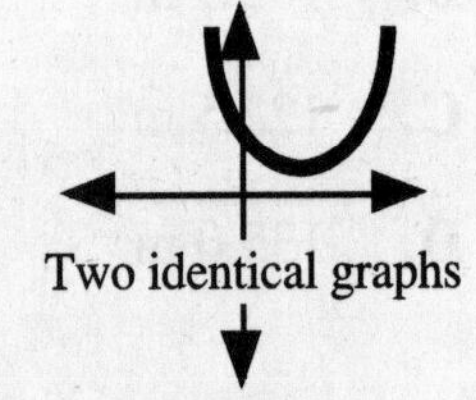

Two identical graphs

3. a) $x = 1, y = 1$ **b)** $x = 2, y = 2$ **c)** $x = -2,\ y = 10$
$x = 2,\ \ y = -2$

4. a) $x = -2,\ y = 1$ **b)** $x = 12,\ y = 32$
$x = 15,\ y = \frac{25}{2}$

5. $\left(\frac{3}{2}, \frac{41}{4}\right)$, $(-5, 20)$ **6.** C **7.** B

8. C **9.** | 2 | | | | **10.** | 7 | | | |

Group Investigation See page 528 for the solution.

Linear and Quadratic Systems and Inequalities Lesson #3: Solving Linear Inequalities in Two Variables Without Technology

The speed limit on a highway is 100 km/h. A car is breaking the speed limit. This means that the speed, s, at which the car is travelling is given by the inequality $s > 100$.

Before studying linear inequalities in two variables, we will review linear inequalities in one variable.

Review *Linear Inequalities in One Variable*

A mathematical inequality must contain one of the following symbols:

$$< \quad \leq \quad > \quad \geq \quad \neq$$

The following are examples of linear inequalities in a single variable :

$4x - 1 > 7 \qquad 1 - 2a \leq 5 \qquad$ etc.

The solution to a single variable inequality can be shown on a number line.

In this unit, unless otherwise stated, we assume that the variables are defined on the set of real numbers.

Class Ex. #1

Consider the inequality $4 - 2(3 + x) > 12$.

a) Solve the inequality algebraically.

b) Check the solution using a test case.

c) Graph the solution on a number line.

Complete Assignment Questions #1 - #2

Linear Inequalities in Two Variables

The following are examples of linear inequalities in two variables :

$2x - 3y \geq 6$ $\quad$ $4p + 3q < 10$ $\quad$ etc.

The solution region to a linear inequality in two variables can be represented on a coordinate plane using a **boundary line** and shading one side of the line.

The boundary line will be solid or broken according to the following rule.

- a **solid boundary line** is used to represent **≥** or **≤**
- a **broken** or **dotted boundary line** is used to represent **>** or **<**

Graphing a Linear Inequality Without Using Technology

The following procedure can be used to graph the solution region of a two variable linear inequality.

1. On a coordinate plane, graph the corresponding linear equation using a table of values, intercepts, or point and slope. Draw the line solid or broken according to the rule above.

2. The line divides the coordinate plane into two regions, called **half planes**. The solution region will be on one side of the line. To determine which side, choose the coordinates of a point not on the line, called a **test point**, and determine if the coordinates of the point satisfy the inequality. If the inequality is satisfied, then the solution is the region from which the point was chosen. If not, then the solution region is the other region.

3. Shade the appropriate region.

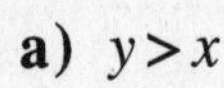

Class Ex. #2

Graph the following two variable inequalities on the grids provided.

a) $y > x$

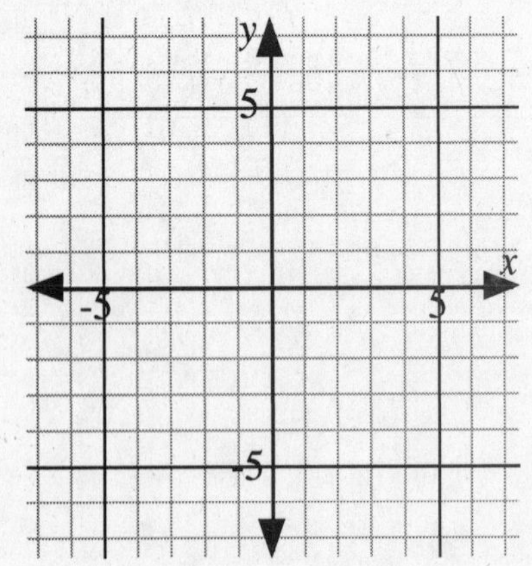

b) $3x - 2y \leq -6$

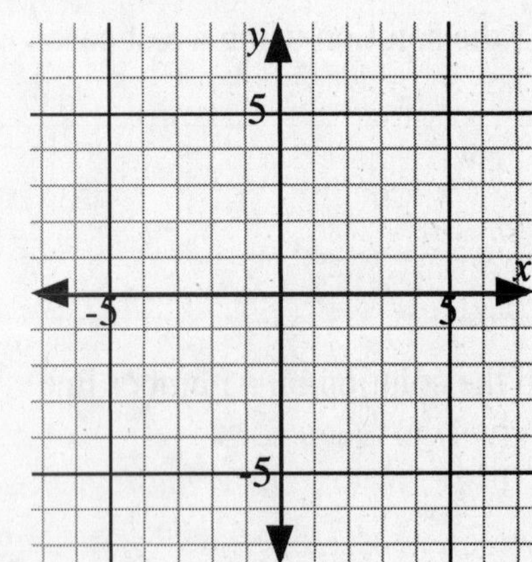

Graph the following inequality without using a graphing calculator.

$$y < \frac{3}{4}x + 3$$

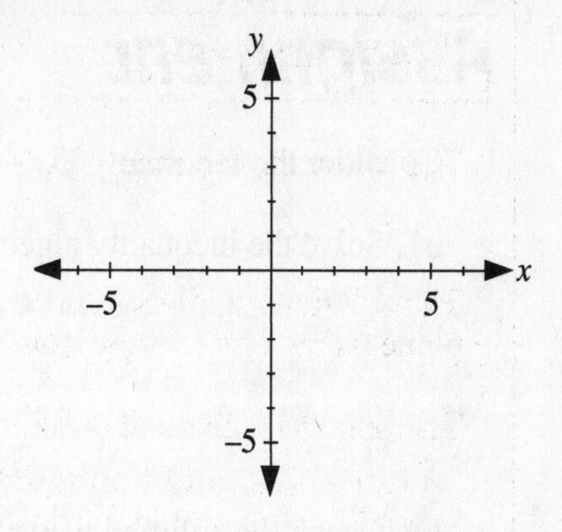

1. If the boundary line is given in the form $y = mx + b$, then:
   - the region <u>above</u> the line represents $y > mx + b$
   - the region <u>below</u> the line represents $y < mx + b$
2. If the boundary line does not pass through the origin, the simplest test point to choose is $(0, 0)$.

The diagram shows the solution region to an inequality. The boundary line has intercepts at $(-2, 0)$ and $(0, 4)$.

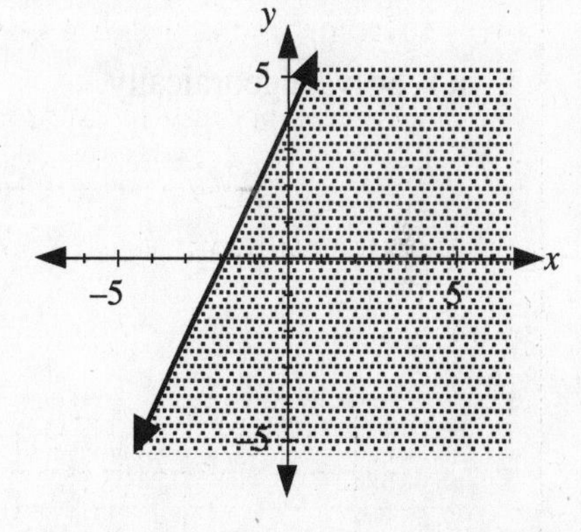

a) Determine the equation of the boundary line.

b) Determine the inequality.

Complete Assignment Questions #3 - #11

Assignment

1. Consider the inequality $5x - 3 \geq 33 - x$.

   a) Solve the inequality algebraically.

   b) Check the solution using a test case.

   c) Graph the solution on a number line.

2. Consider the inequality $\frac{p+4}{4} - \frac{3p-9}{7} < \frac{1}{2}$.

   a) Solve algebraically.

   b) Check the solution using a test case.

   c) Graph the solution on a number line.

3. In each case, show the solution region to the inequality without using technology.

a) $y \geq 3x + 2$ **b)** $y < 5 - x$ **c)** $y > \frac{x}{2}$

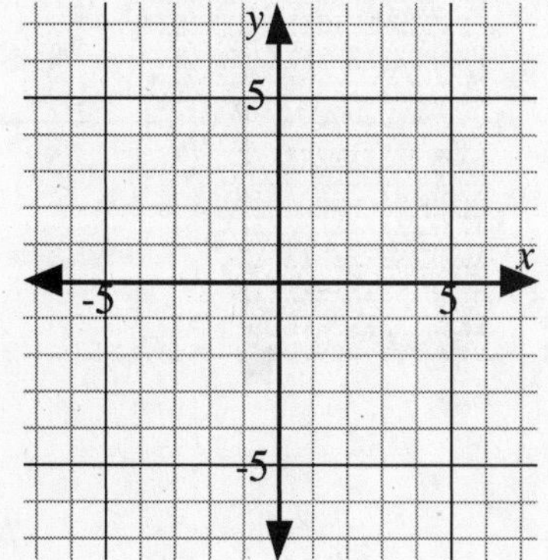

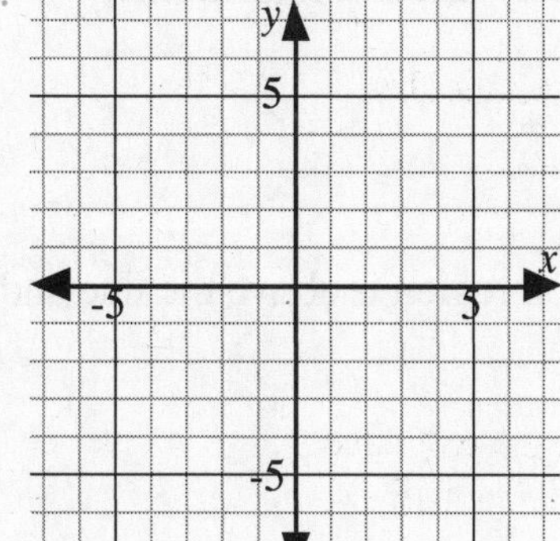

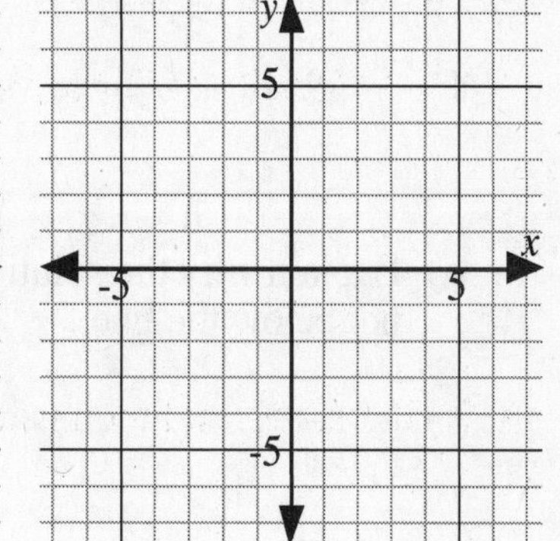

4. In each case, show the solution region to the inequality without using technology.

a) $4x + 3y \leq 12$ **b)** $3p - 5q \geq 30$ **c)** $x < \frac{2}{3}y$

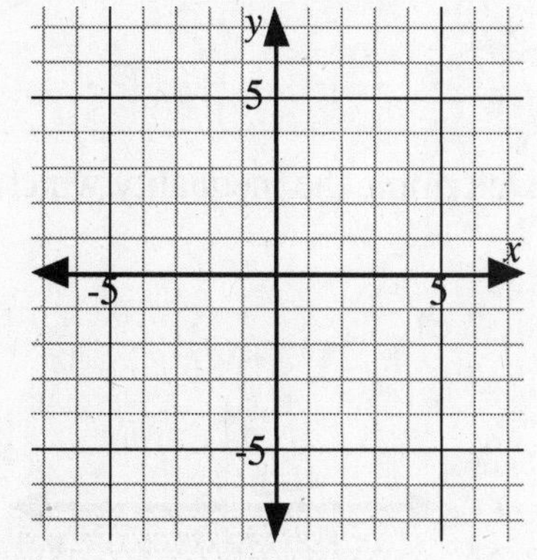

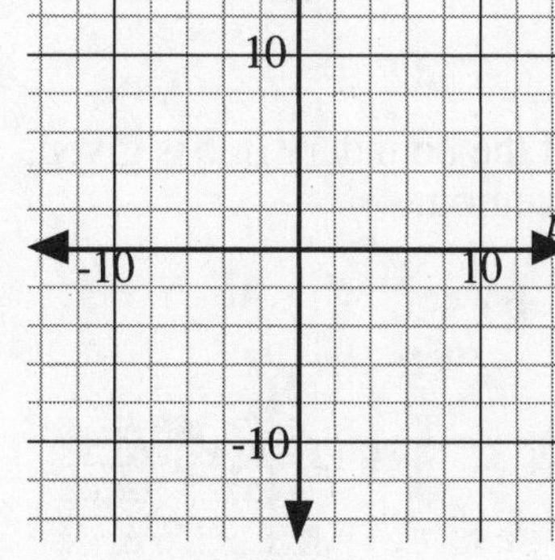

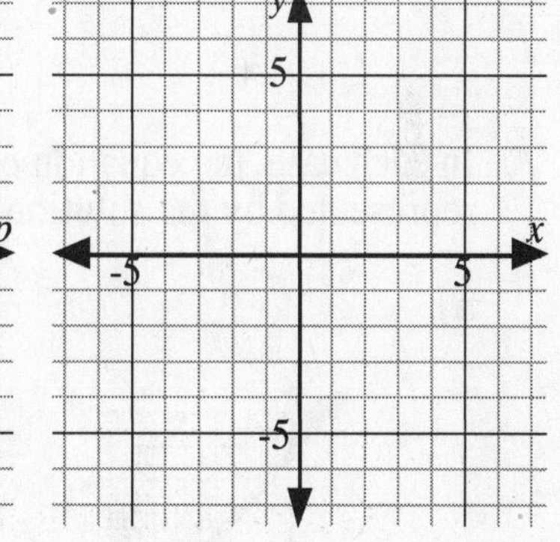

5. The graph shows the solution region to the inequality $5x - 2y < 10$.

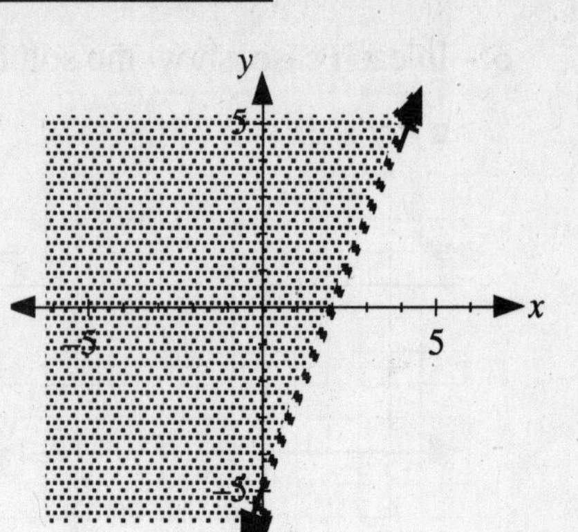

a) Explain why the boundary line is a broken line.

b) Explain why the solution region is above the line and not below the line.

6. Sketch the half-plane represented by the following inequalities:

a) $y > -2$ **b)** $x < 2$ **c)** $x \geq 0$ **d)** $y + 3 \leq 0$

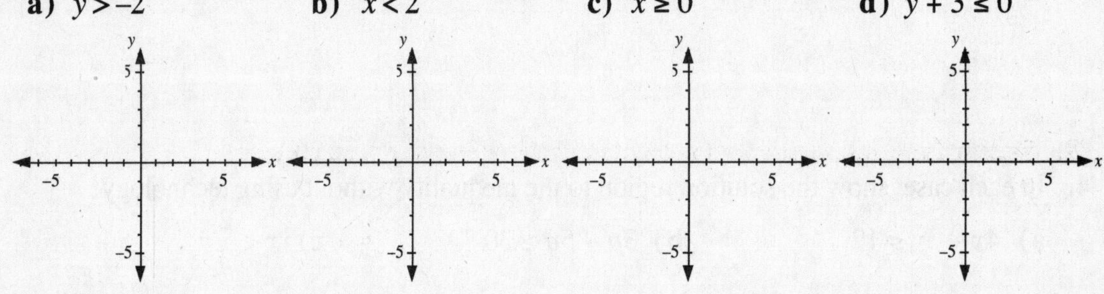

7. In each case, the equation of the boundary line is given. Determine the inequality which is represented by the solution region.

a)

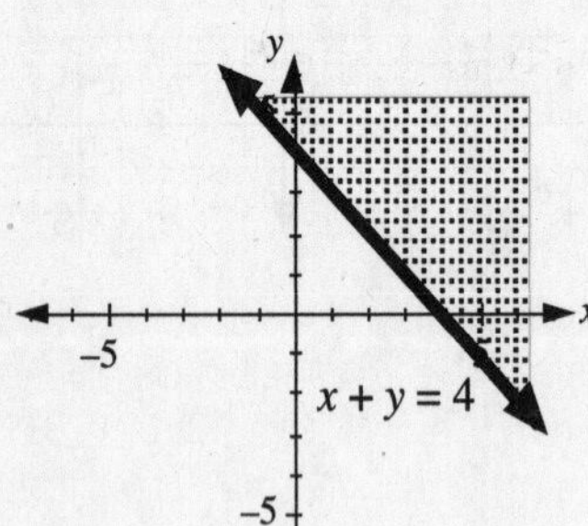

b)

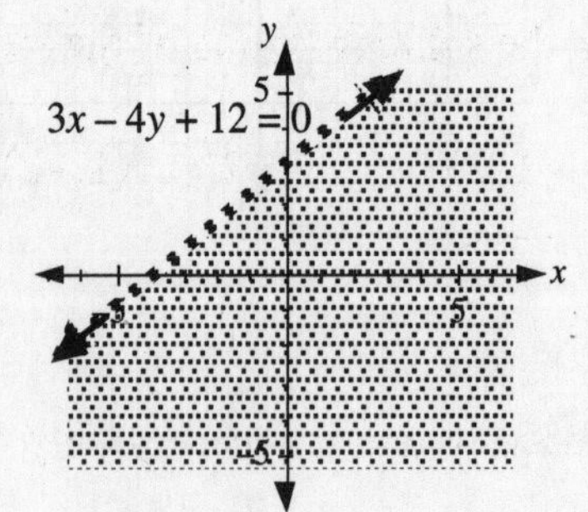

c)

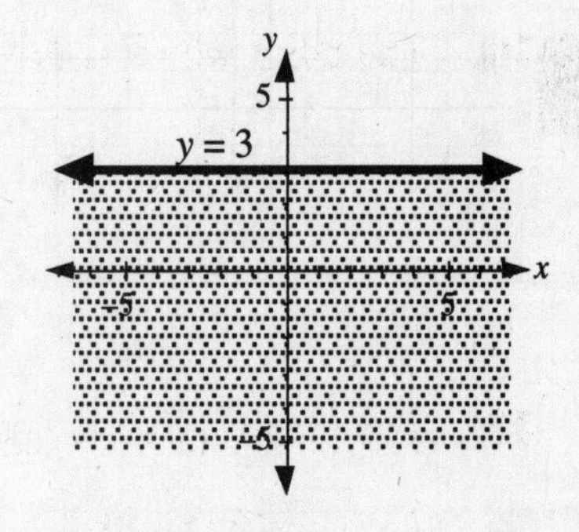

8. In each case, use the information given to determine the inequality.

a)

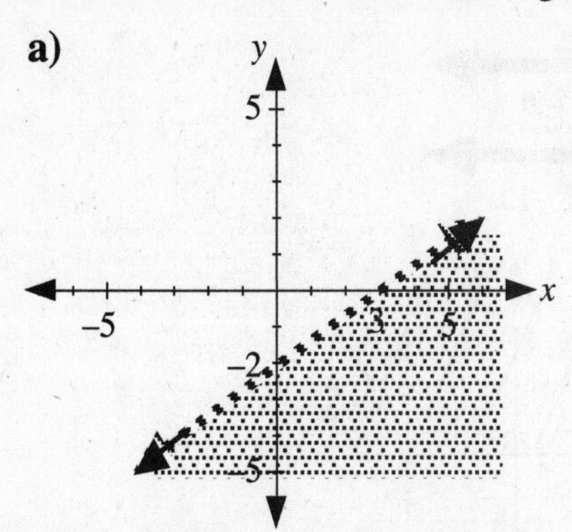

The boundary line has an x-intercept of 3 and a y-intercept of –2.

b)

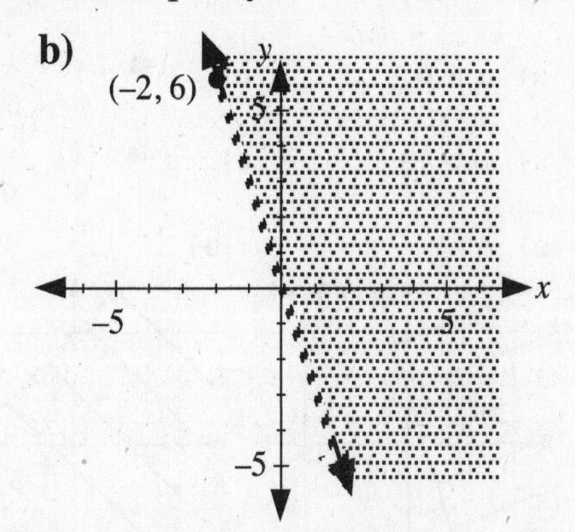

The boundary line passes through the origin and the point (–2, 6).

9. Sketch the solution region represented by the following inequalities:

a) $1 \le y \le 4$

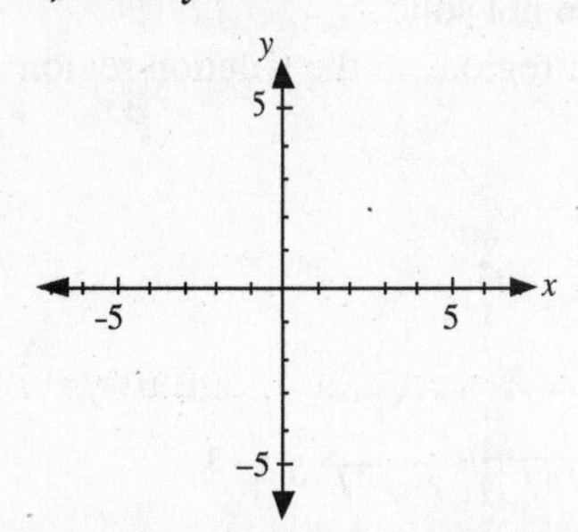

b) $-3 < x < 2$

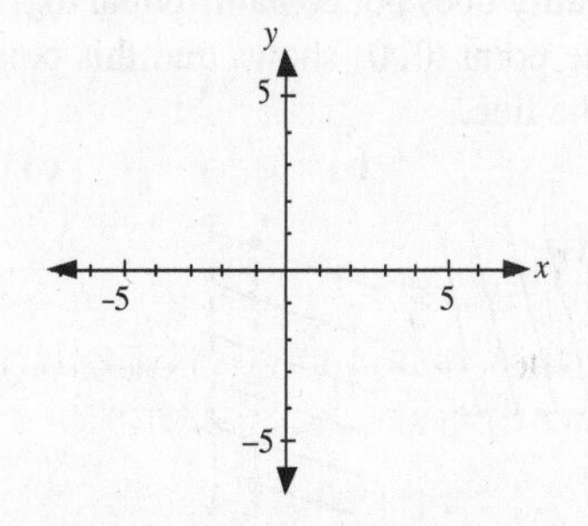

Multiple Choice

10. The point which is **not** in the solution region of the inequality $4x - 3y \le 6$ is

A. (0, 0) **B.** (–1, 2) **C.** (1, –2) **D.** (3, 2)

11. The graph shows the solution region to the inequality

A. $x + 2y \ge -4$

B. $x + 2y \le -4$

C. $2x + y \ge -2$

D. $2x + y \le -2$

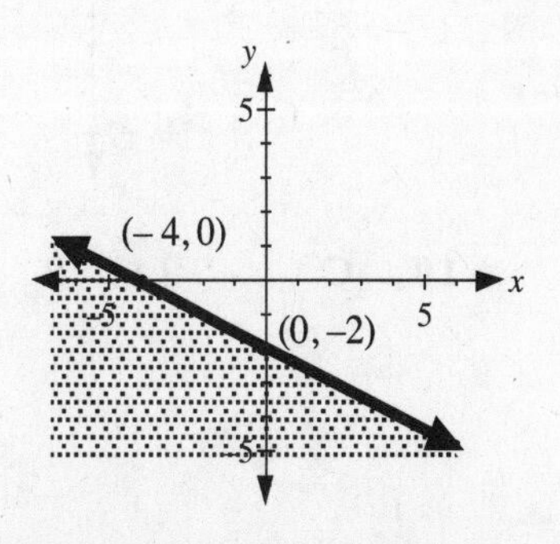

Answer Key

1. a) $x \geq 6$ **c)**

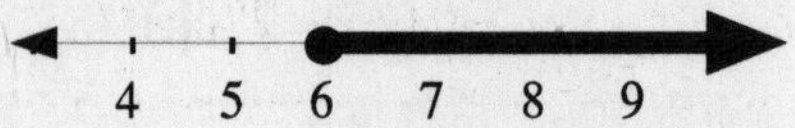

2. a) $p > 10$ **c)**

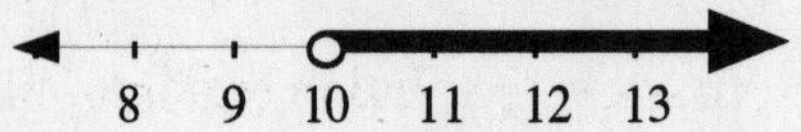

3. a)

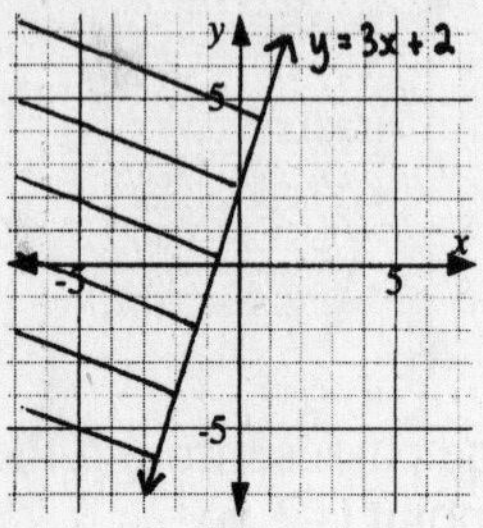

b)

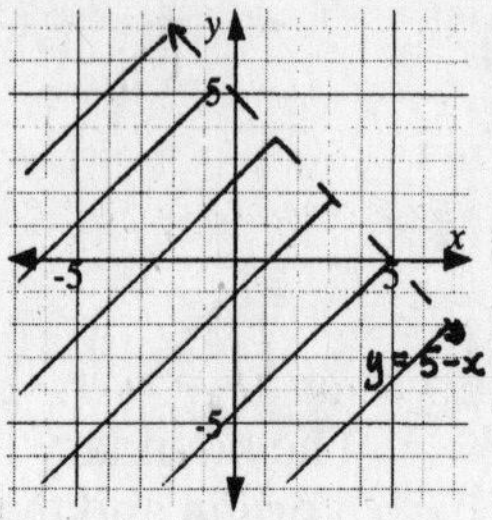

c)

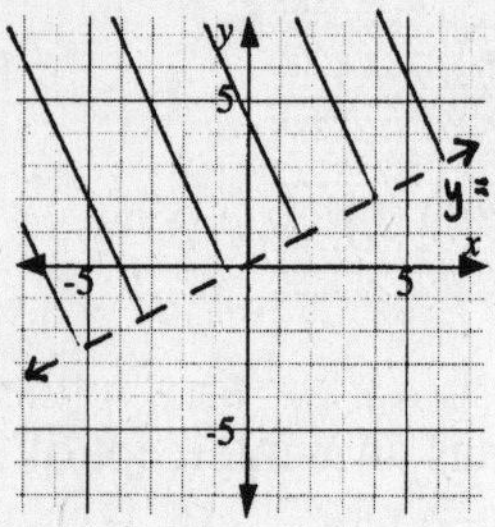

4. a)

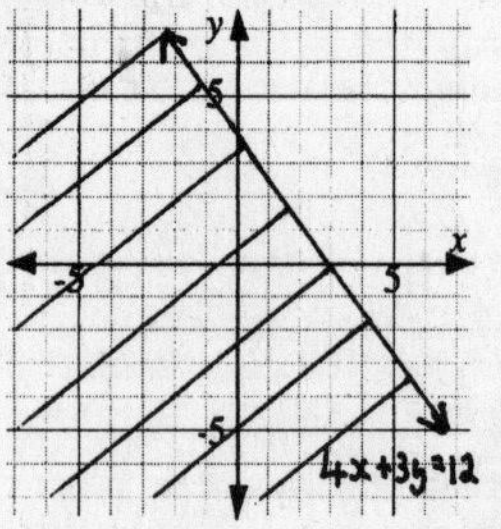

b)

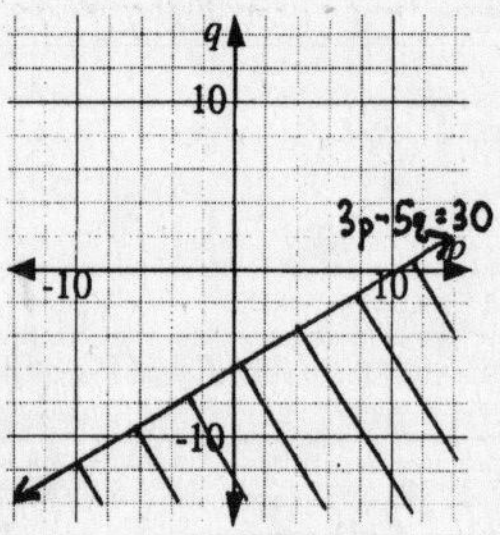

c)

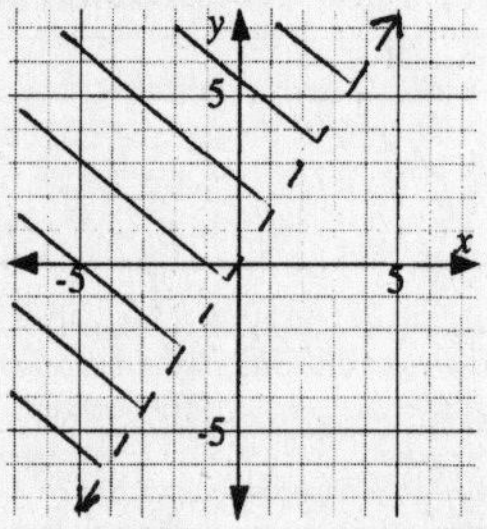

5. a) The inequality does not contain "equal to", so the line is broken not solid.
b) Testing the point (0, 0) shows that this point is in the solution region, so the solution region is above the line.

6. a)

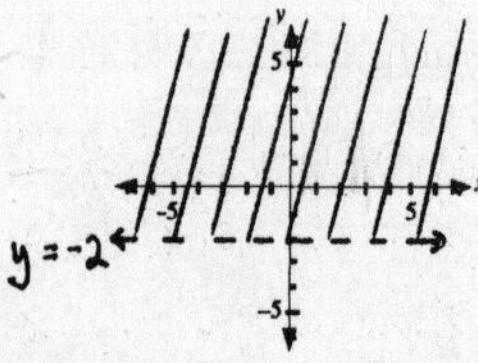

b)

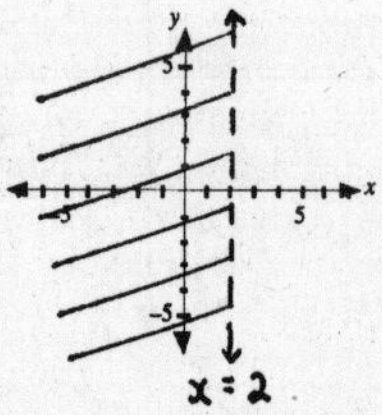

c)

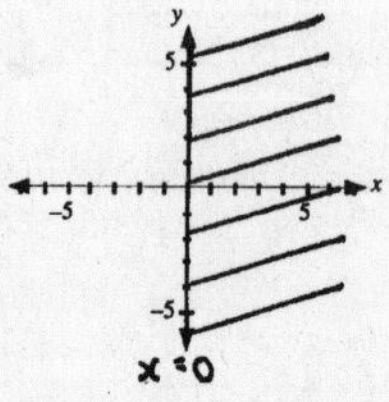

d)

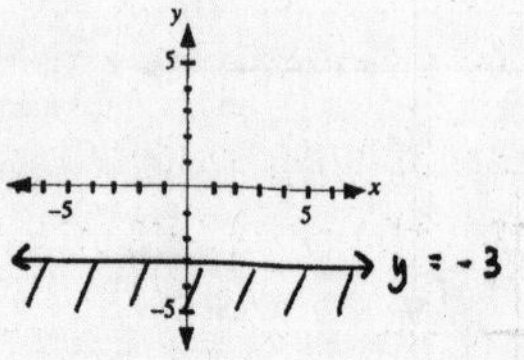

7. a) $x + y \geq 4$ **b)** $3x - 4y + 12 > 0$ **c)** $y \leq 3$ **8. a)** $y < \frac{2}{3}x - 2$ **b)** $y > -3x$

9. a)

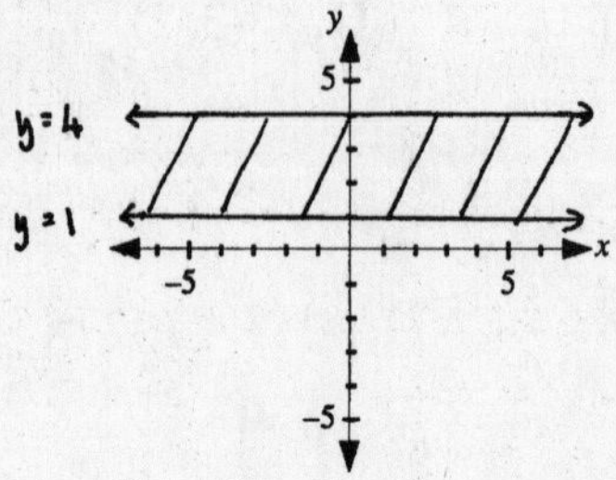

b)

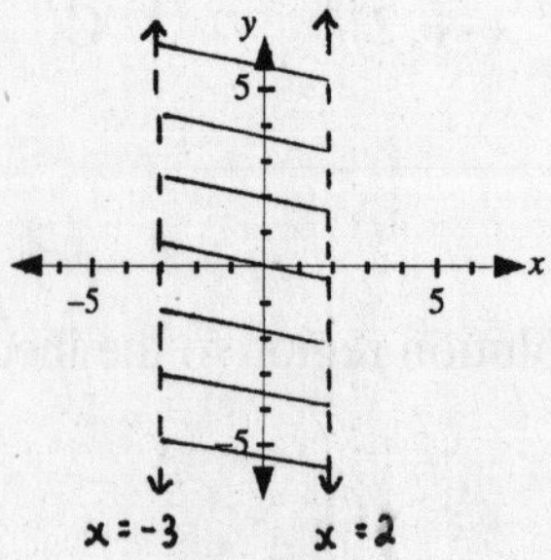

10. C **11.** B

Linear and Quadratic Systems and Inequalities Lesson #4:
Solving Quadratic Inequalities in Two Variables Without Technology

Investigating a Quadratic Inequality in Two Variables

a) Explain why the point $(3,0)$ is in the solution region of $y \geq x^2 - 3x - 4$.

b) Determine whether the following test points are in the solution region of $y \geq x^2 - 3x - 4$ **or** in the solution region of $y \leq x^2 - 3x - 4$.
Write the coordinates of the points in the appropriate row in the table below.

Test Points: $(0,0)$, $(-3,0)$, $(0,3)$, $(0,-7)$, $(1,4)$, $(7,-1)$, $(-4,2)$, $(8,5)$, $(2,-2)$, $(-5,-2)$

Points in the solution region of $y \geq x^2 - 3x - 4$	(3, 0)
Points in the solution region of $y \leq x^2 - 3x - 4$	

The diagrams below show the graph with equation $y = x^2 - 3x - 4$.

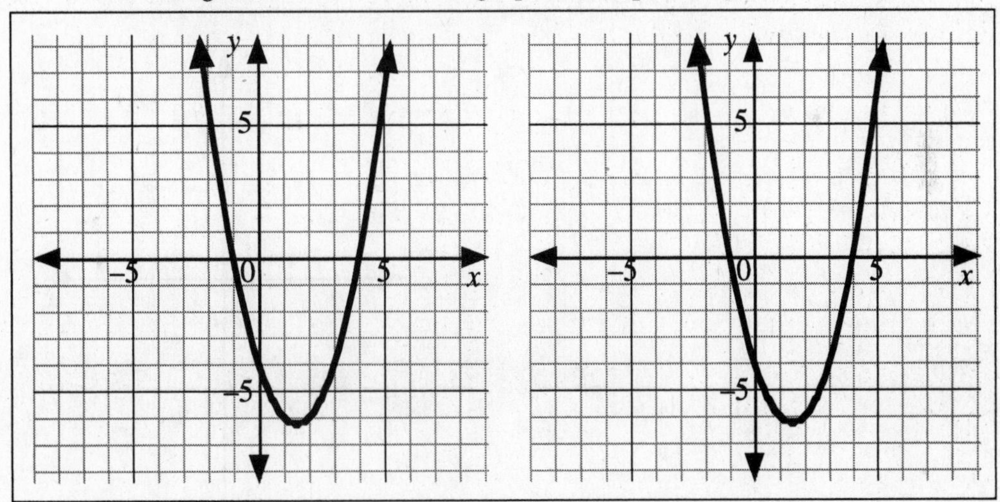

c) i) Plot the points from the top row in b) onto the first grid. These points are in the solution region to the quadratic inequality $y \geq x^2 - 3x - 4$.

ii) Plot the points from the second row in b) onto the second grid. These points are in the solution region to the quadratic inequality $y \leq x^2 - 3x - 4$.

d) i) Shade the solution region to the inequality $y \geq x^2 - 3x - 4$ on the first grid.
ii) Shade the solution region to the inequality $y \leq x^2 - 3x - 4$ on the second grid.

Quadratic Inequalities in Two Variables

Notice from the investigation that the solution to the two variable quadratic inequality is either "inside" the parabola or "outside" the parabola. This means that only one test point is required in order to determine the solution region.

The following procedure can be used to graph the solution region of a two variable quadratic inequality.

1. Draw the graph of the corresponding quadratic equation using intercepts or other means. The graph will be solid or broken according to whether the inequality includes "equal to" or not.

2. Choose a test point that does not lie on the graph of the quadratic equation.

- If the test point **does** satisfy the quadratic inequality, shade the region, inside or outside the parabola, that includes the test point.
- If the test point **does not** satisfy the quadratic inequality, shade the region, inside or outside the parabola, that does not include the test point.

Shade the solution region to the inequality $y < 20 + x - x^2$ on the grid below.

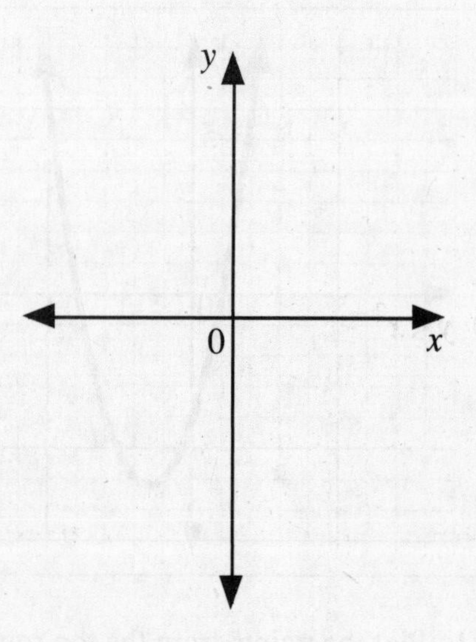

Complete Assignment Questions #1 - #6

Assignment

1. In each case, the equation of the parabola is given.
Determine the quadratic inequality represented by the solution region from the screenshot of a graphing calculator.

a) 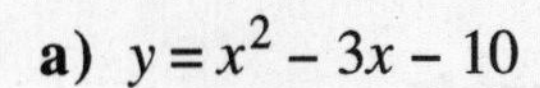 $y = x^2 - 3x - 10$

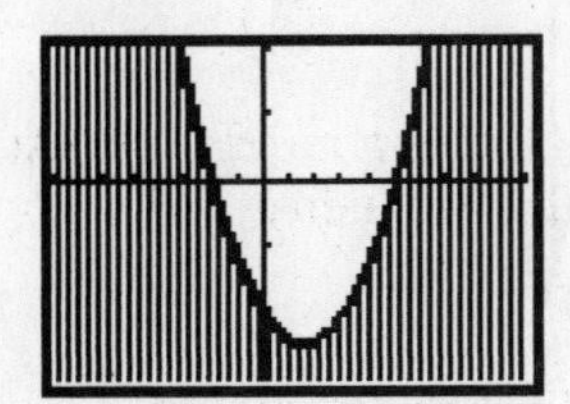

b) $y = x^2 - 10x + 21$

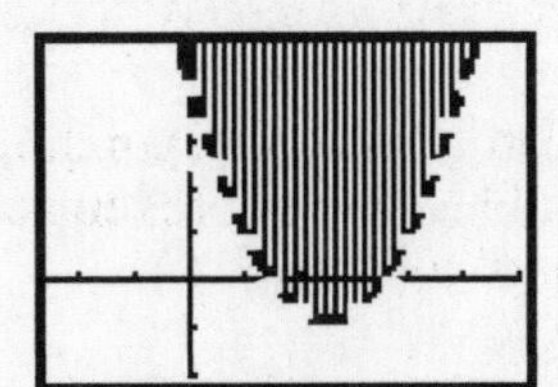

2. In each case, shade the solution region to the given inequality on the grid provided.

a) $y \leq x^2 + 3x - 18$

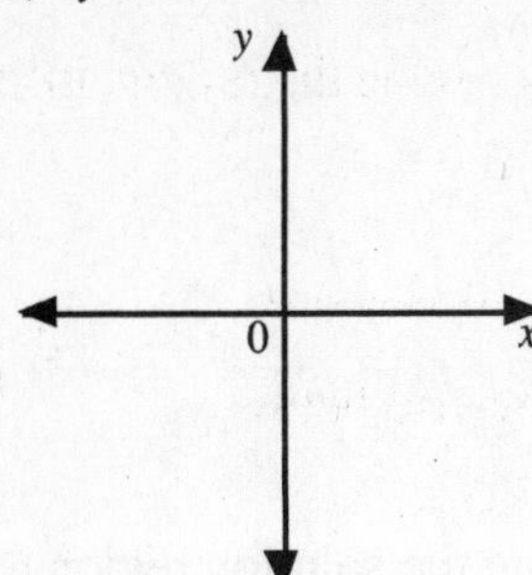

b) 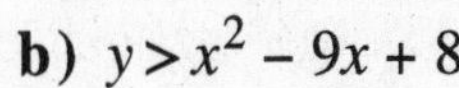 $y > x^2 - 9x + 8$

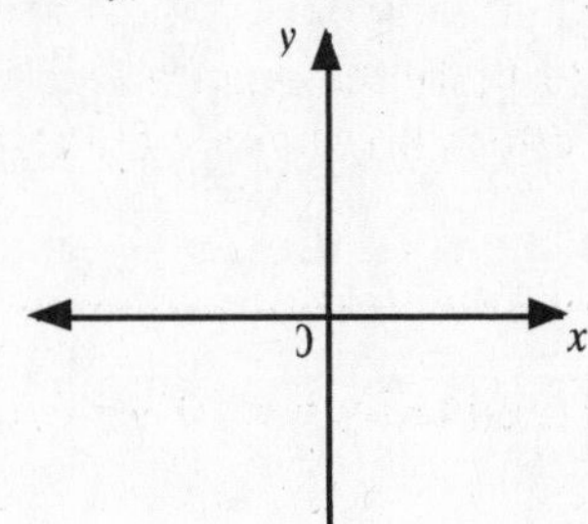

c) $y \geq 15 - 2x - x^2$

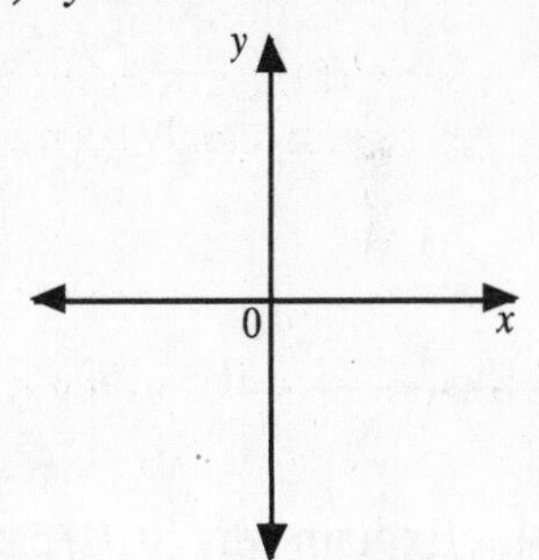

d) $y < x^2 - 6x$

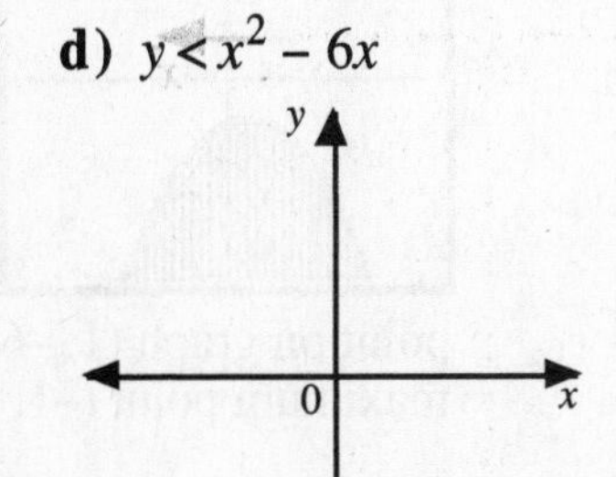

e) $y \leq 16 - x^2$

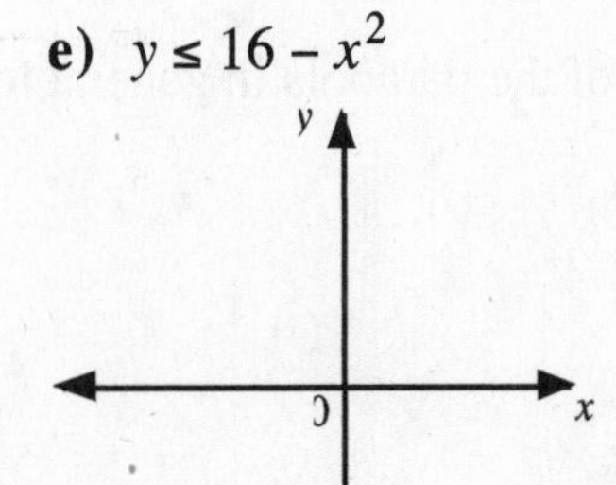

f) $y \leq x^2 - 16$

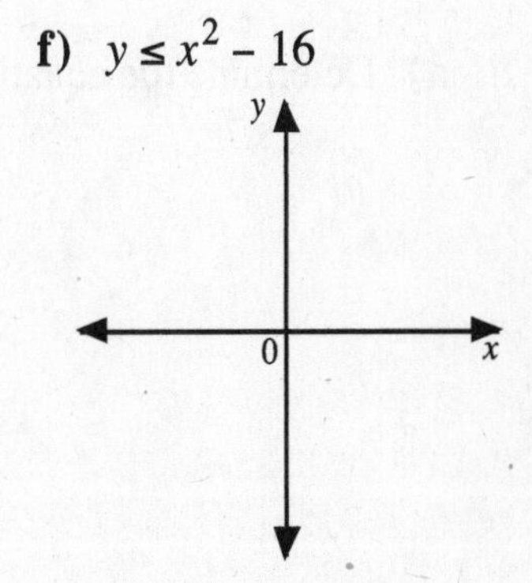

3. In each case, shade the solution region to the given inequality on the grid provided.

a) $y + 24 < 3x^2 + 14x$

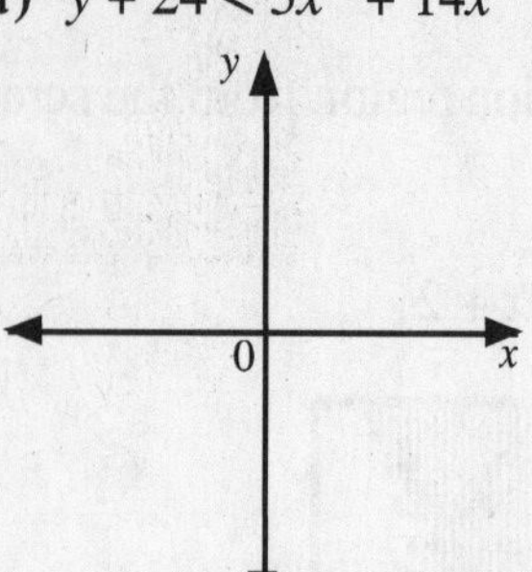

b) $2y \leq 56 - 2x - 4x^2$

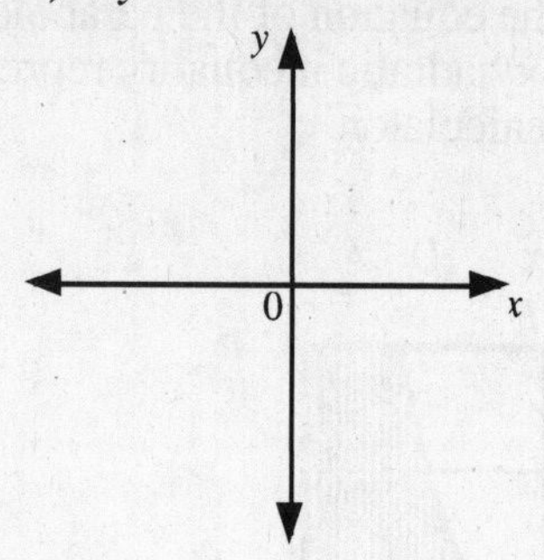

4. Explain why $(0, 0)$ cannot be used as a test point when finding the solution region to the inequality $y > x - 4x^2$.

5. Consider the information shown on the grid.

a) Determine the equation of the parabola in general form.

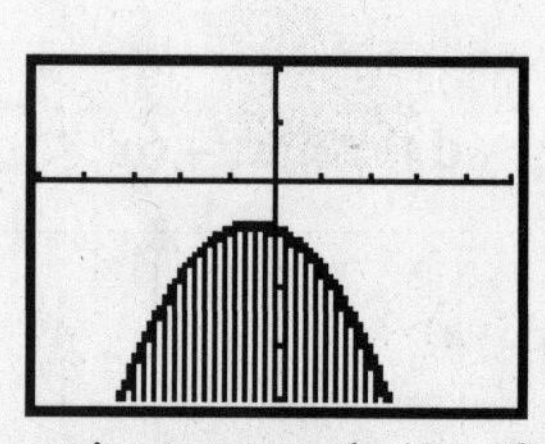

point on graph $(1, -6)$
maximum point $(-1, -4)$

b) Determine the quadratic inequality represented by the shaded region.

Multiple Choice **6.** The shaded area on the grid is the solution region to the inequality

A. $y > x^2 - 6x + 20$
B. $y < x^2 - 6x + 20$
C. $y > 2x^2 - 12x + 20$
D. $y < 2x^2 - 12x + 20$

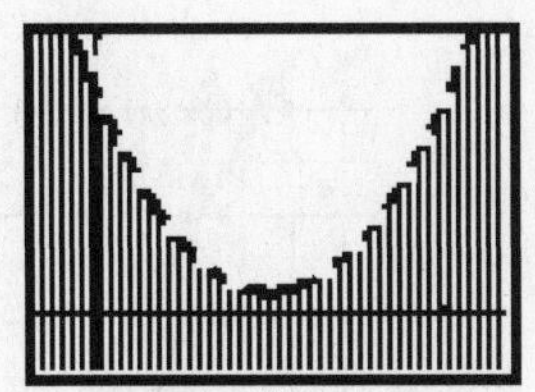

y-intercept = 20
vertex (3, 2)

Answer Key

1. a) $y \le x^2 - 3x - 10$ **b)** $y > x^2 - 10x + 21$

2. a)

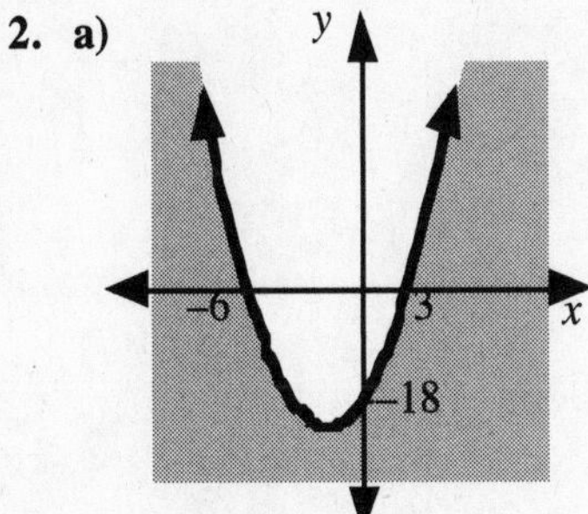

b)

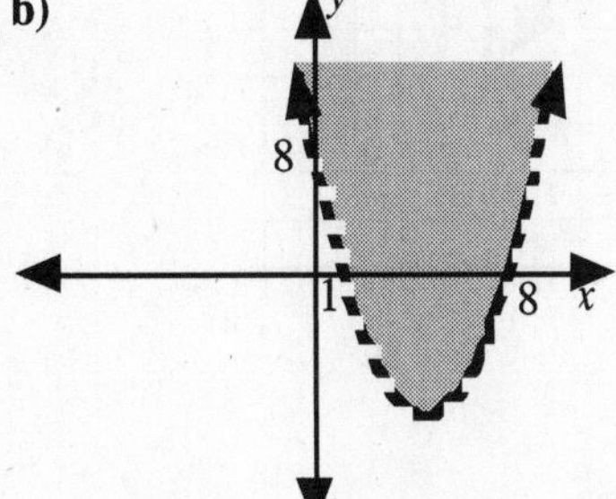

c)

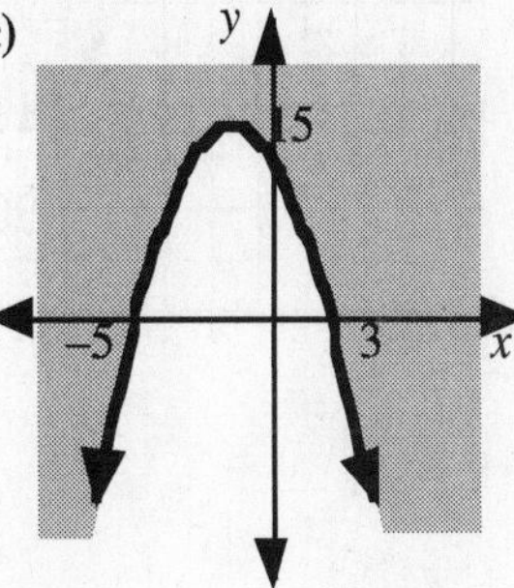

d)

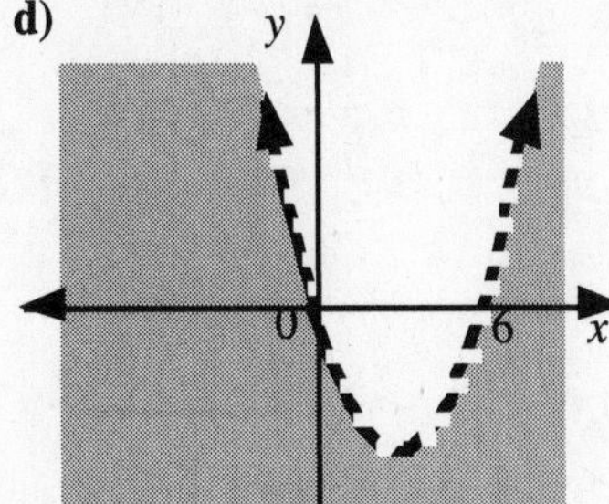

e)

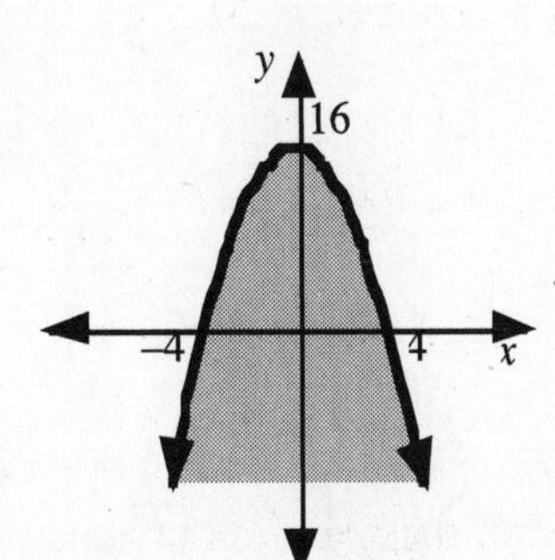

f)

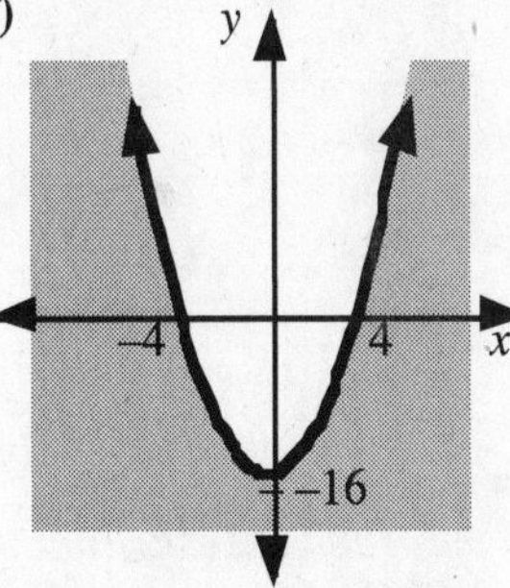

3. a)

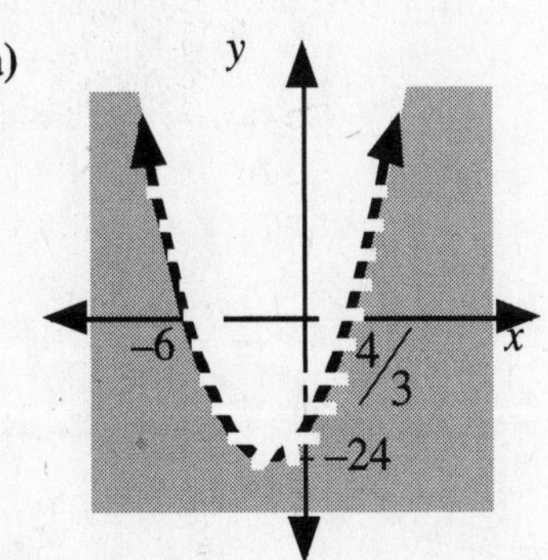

b

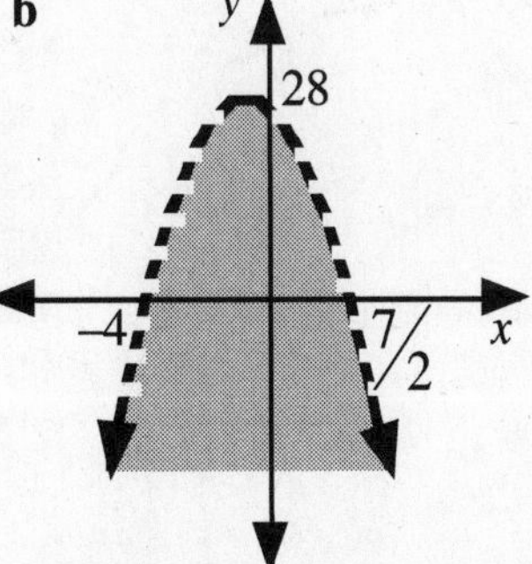

4. The point (0, 0) is on the graph of $y = x - 4x^2$, so it cannot be used to determine when $y > x - 4x^2$.

5. a) $y = -\frac{1}{2}x^2 - x - \frac{9}{2}$ **b)** $y \le \frac{1}{2}x^2 - x - \frac{9}{2}$ **6.** D

The solution to Group Investigation from Lesson #2, page 514.

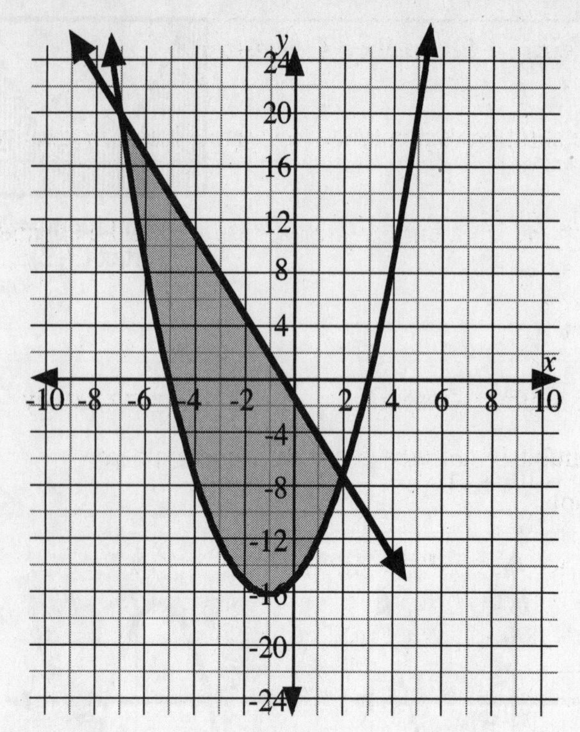

Linear and Quadratic Systems and Inequalities Lesson #5:
Solving Inequalities in Two Variables Using Technology

Graphing a Linear Inequality Using a Graphing Calculator

Use the following procedure to graph the solution region to a two variable linear inequality using a TI-84 graphing calculator.

1. If necessary, rearrange the inequality by isolating y to the left side so that the equation of the boundary line is in the form $y = mx + b$.

2. Input the boundary line equation into Y_1.

3. To the left of Y_1 select the shading which corresponds to the inequality symbol by pressing the [Enter] key continuously until the desired symbol appears.
Use the following inequality symbols:

- For $y \geq mx + b$ or $y > mx + b$ use ◥Y1 = mX +b
- For $y \leq mx + b$ or $y < mx + b$ use ◣Y1 = mX +b

Press the [GRAPH] key.

The graphing calculator does not distinguish between < and ≤ or > and ≥, i.e. broken or solid boundary lines. When sketching a graph from the graphing calculator window on your own grid, use the appropriate type of boundary line.

We use the inequality $x - y > 3$ to illustrate the procedure above.

1. Rearrange the inequality. $x - y > 3$

$-y > -x + 3$

$y < x - 3$

Plot1 Plot2 Plot3
\Y1 = X−3
\Y2=
\Y3=
\Y4=
\Y5=
\Y6=
\Y7=

2. Input the boundary line equation, $y = x - 3$, into Y_1.

3. Press the [Enter] key to the left of Y_1 until the symbol representing "<" appears.

To represent $y < x - 3$,. we input ◣Y1 = X−3 .

Plot1 Plot2 Plot3
◣Y1 = X−3
\Y2=
\Y3=
\Y4=
\Y5=
\Y6=
\Y7=

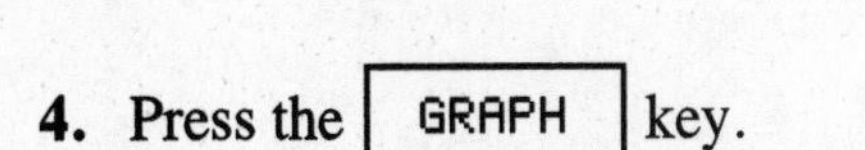

4. Press the [GRAPH] key.

5. On your own grid, sketch the solution region to the inequality with a broken boundary line to represent " less than".

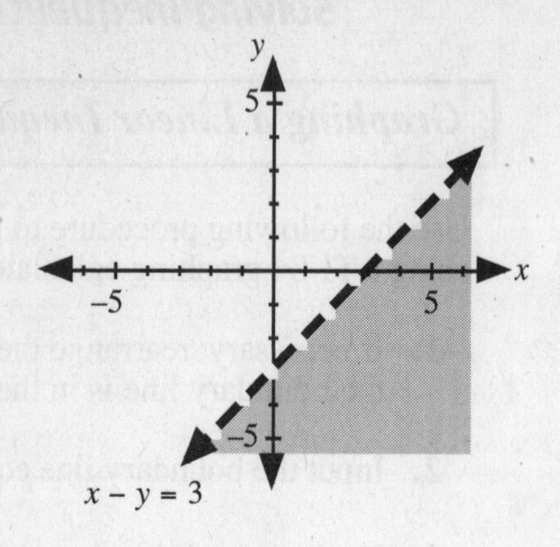

Graphing a Quadratic Inequality Using a Graphing Calculator

Use a similar procedure to graph the solution region to a two variable quadratic inequality. In this case, the equation entered into Y_1 must be in the form $y = ax^2 + bx + c$.

Graph the solution region to the following inequalities on a graphing calculator, and sketch the solution region on the graph provided. Label the *x* and *y*-intercepts on the grid.

a) $2x + 3y - 12 < 0$

b) $y \geq 2x^2 - x - 15$

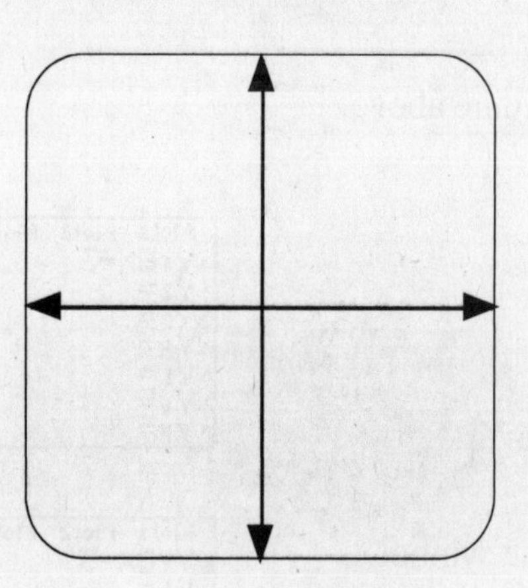

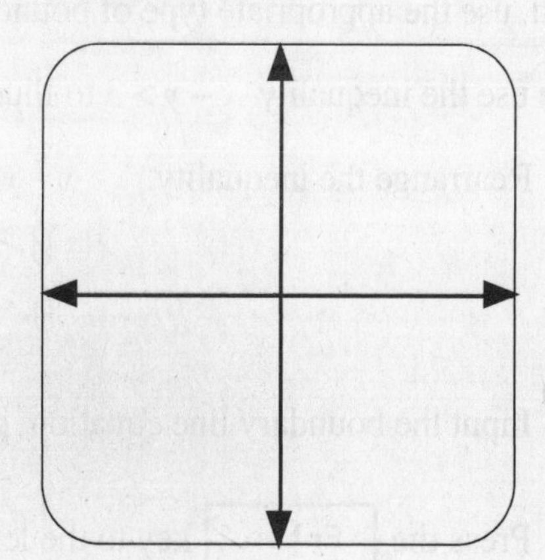

Complete Assignment Questions #1 - #4

Assignment

1. Graph the solution region to the following inequalities on a graphing calculator, and sketch the solution region on the grid provided. Label the x and y-intercepts on the grid.

a) $y \geq \frac{1}{2}x + 1$

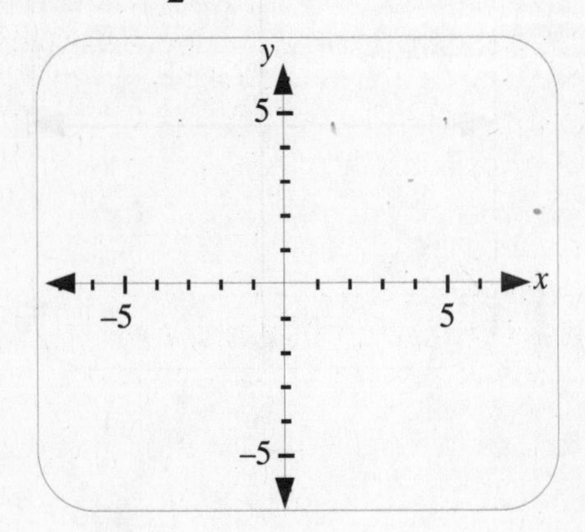

b) $3x - y > 6$

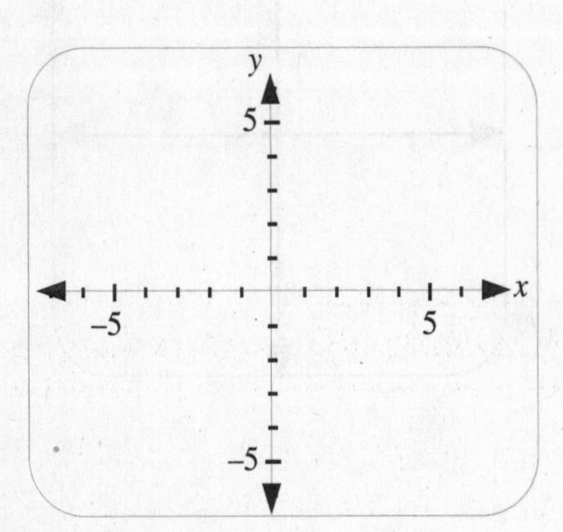

c) $2x + 5y \leq 10$

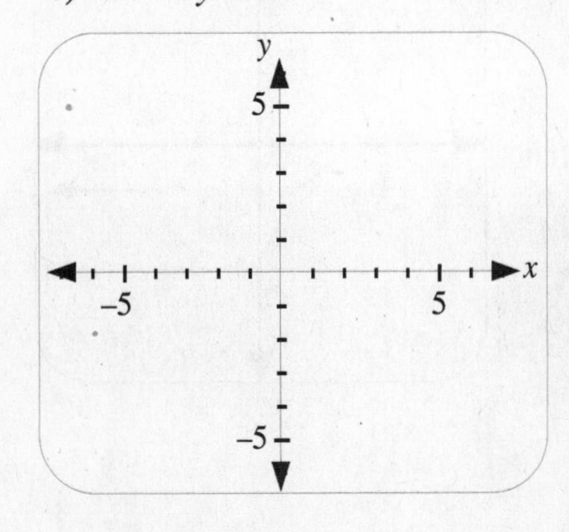

d) $4x - y + 6 < 0$

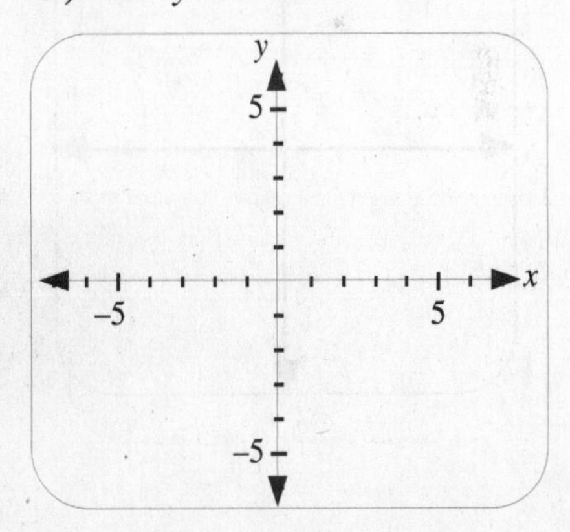

2. Graph the solution region to the following inequalities on a graphing calculator and sketch the solution region on the grid provided.

a) $y \leq x^2 + 4x - 32$

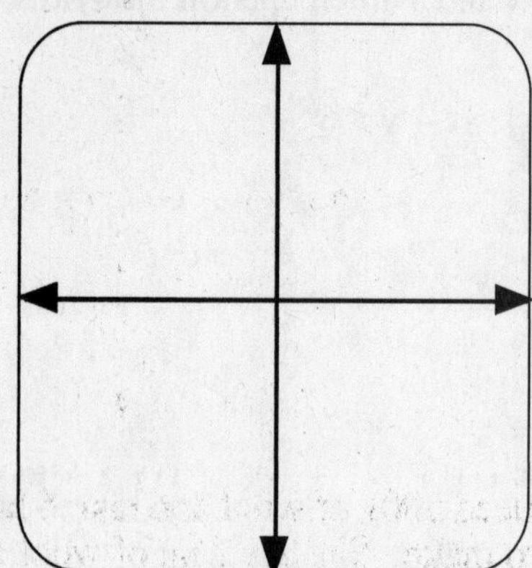

b) $y > -2(4x + 1)(x - 5)$

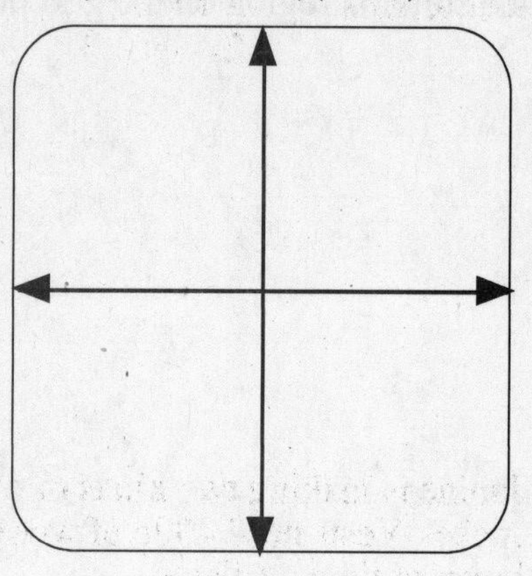

c) $y < -10x^2 + 35x - 15$

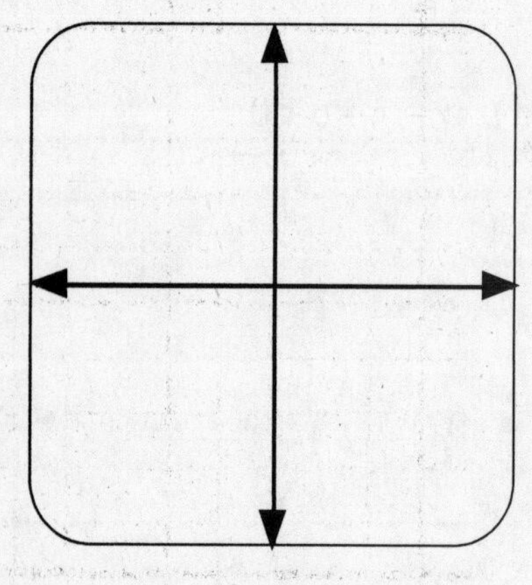

d) $y - 2 \geq (x + 3)^2$

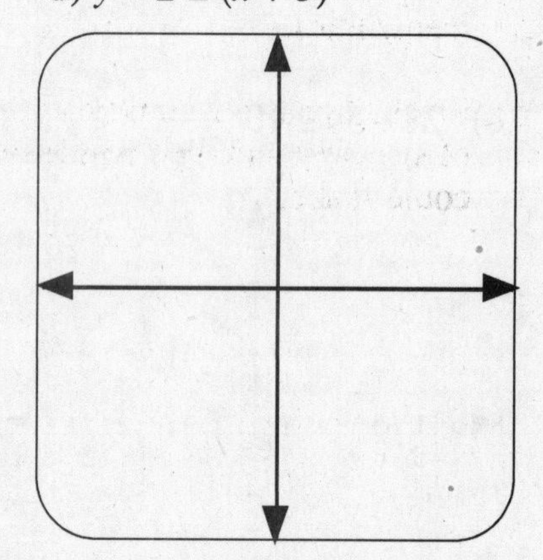

The following questions are extension questions.

Group Work

3. Show the solution region to the following system of linear inequalities. $x + y \geq 6$
$2x - y < 4$

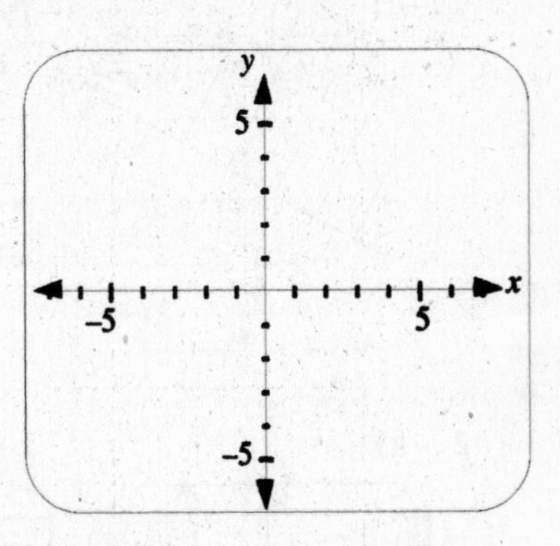

4. Janine is making two kinds of clothing. Sweaters need 500g of wool and take 6 hours to make. Vests need 400g of wool and take 9 hours to make. She has 2 kg of wool and 36 hours of time available.

   a) Suppose she makes x sweaters and y vests. Write down a system of <u>four</u> inequalities which represent the information. Give the inequalities in simplest form.

   b) Graph the solution region of the system of inequalities.

   c) State all possible combinations of the number of sweaters and the number of vests which she could make.

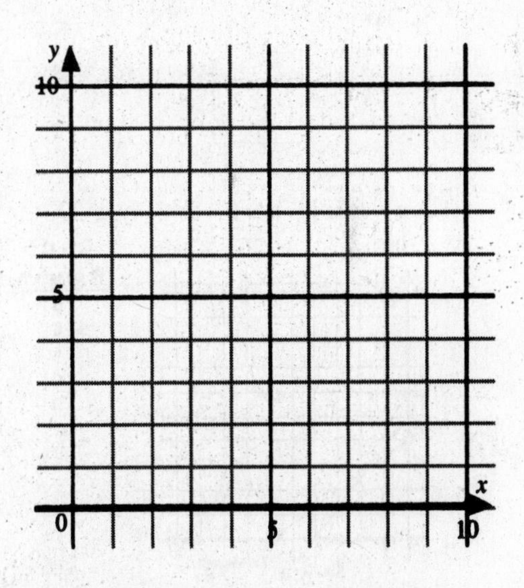

   d) If sweaters sell for \$36 and vests for \$30, how many of each should she make to maximize the value of the items she sells if she must make at least one of each item?

Answer Key

1. a) b) c) d)

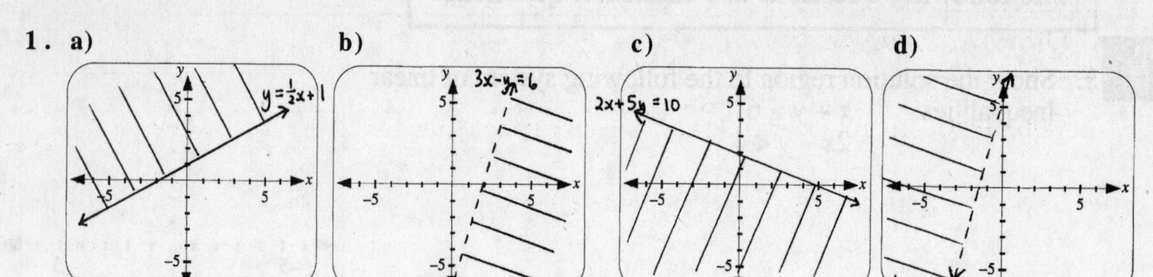

2. a) b) c) d)

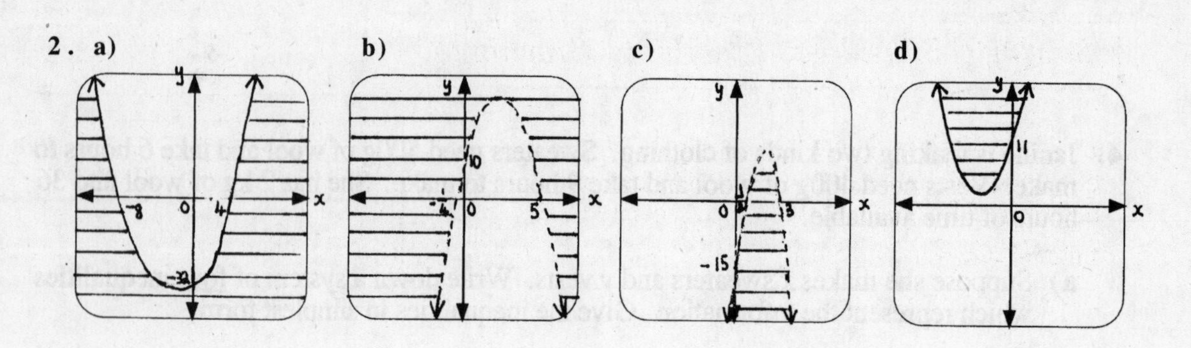

3.

4. a) $x \geq 0,\ y \geq 0,\ 5x + 4y \leq 20,\ 2x + 3y \leq 12$

b) c)

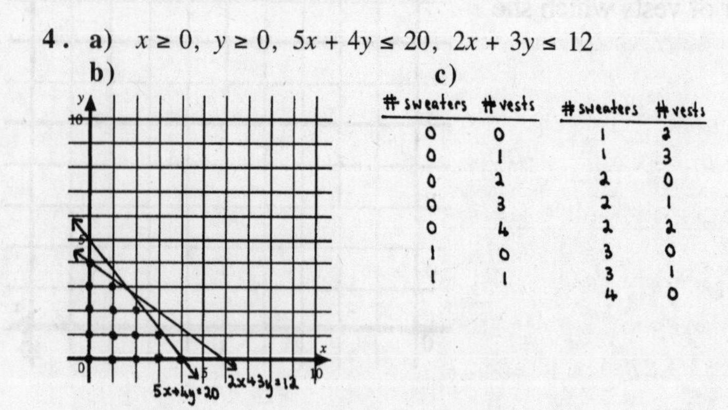

# sweaters	# vests	# sweaters	# vests
0	0	1	2
0	1	1	3
0	2	2	0
0	3	2	1
0	4	2	2
1	0	3	0
1	1	3	1
		4	0

d) Three sweaters and one vest sell for $138.

Linear and Quadratic Systems and Inequalities Lesson #6: Solving Quadratic Inequalities in One Variable by Case Analysis

Quadratic Inequality

A **quadratic inequality** in one variable takes one of the following forms:

- $ax^2 + bx + c < 0$
- $ax^2 + bx + c > 0$
- $ax^2 + bx + c \leq 0$
- $ax^2 + bx + c \geq 0$

Solving Quadratic Inequalities by Graphing

$x^2 + 2x - 8 > 0$ and $x^2 + 2x - 8 < 0$ are quadratic inequalities whose solutions can be determined from the graph of the associated function $f(x) = x^2 + 2x - 8$.

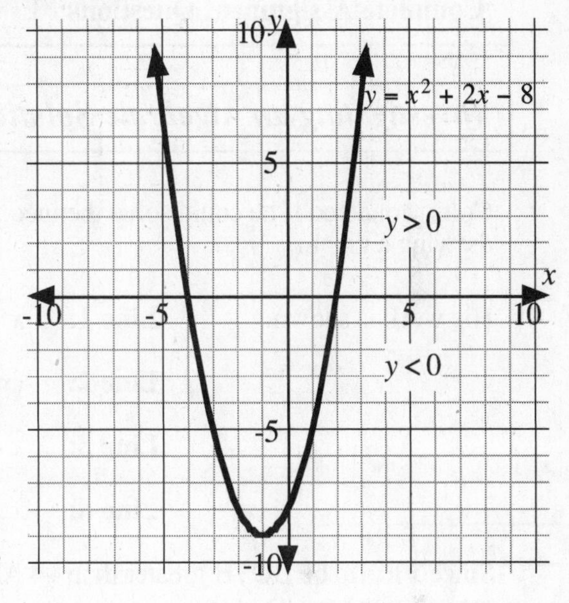

The graph of the function whose equation is $y = x^2 + 2x - 8$ is shown.
The x-intercepts are -4 and 2.

The x-coordinates of the points on the part of the graph which is above the x-axis give the solution to the inequality $x^2 + 2x - 8 > 0$.

The x-coordinates of the points on the part of the graph which is below the x-axis give the solution to the inequality $x^2 + 2x - 8 < 0$.

Complete the following using the above graph:

a) The solution to the inequality $x^2 + 2x - 8 > 0$ is ______________ or ______________ .

b) The solution to the inequality $x^2 + 2x - 8 < 0$ is ______________ .

The solution in a) can be represented on a number line as

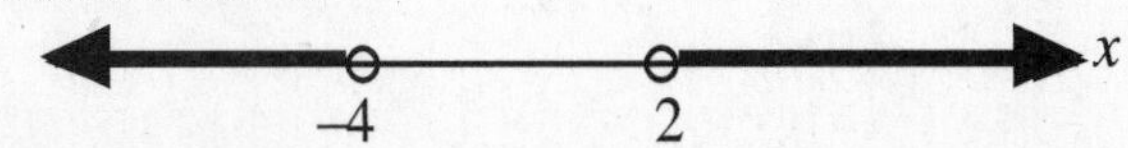

The solution in b) can be represented on a number line as

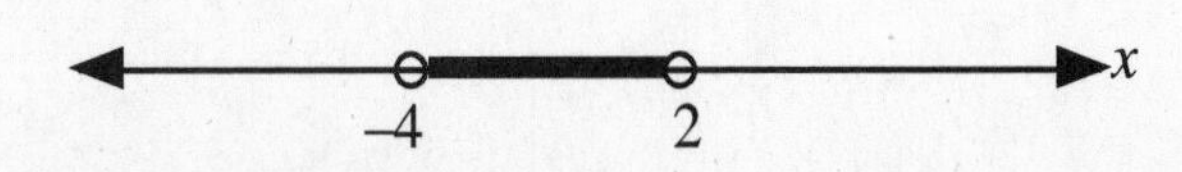

a) Use the graph of the function $f(x) = 12 + 4x - x^2$ to solve the inequality $12 + 4x - x^2 \geq 0$.

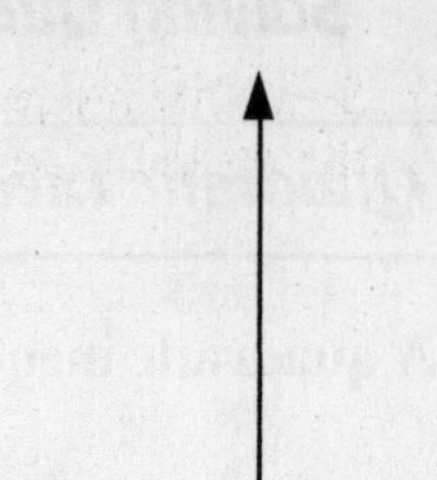

b) Show the solution on a number line.

c) State the solution to the inequality $12 + 4x - x^2 \leq 0$.

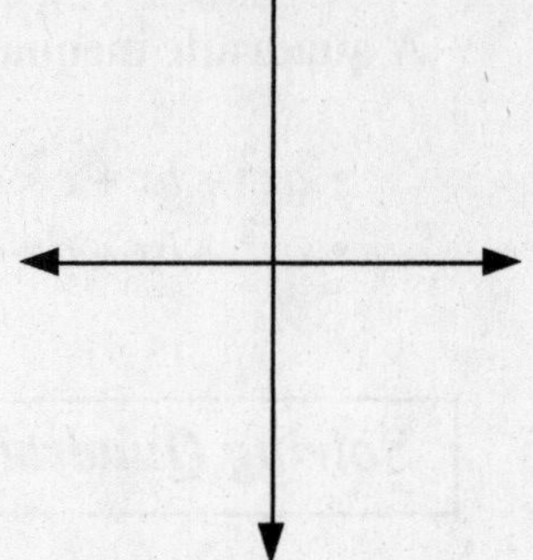

Complete Assignment Questions #1 - #4

Investigating an Algebraic Solution to a Quadratic Inequality

Colin wondered if he could solve the inequality $x^2 + 2x - 8 > 0$ from Class Ex. #1 without drawing a graph.

His work is shown.

Line 1: $x^2 + 2x - 8 > 0$

Line 2: $(x + 4)(x - 2) > 0$

Line 3: $x + 4 > 0$ and $x - 2 > 0$

Line 4: $x > -4$ and $x > 2$

Since x has to be BOTH greater than -4 AND greater than 2, he concluded that the solution was $x > 2$.

When he checked his answer with Class Ex. #1, he discovered that he only had part of the solution.

Colin's answer is incomplete because going from Line 2 to Line 3, Colin concluded that if the product of two quantities is positive (as in Line 2), then both quantities must be positive (as in Line 3).

This is not necessarily the case.

a) Describe the other case that Colin did not consider in going from Line 2 to Line 3.

b) Determine the complete solution to the inequality.

c) Solve the inequality $x^2 - x - 20 \leq 0$ by an algebraic process similar to the investigation on the previous page.

Solving Quadratic Inequalities Algebraically by Case Analysis

The method used in the investigation to solve the quadratic inequality is called **case analysis**.

When the quadratic inequality is ≥ 0.

If the factored form of the inequality results in two factors whose product is positive, there are two cases to consider.

Case 1: Both factors are positive.
Case 2: Both factors are negative.

When the quadratic inequality is ≤ 0.

If the factored form of the inequality results in two factors whose product is negative, there are two cases to consider.

Case 1: The first factor is positive and the second factor is negative.
Case 2: The first factor is negative and the second factor is positive.

Note that when solving a particular case there may be no solution (as in part c in the investigation).

Use case analysis to solve $5 - 14x - 3x^2 \geq 0$.

Complete Assignment Questions #5 - #7

Assignment

1. The graph of $y = x^2 - 9$ is shown.
Write the solution to each of the following.

a) $x^2 - 9 = 0$

b) $x^2 - 9 \leq 0$

c) $x^2 - 9 \geq 0$

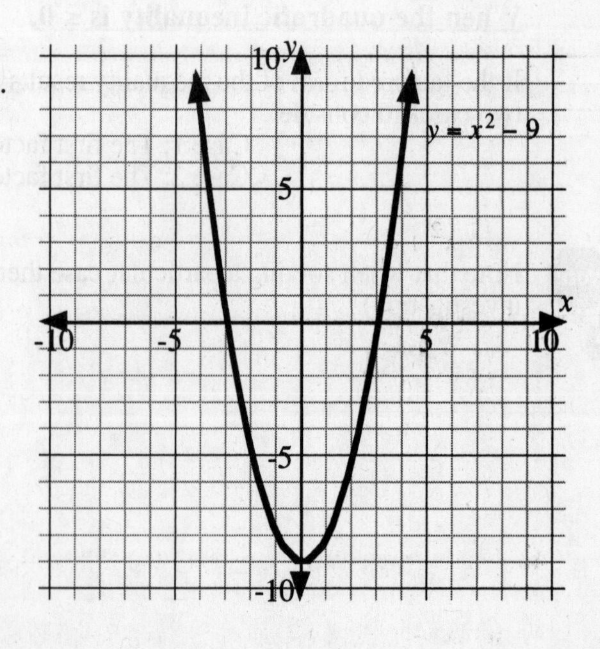

2. The graph of $y = -\frac{1}{5}x^2 + \frac{2}{5}x + 7$ is shown.
Write the solution to each of the following.

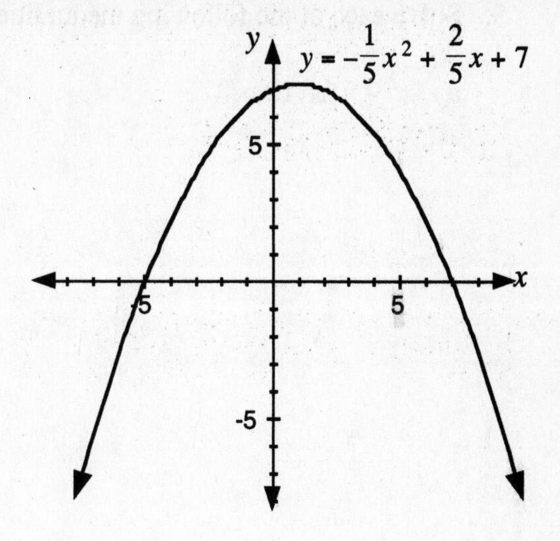

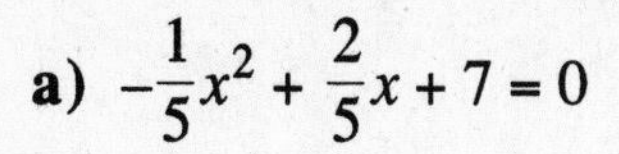

a) $-\frac{1}{5}x^2 + \frac{2}{5}x + 7 = 0$

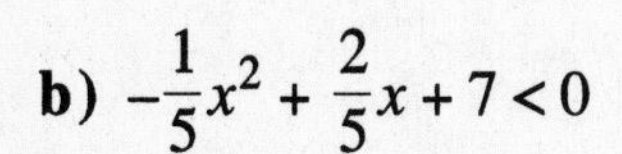

b) $-\frac{1}{5}x^2 + \frac{2}{5}x + 7 < 0$

c) $-\frac{1}{5}x^2 + \frac{2}{5}x + 7 > 0$

3. Use a graph to solve each of the following inequalities, and show the solution on a number line.

a) $x^2 - 4x + 3 < 0$ **b)** $2 + x - x^2 \geq 0$ **c)** $2x^2 + 7x > -5$

d) $x^2 + 4x > 0$ **e)** $x^2 - 6x + 9 \leq 0$ **f)** $-4x^2 - 8x + 21 \leq 0$

4. Use a graph to solve each of the following inequalities. Answer to the nearest tenth.

a) $x^2 - 6x + 1 > 0$ **b)** $7 + 2x - x^2 \geq 0$ **c)** $3x^2 - 9x < 4$

5. Solve each of the following inequalities using case analysis.

a) $x^2 - 7x + 10 > 0$

b) $x^2 + 5x - 14 < 0$

c) $2x^2 - x - 15 \geq 0$

d) $x^2 - 9x \leq 0$

e) $3x^2 + 5x - 2 > 0$

f) $24 - 2x - x^2 < 0$

6. Consider the equation $f(x) = x^2 + mx + 4$. Determine the range of values of m for which the equation has two unequal roots.

Multiple Choice

7. Consider the number line shown

The inequality which has the solution shown is

A. $(x - 1)(x + 3) \leq 0$
B. $(x - 1)(x + 3) \geq 0$
C. $(x + 1)(x - 3) \leq 0$
D. $(x + 1)(x - 3) \geq 0$

Answer Key

1. a) $x = -3$ or 3 **b)** $-3 \leq x \leq 3$ **c)** $x \leq -3$ or $x \geq 3$

2. a) $x = -5$ or 7 **b)** $x < -5$ or $x > 7$ **c)** $-5 < x < 7$

3. a) $1 < x < 3$ **b)** $-1 \leq x \leq 2$ **c)** $x < -\frac{5}{2}$ or $x > -1$

d) $x < -4$ or $x > 0$ **e)** $x = 3$ **f)** $x \leq -\frac{7}{2}$ or $x \geq \frac{3}{2}$

4. a) $x < 0.2$ or $x > 5.8$ **b)** $-1.8 \leq x \leq 3.8$ **c)** $-0.4 < x < 3.4$

5. a) $x < 2$ or $x > 5$ **b)** $-7 < x < 2$ **c)** $x \leq -\frac{5}{2}$ or $x \geq 3$
d) $0 \leq x \leq 9$ **e)** $x < -2$ or $x > \frac{1}{3}$ **f)** $x < -6$ or $x > 4$

6. $m < -4$ or $m > 4$ **7.** C

Linear and Quadratic Systems and Inequalities Lesson #7: Solving Quadratic Inequalities in One Variable by Sign Analysis

In the previous lesson, we solved quadratic inequalities using graphing techniques and by case analysis.

In this lesson, we introduce the technique of **sign analysis** (either by using **test intervals** or by using a **sign chart**) to solve quadratic inequalities.

Solving Quadratic Inequalities in One Variable Using Test Intervals

Part One

The graph of a quadratic function with equation $y = x^2 + 2x - 8$ is shown below.

The zeros of the function, –4 and 2, can be used to divide the x-axis into three intervals. In each interval, the function is either always positive or always negative.

a) Use the graph to select the correct alternative in the statements below.

- On the interval $x < -4$, the function is (positive / negative).
- On the interval $-4 < x < 2$, the function is (positive / negative).
- On the interval $x > 2$, the function is (positive / negative).

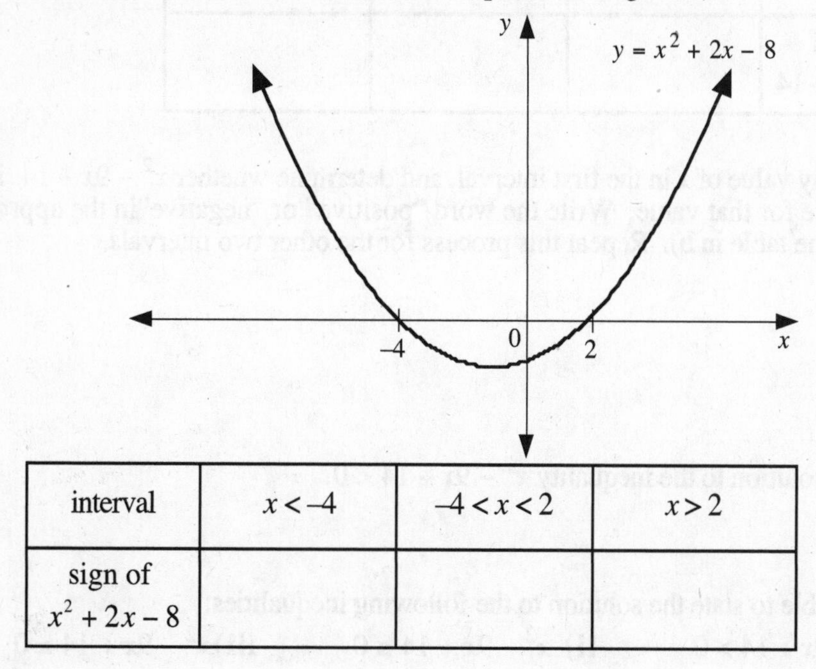

interval	$x < -4$	$-4 < x < 2$	$x > 2$
sign of $x^2 + 2x - 8$			

b) Write the words "positive" or "negative" in each of the spaces in the chart above.

c) Complete the following:

- The solution to the inequality $x^2 + 2x - 8 > 0$ is ____________ or ____________ .
- The solution to the inequality $x^2 + 2x - 8 < 0$ is ____________ .

The intervals determined by the zeros of the function are called **test intervals**.
In solving a quadratic inequality without graphing, we use a value of x in each of these test intervals to determine whether the quadratic function is positive or negative as shown in the example below.

Part Two

Consider the inequality $x^2 - 9x + 14 < 0$.

a) Write the inequality in factored form, and determine the roots of the equation $x^2 - 9x + 14 = 0$.

b) Use the roots of the equation to determine three test intervals, and write these intervals in the table below.

interval			
sign of $x^2 - 9x + 14$			

c) Choose any value of x in the first interval, and determine whether $x^2 - 9x + 14$ is positive or negative for that value. Write the word "positive" or "negative"in the appropriate space of the table in b). Repeat this process for the other two intervals.

d) State the solution to the inequality $x^2 - 9x + 14 < 0$.

e) Use the table to state the solution to the following inequalities:
i) $x^2 - 9x + 14 > 0$ **ii)** $x^2 - 9x + 14 \leq 0$ **iii)** $x^2 - 9x + 14 \geq 0$

The values we use to determine whether a quadratic expression is positive or negative are called **test points**.

Solve the inequality $8x - x^2 \leq 0$ using test intervals.

Complete Assignment Questions #1 - #2

Solving Quadratic Inequalities in One Variable Using a Sign Chart

At the beginning of this lesson, in Part 1 c), Colin solved the inequalities $x^2 + 2x - 8 > 0$ and $x^2 + 2x - 8 < 0$ using using test intervals. His elder brother, who had just completed high school, showed him a different method which was useful in solving more complicated inequalities.

The method for solving $x^2 + 2x - 8 > 0$ is shown below.

Step 1: Factor the quadratic expression. $(x + 4)(x - 2) > 0$

Step 2: Determine the zeros of the quadratic expression. -4 and 2

Step 3: Use a **sign chart** which shows the sign of each factor (+, 0, –) to the left and right of each of the zeros.

x	←	-4	↔	2	→
$x + 4$	–	0	+	+	+
$x - 2$	–	–	–	0	+
Product	+	0	–	0	+

Step 4: Since the original inequality symbol is > 0, look for the solution under the + in the product row. The solution is $x < -4$ or $x > 2$.

Although this method may appear complex at first, it is easier to use when solving more complex polynomial inequalities and rational inequalities in higher level math courses. In Calculus, it is used to determine where functions are increasing and decreasing, and to determine maximum and minimum points, and changes in concavity.

Use the above chart to state the solution to the inequality $x^2 + 2x - 8 < 0$.

a) Factor fully the expression $-6x^2 - 39x - 18$.

b) Solve the inequality $-6x^2 - 39x + 18 \leq 0$ by using sign analysis with a sign chart.

Complete Assignment Questions #3 - #11

Assignment

1. Solve the following inequalities using sign analysis with test intervals.

a) $x^2 - 8x + 15 < 0$

b) $9x^2 + 2x \geq 0$

2. Solve the following inequalities using sign analysis with test intervals.

a) $3x^2 - 10x - 8 \leq 0$

b) $32 - 4x - x^2 > 0$

3. Solve the following inequalities using sign analysis with a sign chart.

a) $x^2 - 5x - 24 \leq 0$

b) $x^2 + 5x + 6 > 0$

4. Solve the following inequalities using sign analysis with a sign chart.

a) $3 + 2x - x^2 \leq 0$

b) $9x^2 - 3x < 0$

5. Solve using sign analysis.

a) $x(x + 4) < 0$

b) $x(x + 4) < 21$

c) $-4x(x + 4) < 0$

6. Solve the inequality $x^2 + 12x - 28 > 0$ by the following methods:

a) case analysis

b) sign analysis with test intervals

c) sign analysis with a sign chart

d) graphically

7. Solve the inequality $8x^2 - 26x - 7 < 0$ by an algebraic process.

8. In each case, write a quadratic inequality, with a leading coefficient of one, which has the solution given.

a) $-5 \leq x \leq -1$ **b)** $x < -2$ or $x > 3$

9. The approximate height, h metres, of an object, at time t seconds, is given by the equation $h = 60t - 5t^2$.

a) Calculate t when $h = 0$.

b) Explain why the height of the object cannot be greater than 180 metres.

c) Determine the interval for t such that $h \geq 100$.

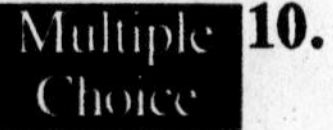

10. Consider the number line shown

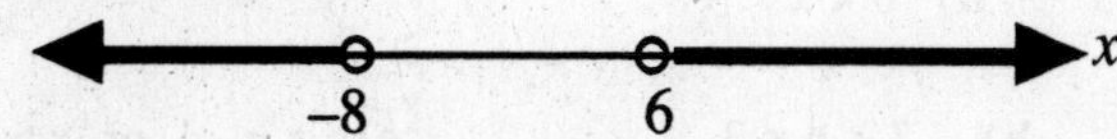

The inequality which has the solution shown is

A. $x^2 - 2x - 48 < 0$
B. $x^2 - 2x - 48 > 0$
C. $x^2 + 2x - 48 < 0$
D. $x^2 + 2x - 48 > 0$

11. Use sign analysis to solve the following inequalities.

a) $-2(x-2)(5-x)(x+3) > 0$ **b)** $\dfrac{x^2+3x}{x-2} \le 0$

Answer Key

1. a) $3 < x < 5$ **b)** $x \le -\frac{2}{9}$ or $x \ge 0$

2. a) $-\frac{2}{3} \le x \le 4$ **b)** $-8 < x < 4$

3. a) $-3 \le x \le 8$ **b)** $x < -3$ or $x > -2$

4. a) $x \le -1$ or $x \ge 3$ **b)** $0 < x < \frac{1}{3}$

5. a) $-4 < x < 0$ **b)** $-7 < x < 3$ **c)** $x < -4$ or $x > 0$

6. $x < -14$ or $x > 2$ **7.** $-\frac{1}{4} < x < \frac{7}{2}$

8. a) $x^2 + 6x + 5 \le 0$ **b)** $x^2 - x - 6 > 0$

9. a) $t = 0$ or $t = 12$ **b)** The maximum height is at $t = 6$, where $h = 180$ **c)** $2 \le t \le 10$

10. D **11. a)** $-3 < x < 2$ or $x > 5$ **b)** $x \le -3$ or $0 \le x < 2$, (Note that x cannot equal 2)

Linear and Quadratic Systems and Inequalities Lesson #8: Practice Test

1. The x-coordinate of the point of intersection of the graphs with equations $y = x^2 + 15x - 20$ and $y = 5x^2 - 13x + 29$ is

A. $-\frac{2}{7}$

B. $\frac{2}{7}$

C. $-\frac{7}{2}$

D. $\frac{7}{2}$

1. To the nearest tenth, the sum of the x-coordinates of all the points of intersection of the system $\begin{array}{l} y = x^2 - 3x - 3 \\ y = x + 1 \end{array}$ is ______ .

(Record your answer in the numerical response box from left to right.)

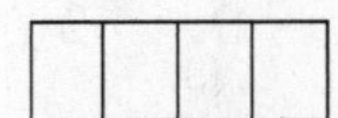

2. The number of solutions of the system $\begin{array}{l} y = x^2 - 2x + 3 \\ y = x - 5 \end{array}$ is

A. 0

B. 1

C. 2

D. infinite

3. When solving the system $\begin{array}{l} y = 3x^2 - 4x + 2 \\ y = 3 - x \end{array}$ a quadratic equation which requires to be solved is

A. $3x^2 - 3x + 5 = 0$

B. $3x^2 - 3x - 1 = 0$

C. $3x^2 - 5x + 5 = 0$

D. $3x^2 - 5x - 1 = 0$

Numerical Response **2.** To the nearest hundredth, the positive x-coordinate of the solution to the quadratic-quadratic system of equations $\begin{matrix} y = 4x^2 - 7x + 12 \\ y = 13 - 2x - x^2 \end{matrix}$ is ______.

(Record your answer in the numerical response box from left to right.)

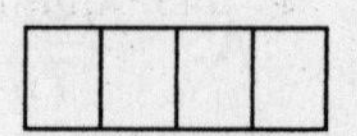

4. The line $y = kx + 3$ is a tangent to the parabola $y = x^2 + 8$. A possible value of k is

A. $\sqrt{5}$

B. $2\sqrt{5}$

C. $\sqrt{11}$

D. $2\sqrt{11}$

Numerical Response **3.** The quadratic-quadratic system of equations $\begin{matrix} y = 2x^2 - 7x + 3 \\ y = x^2 + 3x - k \end{matrix}$ is satisfied by $x = 4$ and by $x = 6$. The value of k is ______.

(Record your answer in the numerical response box from left to right.)

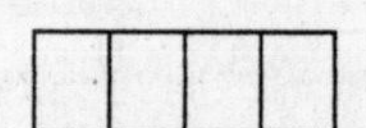

5. The point which is NOT in the solution region of the inequality $3x - 5y \geq 2$ is

A. $(3, -5)$

B. $(-3, -5)$

C. $(-3, 5)$

D. $(5, -3)$

4. When solving the system $\begin{array}{l} y = 2x^2 - 3x - 6 \\ y = 7 - 4x \end{array}$ a quadratic equation is formed which requires to be solved.

If this equation is written in the form $2x^2 + bx + c = 0$, then value of $b - c$ is _____ .

(Record your answer in the numerical response box from left to right.)

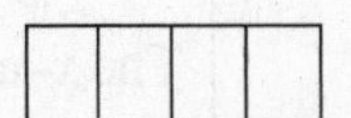

6. Which of the following points is in the solution regions of both $y > 2x + 8$ and $y \leq x^2 - 3x + 2$?

A. $(0, 10)$

B. $(-1, 6)$

C. $(-2, 4)$

D. $(-3, 20)$

Use the following information to answer the next question.

The illustration shown is the screenshot from a graphing calculator.

The parabola on the screenshot has the equation $y = x^2 - 5x - 11$.

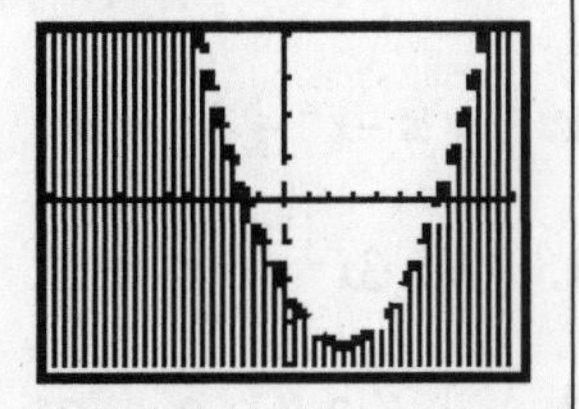

7. The shaded region represents the solution to the inequality

A. $y < x^2 - 5x - 11$

B. $y > x^2 - 5x - 11$

C. $y \leq x^2 - 5x - 11$

D. $y \geq x^2 - 5x - 11$

Use the following information to answer the next question.

Stephane graphed an inequality on his calculator.

The x- and y-intercepts of the straight line are 2 and –4 respectively.

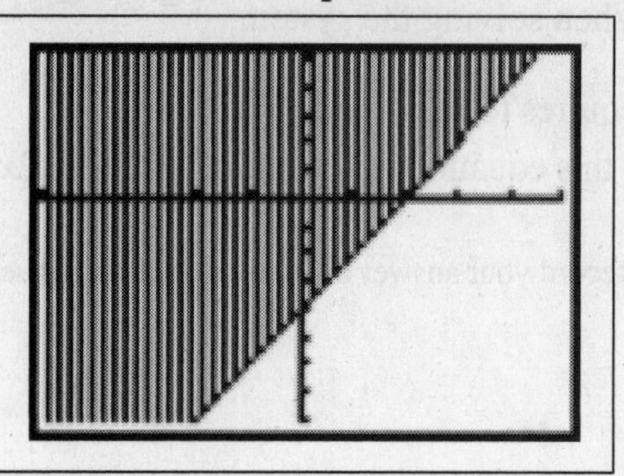

8. The graph shows the solution to the inequality

A. $2x - y \geq 4$

B. $2x - y \leq 4$

C. $x - 2y \leq 8$

D. $x - 2y \geq 8$

9. The shaded area shows the solution region to a two-variable inequality. The x-intercepts of the parabola are –5 and 2, and the y-intercept is 30.

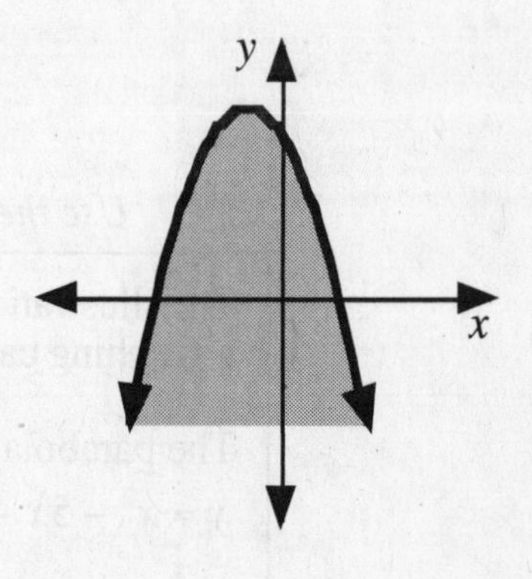

The two-variable inequality is

A. $y \leq -x^2 - 3x + 10$

B. $y \geq 3x^2 + 9x - 30$

C. $y \geq -3x^2 - 9x + 30$

D. none of the above

10. The shaded area represents the solution region to the inequalities

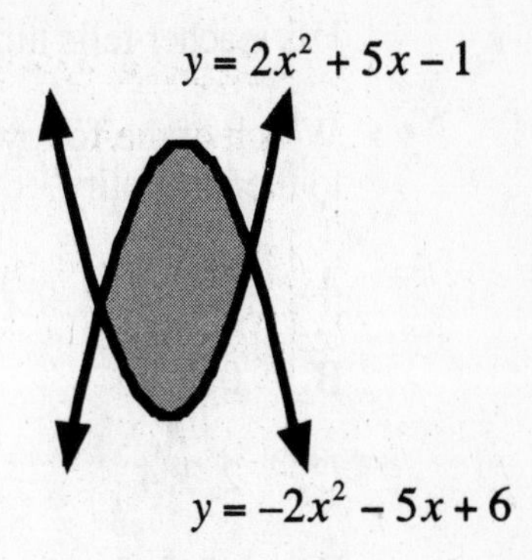

A. $y \le 2x^2 + 5x - 1$ and $y \le -2x^2 - 5x + 6$

B. $y \le 2x^2 + 5x - 1$ and $y \ge -2x^2 - 5x + 6$

C. $y \ge 2x^2 + 5x - 1$ and $y \le -2x^2 - 5x + 6$

D. $y \ge 2x^2 + 5x - 1$ and $y \ge -2x^2 - 5x + 6$

Numerical Response **5.** A dinner theatre is putting on a new show with a maximum capacity of 125 guests. Each guest will pay \$75 to attend the show. The expenses each night can be related to the number of guests, n, by the formula $E = 1800 + 39n - 0.15n^2$.

The number of guests that must attend the show on any particular night in order for a profit to be made can be written as $k \le n \le 125$. The value of k is _____.

(Record your answer in the numerical response box from left to right.)

11. The solution to the inequality $x^2 - x - 90 \ge 0$ is

A. $-9 \le x \le 10$

B. $-10 \le x \le 9$

C. $x \le -9$ or $x \ge 10$

D. $x \le -10$ or $x \ge 9$

12. Consider the number line shown.

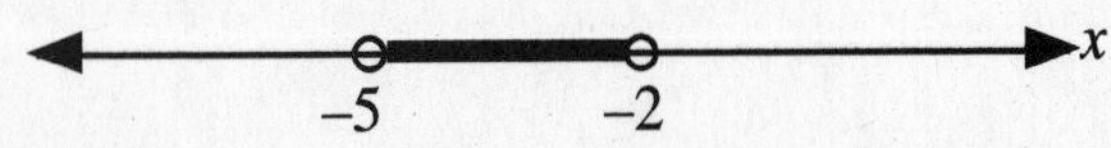

The inequality which is represented by the number line is

A. $(x - 5)(x - 2) < 0$ **B.** $(x - 5)(x - 2) > 0$

C. $(x + 5)(x + 2) < 0$ **D.** $(x + 5)(x + 2) > 0$

13. Hanif is algebraically solving the inequality $18 - 21x + 3x^2 \leq 0$.
His teacher tells him he can only evaluate $18 - 21x + 3x^2$ for three values of x.

Which of the following values of x should allow him to determine the correct solution to the inequality?

A. $-9, -3, 0$

B. $0, 3, 9$

C. $2, 3, 4$

D. $-2, 3, 5$

Use the following information to answer questions #14 and #15.

Corey is solving the quadratic inequality $-5x^2 - 5x + 30 > 0$ using a sign chart.

The outline of her sign chart is shown

x	$\leftarrow$	P	$\leftrightarrow$	Q	$\rightarrow$
-5					
$x + 3$					
$x - 2$			R		
Product					

14. Which of the following statements about P, Q, and R is true?

A. $P = -2, \; Q = 3, \; R = -$ **B.** $P = -2, \; Q = 3, \; R = +$

C. $P = -3, \; Q = 2, \; R = -$ **D.** $P = -3, \; Q = 2, \; R = +$

15. The solution to the inequality $-5x^2 - 5x + 30 > 0$ is

A. $-2 < x < 3$ **B.** $x < -2$ or $x > 3$

C. $-3 < x < 2$ **D.** $x < -3$ or $x > 2$

Written Response - 5 marks

1. • Describe a method, which does not use technology, for determining the solution region to an inequality of the form $y > ax^2 + bx + c$.

• Use your method to sketch the solution region to the inequality $y > 6x^2 + 17x - 45$ on the grid provided.

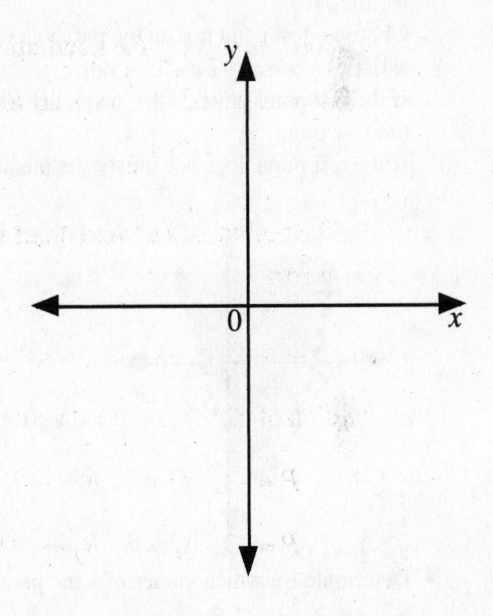

• Explain how to use the graph in the bullet above to determine the solution to the inequality $6x^2 + 17x - 45 < 0$, and state the solution.

Answer Key

1. D 2. A 3. B 4. B 5. C 6. D 7. A 8. B

9. D 10. C 11. C 12. C 13. B 14. C 15. C

Numerical Response

1. | 4 | . | 0 | |

2. | 1 | . | 1 | 7 |

3. | 2 | 1 | | |

4. | 1 | .4 | | |

5. | 4 | 3 | | |

Written Response

- Determine the x-intercepts of the graph of $y = ax^2 + bx + c$ by solving $ax^2 + bx + c = 0$.
  Determine the y-intercept of the graph of $y = ax^2 + bx + c$ by replacing x with 0.
  Use the x and y-intercepts to sketch the parabola with equation $y = ax^2 + bx + c$ (use a broken line for the sketch).
  Choose a test point not on the parabola (choose $(0, 0)$ if possible) and determine whether the test point satisfies $y > ax^2 + bx + c$ or not.
  If the test point satisfies the inequality, shade the region (inside or outside the parabola) containing the test point.
  If the test point does not satisfy the inequality, shade the other region.

- 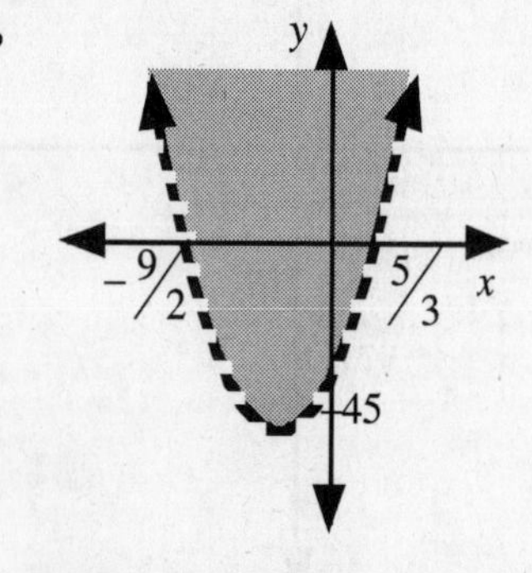

- Determine for which values of x the parabola is below the x-axis.
  $-\frac{9}{2} < x < \frac{5}{3}, x \in R$

Notes Page 1

Notes Page 2

Notes Page 4

Notes Page 7

Notes Page 9